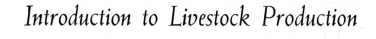

Introduction to Livestock Production

A SERIES OF BOOKS IN *Agricultural Science*

Animal Science Editors: G. W. SALISBURY AND E. W. CRAMPTON

Reproductive Physiology: *Comparative Reproductive Physiology of Domestic Animals, Laboratory Animals and Man*
  A. V. NALBANDOV

Applied Animal Nutrition: *The Uses of Feedstuffs in the Formulation of Livestock Rations*
  E. W. CRAMPTON

The Science of Meat and Meat Products
  AMERICAN MEAT INSTITUTE FOUNDATION

Fundamentals of Nutrition
  E. W. CRAMPTON AND L. W. LLOYD

Physiology of Reproduction and Artificial Insemination of Cattle
  G. W. SALISBURY AND N. L. VANDEMARK

Introduction to Livestock Production: *Including Dairy and Poultry*
  H. H. COLE, Editor

Plant and Soil Science Editors: IVER JOHNSON AND M. B. RUSSELL

Crop Adaptation and Distribution
  C. P. WILSIE

Introduction to Livestock Production

INCLUDING

DAIRY AND POULTRY

H. H. Cole, Editor

University of California, Davis

W. H. Freeman & Company

San Francisco and London

Preface

During the past quarter century the livestock industry has been emerging from "a way of life" to a sound business enterprise based on advances made both in the biological sciences—nutrition, genetics, physiology—and in the sciences concerned with disease control, as well as upon accepted economic principles. Though one may have nostalgic recollections of the good old days, as do the editor and the authors of this volume, it behooves us to acquaint the potential livestock producers of tomorrow with this new and exciting era of the animal, dairy, and poultry husbandman. Large livestock enterprises have become commonplace. Many feed yards, for example, finish over 50,000 head of cattle annually. Yes, this means fewer livestock managers, but at the same time it means more positions of great responsibility comparable to those available in industry. These changes demand a new type of leadership based upon a sound understanding of basic biological principles and an understanding of modern business methods.

In the past, livestock producers raised animals of their choice and sold them for what they could get at the market place. In order to succeed, the livestock producer of today, and of tomorrow, must raise animals that meet consumer specifications and which will retail at a price the consumer is willing to pay. This concept of producing a high quality, standardized product has been developing over a considerable period. For example, as early as 1926, a group of beef producers was organized for the purpose of establishing a federal program for identification of high quality beef. This initial stimulus led to the development of federal meat grading. The introduction of standardized meat, milk, and egg products in the market has played an important part in creating the high consumer acceptability of these products. Much more can and must be done. Furthermore, the economy of production must be emphasized if animal products are to compete successfully with plant products. Though the preference for animal products is high, the consumer does consider price as has been dramatically illustrated in the competition between butter and margarines.

What are the livestock, poultry, and dairy industries doing about improving the quality and economy of their products? The current practices of the poultry industry serve as an outstanding example of the way in which modern concepts of the biological sciences have been used to produce quality products economically; nutritionists, geneticists, physiologists, and disease-control specialists have all been recruited for the task. Other phases of the livestock industry are on the move: the use of the hormone diethylstilbestrol to increase the rate and economy of gain in cattle and sheep; the use of crossbreeding to increase the number of pigs weaned; the use of artificial insemination to hasten improvement through breeding; and the development of drugs and vaccines for disease control are but a few examples of the ways in which advances in the biological sciences are being utilized to increase productivity.

This is the story that unfolds in the succeeding pages; this together with an overall picture of the livestock industry. This book, designed for beginning students interested in some phase of livestock production, is the product of 40 authors, all of whom are accepted leaders in specialized fields. The student has an opportunity, therefore, to become acquainted early with points of view all too frequently reserved for advanced courses. Our aim has been to develop these concepts in a manner understandable to the high school graduate and to arouse in the student early in his training a keen desire to delve deeper into the intriguing possibilities of the further application of the sciences in improving livestock production. Though this text is designed primarily as a beginner's text, livestock producers, I am sure, will find much of interest. In many instances, advances relating to production of one species have not been adapted to others. In reading the manuscript, I have been fascinated by the inherent possibilities of such progress.

Some, no doubt, will decry the lack of emphasis on livestock expositions. In the past, these shows have had a tremendous influence in improving livestock. Somehow they have been left behind. Let us hope that they will rise from the ashes of nurse cows, emphasis on fancy points unrelated to productivity, and subtle means of hiding defects and develop programs which will demonstrate how modern methods can be used in improving our herds and flocks.

The editor is indebted to the authors for their patience in accepting suggested changes; to many colleagues for reviewing different portions of the manuscript; to W. H. Freeman and Company for their cooperation and advice; and to Mrs. June Law, Mrs. Vivian Baker, and Miss Joan Popovich for their assistance in preparing the index and in other matters relating to editing.

> Come shepherd, let us make an honorable retreat;
> Though not with bag and baggage, yet with scrip and scrippage.
> SHAKESPEARE, *As You Like It*

March 1962   H. H. COLE

Contributors

F. N. ANDREWS, *Purdue University, Lafayette, Indiana.*

W. M. BEESON, *Purdue University, Lafayette, Indiana.*

J. M. BELL, *University of Saskatchewan, Saskatoon, Canada.*

O. G. BENTLEY, *South Dakota State College, Brookings, South Dakota.*

G. ALVIN CARPENTER, *University of California, Berkeley, California.*

D. W. CASSARD, *University of Nevada, Reno, Nevada.*

M. T. CLEGG, *University of California, Davis, California.*

H. H. COLE, *University of California, Davis, California.*

HARRY W. COLVIN, JR., *University of Arkansas, Fayetteville, Arkansas.*

P. T. CUPPS, *University of California, Davis, California.*

L. B. DARRAH, *Cornell University, Ithaca, New York.*

RALPH M. DURHAM, *Texas Technological College, Lubbock, Texas.*

R. H. DUTT, *University of Kentucky, Lexington, Kentucky.*

HAROLD GOSS, *University of California, Davis, California.*

DAVID HALLETT, *United States Department of Agriculture, Washington, D.C.*

LORIN E. HARRIS, *Utah State University, Logan, Utah.*

LLOYD HENDERSON, *Foremost Dairies Inc., San Francisco, California.*

F. W. HILL, *University of California, Davis, California.*

K. R. JOHNSON, *University of Idaho, Moscow, Idaho.*

R. G. LOY, *University of California, Davis, California.*

HAROLD P. LUNDGREN, *United States Department of Agriculture, Albany, California.*

S. W. MEAD, *University of California, Davis, California.*

R. J. MEADE, *University of Minnesota, St. Paul, Minnesota.*

J. C. MILLER, *Oregon State College, Corvallis, Oregon.*

C. E. MURPHEY, *United States Department of Agriculture, Washington, D.C.*

A. V. NALBANDOV, *University of Illinois, Urbana, Illinois.*

J. E. NELLOR, *Michigan State University, East Lansing, Michigan.*

A. W. NORDSKOG, *Iowa State University, Ames, Iowa.*

JOHN W. OSEBOLD, *University of California, Davis, California.*

A. M. PEARSON, *Michigan State University, East Lansing, Michigan.*

RALPH W. PHILLIPS, *United States Department of Agriculture, Washington, D.C.*

JOHN C. PIERCE, *United States Department of Agriculture, Washington, D.C.*

G. A. RICHARDSON, *Oregon State College, Corvallis, Oregon.*

G. M. SPURLOCK, *University of California, Davis, California.*

W. J. STADELMAN, *Purdue University, Lafayette, Indiana.*

DEWEY G. STEELE, *University of Kentucky, Lexington, Kentucky.*

D. F. STEPHENS, *United States Department of Agriculture, El Reno, Oklahoma.*

H. H. STONAKER, *Colorado State University, Fort Collins, Colorado.*

CLAIR E. TERRILL, *United States Department of Agriculture, Beltsville, Maryland.*

E. J. WARWICK, *United States Department of Agriculture, Beltsville, Maryland.*

W. O. WILSON, *University of California, Davis, California.*

Contents

Section IV. Physiological Mechanisms and Livestock Production

Section V. Nutrition and Livestock Production

Section VI. Livestock Management

Section VII. Classification, Grading, and Marketing of Livestock and Their Products

Section VIII. Livestock Diseases

Chapter 1

The Livestock Industry: Its Scope and Potential

And the man increased exceedingly, and had much cattle, and maidservants, and menservants, and camels, and asses.

Genesis 30:43

The world's barnyard is large indeed. It comprises some six billion animals and birds—more than twice the number of people in the world.

Livestock and poultry have major places in the economy of practically all countries. They produce the meat, milk, and eggs that constitute important parts of the diet of most peoples. In many countries, much of the power for farm work and for transport of farm products to the market place is still provided by cattle, horses, donkeys, mules, camels, llamas, water buffaloes, and yaks. Wool, mohair, hides and skins, and the numerous by-products of livestock-processing industries are used by man for many purposes. The manure produced by livestock makes an important contribution to the maintenance of soil fertility.

The scope of the livestock industry must be examined from several viewpoints in order to fully appreciate the contributions of farm animals and poultry to human welfare. Data on numbers of livestock and poultry give some indication of the importance of the industry, but global and even national figures are difficult to comprehend; for this reason, data will also be summarized in terms of the number of animals or birds per person in the human population. Although numbers are important, the amounts of usable products actually harvested are of greater significance. So we shall

1

also examine figures for global and national production of animal products. Here, too, the significance of these products to human welfare may be more readily grasped if products harvested are expressed in amounts per person. The efficiency of production is also important and will become more so as competition between foods from animal and plant sources increases.

There are wide variations in the manner in which man utilizes his farm animals and poultry in different parts of the world. There are also wide variations in the productive capacities of different types and breeds. Some of these variations will become apparent as we consider the data on numbers of farm animals and poultry, the amounts of products harvested from them, and the levels of productivity per animal or bird in the livestock and poultry populations. It is against this background of variation that some concept may be formed of the yet unexploited potential of the industry.

If we are to fully appreciate the present and potential contributions of the livestock industry to human welfare, we should let our minds drift back to the time when man had no domesticated animals and birds; when he had to depend upon his prowess as a hunter for his supply of meat, hides, and skins; and when his food other than meat had to be obtained from wild sources or from such domesticated plants as he could cultivate without the aid of animal power.

1-1. THE BEGINNINGS OF LIVESTOCK PRODUCTION

The domestication of livestock was one of man's major steps in his struggle for mastery over his environment. The domestication of crop plants, particularly the cereals, which had preceded the domestication of livestock, gave man a more dependable source of food. The development of these and other crops over the centuries since domestication first took place has greatly increased the number of people the earth could support. The domestication of food-producing animals not only brought man a more dependable source of animal protein than did the produce of the hunt, but enabled him to further expand the potential number of people the earth could support, since those animals provided a means for converting into human food many plants that are not edible by man (Fig. 1-1). The domestication of the horse put a source of speed and power at man's disposal—a source that was not excelled until the invention of the steam and internal combustion engines. Only a few other steps in man's history, such as the mastery of fire, the invention of the wheel, the harnessing of power from electricity, and the achievement of nuclear fission, rank with the domestication of crops and livestock in giving man the means with which to achieve mastery over his environment and to more fully utilize the resources of the earth upon which he lives.

Even though the domestication of livestock took place in prehistoric times, it was in reality a recent event in the long history of man. Reed (1959)

Fig. 1-1. Simmental cattle graze on alpine pastures in Switzerland. These pasture lands are poorly adapted for producing plant foods for human consumption. These sturdy cattle are used for the production of meat and milk and as a source of draft power on Swiss farms and in several neighboring countries.

points out that, in spite of a prolific literature, the central problems concerning the origins and early history of animal domestication remain unsolved. However, on the basis of evidence that he and others have accumulated, Reed concluded that goats were probably domesticated 8000 to 9000 years ago, whereas cattle, sheep, and pigs were domesticated some time thereafter. There is fairly definite proof that cattle had been domesticated by about 5000 to 6000 years before the present, or 3000 to 4000 B.C.

The center of domestication was in the village-farming communities of the hilly, grassy, open-forested flanks of the Near Eastern mountain ranges (Reed, 1959), that is, in the Palestinian, Lebanese, and Zagros Mountains. From this primary center, the village-farming way of life diffused in all directions, carrying with it the practice of cereal agriculture and the basic, domestic food-producing animals. In Egypt, Thessaly, Baluchistan, and the Indus Valley, and probably even in China, or at least North China, the beginnings of village-farming life were established later and seem to have received a cultural stimulus from southwestern Asia. Whether domesticated animals were taken to various other regions or whether only the idea was communicated, we do not know. It seems reasonable to assume that both processes occurred as man took advantage of domesticated animals to produce meat and, eventually, milk, wool, and draft power.

Although the early center of domestication was in the Near East, the actual process must have taken place at many points and under a variety of circumstances. The turkey had been domesticated in southern Mexico before the North American continent was discovered and occupied by Europeans. Such species as the reindeer and the camel's relatives—the llama and the alpaca—must have been domesticated in or near their present habitats. But this is not the place for an extensive discussion of domestication. The objects here are two-fold: to emphasize the relatively recent occurrence of domestication, and to give some indication of the benefits accruing to man as a result of its occurrence.

The potential values of domestication were probably little appreciated in preliterate cultures after the process first began. However, as man advanced in knowledge and understanding, he gradually molded his animals and birds to suit his needs. Thus, long before there was any real understanding of the science of genetics, quite productive animals and birds had been developed, and wide variations in form and function had resulted from the process of selection.

1-2. SIZE OF THE LIVESTOCK INDUSTRY

Statistics for the most important types of farm animals and poultry in the world and in the United States are given in Table 1-1. Most of the totals were taken from the latest tabulations available from the Food and Agriculture Organization of the United Nations (FAO, 1959). Many countries do not have reliable statistics; thus, figures for these countries are based on informed guesses. Since the FAO figures do not include a world total for chickens, this figure has been derived from various sources. The world figures for ducks, geese, and turkeys are probably the least reliable, since they are rough estimates based on figures for various years and, in some cases, on calculations of the proportion of these types of poultry where single figures are given for all poultry types, or where the numbers of ducks, geese, and turkeys are given as a single figure. Although later figures are available for the United States, those published by the FAO have been used to keep the comparisons as valid as possible from the standpoint of the years in which the data were collected. No data for asses are given for the United States, since the number is statistically insignificant. The figure for goats in the United States refers to Texas only. In spite of these and other qualifications that might be given, the data in Table 1-1 give a good indication of the size of the various phases of the livestock industry.

The populations of farm animals and poultry vary a great deal from country to country in relation to the size of the human populations of those countries. It is hardly possible here to show the many contrasts that exist

TABLE *Approximate numbers of the most important types of farm animals*
1-1.   *and poultry in the world and in the United States. Although these*
        data are not for the same year, they represent, in general, the situation
        as of about 1957, except for data on ducks, geese and turkeys, for
        which such recent figures are not available from many countries.

Types of farm animals and poultry	Approximate numbers in—	
	The world	The United States
Cattle	885,000,000	94,802,000
Water buffaloes	94,900,000	
Sheep	936,900,000	30,840,000
Goats	324,300,000	2,835,000
Pigs	399,900,000	51,703,000
Horses	71,000,000	2,466,000
Asses	38,200,000	
Mules	14,600,000	1,108,000
Camels	10,200,000	
Chickens	2,963,533,000	390,131,000
Ducks	116,222,000	12,139,000
Geese	43,000,000	1,152,000
Turkeys	43,300,000	5,799,000

between countries, so comparisons are limited to the average world picture on the one hand and the picture in the United States on the other.

Suppose the farm animals and poultry of the world were divided equally among all the people. How many animals and birds would each person have in his private barnyard? Or, if all those in the United States were divided among the people of this country, how many animals and birds would each person have? The answers are given in graphic form in (Fig. 1-2). Thus, in terms of world figures, each person among the 2,794,800,000 in 1957 would have had a little less than $\frac{1}{3}$ head of cattle (including water buffalo) and slightly more than one chicken; in terms of United States figures, each person would have had a little more than $\frac{1}{2}$ head of cattle and about $2\frac{1}{4}$ chickens. Figure 1-2 also shows that, although there are fewer sheep, goats, horses, asses, and mules per person in the United States than in the world as a whole, the United States has more pigs, as well as more cattle, and poultry per capita than does the world as a whole.

1-3. THE HARVEST OF LIVESTOCK PRODUCTS

Some groups of people in the world still count the value of their livestock in terms of numbers. But it is the amount of usable products harvested that actually determines the value of an animal or a bird to its owner and to

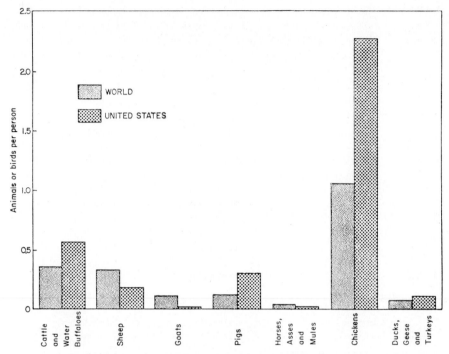

Fig. 1-2. The relative size of the livestock and poultry populations of the world and of the United States in relation to the size of the human populations.

the human race. The size of the annual harvest of some of the most important livestock and poultry products is given in Table 1-2. Data are from the FAO (1959). With the exception of wool, the world figures do not include data from the U.S.S.R.

Since global data are difficult to grasp, the data in Table 1-2 are also expressed in terms of products harvested per person in the world and in the United States. These data indicate the approximate amounts of food of animal origin, and of wool, available to the people of the world each year. They also show that, with the exception of mutton and lamb and milk other than that from cows, the per capita production of food from animals is much higher in the United States than in the world as a whole.

Although the level of production of meat, eggs, and milk is high in the United States in relation to the number of people, other countries rank higher in some products. For example, Australia and New Zealand have a combined annual production of beef and veal of 201.8 lb. per person compared with 92.3 lb. per person in the United States. At the other end of the scale, the countries of Asia, exclusive of the U.S.S.R., produce only 4.8 lb. of beef and veal per person (Phillips, 1960). Australia and New Zealand

TABLE 1-2.	*Products harvested from farm animals and poultry in the world and in the United States, in terms of total production and production per person in the population. World data are exclusive of the U.S.S.R. except for wool, for which data from the U.S.S.R. are included. Estimates of per capita wool production are based on the world total; for all other products, estimates are based on the human population exclusive of the U.S.S.R.*

	Total production (metric tons)		Production per person (lb.)	
Type of product	World	United States	World	United States
Beef and veal	25,510,000	7,054,000	22.0	92.3
Mutton and lamb	4,190,000	322,000	3.6	4.2
Pork	20,970,000	4,755,000	18.1	62.2
Poultry meat	5,800,000	3,244,100	5.0	42.4
Eggs (hen)	10,940,000	3,667,400	9.4	48.0
Milk: cow	238,100,000	57,325,000	206.0	750.0
water buffalo	14,800,000		12.8	
goat	7,500,000		6.5	
sheep	4,800,000		4.1	
Wool: grease	2,230,450	130,330	1.8	1.7
clean	1,295,450	57,360	1.0	.8

also have a higher level of milk production for each person than does the United States—2142 lb. compared with 750 lb. per year. Canada also has a higher level—1060 pounds per person. No adjustments are made in these figures for exports or imports; they merely indicate the levels of domestic production in relation to the sizes of the human populations. In milk production, as in meat production, the countries of Asia are at the other end of the scale. These countries harvest an average of only 25 lb. of cow's milk per person each year.

Water buffaloes, goats, and sheep make important contributions to the milk supply in certain parts of the world; in fact, these three groups of animals taken together produce just over 10% of the world's milk supply (Fig. 1-3). In India, the Murrah and related breeds of water buffalo produce more milk than do cattle (Fig. 1-4). Other types of water buffaloes, such as those in southern China, are used almost entirely for work (Phillips, 1945; Phillips, Johnson, and Moyer, 1945). Some breeds of sheep produce high yields of milk, particularly if some selection has been undertaken to take advantage of high milk-yielding potentials. For example, Finci (1957) reports that 22,519 Awassi ewes in 109 flocks in Israel averaged 615 pounds of milk during the 1955–56 season (Fig. 1-5). The highest yield for one ewe was about 1950 pounds.

Fig. 1-3. An Indian woman prepares chapatties. The food supply is mostly from plant sources, but the urn in lower left corner contains goat's milk which will be passed around during the meal. Although cattle are the main producers of milk, other species such as the goat, sheep, yak, and water buffalo are important producers in various parts of the world. [United Nations photo.]

Although work production is more difficult to measure than food and fiber production, power is another important part of the harvest from livestock each year (Figs. 1-6 and 1-7). Even though much of the power on farms in the more highly developed countries is now supplied by tractors or other mechanical equipment, most of the power used in other parts of the world is still supplied by animals. Estimates derived (Phillips, 1950–51) from data published by Acock (1950) indicate that, at that time, 86.4% of the draft power in agriculture in the world was provided by animals (Fig. 1-8). In the United Kingdom, in North America, and in Oceania, animals provided only 22.7%, 24.5%, and 62.5% of the power respectively, whereas in the U.S.S.R. the figure was 78.7%. Averages for other regions were: Europe, 85.6%; Africa, 98.3%; Near East, 98.9%; Latin America, 99.1%; and Far East, 99.9%. The more advanced countries have moved much further in the mechanization of agriculture since these data were tabulated. Some additional mechanization has also taken place in other areas, but the amounts have been relatively small in most of the countries that depend primarily upon animals for power in agriculture.

Another general measure of the size of the harvest of livestock and poultry products is the amount produced per animal or per bird in the farm animal and poultry populations. Summaries of such measures for the major livestock and poultry products in the world and in the United States are shown in Table 1-3. Leaving aside milk from water buffaloes, goats, and sheep, the livestock and poultry of the United States are generally well above the world average according to this generalized measure of productivity. However, the United States of America does not rank first in all respects. For example, the milk produced per animal in the cattle population in Europe is 2419 lb., and in Canada, 1693 lb., as compared with approximately 1355 lb. in the United States (Phillips, 1960). In Asia (exclusive of the U.S.S.R.), on the other hand, where cattle are used primarily as a source of power, the average production of milk per animal in the population is only 140 lb. For beef and veal, the picture is somewhat different. Compared with 166.7 lb. in the United States, the production per animal is 140.8 lb. in Canada,

Fig. 1-4. Water buffaloes provide power for the preparation of rice fields in Ceylon. Some breeds and types of water buffaloes are used primarily for milk production, others for work. [FAO photo.]

121.5 lb. in Europe, and 26.2 lb. in Asia. The figures for Australia and New Zealand taken together are 1107 lb. of milk and 104.3 lb. of beef and veal per animal.

Such generalized estimates of the productivity of livestock and poultry populations must be taken for what they are. They do not reflect the levels of productivity of specialized groups of animals. Neither do they take into account such factors as the relative portions of the cattle populations in different countries that may be used for milk or beef production, nor the large numbers of bullocks in countries where cattle supply much of the draft power (Figs. 1-9 and 1-10). To make this point entirely clear, and continuing to use cattle as the example, let us examine the production of dairy cows in the United States in relation to the figure of 1354.5 pounds of milk listed in Table 1-3. According to the U.S. Department of Agriculture (1960), there were 20,510,000 dairy cows on farms in the United States in 1957, and their average yield of milk was estimated to be 6162 pounds. At the same time, cows in Dairy Herd Improvement Associations yielded 9688 pounds of milk on the average.

Fig. 1-5. An Awassi ewe. Although sheep are used primarily for meat and wool production, they are an important source of milk in some parts of the world. The Awassi, a Near Eastern breed, is being further developed as a milking breed in Israel. [Finci, 1957.]

Fig. 1-6. Threshing grain by treading in Pakistan. In many parts of the world cattle still provide much of the power for work on farms. [FAO photo.]

TABLE 1-3. *Products harvested annually per animal or bird in the livestock and poultry populations. These are very generalized indications of levels of productivity, derived from livestock statistics and from data on amounts of various products produced annually.*

Product	Production per animal or bird in population (lb.)	
	World	United States
Beef and veal	70.1	166.7
Mutton and lamb	11.6	23.4
Pork	136.7	206.0
Poultry meat	4.4	17.8
Eggs: hen	8.9	21.1
Milk: cow	654.7	1354.5
water buffalo	349.3	
goat	54.4	
sheep	13.3	
Wool: grease	5.3	9.5
clean	3.1	4.2

Fig. 1-7. Zebu oxen being hitched to a cart loaded with rice straw in India. Owing to scarcity of other materials, the straw is used for livestock feed as well as for thatching roofs and for fuel. [United Nations photo.]

1-4. AN INDUSTRY OF DIVERSITY AND CHALLENGE

Although farm animals and poultry are important in practically every country, their roles differ considerably from country to country. In the foregoing discussion, it has been possible only to indicate in part the extreme variations in productivity and to hint at a few of the many reasons behind these variations (Fig. 1-11).

Farm animals and poultry are kept under conditions ranging from those of the high Andes and the Himalayas (Fig. 1-12) to those of the low, steaming tropics; from the far north to the equator; from the lush farm lands of the Corn Belt to the semi-arid ranges of the Navajo reservation. The environment is an important factor in determining the carrying capacity of the land, the kinds of animals or birds that may be used to best advantage, and the upper limits at which they may be expected to produce (Phillips, 1948; 1956; 1958).

The kinds of animals or birds available as breeding stock; the systems of

Fig. 1-8. A Mongolian horse in Chinghai Province, China. Although the draft horse has largely been replaced by tractors in some countries, it is still used extensively for draft, for riding, and as a pack animal in many parts of the world. [Photo by Ralph W. Phillips.]

farming or ranching followed; the skill of the farmers or ranchers; the degree to which diseases and parasites have been brought under control; the extent to which owners have access to new knowledge; the educational and cultural backgrounds of owners, which affect their capacity or their willingness to adopt new methods; and the economic incentives that stimulate the achievement of higher levels of production—all these and other factors play their part in determining levels of productivity (Figs. 1-13 and 1-14).

The Masai tribesman, who herds his cattle in the dry, hot, tribal areas of East Africa, who measures his wealth in terms of numbers of animals rather than in terms of their capacity to produce meat and milk; who on oc-

Fig. 1-9. A Chiana or Chianina bull. These large, active, fast-growing cattle are native to central Italy, where they are used for work, for meat, and to some extent for milk production.

Fig. 1-10. A Charollais bull. This beef breed, which is native to France, is now attracting attention in the United States. This animal was photographed at six years of age, when it weighed approximately 2700 pounds.

casion uses some of his cattle as the purchase price for a bride; who long ago learned to puncture the jugular vein to obtain blood, which he drinks fresh for food and thus retains his animals alive as basic wealth and as a hedge against unusually hard times; and whose animals would have no appeal to specialized producers of beef or milk, is still very much in the cattle business. But the development of his business is limited by many factors, and the level of productivity stands in sharp contrast with the levels of production that have been achieved in the specialized beef and dairy industries of many advanced countries.

The millions of chickens that scavenge for a living—a few to a farm or a village household in many parts of the world, from which the owners harvest perhaps sixty small eggs from each hen each year—make small but important contributions to the supply of animal protein for human consumption (Fig. 1-15). This portion of the world's poultry industry contrasts sharply with the highly specialized chicken industry in the United States—an industry characterized by centralized breeding farms and hatcheries, breeding systems planned and supervised by highly trained geneticists, feeding systems based on the latest results of nutritional research, highly organized processing and marketing systems, and a ready demand for its products based on a level of economic development under which people can afford to buy substantial amounts of eggs and chicken meat.

Equally sharp is the contrast between the system of pork production in China (Phillips and Hsu, 1944; Phillips, Johnson, and Moyer, 1945) and that practiced in the Corn Belt of the United States or the system utilized for the production of bacon-type hogs in Denmark. In both the latter systems, the farmers have access to carefully bred stock, generally practice modern and efficient methods of feeding and management, have access to the feeds from which to provide balanced rations, and either specialize in pork production or fit it into a general farm operation as an important phase of the farm business. And in both countries, there is a ready market for pork products. Pork is a highly favored article of diet among the Chinese (Fig. 1-16). However, the economic level is such that, for most people, pork is a luxury, a feast food to be enjoyed only on special occasions and then in relatively small amounts. The demands made on the land for the production of crops for human consumption are so high that

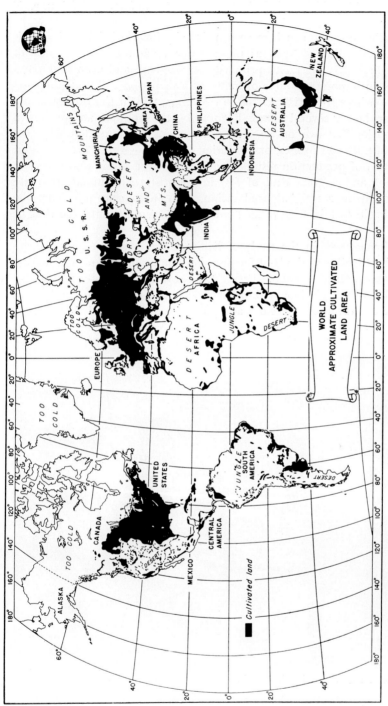

Fig. 1-11. Map showing the approximate cultivated land area of the world. When considering the questions of future world population and how those people are to be fed, it must be recalled that only about 28.3% of the world's surface is land. The land surface is in turn only about 30% arable, while another 30% is devoted to grazing and forests, and approximately 40% is unproductive. Livestock provide the only currently available means of harvesting a crop from much of the earth's land surface.

15

the production of a crop such as corn, primarily for the feeding of pigs, is out of the question. In many areas, pigs are weaned at one to two months of age, after which they are raised primarily on roughage and farm refuse and are used as an important source of manure. This period of "stretching up" may last anywhere from six months to two years, and in the process, a pig may change hands several times. Eventually, the animals are put on a fattening ration for two or three months, often in connection with the operation of mills, oil presses, or breweries, and are then sold for slaughter. Such a system of production results in animals with a minimum of muscle development and a great deal of fat, in contrast with animals that are adequately fed on a well-balanced ration, high in concentrates, from the time they begin to take food other than their dam's milk until the time of slaughter.

It is quite natural, in the study of livestock production, to concentrate upon the breeds, the methods of feeding and management, and the market requirements and methods of marketing that prevail in our own country, and to overlook its interrelations with other aspects of United States and world agriculture. However, our livestock and poultry industries are but a segment

Fig. 1-12. Churning butter from whole milk in the Himalayan highlands of Nepal. Yaks and Yak-cattle hybrids make important contributions to the milk and butter supply in the Tibetan and Mongolian highlands of Asia. [Phillips, Tolstoy and Johnson, 1946. FAO photo by S. Siegenthaler.]

Fig. 1-13. Ankole cattle of East Africa. This unusual-appearing breed is among the many distinct types found in Africa which make important contributions to man's food supply by transforming roughage into meat. [Photo by Uganda Protectorate Department of Information.]

of the national agricultural picture. The total agricultural industry of the United States is in turn but a part of the world picture. Improved communications, high speed transportation, more travel and exchange of information, greater attention to international trade, and other factors are bringing countries and peoples closer and closer together. So it is becoming increasingly difficult if not impossible for the livestock and poultry industries or the overall agriculture of a country to develop in isolation. Thus the scope and potential of our own livestock and poultry industries can be best understood and appreciated if considered against a world background (Fig. 1-17). Moreover, there are important lessons to be learned from the experiences of other countries, and on occasion we may find it profitable to draw upon the sources of germ plasm available in those countries. In the development of our livestock industry, we have depended primarily upon the breeds that our forefathers brought with them from the British Isles and adjacent parts of northwestern Europe. When new stock was desired, we have returned to the same sources. For our poultry breeds, we have ranged somewhat farther afield. But we have made use of relatively few of the sources of germ plasm in the world. For example, our zebu cattle, which we call Brahmans and which came from India rather than from the primary sources

Fig. 1-14. Boran steers in Kenya. This is one of the several African breeds containing a high percentage of Zebu blood which are well adapted to tropical and subtropical grazing conditions in Africa. [Photo by Kenya Department of Information.]

of our other breeds of cattle, are based primarily upon one breed, the Kankrej, with presumably some small admixtures of blood from two or three other zebu breeds. In India, and in Pakistan, there are six major groups and at least 28 more or less distinct breeds of zebus (Phillips, 1944; Joshi and Phillips, 1953). In Africa, there are eight major groups of cattle, comprising some 33 more or less distinct types and breeds. Many of these contain considerable amounts of zebu blood, and some are essentially pure zebu (Joshi, McLaughlin, and Phillips, 1957).

The livestock industry is not only diverse, but it is subject to change. It has shared in the changes that have characterized agriculture in many countries during the present century, and it cannot avoid sharing in further changes that are bound to come. In times of change, today's solution may be inadequate tomorrow.

The agricultural revolution of recent decades is well advanced in the United States and in some of the other more highly developed countries (Fig. 1-18). Less developed countries are striving to bring about similar revolutions in their own agriculture (Fig. 1-19). This is a process that will continue for many years and which is having marked effects on cropping and livestock-production systems and on both rural and urban peoples.

In 1910, the people on farms in the United States constituted 34.9% of the country's population. By 1959, the number of people on farms had dropped to 12% of the population. This in itself is an indication of the marked shift that has come about in the amount of food and other agricultural products one farmer can produce. In this shift, the farmer has become more and more dependent upon mechanical power and equipment. In 1910, there were 24,211,000 horses and mules on farms in the United States. This number increased to a peak of 26,723,000 in 1918, then gradually declined. By 1959, the number had dropped to 3,079,000, or only about 11.5% of the peak number in 1918. This is but one indication of the extent to which farmers have altered their methods to take advantage of modern technical and scientific developments and to meet competition. In this whole process, there has been a remarkable shift in the productivity per

Fig. 1-15. Vaccination of chickens against Newcastle disease in Thailand. The large basket contains birds awaiting their turn. In contrast with the situation in countries where typical production units have large numbers of chickens kept under conditions of intensive management, many chickens (as well as other poultry) are kept in small groups—a few to a farm or a village household—in many parts of the world and these birds are important sources of animal protein, particularly in the underdeveloped parts of the world. [FAO photo by S. Bunnag.]

Fig. 1-16. A fat hog being delivered to market by wheelbarrow in Chengtu, China. Pork is a favorite food of the Chinese. Production is carried out in association with intensive rice culture in the south and with wheat and other cereal culture in the north. Every effort is made to avoid loss of weight in transit to market. [Photo by Ralph W. Phillips.]

worker. In 1820, one farm worker produced enough to meet the needs of four persons. By 1940, the number had increased to 11; by 1958, one farm worker was producing enough for 23 persons. Comparing automation on our larger farms with the relatively inefficient operations on most smaller units, one can visualize further marked increases in productivity per worker in the United States and in other countries.

Although there has been a marked decrease in the number of draft animals, other classes of livestock have maintained important places in the agricultural economy of the United States. But they have not been without competition. The development of synthetic fibers has had its effect on the wool trade. Vegetable fats and oils are competing to an increasing degree with fats of animal origin. Improvements in both processing and transportation and developments in international trade are leading other countries to offer more specialty livestock products on the American market. Changes in consumer demand have resulted in changes in animal type and in the management and feeding of livestock and poultry. Over the last several decades, there has been a decided shift from the lard type to the leaner type of hog. Beef steers go to market at a younger age than they did at the beginning of the century. Turkeys are smaller and more compact. Competition among the various livestock products for their share of the consumer's dollar seems certain to continue.

Human populations will continue to increase. The world is experiencing a population explosion the results of which cannot be fully predicted, but it is certain to have its effect upon the way people live, on the amount of land available for food production, and may have substantial effects upon the kinds of food people eat. The human race required 1,750,000 years, or perhaps more, to build up to the 2.5 billion mark; yet at the present rate of increase, it will add another 2 billion in only thirty years. It is estimated that by the year 2000 the population level will have reached approximately 6,280,000,000 (United Nations, 1958). The United States is sharing actively in this increase. Earlier it was pointed out that there are more than twice as many farm animals and poultry in the world than there are people. But

Fig. 1-18. Merino "hoggets" in the yards at Glentanner Station in New Zealand. Ben Ohau Range, in the background, rises to 8,000 feet. These sheep are part of a flock of eight to nine thousand, mostly Merinos, that graze the foothill country on this station. Their fine wool stands in sharp contrast with the wool of the Barbary sheep, shown in Fig. 1-19, which is used primarily for carpets.

(1956), are worth noting: Pork, 20%; Milk (from dairy cows), 15%; Eggs, 7%; Poultry meat, 5%; Beef, 4%; and Lamb, 4%. These estimates were based on somewhat better than average production, under good feeding practices. Granted that it may be possible to maintain the present level of consumption of animal products per person, will the larger amounts required as the result of population increases be produced as a result of proportionate expansions in livestock and poultry numbers? If this solution were adopted, could room be found for the numbers of animals and birds that would be required? Or can improvements in breeding, feeding, and management be brought about fast enough so that present numbers of livestock and poultry can produce at sufficiently higher average levels to meet the requirements of expanding human populations? At what levels will human populations plateau in various countries? When they do plateau,

Fig. 1-17. An Indian villager herds a sow into an underground hog house. This type of housing is used to protect the animals from the extreme summer heat of the plains of central India. Although swine make very important contributions to man's food supply in many parts of the world, pork is used only to a limited extent in India. [Photo by Ralph. W. Phillips.]

by the turn of this century, it is expected that the number of people will exceed the present total number of farm animals and birds. In the few decades that remain before this century ends, therefore, it seems certain that some very critical questions will have to be answered.

How much productive farm and grazing land will be used for dwelling space, for factories, for highways, for air fields? To what degree will farmers have to start using lands for crop production that are now in pasture or forest, or are not sufficiently productive to be used at all under present circumstances? As population pressures build up, can those peoples who now enjoy high levels of animal products in their diets continue to do so? Or will they have to shift gradually to diets containing higher proportions of foods of plant origin? Can people in countries which now use only small amounts of animal products per person maintain those levels or will they have to depend almost entirely on foods of plant origin? In this connection, the following average percentages of the gross energy in feed eaten by various kinds of animals that are converted into human food, as given by Morrison what kinds of balances will have developed between crop and livestock production?

These are complex problems, and their solutions will not be simple. The solutions may be quite different in different countries; for example, it is possible that some countries that have relatively small human populations may concentrate even more on livestock (Figs. 1-16 and 1-17) and/or poultry production for domestic consumption and/or export, whereas other countries that have dense human populations may find it necessary to increase the proportions of foods of plant origin in the average diet. But the object here is not to provide or even to suggest answers; rather, it is to indicate something of the challenge that lies ahead for the producers of livestock and poultry and for those who serve these industries.

The producer of livestock and poultry, in this world of agricultural change, must draw to an ever increasing degree upon knowledge from many sources if he is to put on the market the kinds of products consumers want, and if he is to breed, feed, and manage his animals or birds in such ways

Fig. 1-19. Barbary sheep in Libya. In many parts of the world sheep make important contributions to man's food and fiber supply, utilizing much land that is unsuited to intensive agriculture. [FAO photo.]

that they will produce efficiently and bring him a reasonable profit. To produce high quality products that will not be unduly out of line with plant products on a cost basis, he must have an understanding of animal genetics, of the physiology of reproduction and nutrition, and of the complex problems of feeding, management, and marketing. Butter affords an excellent example of a superior animal product that declined in popularity because of the disparity between its price and that of plant substitutes. Today, meat products, milk, and eggs stand unsurpassed from the standpoint of consumer preference, but the livestock producer cannot stand on his laurels. He must, by individual and cooperative effort, improve still further the quality of his products and simultaneously increase the efficiency of production in order that they will not be priced out of the market. In these circumstances, the livestock producer must have an understanding of the laws of supply and demand and of the overall economic situation in his own and other countries, so that he may assess short- and long-term demands for his products, as well as possible shifts in consumer preferences and in the conditions of production. It is against this background that we undertake the study of the various aspects of livestock and poultry production.

REFERENCES AND SELECTED READINGS

References marked with an asterisk are of general interest.

*Acock, A. M., 1950. Progress and economic problems in farm mechanization. Food and Agriculture Organization of the United Nations, Rome, Italy, pp. 1–88.

*FAO, 1959. Production yearbook, 1958. Food and Agriculture Organization of the United Nations, Rome, Italy, pp. 1–475.

Finci, M., 1957. The improvement of the Awassi breed of sheep in Israel. Bull. Research Council of Israel, Section B, Biology and Geology, 6B, No. 1–2:1–106.

*Joshi, N. R., E. A. McLaughlin, and R. W. Phillips, 1957. Types and breeds of African cattle. Agricultural Studies no. 37, Food and Agriculture Organization of the United Nations, Rome, Italy, pp. 1–297, illus.

*Joshi, N. R. and R. W. Phillips, 1953. Zebu cattle of India and Pakistan. Agricultural Studies no. 19, Food and Agriculture Organization of the United Nations, Rome, Italy, pp. 1–256, illus.

*Morrison, F. B., 1956. *Feeds and Feeding.* The Morrison Pub. Co., Ithaca.

Phillips, R. W., 1944. The cattle of India. *J. Heredity,* 35:273–288.

———, 1945. The water buffalo of India. *J. Heredity,* 36:71–76.

*———, 1948. Breeding livestock adapted to unfavorable environments. Agricultural Studies no. 1, Food and Agriculture Organization of the United Nations, Rome, Italy, pp. 1–182, illus.

———, 1950–51. Expansion of livestock production in relation to human needs. *Nutrition Abstracts and Reviews,* 21:241–256.

*——— (Editor), 1956. Recent developments affecting livestock production in the Americas. Agricultural Development Paper no. 55, Food and Agriculture Organization of the United Nations, Rome, Italy, pp. 1–181, illus.

———, 1958. The effects of climate on animals and their performance: an introduction to a symposium. *J. Heredity,* 49:47–51.

———, 1960. Man and his cattle. *The Cattleman,* 46:21–25, 72, 74, 76, 78–80, 82.

————, and T. Y. Hsu, 1944. Chinese swine and their performance compared with modern and crosses between Chinese and modern breeds. *J. Heredity*, 35:365–379.

*————, R. G. Johnson, and R. T. Moyer, 1945. The livestock of China. U.S. Department of State Publication 2249, Far Eastern Series 9, pp. 1–174, illus.

————, I. A. Tolstoy, and R. G. Johnson, 1946. Yaks and yak-cattle hybrids in Asia. *J. Heredity*, 37:162–170, 206–215.

Reed, C. A., 1959. Animal domestication in the prehistoric Near East. *Science*, 130: 1629–1639.

*United Nations, 1958. The future growth of world population. United Nations, New York, pp. 1–75.

USDA, 1960. Agricultural Statistics, 1959. United States Department of Agriculture and Government Printing Office, Washington, D.C.

Section I

Livestock Products

Chapter 2

Meats

And who abstains from meat that is not gaunt?
SHAKESPEARE, *Richard II*

2-1. INTRODUCTION

The term meat, as used in this discussion, will refer to all parts of the dressed carcass, whether beef, pork, veal, lamb, or mutton. Meat consists not only of muscular tissue, bones, and fat, but also includes the edible glands and organs removed at slaughter.

The sale of meat animals provides the largest single source of farm income, as shown in Fig. 2-1. Meat currently provides 32 cents of every dollar of farm income.

2-2. MEAT CONSUMPTION

In 1959, the per capita meat consumption in the United States was 160 lb. (Fig. 2-2). Twelve pounds of lard were also used per capita, in addition to other edible animal fats. Over 93% of all meat consumed was

MEAT ANIMALS GIVE FARMERS MOST DOLLARS

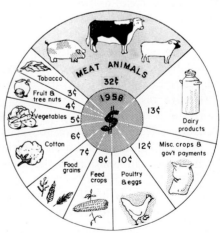

Fig. 2-1. The source of the farmer's dollar. [From the American Meat Institute, Chicago, Ill.]

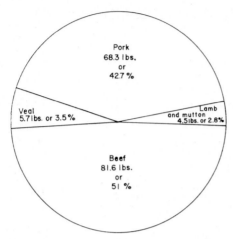

Fig. 2-2. Amount and proportion of various kinds of meat consumed in the United States in 1959. [Data from USDA Supplement for 1959 to Statistical Bull. #320.]

either beef or pork, whereas the consumption of veal, lamb, and mutton totaled less than 7%.

Great variation exists in the per capita meat consumption from one country to the next (Fig. 2-3). Australia, New Zealand, and Uruguay surpassed U.S. consumption by 40 to 65 lb. per person in 1958 and Argentina consumed 6 lb. per capita more. Meat consumption in Argentina dropped from an average of 222 lb. for the years 1951–1955, and from 244 and 242 lb. per capita in 1956 and 1957, respectively, to only 166 lb. per person in 1958. This large decline has been attributed to a drastic reduction in the number of breeding animals, owing to an expanding meat export trade.

2-3. MEAT AS A FOOD

The importance of meat in the diet is well known. Research has shown meat to be an excellent source of most B-complex vitamins, especially niacin. Lean pork contains relatively large amounts of thiamin. The greatest contribution of meat to the diet is related to its protein content, which is important chiefly because it supplies all of the essential amino acids in adequate amounts.

Because of similarities in composition and in nutritive value, meat from swine, sheep, and cattle is often grouped with poultry and fish in evaluating the relative importance of various classes of foods. The data of Clark *et al.* (1947) are presented in this manner (Fig. 2-4). Meat is not only a good source of B-vitamins and amino acids, but also supplies large amounts of iron. Liver is an outstanding source of this nutrient. Of particular interest to a weight-conscious public is the relatively low level of calories supplied by lean meat in relation to the amounts of B-vitamins and high quality protein.

The digestibility of edible meat—normally well over 95%—is sometimes used as a standard for comparison with other foods. Frequently, one hears that fat meat, particularly pork, is indigestible. There is no basis for this claim. However, fat is digested more slowly.

The meat industry should be aware of the problem of atherosclerosis (hardening of the arteries), which is the leading cause of death in the US today. Meat and, more particularly, animal fats have been claimed to increase the blood cholesterol level, which many physicians believe is responsible for atherosclerosis. However, cholesterol is synthesized by the body even in the absence of dietary sources. The best information indicates that the dietary level of cholesterol is only one of a number of contributory factors involved in causing atherosclerosis (Maddox, 1960). At present, indications are that hardening of the arteries can best be avoided by adequate exercise and avoiding obesity. Except for a reduction in total calories, no major dietary changes are generally being recommended.

2-4. COMPOSITION OF MEAT

The American Meat Institute Foundation (1960) gives the average composition of the edible portion of fresh meat cuts at 17% protein, 20% fat, 62% moisture, and 1% ash. Since wide variability in composition exists, an average value serves only as a general guide.

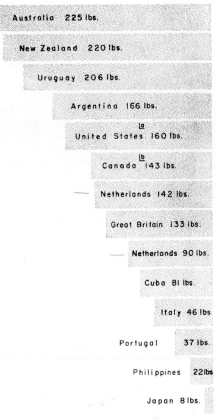

Fig. 2-3. Meat consumption per person for some countries of the world. [Data from USDA "Foreign Crops and Markets" (1959).]

The percentage of separable lean in a carcass or cut varies widely and is inversely related to fat content (Fig. 2-5). It is interesting to note that the percentage of bone and tendon declines directly with muscle, but varies inversely with fatty tissue.

2-5. WHAT THE CONSUMER WANTS IN MEAT

All members of the meat team—the producer, the packer, and the retailer—should keep in mind that they are in business to serve the consumer. Consequently, they should know why the consumer eats meat and what he desires for maximum satisfaction, then gear production, processing, and distribution systems toward best meeting consumer desires. The prestige that meat enjoys in this country depends largely upon its savory character-

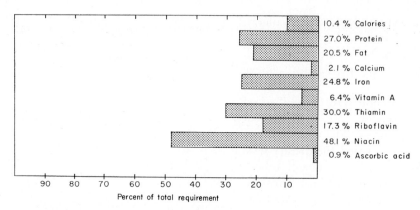

Fig. 2-4. Percentage of total dietary requirement for each nutrient supplied by meat, poultry, and fish.

istics and, to a lesser extent, upon its high nutritive value. Tenderness, flavor, juiciness, leanness, and attractiveness, which includes color and firmness, appear to be the main criteria the consumer considers.

Tenderness. According to consumer studies, tenderness is the most important palatability attribute for acceptance of beef. Tenderness is less critical for veal, lamb, and pork because of less variability from animal to

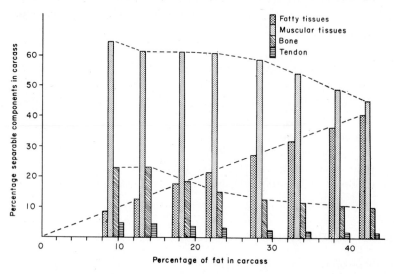

Fig. 2-5. Changes in the proportion of different components as the carcass changes in fatness. [From E. H. Callow. "Comparative studies of meat II. The changes in the carcass during growth and fattening, and their relation to the chemical composition of the fatty and muscular tissues." *J. Agr. Sci.,* 38: 174, 1948.]

animal. Although tenderness can be altered by cooking, aging, and enzyme treatment, only the pre-slaughter factors will be considered at this point. Many characteristics have been suggested as possible indicators of tenderness, among which are conformation, maturity, finish, marbling, and muscle structure.

CONFORMATION. According to recent studies by J. W. Cole (personal communication), body type, or conformation, is unrelated to tenderness. Cole found that Jersey steers of poor beef conformation produce, on the average, more tender steaks than do Angus or Hereford steers of good beef type. Holsteins are less tender than Jerseys. Brahmans produce the toughest steaks.

MATURITY. A number of researchers have shown that younger, more immature beef is more tender. The determination of maturity in the retail market is a difficult task. In the carcass, maturity is estimated by the redness and degree of ossification of the spinous processes. Since about 3–5% of cutter and canner cows are as tender as young beef, it is obvious that maturity is not solely responsible for tenderness. Nevertheless, the marketing of cattle, hogs, and lambs when relatively immature is more likely to produce tender meat.

FINISH OR DEGREE OF FATNESS. Several workers have reported that fatter hogs are more tender than lean hogs, but the relationship is not clear-cut. Some evidence points to a similar relationship for beef. From the standpoint of tenderness, it is doubtful whether additional external finish beyond the amounts needed to permit distribution to retailers without surface drying or slime growth is advantageous.

MARBLING. The amount and distribution of intramuscular fat, commonly called marbling, has been quite generally accepted as an indicator of tenderness by the meat trade. Although evidence was submitted over 20 years ago, however, showing that there is little relationship between marbling and tenderness (Hostetler *et al.*, 1936), general acceptance of the low relationship is relatively recent. A number of workers have shown that marbling accounts for only about 10% of the tenderness variation in beef. Similar values are not available for pork, but the evidence suggests that marbling may be more closely related to tenderness than in beef (Batcher and Dawson, 1960; Harrington and Pearson, 1961).

MUSCLE STRUCTURE. Muscle structure and tenderness may be related, Joubert (1956) found considerable variation in the muscle fiber diameter of different breeds of cattle; however, there seems to be little relationship between tenderness and muscle-fiber diameter (Hiner *et al.*, 1953). Although Adams *et al.* (1960) found a relationship between collagen (white connective tissue) and tenderness, other factors appear to be more important. With the electron microscope and other new tools for studying the structure of meat, the true basis for tenderness may come to light.

EFFECT OF EXERCISE. Contrary to the popular view, Mitchell and Hamilton

(1933) demonstrated that steers exercised for 131 days were slightly more tender and had less collagen in their muscles than similar unexercised animals. This work was later confirmed by Bull and Rusk (1942). Thus, moderate exercise over a considerable length of time does not appear to adversely affect meat tenderness.

Flavor. Flavor is undoubtedly the attribute that contributes most to consumer acceptance, yet personal likes and dislikes vary widely. Generally, flavor becomes more pronounced as an animal matures, as is evidenced by the full flavor of beef as compared with the blandness of veal. As with most foods, meat flavor is a blend of odor and taste. The evidence available suggests that the basic flavor of beef is due to a glycoprotein (a protein conjugated with a carbohydrate), but no doubt a host of chemical substances contribute to the distinctive flavors of meat from the various animals. Research (Kramlich and Pearson, 1958) indicates that fat does not contribute directly to beef flavor; yet fat may possibly enhance and improve flavor during cooking.

Off-flavors in meats are often the result of careless handling, but this discussion will be concerned only with problems related to production. Sex odor, or boar odor, in pork has been the basis for condemnation of boars and stags by the Meat Inspection Division of the USDA. However, the meat from boars is not unhealthful, and both federal and state meat inspectors are presently allowing boar carcasses to be used for processing purposes. This practice has resulted in a narrowing of the price spread between boars and barrows. In sheep, the problem of mutton flavor has unquestionably contributed to the low level of lamb and mutton consumption in the U.S. However, milk-fed lamb has a bland flavor, and educating the public to this fact would probably do much toward increasing the popularity of this excellent product. Beef flavor problems have been largely confined to off-flavors coming from certain feeds, such as wild onions. Removal of most feed flavor can be accomplished simply by taking the animals off of offending feeds for about 10 days prior to slaughter.

Juiciness. Certainly juiciness adds to the overall acceptability of meat, yet the separation of true juiciness from other palatability factors is difficult. Taste panel studies indicate that marbling contributes more to juiciness than to tenderness. On the other hand, neither moisture content nor press fluid have been found to be closely associated with juiciness. In general, it appears that fat covering and both inter- and intra-muscular fat tend to increase juiciness.

Leanness. Numerous consumer studies based upon visual appraisal have shown that the housewife will select lean meat when given a choice between cuts differing widely in fatness. With respect to beef, organoleptic studies have shown, on the contrary, that fatness improves acceptability. It takes more feed to put on a pound of fat than a pound of lean. Thus, from the standpoint of economy, beef producers should concentrate on developing strains of cattle yielding highly palatable meat with a minimum of fat.

Attractiveness. Since the advent of the self-service market, the retailer and meat packer have become increasingly aware of the importance of meat appearance. Color has probably been the most important single factor in attractiveness, thus, two-toned pork and dark or discolored beef and lamb sell for a discount.

Hall *et al.* (1944) studied dark-cutter beef, which fails to brighten on cutting and exposure to air. The color is normally bright at pH 5.6 or below, at 5.7 it becomes shady or dull, and at 6.5 or above it is dark. The ultimate pH of the meat depends on the amount of lactic acid produced after death, which in turn depends upon the amount of glycogen present at the time of death. By preventing undue excitement, by feeding in transit, and by avoiding undue exposure to inclement weather in marketing cattle, the incidence can be greatly reduced.

Pale, watery and two-toned pork has also been related to the glycogen content of different muscles at the time of slaughter (Briskey *et al.,* 1959). A uniformly dark product, which does not appear to be objectionable to the consumer, can be produced by using exercise or other means to deplete glycogen levels prior to slaughter. However, the incidence of spoilage increases as the pH is raised (Ingram, 1948); thus, this method of achieving a desirable meat color may not be feasible.

2-6. PROCESSING PRACTICES AND THEIR IMPACT

Today, many housewives hold full time jobs outside the home, with a consequent reduction of time available for housework. This is but one example of the kind of social changes that have altered consumer demand. In addition, other new developments promise to bring about drastic revisions in many trade and processing practices; these revisions have had, or promise to have, a marked influence upon the entire meat and livestock business.

The Super Market. The advent of self-service meats has been a stimulating influence in the development of the meat-type hog and is causing a revision in requirements for beef carcasses. Self-service markets, relying upon meat items as major drawing cards, recognize the importance of providing customer satisfaction. The consumer is offered a wide selection of cuts varying in price and in quality; thus, in making his uncoerced choices from among these items, he reflects his preferences to the packer and producer. High quality meats, attractively packaged and displayed, have increased gross meat sales at the super market.

Tenderization. Naturally occurring meat enzymes tenderize meat during aging, but rapid aging is a recent innovation. The use of ultraviolet lights to control microbial growth at elevated temperatures has permitted faster aging of entire beef carcasses. By speeding up the breakdown of connective tissue, aging can be accomplished in 2–4 days at 60–75°F. Though an increase in tenderization can be achieved, the method is not adapted for use with lower grade carcasses that lack sufficient fat covering. However, recent studies indicate that the concurrent use of antibiotics will permit higher holding temperatures and will allow lower grade meat to be aged in 24 hours or less.

Among the new developments, the one having the greatest potential for revolutionizing the production, processing, and distribution of meats today is a tenderizing method that utilizes exogenous enzymes. Goeser *et al.* (1960) make use of pre-slaughter injection of a proteolytic enzyme preparation into the vascular system of the animal. Apparently the enzyme preparation used does not result in shock on being administered to the animal and does not become active until the temperature is raised during cooking. This method presumably tenderizes low grade beef, as well as the cheaper cuts from the front quarter.

The post-slaughter injection method has also been used for tenderizing both carcasses and cuts. However, in this method, greater difficulties have been encountered in making the injection than in the live-animal procedure. None the less, large quantities of low grade meat are now being dipped or injected with enzyme solutions for tenderization.

Sausage Production. According to estimates, one twelfth of all meat is consumed as sausage. Sausage production has shown an increase for several years. This can be attributed to an increased demand for convenience items, such as lunch meats and frankfurters. Increased sausage consumption has provided a good market for boneless meat from low grade beef and heavy hogs.

2-7. THE MEAT ANIMAL AND ITS PRODUCTS

The yield of an animal, or the dressing percentage, is defined as follows:

$$\text{Dressing } \% = \frac{\text{Carcass weight}}{\text{Live weight}} \times 100.$$

Carcass yield varies considerably, depending upon a large number of factors. Weighing conditions of both the animal and the carcass will have considerable effect upon the yield. Such factors as the amount of fill (water and/or feed) before weighing of the live animal and the length of time the carcass is held in storage before it is weighed are determinants. Thus, dressing percentage has little meaning unless the conditions of weighing are accurately described. The method of dressing, the inherent size of the digestive tract and other vital organs, and the amount of finish also affect dressing percentage.

Cattle. Dressing percentage for different grades of beef are shown in Table 2-1. With the exception of the commercial grade, dressing percentage declines directly with grade, but there is considerable overlap between adjacent grades. The carcasses of many fat cows are graded as commercial, because their age prevents them from being graded as U.S. Good or higher. That is, many animals within this grade have finish enough for the higher grades, but are too old to qualify. Fat animals in this grade, therefore, have a high dressing percentage.

RELATIVE AMOUNTS AND VALUES OF PARTS. A sketch of a beef animal hanging from the rail is shown in Fig. 2-6. The carcass, which usually constitutes only 50–60% of the live weight, accounts for about 90% of the live animal's value (Table 2-2). The hide is the most valuable by-product, composing 6–11% of the weight and about 5% of the total live value. Other by-products account for only a small amount of each animal's total value. The round, loin, and rib make up 27–29% of the live animal's weight, but because they are preferred for steaks and oven roasts, they represent 62–67% of the total value of the carcass (Table 2-3). The chuck is the other major contributor, making up about 13–16% of the weight and accounting for 25–29% of the value. Thus, approximately 90% of the total carcass value of the animal is obtained from the loin, round, rib, and chuck, which represent only 39–45% of the live weight. Approximately 17–18% of the live weight consists of the kidney knob, brisket, navel, flank, and fore shank,

TABLE 2-1. | *Dressing percentage of slaughter cattle for various U.S. grades.*

Grade	Dressing percentage*
Prime	62–66
Choice	58–62
Good	56–58
Standard	52–56
Commercial	56–60
Utility	45–52
Cutter and Canner	40–48

* A normal range is given, but much larger variation occurs within any given grade.

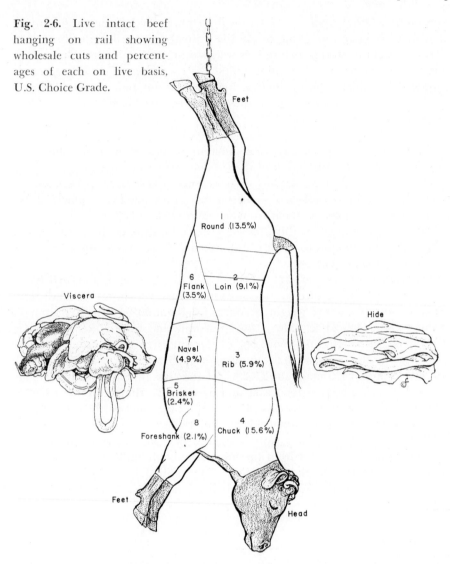

Fig. 2-6. Live intact beef hanging on rail showing wholesale cuts and percentages of each on live basis, U.S. Choice Grade.

but these parts account for only 10% of the total value of the live animal. The hind quarter makes up only 25–30% of the live weight, yet it constitutes about 52–57% of the value.

Helser and coworkers reported on the effect of fattening on the yield of various wholesale cuts. Carcass yield and the percentages of loin, flank, kidney knob, and plate all increased markedly with higher levels of finish; the percentage of rib increased slightly. On the other hand, the percentage of chuck and fore shank were not greatly influenced by finish. The percentage of round declined with increased fatness.

STEER VERSUS HEIFER BEEF. Beef heifers of the English breeds fatten at an

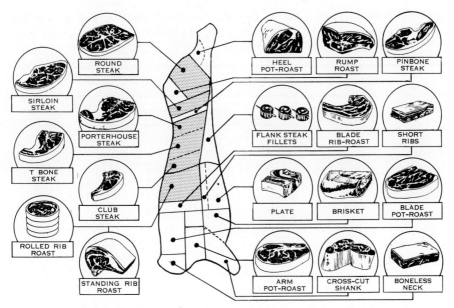

Fig. 2-7. Location of retail cuts of a beef carcass. [Courtesy National Livestock and Meat Board.]

earlier age and at a lighter weight than steers; if carried in the feed lot much beyond 900 lb. live weight, they become excessively fat and take on many of the carcass attributes of older cows. In addition to the discounting for overfatness, heifers sell for less than steers of equal quality and grade.

TABLE 2-2. *Weight and value of the carcass and non-carcass parts of cattle expressed as percentages of the weight and value of the live animal.*

	% live weight	% live value
Hide	6.0–11.0	4.6
Feet	1.3–1.8	0.1
Heart	0.3–0.5	0.3
Caul fat	0.0–3.0	0.3
Liver	0.9–1.2	0.8
Lungs	0.9–1.3	0.2
Kidneys	0.4–0.6	0.2
Head		
tongue	0.2–0.4	0.3
head and cheek meat	0.3–0.5	0.4
head bones	2.3–2.5	0.2
Remainder of viscera	17.0–28.0	2.6
Carcass, dressed *	50.0–62.0	89.7

* Based on U.S. Good carcass with no allowance for costs of slaughtering.

TABLE
2-3.

Weight and value of fore quarters, hind quarters, and high priced cuts, expressed as percentages of the weight and value, respectively, of live animals in the various grades.

	High priced cuts*		Fore quarter		Hind quarter	
	Weight	Value	Weight	Value	Weight	Value
Prime	28.6	65.3	32.5	44.9	29.6	55.1
Choice	28.5	66.7	30.9	43.8	28.3	56.1
Good	28.6	66.5	28.5	43.3	28.0	56.7
Standard	27.7	63.5	27.4	45.8	26.8	54.1
Commercial	28.0	59.5	30.3	48.1	27.4	51.7
Utility	26.7	62.2	24.6	45.5	25.4	54.6

* High priced cuts include the loin, rib, and round (rump on).

Carcass cutting tests made at a number of stations have shown that heifers of similar grade and quality are equal in every way to steers. Thus, this discrimination does not appear to be justified. The trade practice of penalizing heifers is no doubt an outgrowth of the lowered dressing percentage associated with pregnancy.

TYPE AND YIELD. The claim is frequently made that "beef-type" cattle produce carcasses yielding a greater proportion of high-priced cuts. The work of Wilson and Curtis (1893) at Iowa has often been cited to support this claim, yet their data show little difference between beef-type and dairy-type steers. This work was done nearly 70 years ago. More recent work (Butler, 1957; Butler *et al.,* 1956; Stonaker *et al.,* 1952; Willey *et al.,* 1951) indicates that there are no major differences in regard to wholesale cut-out percentages between comprest and conventional-type beef cattle or between cattle containing various proportions of Hereford and Brahman stock. Similarly, a comparison of the percentages of front and hind quarter in cattle of different types has revealed little difference (Stroble *et al.,* 1951; Stonaker *et al.,* 1952).

Hogs. Table 2-4 gives the percentages of the different wholesale cuts by weight and value on the basis of live weight for three grades of pork. Since the grade standards are based chiefly on backfat thickness, the differences noted depend primarily upon differences in fatness. The lean cuts, and to a lesser extent the primal cuts, decline as fatness increases, whereas the percentage of fat trim increases.

AMOUNTS AND VALUES OF PARTS. The lean cuts make up 39% of the weight but 73% of the value of a U.S. No. 1 pig, as compared to 37% of the weight and 72% of the value for a U.S. No. 3 pig. The U.S. No. 2 pig is interme-

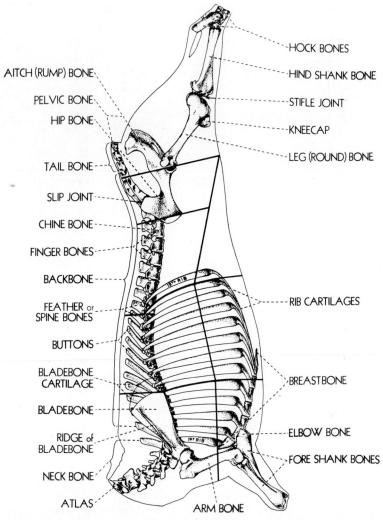

AITCH (RUMP) BONE

PELVIC BONE

HIP BONE

TAIL BONE

SLIP JOINT

CHINE BONE

FINGER BONES

BACKBONE

FEATHER or SPINE BONES

BUTTONS

BLADEBONE CARTILAGE

BLADEBONE

RIDGE of BLADEBONE

NECK BONE

ATLAS

HOCK BONES

HIND SHANK BONE

STIFLE JOINT

KNEECAP

LEG (ROUND) BONE

RIB CARTILAGES

BREASTBONE

ELBOW BONE

FORE SHANK BONES

ARM BONE

Fig. 2-8. Trade terminology of the bony structure of a beef carcass in relation to the principal wholesale cuts. See Fig. 2-6 for the names of the wholesale cuts. [Courtesy National Livestock and Meat Board.]

diate between the two. The percentage of fat trim increases from 17% of the weight and 5% of the value for the U.S. No. 1 pig to 21% of the weight and 7% of the value for the U.S. No. 3 pig. The increase in the percentage of fat trim tends to compensate for the decline in the percentage of lean cuts. As a result of the increased value of the fat trim and an increase in dressing percentage as fatness increases, the spread in value between grades becomes narrower, often causing farmers to comment that packers do not

| TABLE 2-4. | *Weight and value of wholesale pork cuts expressed as percentages of the weight and value of live hogs in the various grades.** |

	U.S. No. 1		U.S. No. 2		U.S. No. 3	
Dressing %	74.24		74.74		75.05	
Av. backfat thickness (in.)	1.42		1.72		1.96	

	Percentages					
Wholesale Cut	Wt.	Value	Wt.	Value	Wt.	Value
Ham, skinned	14.7	30.3	13.7	28.8	13.0	28.0
Loin	11.8	24.9	11.5	24.7	11.1	24.5
N.Y. shoulder†	12.8	18.0	13.0	18.6	12.9	19.0
Belly	10.0	14.1	10.1	14.5	9.7	14.3
Lean trim	1.8	1.8	1.6	1.6	1.4	1.5
Fat trim plus leaf fat	16.6	5.0	19.2	5.9	21.4	6.7
Spareribs	1.9	3.5	1.9	3.6	1.9	3.7
Jowls	2.0	1.1	2.0	1.1	2.0	1.2
Neckbones	1.3	0.6	1.3	0.6	1.3	0.6
Feet	1.9	0.6	1.9	0.6	1.9	0.6
Lean cuts**	39.3	73.2	38.2	72.1	37.0	71.5
Primal cuts‡	49.3	87.3	48.3	86.6	46.7	85.8

* Data taken from hogs slaughtered at Michigan Agricultural Experiment Station, Meats Laboratory.
† New York shoulder is essentially the same as the Boston butt plus picnic, but is left in one piece.
** Lean cuts include loin, ham, and N.Y. shoulder.
‡ The term primal cuts means major cuts from value standpoint and includes lean cuts plus belly.

pay for quality. Be this as it may, pork consumption has gone down in recent years, owing to consumer resistance to fat pork; thus, it behooves the producer to market leaner hogs.

LEAN OR PRIMAL CUTS. Any improvement of pork carcasses must necessarily be based upon proper methods of evaluation. One of the controversies has been whether the most rapid progress could be made by using lean or primal cuts. Primal cuts include the belly (a fat cut), in addition to the lean cuts. Thus, using primal cuts tends to slow down improvement for leanness, but at the same time tends to circumvent production of underfinished carcasses. The belly, though considerably less valuable than loin and ham, is about equal to the shoulder per unit of weight. The question is still unresolved, but the tendency has been to use lean cuts because of more rapid improvement in leanness.

LEANNESS AND DRESSING PERCENTAGE. On the average, fatter hogs have a higher dressing percentage than lean ones; however, the relationship is relatively low. A truly meaty hog may have a high dressing percentage, whereas a hog that is lean but which lacks muscling will have a low carcass yield,

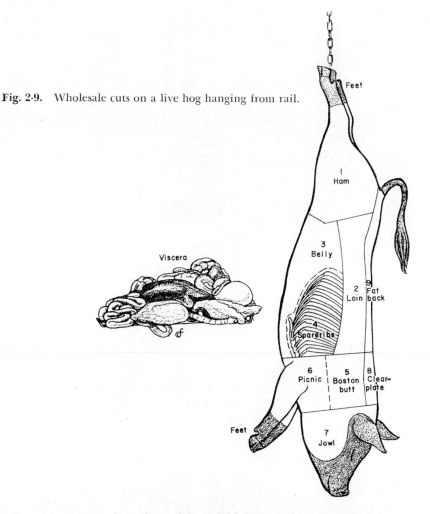

Fig. 2-9. Wholesale cuts on a live hog hanging from rail.

Thus, breeders must reject sires of low-yield hogs lacking in muscling or meatiness.

LENGTH OF CARCASS. A few years ago, length of carcass was given great emphasis in progeny evaluation programs and in carcass judging. More recent evidence shows that the relationship between length of carcass and the percentage of lean or primal cuts is low, although positive. In view of present evidence, the use of length in swine carcass evaluation is of questionable value.

Lamb and Mutton. Generally, the carcass yield of U.S. Prime and Choice grade lambs is 50–54%. Variations outside this range are due to the weight of the fleece and to weighing conditions. U.S. Good lambs usually dress

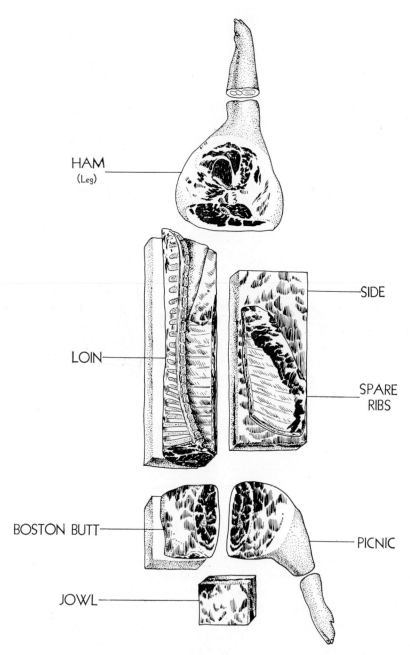

Fig. 2-10. Location of wholesale cuts of pork. Note that the spareribs are removed from the overlying flesh leaving the side or clear belly for processing of bacon. [Courtesy National Livestock and Meat Board.]

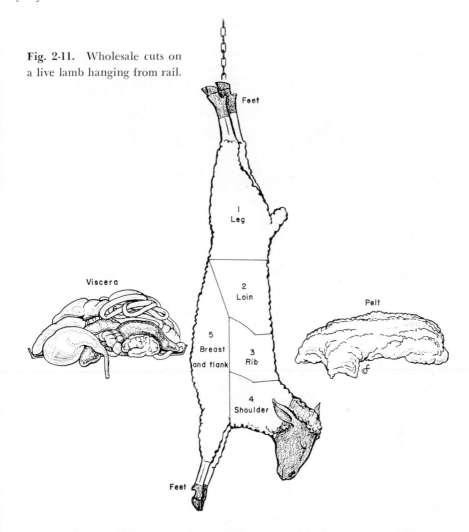

Fig. 2-11. Wholesale cuts on a live lamb hanging from rail.

47–50%. Dressing percentage for the lower grades tends to decline directly as grade decreases.

The value of lamb and mutton by-products is more variable than for the other species. The variation is due to differences in quality of the pelt and to the fluctuations in wool prices. Many lambs are sold following shearing, when the pelt is of little value, whereas others are sold in full fleece. Since the full fleece often weighs 6–8 lb. or more, great variability in value occurs. The amount of wool also has a marked influence on the dressing percentage.

THE PERCENTAGE AND VALUE OF CUTS. Although the method of cutting lamb differs from that used for beef, the differences in value between desirable and less desirable cuts are probably very much alike (Table 2-5). Although the leg, loin, and rack make up only a little over 29% of the live weight,

TABLE 2-5. | *Weight and value of wholesale cuts of lamb expressed as percentages of the weight and value of the live animal.**

	Percentage	
	Weight	Value
Leg (long cut)	16.7	43.2
Loin	7.3	22.2
Hotel rack	5.2	10.4
Shoulder	13.3	6.7
Breast and shank	9.5	17.4

* Based on a dressing percentage of 52.

they constitute about 76% of the total value of the carcass. The wholesale cuts for lamb are shown in Fig. 2-11.

MUTTON VERSUS LAMB. In the United States, any sheep carcass that fails to show the break joint is classified as mutton. Consequently, there is wide variation in fatness, weight, conformation, flavor, and other characteristics among mutton carcasses. The trade has generally paid a premium for lamb and has discounted mutton severely regardless of age. Old crop lambs (sold

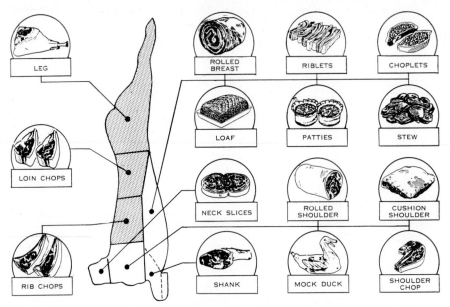

Fig. 2-12. Location of retail cuts of lamb. Wholesale cuts are indicated by heavy lines, but are not labeled. [Modified from figure supplied through courtesy of National Livestock and Meat Board.]

at about a year of age after fattening on irrigated pasture or in dry lot) sell considerably lower than milk-fed early spring lambs.

INFLUENCE OF CONFORMATION. Ljundahl (1942) and Henneman (1942) found that long-legged rangy lambs have a higher percentage of leg than compact short-legged lambs. On the other hand, the shorter-legged lambs have a greater percentage of loin and rack, with no great difference in shoulder. Thus, it appears that conformation has little effect on the yields of high priced cuts.

Veal and Calf. The major difference between beef, calf, and veal is a matter of maturity or age. In general terms, veal is under 3 months of age, calf is less than 12 months, and beef over 12 months at the time of slaughter. In comparison with beef, both veal and calf are lighter colored, have less fat, have less flavor and firmness, and are more watery. Since calf is older than veal, the flesh more nearly resembles beef. Owing to seasonal production, veal and calf have not been promoted, and demand has remained relatively low. Although little research has been conducted on the composition and quality of the meat, consumer demands probably parallel those for beef. The term "baby beef" has been used in the past to denote cattle finished on full feed at 12–18 months of age. However, the use of the term "baby beef" has become less common. Since many calves go direct to the feed lot for fattening at weaning time, much of the beef consumed today would have been classed as "baby beef" twenty years ago.

2-8. RECOGNITION OF CARCASS TRAITS IN LIVE ANIMALS

The improvement of meat animals could be most effectively achieved if superior animals could be recognized on foot. As a partial solution of the problem, several methods for determining fat content of the live animal have been proposed.

Live Probe. The live probe method of measuring backfat thickness on hogs was developed by Hazel and Kline (1952). A steel ruler is inserted through a skin incision. The method is a good indicator of lean cuts of pork and has been widely used by the swine industry. It has been criticized on the basis that it measures fatness directly and leanness indirectly. The method is not effective in sheep or cattle.

Lean Meter. This technique, developed by Andrews and Whaley, permits measurement of subcutaneous fat thickness, using a needle that indicates differences in electrical conductivity for fat and lean tissues. It appears to offer little or no advantage over the live probe method and is more expensive.

Thermistor Probe. The thermistor probe measures subcutaneous fat thickness by showing temperature changes as the needle passes from fat to lean tissues (Warren *et al.,* 1959). The method has appeared to be useful in measuring fatness in cattle.

Ultrasonics. Ultrasound has been used extensively by the steel industry for the detection of flaws and, more recently, by the medical profession for locating and studying abnormal tissues. Basically, sound waves are generated and sent out through the tissues; whenever a change in density occurs, a reflection is returned and amplified on an oscilloscope. Temple and co-workers (1956) used the instrument to measure fat thickness in cattle. Since then, it has been used successfully in lambs and hogs.

Stouffer (1959) has developed a method of plotting the cross-sectional area of the rib-eye muscle from ultrasonic reflections and angular readings in hogs, lambs, and cattle. Even though the method is effective, its usefulness is questionable, since Cole *et al.* (1960) found rib-eye area to have a low predictive value for total carcass lean.

Live-Animal Measurement. Extensive measurements on live animals have been made and related to carcass traits, but, in general, they have not proven useful. It is questionable whether further investigation on live measurements is warranted.

Potassium-40. The naturally occurring radioisotope K^{40} is found in all living cells and is therefore concentrated in the lean tissues. Since the background radioactivity interferes, special shielding and counting equipment is needed. Although the method has been found to be useful in measuring extreme differences in fatness (Kirton *et al.,* 1961), the cost of satisfactory counters and equipment would demand extreme sensitivity in order to justify its use in preference to cheaper methods.

Antipyrine and Other Body-water Diluents. A method that involves injecting antipyrine (or injecting one of several other compounds, such as urea) and noting its dilution has been investigated as a means of predicting fatness or leanness. However, the reports on its accuracy are conflicting.

Specific Gravity. Specific gravity or relative density has long been recognized as a good measure of leanness. Carcass density can be accurately determined by underwater weighing, but this procedure obviously cannot be used with live animals. The determination of specific gravity by measuring body volume on the basis of air displacement (Liuzzo *et al.,* 1958) or by helium dilution (Siri, 1956) have been proposed. Although these methods appear sound, mechanical problems have prevented the desired accuracy.

Creatinine Excretion. The creatinine coefficient (mg of creatinine excreted in 24 hr per kg of body weight) is theoretically proportional to leanness. Studies with farm animals have failed to show the method to be sufficiently accurate for practical improvement programs (Saffle *et al.,* 1958).

Conformation. According to information reported by Pierce (1957) and unpublished data of Carroll and Clegg, animals of good conformation yield a higher proportion of retail cuts than animals of poor conformation. For example, Carroll and Clegg have data on a limited number of steers showing that the percent of trimmed retail shortloin, sirloin, top round, bottom round, and knuckle accounts for 66.3% of the hindquarter weight for Herefords as compared to 61.6% for Holsteins. Although this difference would not be expected, in view of the similarity in percentage of wholesale cuts between cattle differing in conformation, the differences were statistically significant. To summarize the information on recognition of carcass traits in the live animal, we might say that although some advances in estimating fat content have been made, the problem remains, for the most part, unsolved.

REFERENCES AND SELECTED READINGS

References marked with an asterisk are of general interest.

Adams, R., D. L. Harrison, and J. L. Hall, 1960. Comparison of enzyme and waring blender methods for determination of collagen in beef. *Agr. and Food Chem.,* 8:229.

*American Meat Institute Foundation, 1960. *The Science of Meat and Meat Products.* Freeman, San Francisco.

Andrews, F. N. and R. M. Whaley, 1954. *A Method for the Measurement of Subcutaneous Fat and Muscular Tissues in the Live Animal.* Purdue Univ. Press.

Batcher, O. M. and E. H. Dawson, 1960. Consumer quality of raw and cooked pork. *Food Tech.,* 14:69.

Briskey, E. J., R. W. Bray, W. G. Hoekstra, R. H. Grummer, and P. H. Phillips, 1959. The effect of various levels of exercise in altering the chemical and physical characteristics of certain pork ham muscles. *J. Animal Sci.,* 18:153.

*Bull, S., 1951. *Meat for the Table.* McGraw-Hill, New York.

———, and H. P. Rusk, 1942. Effect of exercise on quality of beef. Ill. Agr. Expt. Sta. Bull. 488.

Butler, O. D., 1957. The relation of conformation to carcass traits. *J. Animal Sci.,* 16:227.

———, B. L. Warwick, and T. C. Cartwright, 1956. Slaughter and carcass characteristics of short-fed yearling, Hereford, and Brahman X Hereford steers. *J. Animal Sci.,* 15:93.

Clark, F., B. Friend, and M. C. Burk, 1947. The nutritive value of per capita food supply. USDA Misc. Publ. 616.

Cole, J. W., L. E. Orme, and C. M. Kincaid, 1960. Relationship of loin eye area, separable lean of various beef cuts, and carcass measurements to total carcass lean in beef. *J. Animal Sci.,* 19:89.

Goeser, P. A., H. F. Bernholdt, M. Hogan, and G. E. Brissey, 1960. Tendered meat through antemortem vascular injection of proteolytic enzymes. *Food Tech.*, 14:41 (Abstract).

Hall, J. L., C. E. Latschar, and D. L. Mackintosh, 1944. Quality of beef. Part IV: Characteristics of dark cutting beef. Survey and preliminary investigation. Kansas Agr. Expt. Sta. Tech. Bull. 58.

Harrington, G. and A. M. Pearson, 1962. The chew count as a measure of tenderness in pork loins with varying degrees of marbling. *Food Sci.*, 27 (in press).

Hazel, L. N. and E. A. Kline, 1952. Mechanical measurement of fatness and carcass value on live hogs. *J. Animal Sci.*, 11:313.

Helser, M. D., P. M. Nelson, and B. Lowe, 1930. Influence of the animal's age upon the quality and palatability of beef. Iowa Agr. Expt. Sta. Bull. 272.

Henneman, H. A., 1942. The relationship of rate of growth in lambs to body measurements and carcass value. Mich. State Univ., M.S. Thesis.

Hiner, R. H., O. G. Hankin, H. S. Sloane, C. R. Fellers, and E. E. Anderson, 1953. Fiber diameter in relation to tenderness of beef muscle. *Food Research*, 18:364.

*Hinman, R. B. and R. B. Harris, 1942. The Story of Meat. Swift and Company, Chicago.

Hostetler, E. H., J. E. Foster, and O. G. Hankins, 1936. Production and quality of meat from native and grade yearling cattle. N.C. Agr. Expt. Sta. Bull. 63.

Ingram, M., 1948. Fatigue musculaire, *p*H et prolifération bactérienne dans la viande. *Ann. Inst. Pasteur.*, 75:139.

Jourbert, D. M., 1956. An analysis of factors influencing post-natal growth and development of the muscle fiber. *J. Agr. Sci.*, 47:59.

Kirton, A. H., A. M. Pearson, R. H. Nelson, E. C. Anderson, and R. L. Schuch, 1961. Use of naturally occurring potassium-40 to determine carcass composition of live sheep. *J. Animal Sci.*, 20:635.

Kramlich, W. E. and A. M. Pearson, 1958. Some preliminary studies on meat flavor. *Food Tech.*, 23:567.

Liuzzo, J. A., E. P. Reineke, and A. M. Pearson, 1958. Determination of specific gravity by air displacement. *J. Animal Sci.*, 17:513.

Ljundahl, W. A. Significant factors in the determination of carcass quality in lamb. Mich. State Univ. M.S. Thesis (1942).

Maddox, G., 1960. Effects of fats on heart disease. *Food and Nutr. News*, 31(7):1.

Mitchell, H. H. and T. S. Hamilton, 1933. The effect of long-continued muscular exercise upon the chemical composition of the muscles and other tissues of beef cattle. *J. Agr. Research*, 46:917.

Pierce, J. C., 1957. The influence of conformation, finish, and carcass weight on the percentage yield of wholesale and retail cuts of beef. *Proc. Recip. Meat Conf.*, 10:119.

Saffle, R. L., L. E. Orme, D. E. Sutton, D. E. Ullrey, and A. M. Pearson, 1958. A comparison of urinary and blood serum creatinine with live probe as measures of leanness for live swine. *J. Animal Sci.*, 17:480.

Siri, W. E., 1956. Apparatus for measuring human body volume. *Rev. Sci. Instr.*, 27:729.

Stonaker, H. H., M. H. Hazaleus, and S. S. Wheeler, 1952. Feedlot and carcass characteristics of individually fed comprest and conventional type Hereford steers. *J. Animal Sci.*, 11:15.

Stouffer, J. R., 1959. Status of the application of ultrasonics in meat animal evaluation. *Proc. Recip. Meat Conf.*, 12:161.

Stroble, C. P., C. B. Roubicek, and N. W. Hilston, 1951. Carcass studies of steer progeny. *Proc. West. Sect., Am. Soc. Animal Prod.*, 11:155.

Temple, R. S., H. H. Stonaker, D. Howry, G. Posakony, and M. H. Hazaleus, 1956. Ultrasonic and conductivity methods for estimating fat thickness in live cattle. *Proc. West. Sect., Am. Soc. Animal Prod.*, p. 70.

Warren, R. B., V. H. Arthaud, C. H. Adams, and R. M. Koch, 1959. Thermistor thermometer for estimating fat thickness on live beef cattle. *J. Animal Sci.*, 18:1469.

Willey, N. B., O. D. Butler, J. K. Riggs, J. H. Jones, and P. J. Lyerly, 1951. The influence of type on feedlot performance and killing qualities of Hereford steers. *J. Animal Sci.*, 10:195.

Wilson, J. and C. F. Curtis, 1893. Steer feeding. Iowa Agr. Exp. Sta. Bull. 20.

*Ziegler, P., 1954. *The Meat We Eat*. 5th Ed. Interstate, Danville.

Chapter 3

Milk and Milk Products

He asked water and she gave him milk; she brought forth butter
as a lordly dish.   *Judges 5:25*

3-1. INTRODUCTION

The beginning history of dairying is somewhat obscure, but excavations made by archeologists indicate that the cow was first domesticated by men of the Old Stone Age and that, in prehistoric times, milk and butter were held in high regard as human foods. The selection of cows on the basis of milk production is credited to the nomadic Aryans of Central Asia.

During the intervening centuries, the recognition of the importance of milk and milk products in civilization's progress increased until in 1956 they were established as one of the four groups of foods contributing the essentials of an adequate diet. In the United States, dairy foods account for about 14% of the consumer's food budget.

As the cow population expanded throughout the world and as milk production became a specialized phase of agriculture, methods were developed for concentrating and preserving milk nutrients for future use, for barter, or for international trade. Dairying progressed from an art to a science, employing the disciplines of genetics, chemistry, physics, bacteriology, heat and refrigeration engineering, business, and other branches of knowledge, in order to improve the old, create new, and profitably distribute, dairy commodities in both domestic and world commerce.

In the United States—one of the important dairy countries—the total farm income from dairying in 1959 was approximately 6.7 billion dollars, of which approximately 2.1 billion dollars came from the sale of cows and

52

heifers from dairy herds; the remainder came from the sale of over 124 billion lb. of milk. In 1959, the per capita consumption of all dairy products on the milk equivalent[1] basis was approximately 96.5% of the total milk production, of which approximately 56.6% was consumed as fluid milk, cream, and ice cream; 24.5% as butter; 10% as cream; and 4.5% as evaporated and condensed milks. It is noteworthy that, in spite of the definite decline in per capita consumption of butter and fluid cream during the postwar period, the consumption of fluid milk has remained fairly uniform, whereas the consumption of cheese (especially cottage cheese), frozen dairy foods, and nonfat dry milk has shown substantial gains. Nutritional science, aided by industry-supported research, education, and promotion, and coupled with a healthy economy, is favorably influencing consumer purchasing of dairy products.

3-2. THE PRODUCTION OF MILK

Although milk from nearly every species of domestic mammal has played a part in man's economy, the modern agriculturalist is primarily interested in the dairy cow, the buffalo, the goat, the ewe, and, to a degree, the mare and the sow as sources of milk. The dairy industry has evolved around the first three especially, and of these the dairy cow is of first importance in countries where dairying is of major agricultural significance. Since milks from these industrially important mammals differ mainly in percentage composition, and therefore in some physical properties (see Table 3-1), the term "milk," as used in the following pages, will refer to cow's milk.

TABLE 3-1. | *Characteristic composition of milks of important mammals.*

	Water (%)	Total Solids (%)	Fat (%)	Protein (%)	Lactose (%)	Ash (%)
Human	87.8	12.2	3.8	1.2	7.0	0.2
Cow	87.3	12.7	3.9	3.3	4.8	0.7
Goat	87.6	12.4	3.7	3.3	4.7	0.7
Water Buffalo	76.8	23.2	12.5	6.0	3.8	0.9
Ewe	81.6	18.4	6.5	6.3	4.8	0.8
Sow	82.4	17.6	5.3	6.3	5.0	1.0
Mare	90.2	9.8	1.2	2.3	5.9	0.4

Milk may be considered to be a secretion of the mammary glands of a mammal, but, since the fore, middle, and last milks differ in percentage

[1] The milk equivalent of a product refers to the amount of 3.5% milk required to produce a unit of product. For example, 1 lb. of butter is equivalent to approx. 22.8 lb. of milk; 1 lb. of Cheddar cheese is equivalent to 10 lb. of milk.

composition, and since the percentage composition may be affected by udder disease and physiological disturbances, all of which may result in changes in physical properties, it is necessary to restrict the definition of milk. Natural milk, as a commodity, is considered to represent the complete secretion of a normal mammary gland. From the analyses of a series of one-day composites taken at monthly intervals throughout the lactation period, it is possible to calculate the lactation yield and the percentage composition of the total milk of the individual animal for the specific lactation. Average values so obtained are meaningful only for this individual. The variation in milk composition, either between cows within a herd of the same breed or between herds of the same breed, for individual composites as well as lactation averages, makes the tabulation of the average composition of breed milks hazardous and of questionable specific value.

Table 3-2 was compiled from the analyses of samples taken at approximately 6-week intervals throughout a year from individual cows in commercial herds in widely separated parts of Oregon. The data represent 1705 samples from 6 Holstein herds, 700 from 3 Guernsey herds, 1417 from 7 Jersey herds, 470 from 2 Brown Swiss herds, and 194 from 1 Ayrshire herd. Yearly yields of milk and of the various components were used in the calculations.

The data in Table 3-2 illustrate the characteristic differences to be expected in breed milks, but they do not indicate the extent of the deviations from these mean values due to the fairly well-understood effects of age, stage of lactation, feed, season, and other environmental factors.

That significant differences in the mean composition of milk from herds of the same breed do exist is illustrated in the study made by Overman *et al.* of 39 herds of Brown Swiss cows located in widely scattered localities in the United States. However, the data and herd records were inadequate to justify attributing these variations to genetic differences alone. The study, of which the data of Table 3-2 are only a part, gives a clear indication that herd differences may be due to individual characteristics and that these are

TABLE 3-2. | *Representative composition of milk from five dairy breeds.*

Breed	Water (%)	Fat (%)	Solids-Not-Fat (%)	Protein (%)	Lactose (%)	Ash (%)
Ayrshire	87.11	4.03	8.86	3.28	4.90	0.68
Brown Swiss	86.79	3.95	9.26	3.51	5.01	0.74
Guernsey	85.76	4.90	9.34	3.66	4.95	0.73
Holstein	87.93	3.53	8.54	3.08	4.78	0.68
Jersey	84.96	5.43	9.61	3.88	4.99	0.74

related to inheritance. Many current studies are inquiring into the heritability of the protein content of milk.

Interrelationships Among Major Milk Constituents. It is recognized that a high positive correlation exists between the percentages of fat and total solids, fat and protein, and protein and solids-not-fat. Somewhat lower and more variable correlations between the fat and solids-not-fat have been found. Attempts have been made, for practical purposes, to express the interrelationships between fat and solids-not-fat by linear regression equations. Thus, $y = a + bf$, where $y =$ percent s.n.f., $f =$ percent fat, and a and b are constants.

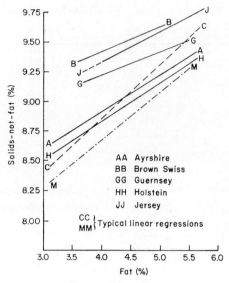

Fig. 3-1. The relationships between the percentages of fat and of solids-not-fat in milks of different breeds.

As illustrated in Fig. 3-1, the equations may fairly represent the interrelationships within individual breeds. It is obvious, however, that a single linear equation, as represented in curves C—C or M—M, is inadequate for calculating the solids-not-fat percentage from the percentage of fat in producer milks, regardless of breed. This becomes increasingly significant as the nonfat solids increase in economic importance.

Some Constancies in Milk Composition. 1. The ratio of the percentage of protein to that of the total solids in herd milks varies only within narrow limits, regardless of breed. For example, in the Oregon study referred to previously, the mean protein content of the yearly milk yield of the 19 herds was 25.73% of the total solids. The percent of total solids may be estimated by multiplying the protein percentage by the factor 3.89.

2. The energy value of natural milk is closely related to its fat percentage and may be calculated using the equation $E = 128.9 + 52.9f$ where $E =$ kilocalories per pound of milk and $f =$ percent fat.

Energy Corrected Milk. Since the feed energy required by the cow for lactation is dependent upon the energy of the milk yield, and since the inheritance of a cow's ability to produce milk may be measured in terms of milk energy yield, the yield of milk from the individual cow or herd is commonly expressed in terms of a reference milk on the basis of its energy value. Overman and coworkers (1933) chose milk containing 4% fat as the

TABLE 3-3. | *Partial evaluation of representative cow's milk.**

	Per 100 ml	Per qt
Water (g)	87.3	826.12
Total solids (g)	12.7	120.18
Fat (g)	3.7	35.01
Solids-not-fat (g)	9.0	85.17
Total protein (g)	3.3	31.23
Caseins (g)	2.6	24.60
β-lactoglobulins (g)	0.34	3.22
α-lactalbumin (g)	0.06	0.57
Other albumin and globulin types (g)	0.3	0.28
Nonprotein nitrogenous compounds (g)	0.02	0.19
Lactose (g)	4.96	46.94
Ash (g)	0.72	6.81
Major components		
Calcium (mg)	122	1182.9
Phosphorus (mg)	96	908.4
Magnesium (mg)	12	113.6
Potassium (mg)	138	1305.9
Sodium (mg)	58	548.9
Chlorine (mg)	103	974.7
Sulfur (mg)	30	283.9
Vitamins		
Fat soluble		
Vitamin A (μg)	34	321.2
Carotenoids (μg)	38	359.6
Vitamin D (U.S.P. units)	2.36	22.3
Vitamin E (mg)	0.06	0.57
Vitamin K Dam-Glavind units	100	946.3
Water-soluble vitamins		
Ascorbic acid (mg)	1.6	15.1
Biotin (μg)	3.5	33.1
Choline, total (mg)	13	123.02
Folic acid (μg)	0.23	2.2
Inositol (mg)	13	123
Nicotinic acid (μg)	85	840.36
Pantothenic acid (μg)	350	3312.05
Pyridoxine (μg)	48	454
Riboflavin (μg)	157	1485.7
Thiamine (μg)	42	397
Vitamin B_{12} (μg)	0.56	5.3
Other Accessories		
Phospholipids (as lecithin) (g)	0.057	0.539
Cholesterol (g)	0.014	0.1325

TABLE | *Partial evaluation of representative cow's milk (continued).*
3-3.

	Per 100 ml	Per qt
Energy		
Combustible (kcal)	72	681
Physiological (kcal)	66	625
Enzymes of known significance		
Catalase, peroxidase, xanthine oxidase		
phosphatases, lipases, protease(s)		

* Revised from Macy, Kelly, and Sloan (1953).

reference milk and, from an equation similar to the foregoing, developed and introduced the Fat Corrected Milk (4%) formula: $FCM = 15F + 0.4M$, in which FCM = pounds of milk equivalent in energy to the reference milk, M = pounds of milk, and F = pounds of fat in the milk being compared. This relation may also be expressed as $FCM = M(0.15f + 0.4)$, where f = percent fat. It is perhaps unfortunate that the term Energy Corrected Milk (ECM) was not used. It might also be suggested that the formula $ECM = 15.5F + 0.33M$ appears to be more representative than the simplified formula. Future students of dairy husbandry might find interest and reward in pursuing the idea suggested by Gaines and Overman (1938), namely, that since the energy yield of milk tends to be a simple multiple of the protein yield (kilocalories per pound of milk = 102.6 × percent protein), more significance might be attached to the protein–energy relationship than to the fat–energy relationship. Certainly it merits consideration in studies concerned with the heritability of milk components.

3-3. CHEMICAL COMPOSITION OF MILK

In the previous section, the variation in the quantitative gross composition of milk due to environmental and genetic factors has been considered. These variations are important to producers, milk dealers, and, to a degree, to nutritionists, but for a full appreciation of the composition of milk, it must be considered in its entirety. An approach to this may be found in the compilation made by Macy, Kelly, and Sloan (1953), in which representative values for more than 100 components of human, goat, and cow milks are tabulated and summarized. In Table 3-3, many of these data have been condensed and, in some instances, slightly revised in light of recent findings; enzymes are also listed.

It must be recognized that the data in Table 3-3 do not represent average values. The values may be expected to fall within the range of values characteristic of normal milk as secreted by healthy cows. Much information of particular interest to the nutritionist has been omitted. For example, the mere summation of fat and protein values fails to indicate either the wide distribution of fatty acids (saturated and unsaturated) in milk fat or the completeness of the proteins in dispensable and indispensable amino acids. The original reference must be studied to appreciate milk as a symphony of nutrients that is well balanced with respect to both concentration and type. This latter consideration is the basis for much of the opposition to milk fortification by nutritionists and members of the medical profession.

3-4. THE PHYSICAL PROPERTIES OF MILK

The complexity of its chemical composition suggests that milk possesses interesting physical properties and leads one to wonder how it can be a stable system. It is supersaturated as to milk fat, proteins, and calcium phosphate salts.

TABLE 3-4. *Structural composition of milk.*

Constituent	State	Visibility
Fat as secreted; Av. dia. of globules = 2500–3000 mμ.* *Fat* in homogenized milk; Av. dia. = approx. 250 mμ.	Emulsion	Readily visible under microscope
Calcium caseinate Calcium phosphate } 5–100 mμ	Colloidal Colloidal	Visible under ultramicroscope
Lactalbumins and Lactoglobulins, that is, whey proteins 5–15 mμ	Molecular, but having colloidal properties	
Lactose	Molecular solution	Invisible
Mineral salts	Ionic solution	

* 1 mμ = about 4 × 10^{-8} in.

Structure. As indicated in Table 3-4, milk is a colloidal system[1] in which an aqueous solution of mineral salts, lactose, and some of the serum proteins constitutes the continuous phase. Calcium caseinate, calcium phosphate,

[1] A colloidal system is heterogeneous and consists of a continuous phase and at least one dispersed phase. The dimensions of the dispersed particles are larger than ions and simple molecules, but are small enough to combat the force of gravity. The stability of the system is dependent upon Brownian movement and electrostatic repulsion forces within the dispersed phase.

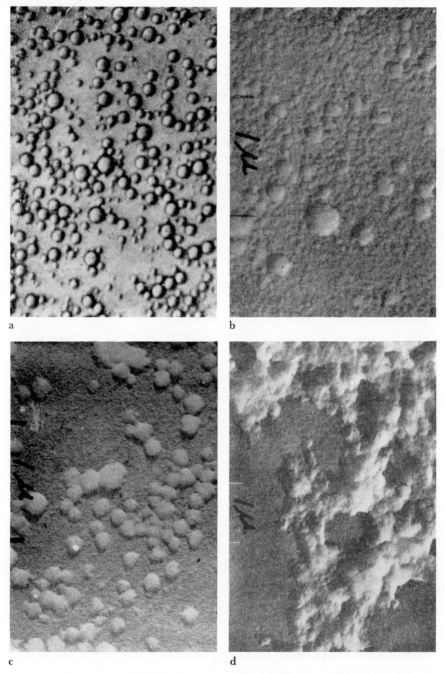

Fig. 3-2. Microphotograph (a) and electron microphotographs (b), (c), (d) of coarse and colloidal dispersions in milk. (a). Fat globules, approximately 600 X; (b) dry nonfat milk, approximately 60,000 X; (c) calcium caseinate-calcium phosphate, approximately 60,000 X; (d) acid whey proteins (coagulated), approximately 28,000 X.

and probably calcium citrate, in various degrees of association, form a dispersed phase; the milk fat forms a more coarsely suspended phase. The dispersions are illustrated in Fig. 3-2. The system is stable as secreted, but the emulsified fat may be separated as cream, either by natural sedimentation or by centrifugation; the calcium complex, as well as the serum proteins, may be isolated by ultrafiltration.

The Milk Fat Emulsion. Although the fat is coarsely dispersed by colloidality standards, it is present in milk in tiny spheres emulsified in an aqueous medium. The emulsion is stabilized by a rather complex material that confers to the emulsion properties characteristic of colloidal systems. The composition of the so called fat globule "membrane" is not entirely understood, but it may be regarded as consisting mainly of a phospholipid-protein complex that serves as a bridge between the fat and aqueous phases. Although the bridge is not securely anchored at either end, it serves well its primary purpose of keeping the fat emulsified before and during nursing by the young. It serves also to protect the fat against oxidation and the action of milk lipase. However, its fragility is such that care must be taken in handling milk by both producer and processor if rancidity, cream plug, and oxidation flavors are to be avoided.

Cream, the emulsified fat concentrated in milk plasma, properly handled, is a stable product and will withstand pasteurization, freezing, and careful drying.

Milk Plasma. When the fat is removed from milk as cream, the portion remaining is known as separated milk, skim milk, nonfat milk, or milk plasma. As previously indicated, it consists of proteins and calcium phosphate colloidally dispersed in milk serum, the latter being a water solution of lactose, mineral salts, and molecularly dispersed serum proteins. In the main, the physical properties of the plasma determine those of the whole milk.

With the exception of butter, the manufacture of dairy products, including the specialties, is based on an understanding of the physical and chemical properties not only of the milk plasma as a whole but also of its major components. For example, the milk plasma is stable under heating and drying conditions, thus permitting the manufacture of pasteurized skim milk, condensed skim milk, and nonfat dry milk. On the other hand, the addition of a very small quantity of rennet to warm milk or milk plasma renders the system so unstable that a clot quickly forms, which later shrinks, exudes whey, and becomes the curd—the raw material for most cheeses. When lactose-fermenting organisms are allowed to develop acidity in milk plasma, the increased concentration of cations results in the coagulation of the main protein—casein. This is the basic reaction in the manufacture of cottage cheese. The quality of such dairy products is dependent upon precise scientific control of the reactions involved.

Useful Physical Properties

SPECIFIC GRÅVITY. Owing to the wide variation in percentage composition, the density of milk varies considerably. A value of 1.032 for the specific gravity (15°C/15°C) is considered sufficiently representative for practical purposes. By assuming that the composition of milk fat and the relationship between the lactose, proteins, and mineral salts of the plasma are constant and, consequently, that definite values for the specific gravities of the fat and the plasma solids may be accepted, many formulas have been recommended for calculating the total solids content of milk from the fat percentage and the lactometer or densitometer readings under specific temperature conditions. No one formula appears adequate for precise calculations under all conditions. The lactometer is a useful tool for detecting gross watering of natural milk.

ELECTRICAL CONDUCTANCE. The ability of milk to conduct an electric current is dependent upon the concentration of certain ions, especially the chloride ion. This property has been applied in the detection of mastitis, but its usefulness is limited owing to the variation in the conductance of normal milks.

SURFACE TENSION. The presence in milk of hydrophilic proteins and phospholipids results in a reduction in the surface tension from that of water. A figure of 52 dynes/cm at 25°C may be considered representative. A progressive lowering of surface tension is a fairly reliable indication of lipase action and of the development of rancidity in cooled milk.

FREEZING POINT. The freezing point of milk is below that of water; thus the addition of water to milk is reflected in a rise in the freezing point. An exact method for determining the freezing point has been developed and accepted by the Association of Official Agricultural Chemists (1960) as the official method for detecting the addition of water to milk.

3-5. ENZYMES OF MILK

During milk secretion, the fat, proteins, and sugar are simultaneously and continuously formed from dissimilar materials provided by the blood. The complex chemical reactions are catalyzed by efficient individual enzymes and enzyme systems and it is not surprising that they find their way into milk. Those of recognized significance to the producer and processor are listed in Table 3-3.

Catalase. The catalase content varies probably more than any other enzyme and is increased in the case of udder disturbances, which result in increased leucocyte counts. A high catalase test is not necessarily indicative of mastitis.

Oxidases. The peroxidase content is fairly constant, and since the enzyme is not inactivated below high heat-treatment temperatures, application is sometimes made to detect or regulate such heat treatment. The content of xanthine oxidase is quite variable, but its presence is of considerable significance. It is closely associated with the fat globules and, being fairly resistant to heat, conceivably plays an important role in the development of flavor defects of an oxidative nature.

Protease(s). The presence of at least one protease (galactase), not of bacterial origin, is now generally accepted. For the extensive conversion of simple nitrogenous compounds to the complex proteins of milk during milk secretion, it must be assumed that an efficient protease system is involved. It is surprising, therefore, that proteases are not among the prominent enzymes of milk. Galactase is considered to play a small part in the ripening of cheese made from raw milk.

Phosphatases. Of the phosphatases present in milk, the greatest significance is attached to the alkaline class. Its concentration in normal milk is fairly constant, and its activity is greatly reduced under the conditions of pasteurization. The phosphatase test, therefore, has been found to be the most reliable for assuring proper pasteurization, providing that precise methods of testing and proper interpretation of the results are followed.

Lipases. Milk possesses the ability to catalyze the hydrolysis of a wide range of esters and fats. The very extensive literature on the subject was reviewed by Herrington (1954). However, the results of current research may reveal much about the lipolytic activity of milk. So far, it is recognized that milk probably contains at least two true lipases, which, through their action on the complex triglycerides of milk fat, release fatty acids, some of which confer odors and flavors that are undesirable in most dairy products but which are desirable in certain types of cheese. Normally, the emulsified fat as secreted is protected against lipolysis. However, if the milk is subjected to undue agitation in the milking process, or if the cooled milk is warmed and cooled with even mild agitation, the natural protection is weakened, and rancidity is likely to occur. The milk from cows in advanced lactation occasionally becomes rancid on mere cooling.

3-6. MILK PRODUCTS

Milk is a unique fluid not merely because of its chemical composition and physical properties but also because it provides the materials for a wide variety of foods. Milk as secreted is already a prepared food, manufactured by the cow from raw materials, many of which are nonedible to humans.

Dairy products are designed to provide concentrated components, tasty variations, or readily preserved commodities.

Creams, Butter, Milk Fat, Buttermilk. The fat in milk may be concentrated by centrifugation to form light, medium, heavy, or plastic cream; by churning the cream, the fat may be further concentrated to form butter, with buttermilk as a by-product. Beginning with cream or butter, the fat may be isolated as practically pure milk fat. No chemical reactions are involved in any of these processes.

Cheeses. The cheese of early Biblical times was probably little more than coagulated milk proteins (curd) admixed with fat and whey. As man learned to harness and control the activities of bacteria, molds, enzymes, and hydrogen ions, many different varieties of cheese were developed. Today, of the 800 or more named cheeses, 400 have been described, of which all but about 30 have commercial significance either as staple foods or as the gourmet's delight. For convenience, they may be classified as very hard (Romano), hard (Cheddar, Swiss), semi-soft (Brick, Trappist, Blue) and soft (Camembert, Neufchatel, Cottage, Mysost).

Casein. Approximately 80% of the total protein of milk consists of colloidally dispersed calcium caseinate. It can be precipitated as calcium paracaseinate by the addition of rennet to skim milk; this precipitate may then be processed into cheese or commercial "rennet casein." The latter, at one time, found extensive industrial use in plastic manufacture. More commonly, the caseinate is converted to casein by acidifying skim milk under carefully controlled conditions. The precipitated casein may be processed into cottage cheese, edible casein products, or dried for industrial usage. The expanding markets for nonfat milk as a food have so increased the market quotation for casein that the industrial use of casein has become more or less restricted to paper coating, glue, and paints, even though research has developed methods for its use in the manufacture of casein wool, paint brush bristles, and other fibers. It is fortunate that the necessity of utilizing this high-quality protein for industrial use is rapidly declining.

Whey Proteins. Approximately 50% of the milk solids of the original milk are retained in the serum, or whey, remaining after the removal of the casein. These consist of the serum proteins, lactose, mineral salts, and water-soluble vitamins. The major portion of the proteins may be removed either by heating and filtering the acidified whey, or by other less simple means.

Milk Sugar. The mineral salts that remain in the filtrate may be removed by ion-exchange treatment. Lactose, the main solute in the effluent, may be isolated by crystallization and drying methods, depending upon the purity desired. Besides being low in sweetness, lactose has distinctive nutritional qualities.

Dried and Condensed Products. As pointed out previously, milk, although a complicated system, is remarkably stable as to physical properties. The individual components possess good chemical stability. Thus, by employing sound engineering principles, milk, cream, skim milk, and whey may be condensed, dried, or frozen, without chemical treatment of any kind. The products are physically tailored according to the ultimate use. The instantizing process for dry milk solids, for example, induces physical rather than chemical changes.

Cultured Products. Milk, separated milk, and whey are good culture media for several types of bacteria and yeasts. By judicious selection of cultures and careful control of their activity, a wide variety of dairy products has been developed. These range from the relatively simple acid and alcoholic fermented beverages, such as cultured buttermilk and Kefir, to the semi-solid products, such as yoghurt and certain soft cheeses. The characteristic flavors and textures of these products result from the chemical changes in the lactose, proteins, and fat brought about by the microorganisms.

Frozen Dairy Products. Unlike essentially all other dairy products, ice cream, sherbets, and ice milks are compounded dairy products. But, except for the added fruits, nuts, eggs, chocolate, flavorings, sugar, stabilizers and emulsifiers, all ingredients are of milk origin.

For the student who desires to delve more deeply into the production, processing, or distribution of milk and milk products, there is available a good selection of textbooks dealing with specific dairy commodities. If he is interested in developing new dairy products or in salvaging the components of milk that are not now completely utilized as human or animal foods, he will find the book by Whittier and Webb (1950) very helpful. It is well to recognize, however, that the dairy foods market is very highly regulated for the protection of the consumer and that federal and state standards (Agricultural Marketing Service, 1959) have been established for the minimum composition of nearly 100 milk and non-milk-fat products (1959).

Although tables showing the composition of dairy foods are readily available, it should be recognized that the values are based on milks of an average fat content of approximately 3.9%, and though acceptable for most nutritional purposes, they are not indicative of the wide variation likely to exist in the composition of dairy products. The compiled values shown in Table 3-5 may be used to calculate the yield and composition of products

TABLE 3-5. | *The solids-not-fat, protein, milk sugar, calcium, and phosphorus contained in natural (unstandardized) milks and their skim milks and creams.*

Fat Test of Milk (%)	3.0	3.5	4.0	4.5	5.0	5.5	6.0
% solids-not-fat							
in milk	8.43	8.60	8.84	9.20	9.50	9.62	9.74
in skim	8.69	8.91	9.21	9.63	10.00	10.18	10.36
in cream (40%)	5.21	5.35	5.53	5.78	6.00	6.11	6.22
% protein							
in milk	3.02	3.14	3.33	3.60	3.83	3.95	4.01
in skim	3.12	3.25	3.47	3.75	4.03	4.15	4.27
in cream (40%)	1.87	1.95	2.08	2.25	2.42	2.49	2.56
% lactose							
in milk	4.74	4.78	4.82	4.89	4.94	4.98	4.99
in skim	4.90	4.95	5.02	5.09	5.20	5.27	5.31
in cream (40%)	2.84	2.87	2.89	2.95	2.97	2.98	2.99
% calcium							
in milk	0.112	0.117	0.122	0.128	0.133	0.139	0.144
in skim	0.115	0.121	0.127	0.134	0.140	0.146	0.153
in cream (40%)	0.069	0.073	0.076	0.080	0.084	0.088	0.092
% phosphorus							
in milk	0.088	0.089	0.091	0.092	0.094	0.095	0.097
in skim	0.091	0.093	0.095	0.097	0.099	0.101	0.103
in cream (40%)	0.054	0.056	0.057	0.058	0.059	0.061	0.062

$$\% \text{ SNF in skim} = \frac{100}{100 - \text{fat } \% \text{ in whole milk}} \times \% \text{ SNF in whole milk.}$$

$$\% \text{ SNF in cream} = \frac{100 - \text{fat } \% \text{ in cream}}{100} \times \text{SNF } \% \text{ in skim.}$$

$$\% \text{ constituent in skim} = \frac{\% \text{ constituent in whole milk} \times \text{water } \% \text{ in skim}}{\% \text{ water in whole milk}}.$$

$$\% \text{ constituent in cream} = \frac{\% \text{ constituent in whole milk} \times \text{water } \% \text{ in cream}}{\% \text{ water in whole milk}}.$$

made from milks of different fat content and to determine the results of standardization, by the addition or removal of cream, the addition or removal of skim milk, or the addition of nonfat solids of such milks to predetermined fat solids-not-fat or protein contents.

REFERENCES AND SELECTED READINGS

References marked with an asterisk are of general interest.

Agricultural Marketing Service, USDA, 1959. Federal and state standards for the composition of milk products (and certain non-milkfat products). Agr. Handbook no. 51.

Association of Official Agricultural Chemists, 1960. *Official Methods of Analysis.* 9th Ed. Washington, D.C., pp. 192–196.

Carskadon, T. R., 1946. The juice of life. *Esquire,* Aug. pp. 44–45.

Federal Reserve Bank of Philadelphia, 1955. The cow: a source of wealth, of health, a ward of the state. *Business Review,* April, May, June.

Gaines, W. L. and O. R. Overman, 1938. Interrelations of milk-fat, milk-protein and milk-energy yield. *J. Dairy Sci.,* 21(6):211–274.

Hannay, E. E., 1928. Dairying and Civilization. California Dairy Council, San Francisco.

Herrington, B. L., 1954. Lipase, a review. *J. Dairy Sci.,* 37(7):770–789.

Hoard's Dairyman, 1937. Milk through the centuries. 82(17):479, 501.

Landman, D., 1955. Cheese and the man with the tasty tongue. *True; the man's magazine,* 35(212):22–25, 72–76.

Macy, I. G., H. J. Kelly, and R. E. Sloan, 1953. The composition of milks. Natl. Acad. of Sci., Natl. Research Council, Pub. 254. Washington, D.C.

*Milk Industry Foundation, 1960. Milk facts. Washington, D.C.

*National Dairy Council, 1960. *How Americans use their dairy foods,* Chicago.

Overman, O. R., R. J. Keers, and E. M. Craine, 1953. Composition of herd milk of the Brown Swiss breed. Ill. Agr. Expt. Sta. Bull. 567.

Overman, O. R. and W. L. Gaines, 1933. Milk energy formulas for various breeds of cattle. *J. Agr. Research,* 46(12):1109–1120.

———, 1948. Linearity of regression of milk energy on fat percentage. *J. Animal Sci.,* 7:55–59.

Page, L. and E. F. Phipard, 1956. Essentials of an adequate diet. Agr. Inf. Bull. 160, USDA.

*Pirtle, T. R., 1926. *History of Dairying.* Mojonnier Bros. Co., Chicago.

Regan, J. C., 1940. Milk. *Bull. Medical Soc. of the County of Kings, N. Y.,* 19(7):1–8.

*Rogers, Associates of, 1935. *Fundamentals of Dairy Science.* 2nd Ed. Reinhold, New York.

*Sanders, G. P., 1953. Cheese varieties and descriptions. Agr. Handbook No. 54, USDA.

Watt, B. K. and A. L. Merrill, 1950. Composition of foods. Agr. Handbook No. 8, USDA.

Webster, G., 1959. Nature's strangest chemical. *Codfish, Cats and Civilization.* Doubleday, Garden City, pp. 144–160.

Whittier, E. O. and B. H. Webb, 1950. *Byproducts from milk.* Reinhold, New York.

Chapter 4

Wool and Mohair

We must cut our coat according to our cloth, and adapt ourselves to changing circumstances.

DEAN W. R. INGE, *Anglican Prelate (1860–1954)*

4-1. INTRODUCTION

Those accustomed to handling bulk wool are able to judge its important qualities, such as fineness, length, crimp, "soundness," and color, by feel and appearance. In fact, most wool is bought and sold on the basis of such judgments. Although this information does certainly go a long way toward predicting wool's processing behavior and the attractiveness and service-ability of manufactured wool products, there is need for greater refinement of these judgments. There is need for more precise and quantitative infor-mation on the wool fibers as a raw material for modification and for manu-facture.

Wool is facing serious competition from other fibers in the textile market. To meet this competition most effectively, it is essential that there is made available as complete a picture as possible of the fiber and its behavior, including fiber damage, distortion, and weakening, under the diverse con-ditions it encounters in processing and in use. It is necessary, for example, to know not only the distribution of fiber lengths, diameters, and crimp, but also such information as fiber-surface characteristics, chemical stability, stability to heat and light, color characteristics, moisture content, strength, and elastic properties (Fig. 4-1). Such information enables the mill and the scientist to devise better ways to modify and manipulate wool in their en-deavor to adapt it to changing circumstances. This is the basis for research

67

Fig. 4-1. The fiber test instrument is used to study the stress-strain behavior of the wool fibers. It records the force required to stretch a fiber. This force is related ultimately to the structure of the various fiber components. When fibers are tested in this instrument, information is plotted electrically. The information obtained (see lower part of Fig. 4-8) is a load-elongation autograph of the wool fiber. It shows that, as you apply force to stretch a wool fiber, it elongates, first of all very slowly. Finally, it suddenly begins to yield and then elongates more rapidly. It slows down somewhat at around 30% stretch .The important thing is that the fiber recovers its original length if the force is removed. This is one of the characteristics which distinguishes wool from most other fibers. From a comparison of these autographs of wool fibers, some untreated and some purposely modified with chemicals, important information is derived, leading to a better understanding of how wool behaves in processing and in use.

aimed to help the wool industry keep abreast of the trend in modern manufacture, which demands greater efficiency and new and superior products made with the highest degree of uniformity.

In the several wool research laboratories throughout the world, scientists are using highly specialized tools to gain the needed information. For example, they are using the optical microscope, the electron microscope, the X-ray diffraction camera, the electron spin resonance spectrometer, the nuclear magnetic resonance spectrometer, the ultraviolet and infrared spectrometers, and specialized test equipment to measure such mechanical properties of fiber, yarn, and fabric as strength and elasticity. Aided by such information, other scientists are using chemical means to modify wool structure, by introducing new chemical groups to the molecules of wool, by attaching resins to the surface, and by blocking chemical centers that cause wool to break down. As a result of all this work, wools are being manufactured that have new desired properties, such as easy-care performance in fabrics.

This discussion is intended as a glimpse into what the scientists are learning and doing about wool. The information being obtained on wool applies, in general, to mohair, the fiber from the Angora goat. Mohair is similar to wool in origin, structure, composition, stability, and behavior. A main difference is the greater surface smoothness of mohair, which is responsible for its relatively high luster.

4-2. GENERATION AND MORPHOLOGY OF WOOL FIBERS

Wool is the end product of a remarkable process that occurs in the tube-like sac—the follicle—located in the outer layers of the sheep's skin (Fig. 4-2). The starting materials for the wool fiber are individual pre-wool cells, which are generated continuously in the bulblike base of the follicle. Pre-wool cells are similar to other living cells in that they are spherical in shape and contain a nucleus suspended in fluid protoplasm. The formation of

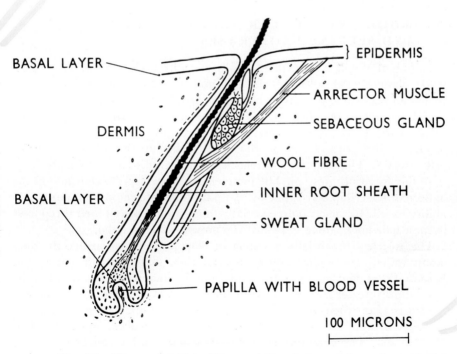

Fig. 4-2. The wool follicle. The wool fiber is formed from the epithelial cells of the follicle.

new cells forces the older ones outward through the follicle channel. During this passage, the cells die; some of them elongate in shape, some of them flatten; the nuclei disintegrate, and the protoplasm becomes fibrous; in the end, the assembly of modified cells is fused to form a continuous, complex filament—the wool fiber. Although complex in morphology, the greater part of the fiber is made up of insoluble, sulfur-containing proteins, the so called keratins. The molecules of these proteins differ significantly in size, composition, and properties from one part of the fiber to another. For the most part, the molecules are threadlike and coiled.

Similar threadlike keratin molecules are the building blocks of which hair, feathers, nails, skin, horn, and hoofs are made. In these substances, too, the chemical composition varies, but the differences are relatively small compared with the wide differences in physical structure of these materials. The manner in which the keratin molecules are cemented and hooked together accounts for the wide differences in the structure of these materials. Similarly, it is true that, by modifying the manner in which the yarns are made and woven, the texture and the performance characteristics of wool can be varied; nevertheless, the unique properties of wool fabrics, such as tailorability, comfort, softness, appearance, and ease of recovery from elongation depend upon specific properties of the keratin building blocks.

4-3. WOOL'S MOLECULAR ARCHITECTURE AND SPECIAL PROPERTIES

Felting of Wool. If we explore wool's structure under an ordinary microscope, observing the outside of the fiber and cut sections of the fiber, we see that wool consists of two distinct components, the outer sheath—the cuticle —and the inner core—the cortex. The scales or cuticle surround the spindle-shaped cortical cells (Fig. 4-3). One kind of cortical cell makes up the hard segment called para cortex; another kind makes up the soft segment, the ortho cortex. The difference in elasticity of the adjoining segments is responsible for crimp in wool. The more elastic layer of ortho cells lies on the outside of the crimp wave. The overlapping scales are responsible for wool's ability to felt. In some wools, especially those from less well-bred sheep, and in most hair fibers, there is a third component—the medulla.

The cuticle is essentially a system of close-packed, flattened cells, commonly called scales. They overlap one another, similar to tiles on a roof. Because the scale edges are rather well defined, the surface of wool exhibits significantly greater friction when the fibers are moved in a direction against the scales than when moved in the opposite direction. The net effect is a tendency of wool fibers to entangle when they are moved, especially when wet and soft. The entanglements are called felt. Felting can occur on the sheep's back, where it appears as cots. The felting of wool fibers occurs in yarns and fabrics, as well as in unprocessed wools. Felting is one of the

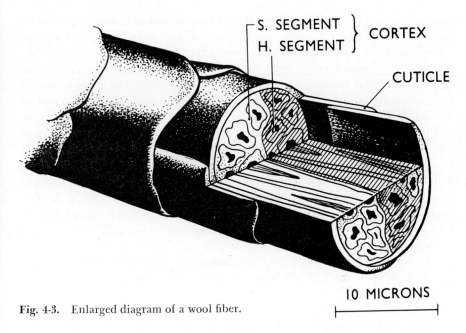

S. SEGMENT
H. SEGMENT } CORTEX

CUTICLE

IO MICRONS

Fig. 4-3. Enlarged diagram of a wool fiber.

main causes of shrinkage when wool fabrics are laundered. Although such shrinkage is a very undesired property of wool, felting can be a desired property in finishing wool fabrics after weaving. If desired, a controlled degree of felting can be applied during finishing, to impart a "body" to the fabric. Such effects are not obtainable in synthetic fabrics. The controlled felting of wool fabrics is called fulling.

Moisture Absorption and Water-shedding Properties. When examined under the electron microscope, another feature of the fiber cuticle is seen, namely, the presence, on the outside surface, of a very thin membrane—the epicuticle (Fig. 4-4). This membrane is protein; yet its composition and structure are such that it repels water, whereas the rest of wool's protein is capable of absorbing relatively large amounts of moisture. Paradoxically, this moisture can pass in and out of the epicuticle. Wool's ability to "breathe" and hold moisture contributes to the comfort in wearing wool garments. And, certainly, the relative ease with which it sheds water is also important.

Elastic Properties and Softness. The cortex of the wool fiber constitutes as much as 90% of the wool substance in some fibers. It is responsible for wool's elastic behavior and its crimp. The cortex is essentially a thread of fused, needle-shaped cells. Because of their shape, they are commonly called spindle cells and frequently contain remnants of nuclei. These cells can be separated from wool by treatment with acid or with proteolytic enzymes such as papain (Fig. 4-5). Each of these cells consists of a bundle of fibrils; the fibrils, in turn, are made up of smaller fibrils, called microfibrils; and the microfibrils, in turn, consist of bundles of the threadlike keratin molecules. The fibrous elements are embedded in an amorphous cementing material of different composition. This cementing protein has a higher sulfur content and is smaller in molecular size than the threadlike molecules of the fibrils and microfibrils.

The cortex of crimped wool fibers has a bilateral structure; that is, it consists of two distinct regions in which the cortical cells have different elastic properties. The cells of these regions are called ortho cells and para cells (Fig. 4-6). The manner in which these two kinds of cells are distributed determines the degree and character of the fiber crimp. Crimp in wool is important in that it contributes to the softness of the fiber and of fabrics, and it probably contributes to wool's spinnability.

Some wool fibers, and hair fibers in general, contain a third main component—the medulla. The medulla consists of a group of air-filled cells and, when present, is found at the center of fibers. Kemp is a kind of hair normally produced by some sheep. It is an extreme form of medullated fiber in which the interior is almost all medulla. Kemp fibers are often flattened in shape and exhibit a shallow crimp. These fibers are highly undesired in wool because they are chalky in appearance, weak in strength, and exhibit

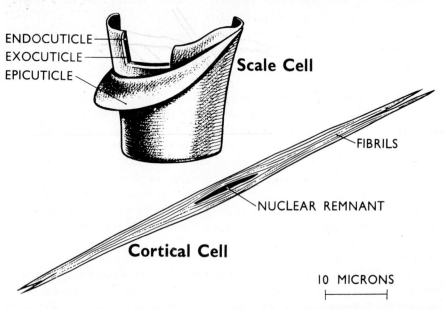

Fig. 4-4. Wool fiber components. The scale itself is shown. It is made up of at least three distinct structures, the epicuticle, exocuticle, and endocuticle.

Fig. 4-5. Spindle cells isolated from wool exhibit special optical properties (birefringence) in polarized light because the thread molecules of which the cells are composed lie in one direction. The ortho and para cells are not distinguishable in this picture.

poor dye receptivity. In most well-bred sheep, kemp fibers are virtually absent.

4-4. CHEMICAL STUDIES ON WOOL FIBERS

Although microscopic methods reveal important information about wool's cuticle, cortex, and medulla, other methods are required to determine the composition, structure, and behavior of the keratin molecules that make up these structural units.

The X-ray diffraction camera shows that some of the threadlike keratin molecules are coiled and that they uncoil when wool is stretched. Moreover, when the extending force is released, the threads recoil. This uncoil-

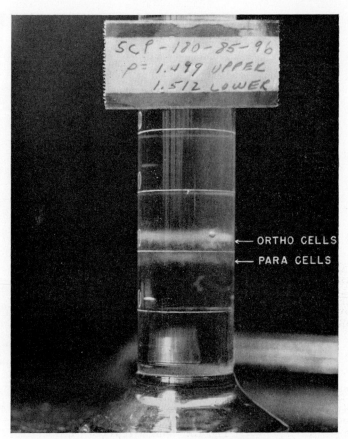

Fig. 4-6. Separation of ortho and para spindle cells is made possible by placing the mixture in a liquid column of varying density, which causes the cells to fall into layers according to their density.

ing and coiling is the basis for the relatively long-range elasticity exhibited by wool. The ability of wool garments to "hang out" wrinkles relates to the recovery of the molecules from uncoiling.

In some chemical environments, the coiled thread molecules in wool become disrupted and the threads collapse into random shapes. The result is a shortening of the fiber. Fibers can be made to shorten as much as 40% by such treatments. This shortening phenomenon is called supercontraction. It results when the chemical environment causes cleavage of chemical bridges that maintain the coiled structure. Two kinds of bridges are recognized: the disulfide bridges |—S—S—| in which two sulfur atoms hold the thread molecules together, and the hydrogen bonds |—H--O=|, which connect hydrogen atoms anchored on one molecule to neighboring atoms, such as oxygen, anchored on another (Figs. 4-7 and 4-8). When wool is ex-

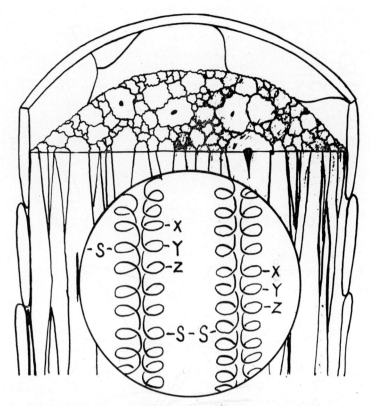

Fig. 4-7. The heart of the wool fiber, shown schematically. In the circle diagram in the center is an illustration of the coiled, threadlike keratin molecules that make up the fibrillar structures in the cortex. The coils are cemented together, back to back, by hydrogen bridges. Groups of coils are tied together by two sulfur atoms of a disulfide bridge. It is very interesting to compare natural rubber with wool. Rubber is similarly made up of coiled thread molecules. But the natural rubber that comes from the tree is a sticky material, of no use to man. About a hundred years ago, Goodyear discovered that addition of sulfur would improve the qualities of rubber and make a material that had elastic characteristics. This process became known as vulcanization, a good example of chemical modification of a natural substance. Over the years, the vulcanization process has become better understood. We now have rubber materials with wide range in properties, depending upon the amount of sulfur that ties together the chains of atoms. The sulfur atoms in the heart of the wool fiber determine its quality in the same way. If the two sulfur atoms are separated (and they split very easily), wool no longer is useful.

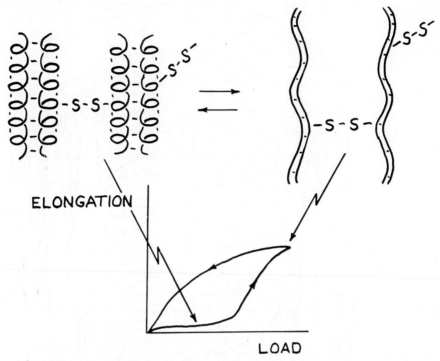

Fig. 4-8. Wool's mechanical behavior in relation to molecular structure. Sulfur atoms keep wool from pulling apart even though the coiled thread molecules are stretched out. The sulfur atoms also help in recovery of the fiber when the force is removed, as illustrated in the load-elongation record shown below.

posed to extreme conditions in a solution which favors breaking the maximum number of disulfide and hydrogen bonds, the fiber not only super-contracts but falls apart, thus freeing the keratin protein molecules from one another, after which they dissolve in the solution.

Using solutions of the dissolved wool protein, scientists are determining the sizes, shapes, and electrical charges of the molecules and their tendency to interact with themselves and with other molecules. To do this, several kinds of specialized equipment are required. One such piece of equipment is the ultracentrifuge, in which the protein solutions are whirled at speeds up to 60,000 revolutions per minute (Fig. 4-9). The high centrifugal force causes the larger molecules to separate from the smaller ones in a manner similar to the separation of cream from milk. By the use of special optical methods, the rates at which these molecules separate in the solutions are measured. From such measurements, the weights and shapes of the molecules are calculated. The thread molecules of wool differ from those of silk, yet both are protein. Silk has no sulfur. The thread molecules of wool and silk are different from the thread molecules of cotton, which is cellulose and not protein. The cellulose molecules are not as flexible. For this reason cotton does not exhibit the extensibility of wool.

Similar optical measurements are made using electrophoresis equipment, in which the protein solutions are subjected to electrical fields that separate molecules having different electrical charges.

Altogether, the information on molecular sizes, shapes, and charges, and on other properties, including the interactions of the molecules with themselves and with molecules entering wool, is providing an understanding of the differences in the elastic behavior and other properties observed among wools.

In other studies, keratin protein molecules are further degraded into their constituent amino acids by boiling them in acid solution. So far, eighteen amino acids have been recognized as building blocks of the wool proteins. Chromatographic techniques are being used to determine the number, kind, and distribution of the amino acids in the keratins that have been isolated from different parts of the wool fiber.

It is known that the amino acids lysine, histidine, and arginine contribute to wool's affinity for acid dyes; other amino acids, aspartic acid and glutamic acid, contribute to wool's ability to bind basic dyes. Moreover, moisture

Fig. 4-9. The ultracentrifuge is one of the instruments used to separate and study the keratin molecules isolated from wool.

binding in wool is similarly related to the number, kind, and distribution
of specific amino acids. Important supplementary information on the different degrees of moisture binding in wool is being obtained from studies
using nuclear magnetic resonance—a new and powerful physical tool that
enables determination of the effects of molecular structure on the mobility
of the hydrogen atoms of water.

4-5. IMPROVING WOOL PRODUCTS THROUGH THE MODIFICATION OF PHYSICAL AND MOLECULAR STRUCTURE

In their studies to develop wool fabrics having new textures and properties, such as built-in ease-of-care properties (including resistance to muss-
ing and pilling), scientists are taking care that they do not alter wool's desirable qualities while they build in new desired characteristics.

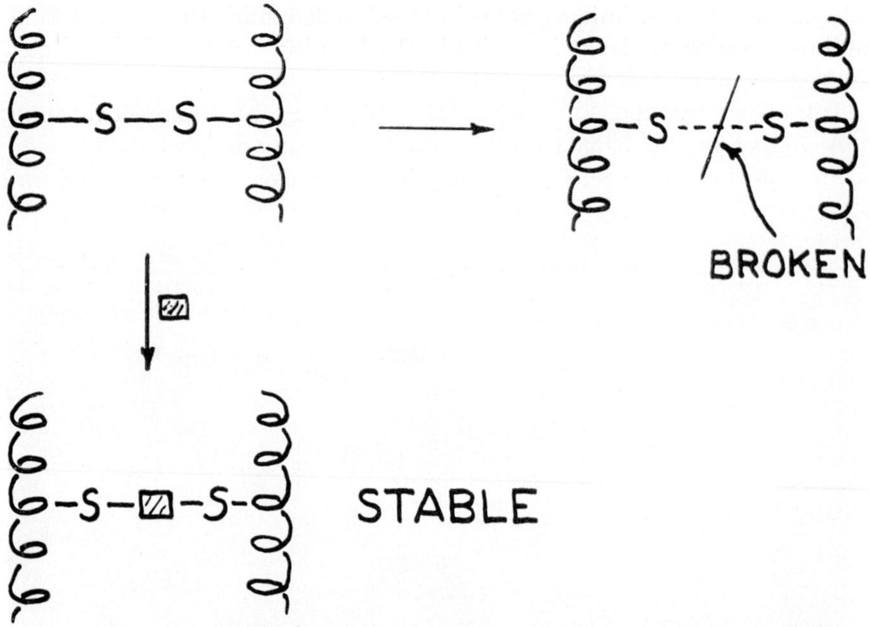

Fig. 4-10. How chemical modification can improve wool's stability to
alkaline solutions. The alkali splits the two sulfur atoms that tie together
the coils of threadlike molecules in the heart of the cells of these fibers.
When we place a fabric in alkali, first it becomes harshened and weakened,
and then, on longer contact with the alkali, falls apart. If the fiber is modified by inserting a chemical between these two sulfur atoms (as illustrated
at the bottom of the figure), the fiber looks and behaves the same as normal
wool, but is stable to alkali. The modification of chemically reduced wool
with bismaleimides does this.

Fig. 4-11. Laboratory comparisons of new treatments for easy-care wool fabrics. The two fabrics shown have just been wetted out in warm soapy water. The fabric on the right emerges smooth and with a durable pleat. The control (untreated) fabric on the left emerges mussy and a crease previously present is missing. The treated fabric is shrink-resistant to repeated home laundering.

Research on wool is underway to explain fiber yellowing and to find effective ways to prevent it. Yellowing of wool fibers can be caused by a number of agents and conditions that wool encounters. It occurs on the sheep's back, in processing, and in use by the consumer. In the fleece, yellow stains are caused by normal urine and fecal pigments, as well as by the end products in urine of phenothiazine, which is used for control of parasites. Fleece yellowing also results from stains caused by pigments produced by bacteria and fungi growing in the fleece. Similar stains can occur in wool products. Alkali and light can also cause yellowing. Most of these stains cannot be removed by washing and are difficult to remove by present bleaching methods. Bleaching, at best, is costly and damaging to fiber quality.

Each kind of yellowing involves either the chemical interaction of wool protein with a colored substance or the generation in the fiber of a colored chemical group that becomes anchored to the wool protein. As the chemical mechanisms of discolorations become better understood, the work being done to devise effective and economical ways to minimize or overcome these reactions is facilitated. The chemical blocking of amino acid tyrosine residues in wool sometimes inhibits yellowing by light. Work is in progress to develop even more effective treatments.

Special emphasis is being given to finding improved treatments to prevent the shrinkage of wool. Some treatments involve the use of protein-degrading agents such as chlorine. These agents break down the keratin protein. Handled correctly, they reduce the sharpness of the scale edges and reduce the differential-friction effect and, hence, the felting shrinkage. The one problem with these agents is that they also decrease fiber strength. A new treatment for control of laundering shrinkage, which does not decrease fiber strength, has been developed by the U.S. Department of Agriculture's Wool and Mohair Laboratory at Albany, California. This treatment is attracting wide commercial interest. Originally called the "IFP" process (interfacial polymerization), it is now called the "Wurlan" process and involves formation of an ultrathin resin film on the fibers. The film is anchored chemically on the fiber surface, so that it is durable to repeated

Fig. 4-12. Pilot plant for mechanical processing of wool. This room houses equipment for experimental studies of the operations of processing scoured wool into worsted fabrics. The operations include: carding, drawing, combing, gilling, roving, spinning, twisting, slashing, beaming, and weaving. With this machinery, research is carried out on the processing of natural and chemically modified wools.

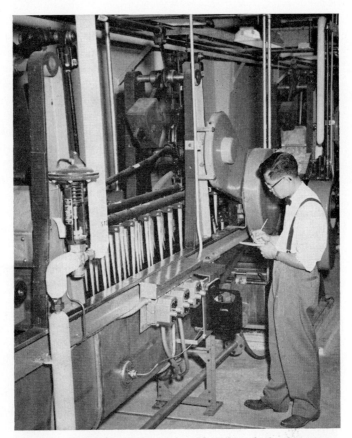

Fig. 4-13. Experimental scouring of raw wool, the first operation in wool processing, involves removal of grease and dirt by washing in an aqueous detergent solution. The first bowl of the scouring train is shown here. In this bowl, warm-water soaking loosens dirt so that it drops through a screen into a settling basin. Chemical agents in the next two bowls remove grease and suint (dry perspiration). The final bowl rinses the wool. Between bowls the wool passes between high-pressure rolls. A "stock dryer" returns the wool to its normal moisture content before it is processed further. One of the aims of scouring studies is to find ways to minimize fiber felting during scouring; another aim is to find better ways of treating scouring-waste liquors.

laundering and dry cleaning. This film not only prevents fabric felting shrinkage but also confers improved smoothness of drying and increased wearlife—all of this without sacrificing wool's good qualities of softness and strength.

New wool products are being developed from wools that are chemically modified to improve their resistance to acids, alkalies, and bleaches. Alkali, for example, splits the pairs of sulfur atoms that tie together the coils of threadlike molecules. Wool fabric is harshened and weakened and falls apart by exposure to alkali. But when the sulfur bridges are modified by inserting an appropriate chemical between the sulfur atoms the treated fabric now looks and behaves the same as normal wool, but is stable to alkali (Fig. 4-10). Faster and more effective methods of dyeing wool are now possible through the use of special chemicals as dye-assisting agents. These agents facilitate the penetration of wool by the dye.

Significant advances have been made toward incorporating durable pleats and creases in wool garments. In principle, the setting-in of pleats or creases is the same as the setting of waves in hair. Chemicals are used to promote rearrangements in fiber structure. During this rearrangement, the disulfide bridges are opened and new bonds are formed. Durable pleats and creases

Fig. 4-14. Pilot-scale processing study of easy-care wool fabircs. Fabric is first impregnated with resin by leading it through a trough containing the liquid and then squeezing the cloth between high-pressure rolls. After this treatment the fabric is led through a drying chamber to heat-set the treating chemical. Similar studies are made on variously treated wools to develop information of direct use to the wool industry.

can be set into goods that have received treatment for shrink resistance well as into untreated goods (Fig. 4-11).

Research is underway to evaluate numerous new and cheaper chemicals and a very large number of so-called textile auxiliaries that are potentially capable of improving the processing of wools and of altering the appearance, feel, and serviceability of fabrics. The number of new and improved wool textiles that may be obtained by chemical modification is very great.

An enormous field of modification of wool and mohair remains to be explored. Treatment of wool fibers, yarns, and fabrics with chemicals results in the formation of products having new and improved performance characteristics while retaining the useful fibrous form of the original materials.

The chemical treatment of wool and mohair thus affords the opportunity to increase their adaptability to changing circumstances, by minimizing fiber damage in processing and by tailoring these fibers to particular uses. This would enable them to maintain their present markets, to regain those lost to synthetics, and to fulfill new uses as needs arise. The modification of wool and mohair gives great promise of increasing the utilization of these fibers by extending their usefulness (Figs. 4-12, 4-13, and 4-14).

REFERENCES AND SELECTED READINGS

Alexander, P. and R. F. Hudson, 1954. *Wool and its Chemistry and Physics.* Reinhold, New York.

Bergen, W. von and H. R. Mauersberger, 1948. *American wool handbook.* Textile Book Publishers, Inc., New York.

Harris, M., 1954. *Handbook of Textile Fibers.* Harris Research Laboratories, Inc., Washington, D.C.

Kaswell, E. R., 1953. *Textile Fibers, Yarns, and Fabrics.* Reinhold, New York.

Matthews, J. M., 1947. *Textile Fibers, their Physical, Microscopical, and Chemical Properties.* Wiley, New York.

Meredith, R., 1956. *The Mechanical Properties of Textile Fibers.* North-Holland Pub. Co., Amsterdam.

Moncrieff, R. W., 1954. *Wool Shrinkage and its Prevention.* Chemical Pub. Co., Inc., New York.

Neurath, H., and K. Bailey, 1954. *The Proteins.* Vol. II, Chapter 23. Academic, New York.

Preston, J. M., 1953. *Fibre Science.* The Textile Institute, Manchester, England.

Proceedings of the First International Wool Textile Research Conference, Australia, 1955. Commonwealth Scientific and Industrial Research Organization, Melbourne, Australia.

Proceedings of the Second Quinquennial International Wool Textile Research Conference, England, 1960. The Textile Institute, Manchester, England.

Review of the Textile Progress (Annual Review). The Textile Institute, Manchester, England, and The Society of Dyers and Colourists, Bradford, England.

Speel, H. C. and E. W. K. Schwarz, 1957. *Textile Chemicals and Auxiliaries.* Reinhold, New York.

Chapter 5

Eggs and Poultry Meats

It's as full of good-nature as an egg's full of meat.
RICHARD B. SHERIDAN, *A Trip to Scarborough (1777)*

Until quite recently, the production of poultry meat or eggs was primarily a small operation and was a minor source of income on most farms. However, specialized poultry farms have now come into being, largely as a result of improvements in technology. As late as 1950, a sizable percentage of the chicken meat produced was a by-product of the egg industry, but by 1960, the poultry industry had become highly specialized, owing to the development of units for the production of eggs or of chicken, turkey, or duck meat. Seldom are any two phases of the industry found on a single farm.

5-1. THE EGG INDUSTRY

Egg production has long been concentrated in the North Central States, Iowa leading the nation. The areas of production are shown in Fig. 5-1. The production of eggs for freezing and drying is largely confined to the central states. Market egg-production centers are found along both coasts and in recent years have been expanding rapidly in the southeastern states.

Chemical Composition and Nutritive Value of Eggs. The egg is composed of three principal parts—shell, albumen or white, and yolk. Each of these major parts is subdivided further as shown in Fig. 5-2. The shell and its membranes serve as a package for the edible portions. The package is not perfect and can be penetrated by gases, water, and bacteria; for this

84

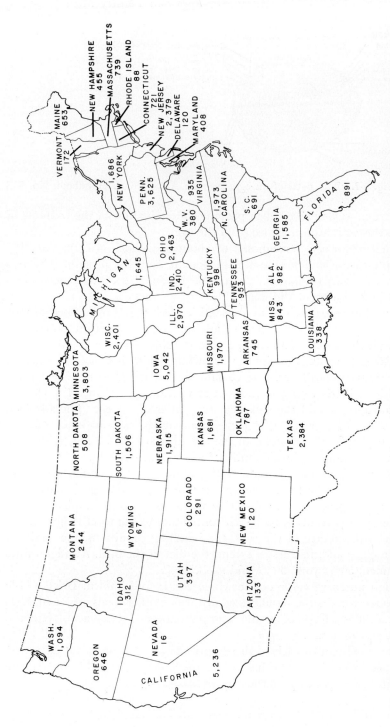

Fig. 5-1. Egg production (millions of eggs) in continental United States; total production for the 48 states in 1959 was over 5 billion dozen. [Sources: AMS, USDA.]

85

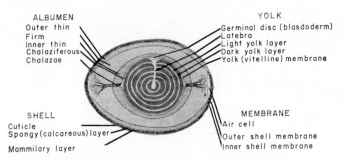

Fig. 5-2. The parts of an egg. [Source: AMS, USDA Handbook No. 75.]

reason, care must be exercised to prevent contamination of the contents of eggs or excessive loss of moisture from the egg.

The shell of an egg is composed of about 94% calcium carbonate, 1% calcium phosphate and magnesium carbonate, and 4% protein. The two shell membranes are composed primarily of protein fibers. These membranes form the inner lining of the shell.

The egg albumen, or white, as observed in fresh eggs, is composed of four layers. The layer nearest the shell membrane is the outer thin white. The next layer is the outer thick white. Inside the thick white is the inner thin white; next to the yolk is the inner thick white, which is sometimes referred to as the chalaziferous layer. The chalaza are connected to the inner thick white, which adheres closely to the yolk or vitelline membrane. The chalaza serve as anchors to hold the yolk near the center of the egg. The albumen contains about 87% water, 12% protein, about 1% carbohydrate, and less than 1% minerals. The proteins of the albumen are ovalbumin, ovomucin, conalbumin, ovomucoid, ovoglobulins, lysozyme, and avidin.

The egg yolk is composed of about 48% water, 17.5% protein, 32.5% fat, and 2% minerals. The total chemical composition of the egg is greatly influenced by the percentage composition with respect to shell, albumen and yolk. The exact percentage that each contributes to the total weight of the egg varies with the age of the eggs, the handling conditions, the strain of chicken, the age and, to a lesser extent, the diet of the bird. Average values are: albumen, 60%; yolk, 30%; and shell, 10%.

The high nutritive value of the whole egg is well known. Dried whole eggs are often used as the standard against which other foods are rated. Eggs are an excellent source of amino acids, unsaturated fatty acids, essential vitamins, and minerals.

The exact content of each of these nutrient groups can be varied widely by modifying the diet of the hen. A detailed review of studies on the nutritive value of eggs was published by Everson and Souders (1957).

Shell Eggs. Most of the eggs produced are marketed in the shell. Since the shell is not removed until just prior to use, the handling practices that prevail on the farm and on the way to market exert a major influence on egg quality. Grade specifications require that all eggs have clean shells. With good management of a laying flock, a majority of all eggs can be produced with clean shells. In wet weather, or with poor management, the percentage of eggs requiring cleaning will be high; in such instances, all eggs are usually cleaned. The cleaning of dirty shells is one of the egg industry's major problems.

When laid, the fluid contents of an egg completely fill the shell. As the egg cools, the contents shrink slightly. This results in the formation of an air space (called the air cell) between the two shell membranes, usually in the large end of the egg. The air cell continues to increase in size as moisture is lost from the egg through the porous shell.

Microbiological Problems. The egg has several natural barriers to microbiological contamination. The first defense is the shell. As long as the egg is dry, bacteria cannot penetrate the shell. However, eggs are moist when laid and are frequently cleaned in water. In addition, moisture condenses on eggs as they are moved from cool areas to warm, humid areas. If bacteria get through the pores of the shell, the membranes serve as another defense. The third line of defense is the albumen, which contains the proteins lysozyme, avidin, and conalbumin. Lysozyme protects the egg by breaking down the bacterial cell wall, whereas avidin inhibits bacterial growth by tying up the vitamin biotin, which the organisms require for growth. Conalbumin also functions as an inhibitor, by combining with any iron present.

Eggs are normally sterile at the time of production. They are exposed to microorganisms that exist in the nest bedding, on the dust in the air, or on the wires of cages. When eggs are cleaned, the protein material sealing the pores is largely removed. As long as the egg is dry, this presents no problem, but if the eggs are

Fig. 5-3. An immersion type of egg washer used for on-farm cleaning of eggs in wire baskets. [Courtesy of Chore Time Equipment Co., Milford, Ind.]

Fig. 5-4. A brush-type egg washer used for cleaning of individual eggs. [Courtesy of Oakes Manufacturing Co., Tipton, Ind.]

washed, or if eggs are allowed to sweat during marketing, bacteria might penetrate the shell.

Two commonly used types of cleaners are the immersion (shown in Fig. 5-3) and the brush type (shown in Fig. 5-4). When using either type of washer great care must be taken to maintain strict sanitation and to use recommended sanitizers with the cleaners. Eggs can be washed without setting up conditions that will result in rotting; however, according to most reports, bacterial spoilage (either green or black rot) can be traced to improper cleaning methods. Much research has been devoted to egg cleaning, most of which is summarized in a report by Kahlenberg *et al.* (1952).

Chemical and Physical Factors Related to Shell Eggs. Egg quality is highest at the time it is laid. The decrease in quality is a result of chemical reactions, which follow the general laws relating to rates of chemical reaction. The most commonly observed changes in quality are a thinning of the outer thick albumen and a flattening of the yolk. These changes proceed at varying rates, depending on the temperature and the rate of respiration of the egg. A fresh egg has a pH of about 7.6 when laid. This increases to about 8.3 in 24 hours and to about 9.2 after 3 weeks. The higher the pH, the more rapidly the albumen thins. The pH rise is largely attributable to loss of carbon dioxide from the egg. The rate can be reduced by using mineral oil to partially seal the pores of the shell.

One physical quality-factor that causes much concern is shell strength. As egg handling becomes more and more mechanized, shell becomes an increasingly important factor. The degree of mechanization in egg grading varies as indicated by Figs. 5-5 and 5-6. Shell strength is influenced by the diet, strain, and age of the hen.

Two of the factors that influence consumer satisfaction with eggs are flavor and yolk color. Flavor can be altered during storage, particularly if the eggs are stored with odiferous products, such as apples, cabbage, onions, or gasoline. Yolk color is influenced most by the diet of the hen. A feed containing large amounts of highly pigmented ingredients can produce dark orange yolks. Most consumers prefer a relatively light yellow yolk.

Egg Products. Eggs that do not meet the requirements of the shell egg trade are frequently sold to egg breakers. In times past, the egg breakers relied on farm-flock production to supply their needs. There are indications that with the decrease in farm flocks the commercial egg breakers will have flocks specifically producing for their needs.

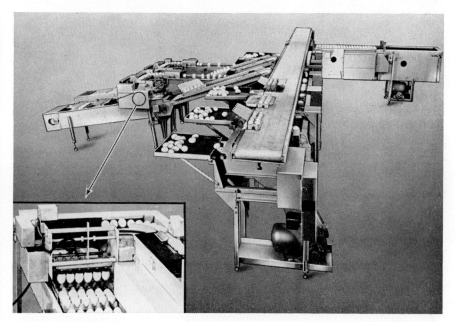

Fig. 5-5. One type of mechanical egg handling and grading equipment. [Courtesy of Barker Poultry Equipment Co., Ottumwa, Iowa.]

Fig. 5-6. Mechanization in egg handling and cartoning. [Courtesy of Food Machinery and Chemical Company, Packaging Division, Riverside, Calif.]

Egg products come in a variety of forms for many applications. The list of egg products, with their specifications and principal uses, shown in Table 5-1 was compiled by Koudele and Heinsohn (1960).

Liquid and Frozen Egg Products. A few eggs are sold as liquid non-frozen products, but these are of little importance on the total market. There is sometimes a very favorable local market for small quantities. The major problems encountered in producing liquid and frozen eggs are sanitation and making a complete separation from the yolks. Egg breaking is accomplished either by hand or by mechanical equipment.

Quality of these products is determined by testing the performance of samples. Albumen is tested to determine the volume of a whipped quantity. Yolk or whole-egg quality is frequently rated on the basis of the deepness of the orange-yellow color. Wholesomeness is indicated by a low bacterial count.

Egg Solids. The production problems of the frozen-egg business are also found when producing egg solids. Handling of the product during the drying operation brings about additional problems requiring that special tech-

TABLE 5-1. | *Egg products and their uses.*

Egg product	Specifications	Principal uses
Frozen whole eggs	A mixture of whites and yolks in natural proportions, with no additives; contains a minimum of 25.5% egg solids.	In cakes, milk pies, cookies, sweet doughs, and other pastries.
Frozen, fortified whole eggs	Whole eggs to which extra yolks and sugar, salt, or syrup have been added. Made according to packers' own formulas.	Same as for whole eggs
Standard frozen whites	Whites with a minimum of 11.5% egg solids, and fat content not over 0.03%.	In angel food and white cakes, meringues and icings; in candy making.
Quick-whipping frozen whites	Whites specially processed prior to freezing, to produce quicker whipping than regular whites.	In angel food cakes.
Frozen plain yolks	Yolks with a minimum of 45% egg solids and no additives. "Dark Yolk" must show No. 4 or No. 5 NEPA* color.	In egg noodles, which by law must contain $5\frac{1}{2}$% egg solids; also in baby foods.
Frozen sugared yolks	Yolks with a minimum of 43% egg solids, containing 10% sugar.	In cakes, milk pies, sweet goods, and other pastries; in French ice cream; also in baby foods.
Frozen salted yolks	Yolks with a minimum of 43% egg solids, containing 10% salt.	In mayonnaise.
Whole-egg solids	Whole eggs in natural proportions, dried by a spray drier; in powdered form, with 2–4% moisture.	Limited use in cake mixes. Used for human relief feeding.
Glucose-free whole-egg solids	Same as whole egg solids, except that glucose has been removed from the liquid before drying.	Used mostly in school lunch programs.
Fortified whole-egg solids	Whole eggs to which extra yolks and sugar, salt, or syrup have been added. (These additives help the dried product retain its lifting ability in cake making) Made according to packers' own formulas.	In cakes.
Flake albumen solids	Albumen dried on pans in cabinet driers; in flake form, with 12–14% moisture.	In candy making.

TABLE | *Egg products and their uses (continued).*
5-1.

Egg product	Specifications	Principal uses
Standard powdered albumen solids	Flake albumen ground to a fine powder.	In confections, meringue powders, and cake icings; sometimes mixed with spray dried albumen for making angel food cake mixes; also exported.
Spray-dried albumen solids	Whites with fat content not over 0.03%, dried in the spray drier; a fine powder, with 5–8% moisture. Sometimes it is blended with powdered flake albumen.	In angel food cakes; in angel food cake mixes; also exported.
Standard yolk solids	Yolks with 45% solids dried in the spray drier; in powdered form, with 3–5% moisture.	In doughnut and other cake mixes; in sweet doughs and Danish pastry; also in noodles.
Glucose-free yolk solids	Same as standard yolk solids except that glucose has been removed from the liquid before drying.	Same as for standard yolk solids.

* National Egg Products Association.

niques and precautions be used to insure the yield of a high quality product. Many egg solids are exported, and the importers in other countries demand a product free of *Salmonella sp.*[1] The need for the production of egg products low in bacteria has led to the increased use of pasteurization of the liquid egg.

The name Egg Solids was officially adopted by egg processors for their dried products in 1952. The technological improvements made in the methods used in the production of dried eggs in the late 1940's have made it possible to obtain stable, flavorful egg solids such as albumen, yolk or whole egg.

New Egg Products. Members of the egg industry are attempting to increase the per capita egg consumption by developing new egg products. The entire food industry is continuing to offer more heat-and-serve and ready-to-eat items. The new egg-rich products are following the same pattern. Among the items suggested as new products are a frozen drink made from orange-egg concentrate, a frozen French toast, a frozen fried egg, and a frozen egg Cantonese. A freezer-dried scrambled egg is another convenient, quality egg product that is now available.

[1] The Salmonella are a genera of bacteria, many species of which when eaten cause severe gastrointestinal disturbances.

5-2. THE POULTRY MEAT INDUSTRY

The per capita consumption of poultry meat increased rapidly between 1940 and 1960. The actual increase was from 14.1 lb. per person in 1940 to 28.9 lb. per person in 1959. Numerous reasons are given for this dramatic increase. Several trade organizations did outstanding jobs in promotion. Poultry breeders improved the market types of meat birds, and the nutritionists formulated more efficient diets. Improvements in management, preventive medicine, and medication also played major roles. The overall effects on production efficiency can best be shown by comparing the 1940 standard of 5% mortality, 5 lb. of feed per lb. of meat (live weight), and a 3 lb. bird at 12 to 14 weeks of age with the practical results of 1960. In 1960, broiler growers figured on less than 2% mortality, 2.5 or less lb. of feed per lb. of meat (live weight), and a 3.5 lb. bird in about 9 weeks. The improvement in the turkey industry has been comparable. In 1940, poultry processing consisted of killing the birds and hand picking them, either with or without dipping them in scalding water to loosen the feathers. Very few birds were eviscerated in processing plants. The evisceration was left for the butcher or for the housewife. Today, almost all poultry is fully eviscerated at the processing plant, and much of it is cut up to be sold as parts.

Fryers or Broilers. Broilers or fryers are young, usually 8- to 10-week-old chickens. The commercial broiler-production centers have shifted over the years. The three states around Chesapeake Bay (Delaware, Maryland, and Virginia) are known as the Delmarva area. This area was the first concentrated broiler-production center. More recently, the Southeastern states, principally Georgia and Alabama, have taken the lead in total production. The distribution of production in 1959 is shown in Fig. 5-7.

As shown in Fig. 5-7, much of the poultry is produced at points quite distant from the market. Chickens cannot be shipped alive economically, so the slaughtering is done close to the site of production, and the birds are shipped completely eviscerated and ready to cook. Processing plants range in capacity from those that process a few hundred birds a day to plants that handle 15,000 chickens per hour. All plants that ship interstate maintain government inspection. Each chicken is individually inspected for wholesomeness, and the federal inspectors see that plant sanitation is maintained.

The processing procedure is quite similar in all plants. The live chickens are delivered to the plant in crates. The birds are hung by both feet on shackles attached to a conveyor that takes the chickens to the killing area, where the throat is cut to allow complete bleeding. The chickens are allowed to bleed until dead before they are moved into a scalder. The water temperature and the scalding time vary, depending on the equipment used. This particular equipment operates at 123°F for a soft-scald. Other com-

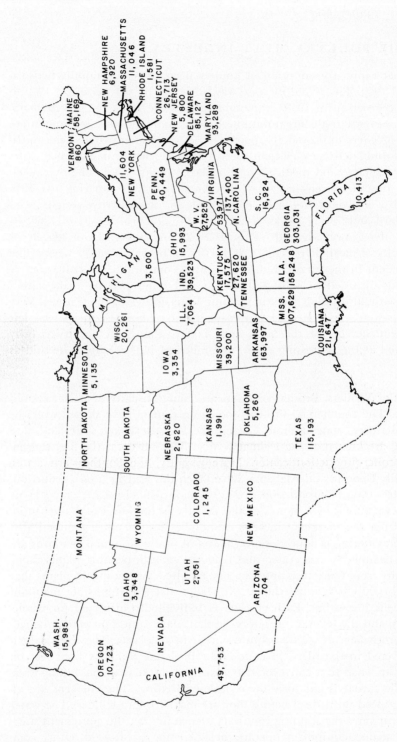

Fig. 5-7. Numbers of broilers (thousands of birds) produced in the continental United States; total production in 1959 was 1.7 billion birds. [Sources: AMS, USDA.]

monly used temperatures are 126–130°F for a semi-scald, 138–142°F for a sub-scald, and, in a few plants, 150°F or more for a hard-scald. The scalding time is reduced as the higher temperatures are used. The exact scalding procedure is important in that excessive scalding reduces tenderness of the muscle tissue (Shannon *et al.,* 1957) and insufficient scalding makes it very difficult to remove the feathers. In some plants, the birds are taken through the pickers on the shackles. Such equipment is shown in Fig. 5-8. After the birds are picked, they are taken from the shackles on the killing, scalding, and picking line and are placed on the eviscerating line. In plants that utilize a different type of picking equipment, the birds are removed from the shackles prior to picking.

Care must be exercised in carefully controlling the picking time and the force exerted by the rubber-finger pickers, since excessive picking results in a less tender muscle tissue. However, it is necessary to remove all feathers and protruding pinfeathers in order to market the birds.

After broilers are picked, they are then shackled to the eviscerating line. On this line, a trained government inspector examines each bird for whole-

Fig. 5-8. Mechanical removal of feathers from chickens. [Courtesy of Gordon Johnson Company, Kansas City, Mo.]

Fig. 5-9. The discharge end of a continuous chiller for poultry meat. [Courtesy of Morris and Associates, Raleigh, N.C.]

someness, by looking at the internal organs and the carcass. After inspection, the inedible portions—the head, feet, digestive system (except for the gizzard), reproductive and excretory systems—are discarded. The heart and liver are cleaned and returned to the packaged bird as edible giblets along with the gizzard. As soon as evisceration is complete, the birds are placed in chilling equipment or in tanks. Poultry meat should be chilled to a temperature of 35–40°F as rapidly as possible. Until 1958, the chilling was done by placing the birds in tanks of ice and water. The water was usually agitated by bubbling air through it or by using a circulating pump. In 1958, mechanical cooling equipment was introduced and was rapidly adopted by the industry. Figure 5-9 shows one type of mechanical chilling equipment.

Ice-Packed or Fresh, Dry-Packed Fryers. Over 80% of the broilers or fryers marketed are sold as ice-packed fresh birds. Such birds are shipped long distances. Wire-bound boxes that hold 24 chickens and about 25 lb. of ice are used for most shipments. The shelf-life of the fresh meat is usually determined by the control of dehydration, discoloration, and microbiological spoilage. As long as the birds are kept in ice, there is little chance that dehydration will take place. Microbiological spoilage is dependent on numerous factors. These are discussed in detail by Dawson and Stadelman (1960).

The most important single factor in the processing and packaging plant is sanitation. If the poultry is packed in ice or in a dry package with relatively few bacteria or fungi present, it will take longer for them to build up to a number that would result in spoilage. One common procedure to improve sanitation is to use chlorinated water containing about 20 ppm of active chlorine for flushing surfaces of equipment that come in contact with the birds. The value of chlorination in a poultry processing plant is discussed by Gunderson *et al.* (1954). Figure 5-10 shows the effectiveness of chlorine in an eviscerating room.

A second factor of importance is the temperatures used for storage of poultry. At a temperature of 32°F, the shelf-life was 18 days; at 37°F, the bacterial spoilage occurred after 11 days; and at 47°F, spoilage occurred after only 6 days. These data were reported by Shannon and Stadelman

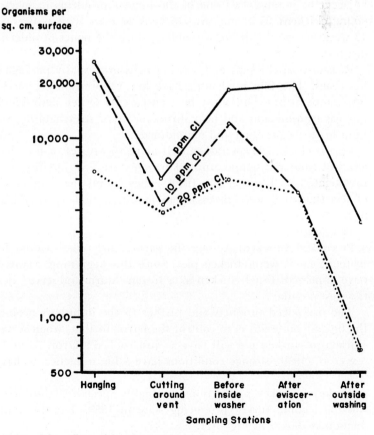

Fig. 5-10. The effect of in-plant chlorination of water on bacterial populations. [Source: Dawson and Stadelman, 1960.]

(1957). Other factors mentioned by Dawson and Stadelman (1960) as having an effect were packaging and the use of antibiotics.

Much consideration is being given to proper packaging of fresh fryers. Most birds are sold as cut-up birds or as whole, eviscerated birds. The whole birds are usually packaged in polyethylene or cellophane bags. In some stores that offer specials, the birds are displayed on crushed ice, without packaging. The cut-up birds are packed in fiber boats and are overwrapped with various types of plastic films. The most satisfactory films for overwrapping can be heat sealed.

In some areas, large volumes of fryers are sold as fresh parts. This type of product requires packaging similar to that for cut-up poultry. Packages of frozen fryer parts are one of the more popular poultry items.

Frozen Chicken. Frozen fryers may be purchased in all forms mentioned for fresh fryers. Discoloration or darkening of the long bones and the meat adjacent to it represents one of the biggest problems in marketing frozen young chickens. With mature chickens or even with roaster-type birds of 13 weeks of age this is not a problem, since the bones of older birds do not discolor.

Roaster-type chickens and stewing hens are usually packaged in flexible film bags. The film used must have low vapor transfer, good strength at low temperatures, and must be transparent. Other desirable features are low gas transmission and heat shrinkability or stretchability, which permit tight fits to be attained and maintained.

Frozen chicken keeps rather well at temperatures of less than 0°F. The effect of time and temperature of frozen storage on quality of chicken was investigated by Klose *et al.* (1959). They found that storage temperatures of less than 0°F were necessary to maintain high quality frozen poultry meat.

Precooked Chicken. Among the earliest precooked frozen foods offered in retail stores were chicken pies. Since this beginning, many other dishes have appeared. Fried chicken as a frozen "warm-and-serve" item is one of the most popular.

The precooked products add further to the industry's problems. One of the biggest problems is to control the flavor so that, when served, the fried chicken or chicken pie will have a "just cooked" flavor. According to Hanson *et al.* (1959), storage conditions have a big influence on flavor.

Turkeys. Turkey production is a highly specialized business. Minnesota was the leading turkey producing state in 1959. The distribution of production is shown in Fig. 5-11.

The turkey industry has gone through several phases. First, production was greatly affected by the disease blackhead prior to the discovery of the

Fig. 5-11. Turkey production (thousands of birds) in continental United States; total production in 1959 was over 81 million turkeys. [Sources: AMS, USDA.]

99

life cycle of the causative organism. Range rotation and the use of medi-
cants have drastically reduced losses from this disease. Then, in 1939, the
Broad-Breasted Bronze turkey was introduced at the Seventh World Poultry
Congress in Cleveland, Ohio, giving the industry a meatier and more efficient bird. During the following decade, the large bronze birds were by far
the most popular variety. The small, family-size varieties next met with
favor, the Beltsville Small White turkey being the most popular. Interest
has recently centered around a large white variety. The large, white strains
offer the advantage of having white pin feathers and a high efficiency of
feed conversion. To obtain small roasters, the large white strains are slaughtered and processed at 12 to 14 weeks of age. One of the major problems
facing the turkey producers is the high cost of poults, which is due to low
egg production and poor hatchability. However, research and improved
breeding techniques are making progress toward the solution of this
problem.

Processing Turkeys. Equipment similar to that for chickens is used for
processing turkeys. The speed of handling turkeys is reduced from the speed
with which chickens are handled. The large plants process up to 2000 turkeys per hour. A turkey eviscerating line is shown in Fig. 5-12.

An electric shock is frequently used to reduce struggling of turkeys during slaughter. The turkeys are stunned with high voltage, low amperage
current just prior to the time their throats are cut. This humane slaughter
treatment reduces the number of bruises on the wings that would otherwise
result from struggling at slaughter.

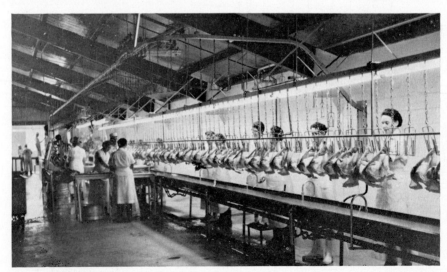

Fig. 5-12. A turkey eviscerating line in operation. [Courtesy of Gordon
Johnson Company, Kansas City, Mo.

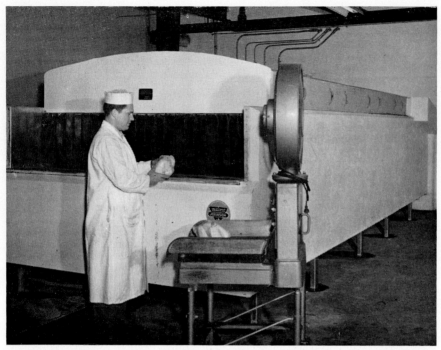

Fig. 5-13.   A spray-type liquid freezer used extensively for turkeys. [Courtesy of Gordon Johnson Company, Kansas City, Mo.]

Over 75% of all turkeys processed are frozen. This requires careful attention to adequate aging of the meat prior to freezing so as to assure tenderness. This requires holding the turkeys at temperatures of 45°F or less for about 20 hours. Turkeys are usually packaged and frozen on the day following slaughter.

Turkeys are frozen either in an air blast freezer (at −30°F) or in a liquid freezer, in which a solution of propylene glycol or sodium chloride is used as the freezing medium. The solutions are usually maintained at about 0°F. One of the liquid freezers available is shown in Fig. 5-13. Prior to freezing, dressed turkeys are packaged in one of the several flexible plastic bags available.

Frozen Shelf-Life of Turkeys. Properly packaged turkey meat keeps well when stored at temperatures of less than 0°F. Turkey fat is more susceptible to becoming rancid than chicken fat, since it contains very little natural antioxidants. By devoting special attention to packaging, thus preventing surface dehydration and "freezer burn," and by maintaining proper temperatures, turkey meat can be stored for 8 months with no detectable rancidity.

Much turkey is used in frozen turkey pies and in turkey rolls. These products are still relatively new, but they have already established themselves as having consumer appeal. Frozen, prestuffed, ready-to-cook turkeys are another product that becomes more widely accepted each year.

Ducks and Geese. The duck production centers of the United States are located on Long Island, New York, and in an area of northern Indiana and southern Michigan. The meat-type Pekin duck is one of the fastest growing of all domestic animals. Commercially produced ducks frequently weigh as much as 7 lb. at eight weeks of age.

The largest goose farm in the United States is in New Mexico. Geese are also grown extensively in the north central states. In many localities, geese are grown to be used for weeding row crops. They have been used successfully for weeding cotton and strawberries.

The large amount of wax in the feathers and the tight feathering make feather removal difficult. In order to get a cleaner picking job, a process known as wax picking is frequently used on ducks or geese. The birds are scalded and partially picked with conventional poultry equipment. They are then dipped into a special hot wax at about 185°F. This is allowed to cool and is then peeled off by hand, removing all down and feathers.

Most ducks and geese are packaged in flexible film bags and are frozen for wholesale or retail distribution.

Other Poultry Meats. There are specialized production centers for Cornish game hens, pheasants, and other game birds. The Cornish game hen is a young broiler-type chicken that is processed at about 5 weeks of age to yield a 1 lb. eviscerated bird.

Game birds are processed, in most instances, with much hand labor. The birds are usually sold as gift packages or to a specialized institutional trade.

REFERENCES AND SELECTED READINGS

References marked with an asterisk are of general interest.

Dawson, L. E. and W. J. Stadelman, 1960. Microorganisms and their control on fresh poultry meat. North Central Regional Publication 112. Michigan State Univ. Tech. Bull. 278.

Everson, Gladys J. and Helen I. Souders, 1957. Composition and nutritive importance of eggs. *J. Am. Dietetic Assoc.,* 33:1244–1254.

*Gunderson, M. F., M. W. McFadden, and

T. S. Kyle, 1954. *The Bacteriology of Commercial Poultry Processing.* Burgess, Minneapolis.

Hanson, H. L., L. R. Fletcher, and H. Lineweaver, 1959. Time-temperature tolerance of frozen foods. XVII. Frozen fried chicken. *Food Technol.,* 12:221–224.

Kahlenberg, O. J., J. E. Gorman, H. E. Goresline, M. A. Howe, Jr., E. R. Baush, 1952. A study of the washing and storage of dirty shell eggs. USDA Circular No. 911.

Klose, A. A., M. F. Pool, A. A. Campbell, and H. L. Hanson, 1959. Time-temperature tolerance of frozen foods. XIX. Ready-to-cook cut-up chicken. *Food Technol.*, 13:477–484.

*Koudele, Joe W. and E. C. Heinsohn, 1960. The egg products industry of the United States. Part I. Historical highlights, 1900–1959. North Central Regional Publication 108. Kansas State Univ. Bull. 423.

Shannon, G., W. W. Marion, and W. J. Stadelman, 1957. Effect of temperature and time of scalding on the tenderness of breast meat of chicken. *Food Technol.*, 11:284–286.

———— and W. J. Stadelman, 1957. The efficacy of chlortetracycline at several temperatures in controlling spoilage of poultry meat. *Poultry Sci.*, 36:121–123.

Types and Breeds
of Livestock

Chapter 6

Breeds of Beef Cattle

6-1. HISTORICAL ASPECTS OF BREED INTRODUCTION AND DEVELOPMENT

Stocks Introduced by Early Settlers. Many of the earliest explorers and settlers of the New World brought cattle. The first to do so was Columbus, on his second voyage in 1493 to the West Indies. Cattle entered what is now the United States by two general routes. Spanish explorers, settlers, and missionaries introduced cattle to the Southwest, to Florida, and to other areas of southern North America. These cattle multiplied and became the basis of the herds of Texas Longhorns which were of great importance to the nation's cattle industry during the years immediately after the Civil War, of range herds in much of the West, and of the "native" range cattle of Florida and other Southern coastal areas.

Settlers from the British Isles and other Northern European countries brought cattle from their homelands into Eastern United States. Later settlers took their descendants westward as settlement proceeded across the nation.

The early importations were predominantly from the British Isles, but were made before specialized beef breeds as we know them today had been developed. In many if not most cases they were valued more for their ability to produce milk and for their usefulness as draft animals than for meat. Indeed, ordinances were passed in some New England areas making it a criminal offense to slaughter an animal for beef before it had passed the age of usefulness for other purposes. A specialized beef industry did develop during colonial times in some eastern areas—notably the Piedmont section of North and South Carolina and Virginia (Towne and Wentworth, 1955).

After the importations by early settlers in the seventeenth century, few additional importations were made for a period of well over 100 years. Historical records are scanty but indications are that little constructive effort was put into developing improved types from the cattle originally imported from either Spain or Northern European areas. Writing of cattle in the Eastern sections of the nation, Allen (1868) said: "As immigration proceeded from the eastern coast to the interior, their neat cattle went with the people, intermixing still more in their new and scattered localities, until they became an indefinite compound of all their original breeds, and composing, as we now find them, a multitude of all possible sorts, colors, shapes and sizes. Thus our 'native cattle' as we call them, have no distinctive character, or quality, although in some of the States, as a stock, they are better than in others." He gave cattle of Spanish descent even less favor in saying: "As for the Texas cattle, we do not name them as an economical beast at all. We have only described them to be shunned "

Early American pioneers were presumably too busy subduing a new land and wresting a living from it to give attention to improvement of beef cattle. When, later in our history, attention was turned to improvement, well-defined breeds were available in other lands, and efforts centered on importation of these breeds and grading up native stocks to them. At present it is useless to speculate whether native cattle in certain areas may have had virtues which would have been worth preserving. They were not preserved and have contributed very little to the nation's present stocks.

Several experiments were conducted during the first third of the twentieth century in which the performance of "native" cattle was compared with that of purebred beef animals and of purebred X native crosses. In all cases the purebreds and their crosses produced animals more nearly meeting market demands, with production efficiencies in most cases equal to or superior to that of the natives (Cullison, 1940). Thus the importation and grading up to purebreds apparently represented a sound decision, although only a few of the many types of natives were used in the comparisons.

Introduction of Purebreds. Earliest importations of representatives of breeds destined to be important beef producers are believed to have been Shorthorns brought to this country from England in 1783, 1791, 1812, and 1817. Large numbers were imported during the general period 1820–1850. Many if not most of these animals were what would today be termed "dual-purpose," but they dominated the beef industry of the United States for much of the nineteenth century and served as the basis for the big "farmers' cow" used for both meat and milk production in farming areas of the country. Bulls of these strains were also used on the Western ranges but rather quickly gave way to the Hereford when sizable numbers of this breed became available during the latter part of the century.

During the nineteenth century, in both Britain and the United States, unfortunate pedigree fads and speculation in pedigrees occurred in the Shorthorn breed. These culminated in an 1873 sale in New York in which

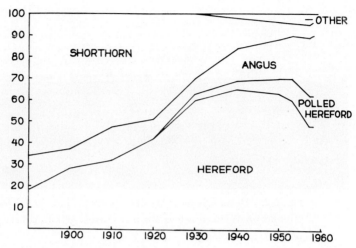

Fig. 6-1. Registrations, 1890–1959, expressed as percentage of total beef cattle registrations accounted for by each breed in each year. Polled Shorthorns are included with Shorthorns. [Graph courtesy of Dr. H. H. Stonaker, Colorado State University.]

109 head of Bates-bred "straight Duchess" cattle averaged $3504 and a cow sold for $40,500. Shortly thereafter the boom collapsed.

In the meantime, Scotch breeders, of whom the most prominent was Amos Cruickshank, had been at work improving the breed for beef purposes through selection for shorter legs, broader backs, earlier maturity, greater feeding capacity, and thicker and smoother fleshing. Scotch cattle were imported to the United States in numbers in the latter quarter of the nineteenth century and quickly assumed a dominant role in the production of beef by Shorthorns. Breeders have continued to rely heavily on stock imported from Scotland except for brief periods of the breed's history in America.

The first Herefords were imported in 1817 by the statesman Henry Clay of Kentucky, but this English breed did not find its way to this country in appreciable numbers until the general period 1850–1890—especially toward the end of this period. The most prominent pioneer herd in the United States was that of Gudgell and Simpson of Independence, Missouri, which operated from 1877 to 1916; many animals were imported by this firm. Following the dispersal of the herd in 1916, particularly after about 1935, a fad for cattle of Gudgell and Simpson breeding developed; cattle that traced in all lines of their pedigrees to this herd (termed "airtight" pedigrees) were in demand.

Angus cattle first came to the United States in 1873, when George Grant of Victoria, Kansas, imported four bulls. Large enough numbers were brought here during the next twenty years to establish the breed firmly. The

Fig. 6-2. Herefords on a Western pasture. This breed has been the most popular on Western ranges for many years. [Photo courtesy, Soil Conservation Service, USDA.]

Angus attained its earliest popularity in the corn belt states, and this area is still its stronghold. Adoption of the breed in other areas has been rapid in recent years, with present use including appreciable numbers on Western ranges.

Other British breeds have been introduced from time to time: the Galloway (1853), the West Highland (1893), the Long-Horns (1817), the Sussex

Fig. 6-3. Angus steers in an Iowa feedlot. The Middle West has long been the area of this breed's greatest popularity. [Photo courtesy American Angus Association.]

Fig. 6-4. Polled Hereford heifers on a Coastal Bermuda grass pasture in Georgia, an area where the breed is popular. [Photo courtesy Georgia Coastal Plain Experiment Station, Tifton, Ga.]

(1884), and perhaps others. These have either disappeared or have to date been maintained in such small numbers as to have had little or no impact on the cattle industry.

The Charolais, a French breed, is first known to have been imported in 1936 from a herd in Mexico; small numbers have been imported since. All have come from Mexico because disease problems in France have prevented direct imports. Numbers are being increased through top crossing on cattle of other breeds. Those with five top crosses are considered purebred. The breed is handicapped in the United States by its limited numbers, but it has attracted considerable attention and cattlemen will follow its future progress with interest.

The only non-European type of beef cattle imported to the United States, and currently of any importance here, is the Zebu. Animals of this type are of the *bos indicus* species. In the United States they are called "Brahmas." The American Brahman breed represents an amalgamation of several breeds imported from India. Brahman cattle are distinctive in appearance, being characterized by a hump over the shoulders, large drooping ears, and loose skin in the dewlap and navel regions. First known importations were in 1849, 1854, and 1885, but the importations which established the breed were in 1905, 1906, and the early 1920's. Only limited numbers were imported and the breed was built up through top crossing on cattle of other breeds. Animals with four top crosses are registered as purebred.

The Brahman has had its greatest usefulness in cross combinations with

Fig. 6-5. Purebred Brahman cattle in a pasture near the Texas-Louisiana border. The picture illustrates some of the colors common in the breed. [Photo courtesy American Brahman Breeder's Association.]

the British breeds and with unimproved cattle, and for this reason it probably exerts a greater influence on the nation's cattle industry than would be indicated by registration figures.

Breeds Developed in America. In many parts of the Southern and Southwestern United States, neither the Brahman nor European breeds are ideal for beef production. The averages of extensive crossbreeding experiments in these areas show conclusively that crosses of Brahman bulls on cows of British breeding will result in calves 25 to 30 pounds heavier at a normal weaning age than British calves; also, crossbred cows will wean calves 60 to 80 pounds heavier. Postweaning growth rates under winter feeding conditions have not exceeded those of British steers and gains have usually been less efficient, but growth on summer pastures has usually been superior. Objective carcass data are not plentiful, but observation and some objective evidence indicate that the carcasses of crossbreds are superior to those of Brahmans in finish, conformation, and palatability of lean tissue—approaching but not equaling British types in these regards. Crossbreds on the average have higher dressing percentages than purebred British types—approaching the Brahman.

The superior growth rates of the crosses are an excellent example of heterosis or "hybrid vigor," since they have exceeded both parental types (Warwick, 1952; Godbey *et al.,* 1959).

In order to eliminate the disadvantages of a continual crossbreeding

Fig. 6-6. A group of Santa Gertrudis yearling heifers, a breed developed in America by the King Ranch, Kingsville, Texas, from a Brahman-Shorthorn foundation. It is usually considered to be the first strictly American breed of cattle. [Photo courtesy Santa Gertrudis Breeders International, P.O. Box 1340, Kingsville, Texas.]

Fig. 6-7. Shorthorn cows on pasture. This breed is the largest of the British breeds. [Courtesy American Shorthorn Association.]

TABLE 6-1. | Total 1959 registrations and leading states in registrations by breed.*

Breed:	Hereford	Polled Hereford	Angus	Shorthorn	Polled Shorthorn	Brahman	Santa Gertrudis
Total registrations:	487,833†	107,293**	233,940	35,729	15,953	14,261	14,658‡
Leading states:	Texas	Texas	Missouri	Iowa	Illinois	Texas	Texas
	Oklahoma	Missouri	Iowa	Illinois	Indiana	Florida	Florida
	Kansas	Illinois	Illinois	Kansas	Iowa	Louisiana	Louisiana
	Nebraska	Mississippi	Texas	Missouri	Nebraska		Georgia
	Montana	Oklahoma	Oklahoma	Texas	Missouri		Arkansas

* 1959 registrations of other breeds include: Charolais, 1234; Charbray, 2634; Brangus, 2995; Galloway, 900; Red Angus, 810; Scotch Highland, 475.

† Registrations by American Hereford Association. Includes 133,711 Polled Herefords.

** Registrations by American Polled Hereford Association. An unknown fraction of these is also registered in the American Hereford Association.

‡ Number given is for animals classified rather than registered in the conventional sense

program, several new breeds have been developed with two objectives: of stabilizing as far as possible the vigor, production qualities, and reasonably good carcass qualities of the Brahman-European crossbred types; and of selecting for further improvement in closed populations based on crossbred foundations. The new strains or breeds developed thus far include the Santa Gertrudis, Beefmaster, Brangus, and Charbray. As a group these breeds are larger cattle than the British breeds; they have only a trace of the hump of the Brahman, but they show definite evidence of Brahman ancestry in ear shape, loose skin in the dewlap and sheath areas, and in type of hair coat.

Trends in Breed Popularity. No census data are available to show conclusively the proportions of different breeds of all beef cattle on the nation's farms and ranches. Data on numbers registered in a recent year (Table 6-1) give a good general idea of relative importance but are far from precise as estimates of distribution in the total population. Figure 6-1 shows trends in numbers registered in various breeds for the past 60 years. In the early 1900's the Shorthorn was the most numerous breed, but this position was long ago relinquished to the Hereford. In more recent years the Angus has experienced a great surge in popularity. Although Polled Shorthorns are not shown separately, the polled (hornless) strains of both Herefords and Shorthorns, established during the early years of the present century, have experienced substantial increases in popularity. In 1959, registrations of the polled strains made up approximately 30% of the total registrations in each breed.

The data vividly illustrate the fact that breeds change in popularity. In the long run these changes probably depend upon ability to meet economic needs, although skillful breed promotion and effective selling efforts are doubtless factors of importance, especially over short periods.

6-2. HISTORY AND CHARACTERISTICS OF BEEF CATTLE BREEDS

Most of the older breeds (Table 6-2) were the result of development by one or more breeders in an area of a kind of cattle which were useful and which had characteristics distinguishing them from other strains or breeds. Most breeds were developed from mixtures of various native strains and came to be recognized as breeds only after they had achieved at least some degree of popularity outside the area of origin.

Studies of the genetic histories of the Shorthorn (McPhee and Wright, 1925), Angus (Stonaker, 1943), and Hereford (Willham, 1937) all show that rather intensive inbreeding was practiced during the formative stages. Inbreeding was apparently practiced intentionally in some cases in order to intensify desired traits, but it probably also occurred more or less automatically in some cases—because of limited numbers and because the best

TABLE 6-2. | *Beef cattle breeds imported to the United States or developed from imported breeds.*

Breed	Origin			Importation to U.S.		Breed Standards	
	Country	Approx. date	Foundation stocks	First	In large numbers	Color	Polled or Horned
Aberdeen Angus	Scotland	Late 1700's	Stocks native to area	1873	1878–1900	Black	Polled
Red Angus	United States	Assn. est. 1954	Red segregates from black Angus herds			Red	Polled
Charolais	France	Before 1775	Stocks native to area	1936		Cream to light wheat	Horned
Hereford	Western England	Middle 1700's	Stocks native to area	1817	1850–1890	Red with white face	Horned
Polled Hereford	United States	Early 1900's	Polled mutants or "sports" from horned herds			Red with white face	Polled
Shorthorn	Northeast England	Late 1700's	Stocks native to area	1783	1820–1850	Red, white, or roan	Horned
Polled Shorthorn	United States	Early 1900's	Polled mutants or "sports" from horned herds			Red, white, or roan	Polled
American Brahman	India	Amer. assn. est. 1924	*	1849	1905–1925	Varies, steel gray most common, but reds and darker shades occur	Horned

* The American Brahman was formed by an amalgamation of several breeds from India.

foundation animals were likely to have been related. Whatever the reasons, a few foundation animals in each breed developed high relationships to all the other animals in the breed. In general, much less inbreeding has been practiced by modern breeders. In one of the newer American breeds, the Santa Gertrudis (Rhoad, 1955), similar procedures were followed during the formative stages.

The more recently developed American breeds (Table 6-3) are all based on crossbred foundations, with the crosses made for the purpose of founding a breed—usually after exploratory crosses suggested the desirability of the particular cross.

Breed differences are of two kinds. The readily apparent differences in color, color pattern, and presence or absence of horns serve as breed trademarks and may also have economic value in certain cases. Tables 6-2 and 6-3 summarize information on breed differences of this kind.

Differences between breeds in traits such as fertility, mothering ability, efficiency of gains, or carcass desirability are of potentially more importance to the person making selection of a breed or breeds for his own operation. Adaptability, or the ability to achieve maximum productivity in a given environment, is also of prime importance.

In some cases research information has given us evidence of breed differences in such traits, while in other cases long-time observations have made the existence of such differences seem probable. However, no completely objective comparisons of different breeds have been made in which each breed was systematically sampled and representatives observed under similar conditions for productivity. Again, a great deal of evidence and observation shows immense variation within breeds in productive characteristics. Thus, in spite of the fact that in some cases there may be real differences in breed averages, variation within breed is greater. The selection of a breed then becomes of less importance than selection of productive animals within the breed used.

6-3. ECONOMIC AND ESTHETIC IMPORTANCE OF DIFFERENCES BETWEEN BEEF BREEDS

Color. A uniform color in a group of cattle provides an optical illusion of uniformity of type and conformation. Further, a distinctive color or color pattern characteristic of a breed forms a trade-mark by which it is readily identified; this may serve as an aid in popularizing the breed. It is for these reasons that a majority of breeds have adopted standard colors or color patterns or have limited the number of acceptable colors to a very few. If, however, the color or pattern adopted as standard is difficult or impossible to fix, breeders are forced to practice selection for it and to cull off-color animals regardless of merit in other regards.

The color of the Hereford may be taken as an example. The distinctive

TABLE 6-3. | *Beef cattle breeds developed in the United States from crossbred foundations.*

Breed	Origin			Breed standards		Date registry association founded
	Founder	Approximate date	Foundation stocks	Color	Polled or horned	
Santa Gertrudis	King Ranch, Kingsville, Texas	First crosses 1910. Intensive efforts to form breed started in 1918	$\frac{5}{8}$ Shorthorn, $\frac{3}{8}$ Brahman ancestry	Cherry red	Horned	1951
Beefmaster	Lasater Ranch, Falfurrias, Texas	1908, efforts intensified in 1930's	Brahman, Shorthorn and Hereford breeds*	Varies, is not a factor in selection	Horned	1961
Brangus	Clear Creek Ranch, Welch, Oklahoma	1942	$\frac{5}{8}$ Angus, $\frac{3}{8}$ Brahman ancestry	Black	Polled	1949
Red Brangus	Paleface Ranch, Spicewood, Texas	1946	Angus and Brahman†	Red	Polled	1956
Charbray	Several ranches in Texas	Late 1930's	$\frac{1}{8}$ to $\frac{1}{4}$ Brahman and $\frac{3}{4}$ to $\frac{7}{8}$ Charolais	Light cream or wheat	Horned	1940

* Developed by mass selection in multiple sire herds. Percentages of each breed in ancestry not known.
† No fixed proportion of ancestry of two breeds required, but cattle must be of type intermediate between the two parent breeds.

color pattern of this breed—red body with white face, white underline, and other white markings—is of unknown origin, although there are cattle of other breeds on the continent of Europe with somewhat similar markings. The white face is dominant and calves of any cross between the Hereford and another breed exhibit it to varying degrees. This may well have been a factor in the popularization of the breed. The exact color pattern desired has proved difficult to fix with animals having too much white along the back (linebacks) or too much red on the neck (red necks)—still occasionally occurring. A recent study (Stanley *et al.,* 1958) indicates that the preferred amount of white "is the result of an intermediate genetic situation and that it is not likely that selection of breeding stock for this trait will fix the color pattern for this desired intermediate." Also, in the Hereford breed some breeders have preferred a dark and some a light shade of red. Studies at several experiment stations have shown no relationship between shade of color and productivity. To the extent that selection is made for color, selection pressure for traits of greater economic value is reduced.

The black color of the Angus has likewise been a valuable trade-mark. Black shows a variable degree of dominance in crosses with other breeds. It is dominant over red and in crosses with red Shorthorns gives solid black offspring. Crosses with Herefords are black-bodied, with white faces and some white on other extremities. Crosses with white Shorthorns are usually blue roan (a mixture of black and white hairs), with white spotting sometimes occurring. Brahman crosses are usually solid black, while the offspring of crosses with the Charolais are usually a smoky, dark cream hue.

From the beginning of recorded history of the Angus breed, the predominant color has been black, but a gene for red color is present in low frequency as a recessive and occasional red calves are born. Complete elimination of a recessive gene such as this is very difficult. Reds breed true for color when intermated, and breeders in both Great Britain and the United States have assembled red herds. So far as is known the characteristics of these cattle are the same as those of the parent breed except for color.

Color is related to productivity in some cases. In hot areas with intense sunlight, light coat colors absorb less heat from the sun than darker ones. They thus aid in maintaining normal body temperatures. In the case of Angus cattle, red color may constitute an advantage in warmer areas.

White udders may lead to "snow burn" if cows calve in the spring before snow is gone. Pigment around the eyes in white-faced cattle reduces the incidence of cancer of the eyelid.

Horned versus Polled. Cattlemen have long disagreed on the question of whether beef cattle should be horned or polled. Horns make market animals more difficult to handle and also result in bruises. For this reason most market cattle of horned breeds are dehorned. If performed at young ages this operation is not difficult and if properly done involves little danger of loss. However, the operation constitutes additional work and there is always the danger of infection or insect injury particularly in areas where the screwworm is present.

Advocates of the horned type believe that these cattle have advantages in production. The principal advantage claimed is that in multiple sire herds, especially under range conditions, horned bulls scatter and breed their cows, while polled ones tend to gather in groups and spend their time fighting, resulting in lowered calf crops. It has also been observed that many polled bulls have a tendency to allow the penis or sheath to protrude, with a resulting possibility of injury and temporary or permanent sterility. It is not known whether this tendency is another effect of the gene for polled cattle or whether it is mere coincidence that it occurs in the polled type.

Some breeders feel that horned cows are better mothers under certain conditions, especially in areas where predatory animals are prevalent.

No studies are known to have been made on any of the foregoing ideas. It is quite possible that economic considerations may favor one of the two kinds under some environmental and management situations, while the other type might be favored in other cases.

Within cattle of British origin the hereditary factor for polled behaves in most cases as a simple dominant, although there are exceptions indicating a more complicated mode of inheritance.

Angus cattle are polled and are apparently pure or homozygous for the gene for polled, since in crosses with all breeds except the Brahman or those based on Brahman crossbred foundations, only polled offspring are produced. In crosses of the latter type variable percentages of the calves have horns or heavy scurs, thus further indicating that the inheritance of horns is not a simple one-factor pair situation.

Present-day Polled Herefords and Polled Shorthorns descend entirely from polled mutant or "sport" animals which occurred in the parent horned breeds. The formation of these breeds (or perhaps it is better to term them strains within breeds) is an interesting example of applied genetics. The Polled Hereford was established by Warren Gammon of Iowa, who in 1901 purchased four polled bulls and seven cows he had located by circularization of all Hereford breeders. Other mutants have been utilized as they have appeared from time to time in horned herds. Horned blood was infused during the formative stages of the breed, both to increase numbers of polled cattle and to improve the average quality. In the establishment of the breed it was necessary to use all the few polled animals available, regardless of merit in other regards. Infusion of horned blood has continued to the present time.

Gestation Length and Birth Weight. Gestation periods and birth weights of calves of the same breed vary considerably; for example, the average gestation length in Herefords in different studies has been reported to be from 279 to 286 days (see review by Brakel *et al.*, 1952). It therefore does not seem advisable to attempt to give breed averages for either character. However, trends in within-herd comparisons make it obvious that real breed differences exist.

In purebred Angus cattle gestation length averages three to eight days less and calves on the average are five to eight pounds lighter at birth than the Hereford or Shorthorn. Both traits tend to be transmitted in crosses. Calves from Hereford cows but sired by Angus bulls *on the average* have shorter gestation periods and are lighter at birth than if sired by Hereford bulls (Gerlaugh *et al.*, 1951).

Observations of the above tendencies led to the hypothesis that it would be desirable to breed first-calf heifers of other breeds to Angus bulls, obtain calves with lower birth weights, and thus reduce calving difficulties. Chambers *et al.* (1954a) studied the question and found that while on the average there was less difficulty in calving Hereford heifers bred to Angus bulls, there was a great deal of difference between bulls; some Angus bulls sired calves that were bigger and gave more calving trouble than those sired by some Hereford bulls. To minimize calving troubles in first-calf heifers they recommended using small, fine-boned bulls, with choice of breed a secondary consideration.

Purebred Brahman cattle on the average have gestation periods a few days longer than any British breed, and crossing Brahman bulls on British cows tends to result in longer gestations (Wheat and Riggs, 1958) and heavier birth weights (Godbey *et al.*, 1959) than pure British matings.

Milking and Mothering Ability. As discussed more fully in Chapter 14, weaning weight of calves is a very important factor in profitable beef production. Comprehensive comparisons of British breeds have not been made, but scattered data from several experiment stations and on-the-farm testing programs strongly suggest that Angus cows wean heavier calves than Herefords. The position of present-day Shorthorns is uncertain.

In the Southern states the Brahman cow and Brahman X British crossbreds wean calves considerably heavier than British types (Warwick, 1952; Damon *et al.*, 1959). Cattle of the newer breeds based on Brahman-British foundations have also been shown to raise heavy calves. The superiority of cows with some Brahman background is one of the principal reasons for the popularity of this type in many Southern areas.

Post Weaning Growth. As with other characters, comprehensive comparisons of the British breeds for ability to gain rapidly and efficiently after weaning, either in the feed lot or on pasture, have not been made. Available data suggest some *average* superiority of the Hereford, followed closely by the

Shorthorn and Angus. The Charolais and its crosses have been shown in several trials to grow faster than British types. This is one of the traits which has stimulated interest in the breed. Brahman crossbreds and breeds based on them have generally shown superior gaining ability under Southern pasture conditions.

Meat Quality. Over a period of many years the Angus breed has enjoyed an unequaled record in carcass competition at leading shows. The winning record apparently depends largely upon the high average ability of animals of this breed to marble well without excessive external fat. Recent summaries of data from all entries in carcass contests and from experiment stations where limited breed comparisons have been made indicate some superiority of Angus carcasses in marbling, rib eye area, and carcass grade. But the margin over other breeds is small, with a great deal of overlap.

The Brahman, and to a lesser degree its crosses, has been shown to produce less tender lean than the British breeds but also to have more variability, suggesting the possibility of more rapid improvement (Cartwright *et al.*, 1958). Brahman and Brahman crossbreds usually dress one to three per cent higher than British-type cattle.

Charolais crosses with the British breeds in experiments of limited scope have demonstrated their ability to produce carcasses with high lean content and apparent good eating quality, as judged by tenderness ratings (Damon *et al.*, 1960; Warwick, 1960). These carcasses, however, have less marbling than those of British cattle and in several comparisons have rated lower, by U.S. government grade standards.

Adaptation to Range. Although one breed, the Hereford, has dominated the range cattle industry for many years, all the breeds are being raised successfully under range conditions. Since no comprehensive comparisons have been made, it is uncertain whether the Hereford is truly superior in its adaptation or whether its popularity rests on other factors.

The Hereford originated in an area of West Central England where cattle were produced on grass, with little or no supplementary feeding. It has been surmised that the environment in its native home may have resulted in selection of types especially well adapted to range and pasture management. Under American conditions it is generally recognized that the ability to thrive under the rigors of the range, to survive during periods of adversity such as severe winters, and to maintain satisfactory fertility records under many conditions are characters which have contributed to the breed's popularity.

During recent years the Angus has been increasing in popularity among range operators. How much further this breed will make inroads on the Hereford cannot be predicted at this time.

Heat Adaptation. Cattle of the British breeds were developed in areas of temperate climate and most of them do not have a sufficiently good thermo-regulatory mechanism to maintain normal body temperatures under hot environmental conditions. The Brahman and its crosses are superior in this regard (Rhoad, 1940). Ability to tolerate heat is thought to be one of the reasons Brahmans and their crosses are able to make more rapid summer pasture and feed-lot gains in many areas (Cartwright, 1955).

Problems of beef production under subtropical conditions are complicated, however; in addition to heat tolerance, there are such factors as quality of pasture forage and insect and parasite infestations. Having animals with ability to withstand heat does not automatically solve all beef production problems in these areas.

Hereditary Defects in Beef Cattle. Many hereditary defects have long been known in both beef and dairy cattle (see Rice *et al.*, 1957, and Gilmore, 1950, for listings). Few defects have been frequent enough to constitute major problems, although in some breeds they have occasionally been serious enough to result in extensive culling of animals related to those producing defective animals. It had, however, been generally assumed that such defects were of little importance from an industry standpoint. Events of the past 20 years have made it necessary to modify this view.

During the late 1930's and 1940's a small extra-low-set, compact type of Hereford, generally known as "Comprest"—and apparently due to a semi-dominant mutant gene resulting in an extreme type of dwarf when homozygous (Stonaker, 1954)—appeared in the breed and for a time was popular in show rings. The practical usefulness of this type was so much in question that research on the problem was conducted at several experiment stations. This research, as well as the experience of practical cattlemen, showed conclusively that cattle of this type had little or no carcass superiority and that they had several serious production difficulties—including low weaning weights, slow growth, and production of dwarfs when intermated (Stonaker *et al.*, 1952; Chambers *et al.*, 1954b; Stonaker, 1954). They very quickly lost their popularity. A type known as "compact" in the Shorthorn breed had a similar history. These types were easy to eliminate since animals carrying the gene were phenotypically recognizable and could be culled.

At about the same time, or a little later, a recessive hereditary type of dwarfism (Johnson *et al.*, 1950), popularly known as "snorter," became a problem among Hereford and Angus cattle and possibly occurred in other breeds. Dwarfism of this type has undoubtedly caused more turmoil among purebred beef cattle breeders than any other factor. Research has clearly established that "snorter" dwarfism is inherited as a recessive. Why it occurs frequently enough to constitute a problem is not known with certainty.

However, research at several stations indicates that *on the average* the gene for dwarfism may have some effect in the heterozygous condition and that normal animals carrying the gene in the recessive or hidden form may be slightly shorter in body, head, and legs. While these effects are not definite enough to be diagnostic for the presence or absence of the gene in individual animals, they may be great enough so that if selection were for these characters, carriers would be favored in a greater than chance proportion in the selection of breeding stock, with consequent increase in frequency of the gene. The alternative view is that dwarfism increased in frequency because several prominent animals happened to be carriers and the popularity of their progeny resulted in wide dissemination of the gene.

Much research has been done in attempts to find anatomical or physiological methods of identifying normal carriers of the dwarf gene, but to date no successful method has been found (Bovard, 1960). Breeders have used "clean pedigree" animals—animals with no known carriers in their pedigrees—to reduce the incidence of dwarfism. This has also resulted in culling many otherwise desirable animals who had one or more known carriers in their pedigrees. Some progeny testing of bulls to locate non-carriers has been done by breeding them to groups of known carrier cows.

Other types of dwarfism are also known (Bovard, 1960) but none are believed to have been frequent enough to constitute major problems. There is disagreement among research workers on the genetic relations of dwarfs of these types to the snorter.

Occurrence of another category of defects depends partly upon hereditary tendencies toward susceptibility and partly upon environmental effects. Cancer eye is an example of this kind (Anderson and Chambers, 1957), and it has been a particular problem of the Hereford breed. Selection against cancer eye is difficult since it occurs most frequently in older animals, which may already have several progeny in a herd or dispersed among other herds. The fact that it is partially hereditary, however, indicates that culling the affected animals and their progeny and other close relatives should reduce its frequency. Uterine prolapse is a defect whose elimination is beset with many of the same problems (Woodward and Quesenberry, 1956). Maintaining intensive selection on traits of this kind would greatly reduce the selection intensity which could be put on other traits of economic importance.

The problem of animals which have long sheaths or habitually allow the penis to dangle from the sheath has been referred to earlier in connection with the polled gene. These conditions are not limited to polled cattle. The Brahman breed and many of the newer breeds based on Brahman crossbred foundations have problems in this regard. No studies are known to have been made on the heritability of these conditions, but observation suggests hereditary differences. If these exist, selection for improvement should be effective.

Some beef animals have dispositions which make them difficult to handle under normal management conditions. All breeds have animals of this kind but they are apparently more frequent in the Brahman and related breeds and in the Angus. Again, no scientific studies have been made on heritability of differences in temperament, but observation suggests the desirability of selecting docile animals for breeding purposes.

6-4. SUMMARY

We have given historical material on the beef cattle breeds used in the United States and have briefly discussed the popularity and characteristics of the various breeds. From the material presented it is apparent that all breeds have both strong points and weaknesses and that there is no one best breed for all conditions. While real differences exist between breed averages, there is much hereditary variation within all breeds. Selection of inherently productive animals within a breed is likely to be of as much or more importance than selection of a breed.

REFERENCES AND SELECTED READINGS

References marked with an asterisk are of general interest.

*Allen, Lewis F., 1868. *American Cattle, Their History, Breeding and Management.* Orange Judd Co., New York.

Anderson, David E. and Doyle Chambers, 1957. Genetic aspects of cancer eye in cattle. Okla. Agr. Exp. Sta. Misc. Pub. MP-48, pp. 28–43.

Bovard, K. P., 1960. Hereditary dwarfism in beef cattle. *Anim. Breeding Abstracts,* 28(3):223–237.

Brakel, W. J., D. C. Rife, and S. M. Salisbury, 1952. Factors associated with the duration of gestation in dairy cattle. *J. Dairy Sci.,* 35(3):179–194.

*Briggs, Hilton M., 1958. *Modern Breeds of Livestock.* Revised ed. Macmillan, New York.

Cartwright, T. C., 1955. Responses of beef cattle to high ambient temperatures. *J. Animal Sci.,* 14(2):350–362.

———, O. D. Butler, and Sylvia Cover, 1958. Influence of sires on tenderness of beef. *Proc. 10th Res. Conf.,* Amer. Meat Instit. Found., pp. 75–79.

Chambers, Doyle, J. A. Whatley, Jr., and W. D. Campbell, 1954a. A study of the calving performance of two-year-old Hereford heifers. Okla. Agr. Exp. Sta. Misc. Pub. MP-34, pp. 39–43.

——— and D. F. Stephens, 1954b. Growth and reproductive performance of large- and small-type Hereford cattle. Okla. Agr. Exp. Sta. Misc. Pub. MP-34, pp. 50–54.

Cullison, A. E., 1940. The influence of breeding on the performance of beef calves produced in Mississippi. Miss. Agr. Exp. Sta. Bull. 347.

Damon, R. A., Jr., S. E. McCraine, R. M. Crown and C. B. Singletary, 1959. Performance of crossbred beef cattle in the gulf coast region. *J. Animal Sci.,* 18(1):437–447.

———, R. M. Crown, C. B. Singletary and S. E. McCraine, 1960. Carcass characteristics of purebred and crossbred beef steers in the gulf coast region. *J. Animal Sci.,* 19(3):820–844.

Gerlaugh, Paul, L. E. Kunkle, and D. C. Rife, 1951. Crossbreeding beef cattle. Ohio Agr. Exp. Sta. Research Bull. 703.

Gilmore, Lester O., 1950. Inherited non-lethal anatomical characters in cattle—a review. *J. Dairy Sci.*, 33(3):147–165.

Godbey, E. G., W. C. Godley, L. V. Starkey, and E. D. Kyzer, 1959. Braham X British and British X British matings for the production of fat calves. S. Carolina Agr. Exp. Sta. Bull. 468.

Johnson, L. E., G. S. Harshfield, and W. McCone, 1950. Dwarfism, an hereditary defect in beef cattle. *J. Heredity*, 41:177–181.

McPhee, H. C., and S. Wright, 1925. Mendelian analysis of the pure breeds of livestock. III. The Shorthorn. *J. Heredity*, 16:205–215.

*Ornduff, D. R., 1957. *The Hereford in America*. Printed privately by the author.

*Rhoad, A. O., 1940. A method of assaying genetic differences in the adaptability of cattle to tropical and subtropical climates. *Empire J. Exp. Agr.*, 8:190–198.

*———, 1955. *Procedures Used in Developing the Santa Gertrudis Breed.* In *Breeding Beef Cattle for Unfavorable Environments.* Univ. of Texas Press, Austin, Tex., pp. 203–210.

*Rice, V. A., F. N. Andrews, E. J. Warwick, and J. E. Legates, 1957. *Breeding and Improvement of Farm Animals.* 5th ed. McGraw-Hill, New York.

*Sanders, A. H., 1918. *Short-horn Cattle.* Sanders Pub. Co.

*———, 1928. A history of Aberdeen-Angus cattle. *New Breeders' Gazette,* Chicago.

Stanley, M. E., D. Chambers, and D. E. Anderson, 1958. Inheritance of color pattern and shade of hair color in Hereford cattle. Okla. Agr. Exp. Sta. Misc. Pub. MP-51, pp. 50–54.

Stonaker, H. H., 1943. The breeding structure of the Aberdeen Angus. *J. Heredity,* 34:323–328.

*———, 1954. Dwarfism in beef cattle. *Proc. West. Sect. Amer. Soc. Animal Prod.,* 5:239–242.

*———, M. H. Hazaleus, and S. S. Wheeler, 1952. Feedlot and carcass characteristics of individually fed comprest and conventional type Hereford steers. *J. Animal Sci.,* 11:17–25.

*Towne, C. W., and E. N. Wentworth, 1955. *Cattle and Men.* Univ. of Oklahoma Press, Norman, Okla.

Warwick, E. J., 1952. Crossbreeding with Brahman cattle. Guest Paper. Forty-fourth Annual Meeting, Amer. Soc. Anim. Prod., *Amer. Breed.* 4(11):6–9, 24.

*———, 1958. Fifty years of progress in breeding beef cattle. *J. Animal Sci.,* 17(4):922–943.

*———, 1960. Genetic aspects of production efficiency in beef cattle. Proc. of Conf. "Beef for Tomorrow," Natl. Aca. Sci., Natl. Research Council Pub. 751, pp. 82–92.

Wheat, J. D. and J. K. Riggs, 1958. Heritability and repeatability of gestation length in beef cattle. *J. Animal Sci.,* 17(1):249–253.

Willham, O. S., 1937. Genetic History of Hereford Cattle in the United States. *Jour. Hered.* 28:283–294.

Woodward, R. R. and J. R. Quesenberry, 1956. A study of vaginal and uterine prolapse in Hereford cattle. *J. Animal Sci.,* 15(1):119–124.

Chapter 7

Breeds of Dairy Cattle

"Those who survey the work done in this department will arrive at the conviction that among all of the experiments made, not one has been carried out to such an extent and in such a way as to make it possible to determine the number of different forms under which the offspring appear, or to arrange these forms with certainty according to their separate generations, or definitely to ascertain their statistical relations."

GREGOR MENDEL

7-1. INTRODUCTION

Dairy cattle are well adapted to the types of agriculture practiced in the United States. They are found in every state. According to the latest estimates, dairy cows are found on about 50% of the farms, many of the small herds on farms producing other agricultural products. However, there is a marked tendency for dairy herds to be concentrated around densely populated areas, where they furnish a supply of fluid milk.

Approximately one-third of the cattle in the United States are kept for the production of milk. Of these, approximately 80% belong to the major dairy breeds, 15% belong to the dual-purpose and minor dairy breeds, and 5% are beef cattle or "native" cattle lacking the characteristics of any particular breed. As our agriculture becomes more specialized a greater percentage of the cattle kept for milk production will probably belong to the specialized dairy breeds. Consumer preferences—combined with high costs for labor, equipment, land, and other items used in the production of milk—have created an economic situation favoring the production of a

127

high volume of milk of a composition conforming to the market requirements.

Taxonomically, cattle belong to the class *Mammalia.* They belong to the
order *Arteriodactyla* (even-toed hoofed animals) and are further divided into
the suborder *Pecora,* which includes deer and giraffes. This suborder is
characterized by a specialized four-compartmented stomach, which enables
them to digest and utilize roughages. They belong to the family Bovidae,
which includes sheep, goats, and antelopes, and are characterized taxonomically by hollow horns which contain a bony core and do not shed.
Cattle are further grouped in the genus *Bos,* which differentiates them
from the other genera of this family. Our domestic cattle belong to twc
species within this genus. One is the cattle of European origin, *Bos taurus,*
also called *Bos typicus primigenius.* These animals are characterized by the
absence of a hump over the withers, a flat forehead and poll with the horns
growing from the junction of the lateral and posterior borders of the skull,
a small dewlap, and a lowing cry. The second species—*Bos indicus,* commonly called "Zebu" or "Indian cattle"—are characterized by the large
hump over the withers, a large dewlap, large drooping ears, and a grunting
voice. Most of the dairy cattle in the United States belong to *Bos typicus*
but animals of the Red Sindhi breed, belonging to the *Bos indicus* species,
are being used experimentally in crossbreeding for increased heat tolerance
in the southeastern United States.

The immediate ancestors of our major breeds of dairy and beef cattle
are thought to be the great ox of Europe, *Bos primigenius.* Some authorities
consider that another distinct species, *Bos brachycerus,* also called the Celtic
Ox or Celtic Shorthorn, were the ancestors of some of our modern breeds.
Bos pimigenius became extinct during the seventeenth century and the last
survivors were found in the forests of north central Europe. The semiwild
"White Park Cattle" found in England are considered to be descendants
of the *Bos brachycerus* species.

Whether our breeds arose from one species or two is relatively unimportant with respect to the improvement of our modern breeds but it is
interesting from a historical standpoint. Information on the relationship of
the "White Park Cattle" in England to our modern breeds could be obtained by comparing their respective "blood groups." The blood groups are
based upon antigens in the red blood corpuscles and agglutinins in the
blood sera, which when mixed with blood from other animals cause clumping and hemolysis of the red cells. Their presence in the blood of an animal
is controlled by inheritance, and the finding of an identical blood group
in two different animals indicates that these two animals are genetically
alike for this factor; that is, both animals have the same genetic factors
responsible for this characteristic and are therefore related with respect to
this factor. If some identical blood groups are found in these semiwild
cattle and our modern breeds it would indicate that our modern breeds

descended from these animals or that both had common ancestors; the number of similar groups would give an estimate of the extent of their relationship.

7-2. IMPORTATION OF CATTLE

The early importation of cattle into the United States is discussed in Chapter 6. Although the cattle imported at this time were probably representative of the kinds found in the areas from which the colonists migrated, they were interbred and soon lost their identity. It is not surprising that the early settlers knew nothing of breeding, because the mechanisms governing reproduction and inheritance had not been discovered. Hamm discovered the spermatozoon in 1677 and Von Baer discovered the egg in 1827. Spallan-

TABLE 7-1. | *Origin, importation, and characteristics of the major breeds of American dairy cattle.*

	Ayrshire	Brown Swiss	Guernsey	Holstein	Jersey
Country of origin	Scotland	Switzerland	Island of Guernsey	Holland	Island of Jersey
First importation to U.S.*	1822	1869	1830	1852	1850
Breed Association formed†					
European	1877	1911	1814	1873	1833
U.S.	1875	1880	1877	1871	1868
Herdbook established†					
European	1877	1911	1822	1873	1866
U.S.	1875	1889	1877	1885	1868
Body size (lb.)**					
Female	1200	1400	1100	1500	1000
Male	1850	2000	1700	2200	1500
Av. gestation period (days)	277.9	289.7	283.9	278.8	278.8
Desirable color markings	Red, mahogany brown, or combination of these with white	Solid brown	Fawn, with white markings, yellow skin	Black and white	Fawn, with or without white markings

* Earlier importations occurred but available records indicate these later importations eventually formed the nucleus for the present-day breeds.
† Approximate dates.
** Minimum mature weight in milking or breeding condition. Purebred Dairy Cattle Association.

Fig. 7-1. Ayrshire cow, Neshaminy Miss Phett; she produced 166,941 lb of milk and 7646 lb of fat in 10 lactations. [Courtesy Ayshire Breeders Association.]

zani showed in 1780 that the spermatozoa were necessary for the early development of the young, but the actual process of fertilization was not understood until about 1875. Mendel discovered the fundamental laws governing inheritance in 1866, but his discoveries were ignored when first published, not to be rediscovered until 1900. Thus the modern concepts of breeds and breeding are of recent origin and early animal improvement was based primarily on observations of men who were breeding the animals for various uses.

The second wave of importation of dairy cattle into the United States began about the middle of the nineteenth century (Table 7-1). The cattle imported at this time were probably representative of the improved cattle in their respective areas, and following importation they were mated to maintain their identity. Closely associated with these importations was the formation of the breed associations and the establishment of herd books. In some instances individual breeders kept private herd books for pedigrees. In other cases the breed association recorded pedigrees and established the herd books. They were organized primarily to record pedigrees, to keep the breeds "pure," and to protect the importers from unscrupulous dealers. The present breed organizations continue to register cattle and keep pedigrees, but they perform other functions—discussed in greater detail in a later section.

The country of origin and the approximate formation dates of the modern breeds of dairy cattle are given in Table 7-1. It is of interest to note that herd books, in some instances, were established earlier in the United States than in the country of origin.

7-3. BREEDS

A breed may be defined as a group of animals related by descent and developed for a special function. Thus, dairy cattle breeds are breeds developed primarily for milk production. In the United States, cattle kept primarily for milk production belong to the Ayrshire, Brown Swiss, Guernsey, Holstein, and Jersey breeds. Figures 7-1 to 7-5 are photographs of cows of these breeds. In addition, two dual-purpose breeds, the Milking Shorthorn and Red Polled, are kept for milk, but their numbers are small in comparison with the previously mentioned dairy breeds. The number of animals registered in each of the different breeds for the year 1959 is as follows: Ayrshire 23,050, Brown Swiss 25,667, Guernsey 75,332, Holstein 273,913, Jersey 54,695 and Milking Shorthorn 12,343; a total of 465,000 head. If we assume that the above figures are correct, and that the average life of the cow in the herd is 5 years, the estimated number of registered dairy cattle in the United States should be about 2,225,000. The latest estimate of

Fig. 7-2. Brown Swiss cow, Lee's Hills Keeper's Raven; she produced 34,851 lb milk, 4.53% fat, 1579.3 lb fat 3 times milking in 365 days; age 9 years 9 months. [Courtesy the Brown Swiss Breeders Association.]

Fig. 7-3. Guernsey cow, Lush Acres Hermes' Quest; she produced 14,651 lb of milk and 900 lb of fat in 305 days, 2 times milking. [Courtesy American Guernsey Cattle Club.]

the total number of cattle kept for dairy purposes is about 33,000,000 so that registered cattle comprise approximately $6\frac{1}{2}\%$ of the total number of dairy cows. Data on the actual numbers of cows belonging to the different breeds are not available but the Holstein-Friesian Association estimates that Holsteins, purebred and grade, account for approximately 60% of the dairy cattle in the United States.

Cattle were kept for dairy purposes long before the modern breeds developed. For example, in Holland a butter trade had developed to the extent that specialized buildings, "butterhouses," were constructed for its storage and distribution before 1288. Students of breed history do not agree on the origin of the different breeds of dairy cattle, but animals conforming to our present idea of a specialized breed probably existed in the areas for variable periods of time before they were formally recognized as a distinct breed. The consensus of opinion is that most of the modern breeds were probably formed from crossbred foundation stock—that is, the "native" animals were crossed with animals from other areas. This was probably followed by selection within the group for animals with the desired characteristics, but the methods and preciseness of the selection cannot be determined. Bakewell was one of the first men to apply modern methods to the improvement of animals. Although he worked with beef cattle, his ideas—"Like begets like" and "Breed the best to the best"—were probably

Fig. 7-4. Holstein cow, Princess Breezewood R A Patsy; she produced 36,821 lb of milk and 1866 lb of fat in 365 days, 2 times milking. [Courtesy Holstein Friesian Association of America.]

Fig. 7-5. Jersey cow, Imp. Wonderful Snowdrop; she produced 14,234 lb of milk and 833 lb fat. [Courtesy of the American Jersey Cattle Club.]

applied to the early selection of cattle for dairy purposes and played a role in the selection of animals which eventually became the dairy breeds. Laws prohibiting the importation of cattle to the islands of Guernsey and Jersey probably were important in the formation of these two breeds as we know them today.

7-4. BREED CHARACTERISTICS

Inherited characteristics form the bases that distinguish the individual breeds. Those characters that are easily identified and inherited in a simple manner form many distinguishing characteristics of the different breeds and probably arose because they could be standardized easily. Color markings fall into this category and in many cases they are the trade-mark of the breed. As already mentioned, the origin of our modern breeds is not known but the information available suggests that circumstances giving rise to the various breeds were quite similar. Foundation animals from which the breeds arose appear to have been crossed with animals from other areas. These wide crosses increased the number of different genes in the foundation stocks and formed a wide genetic basis from which animals with the desired characteristics could be selected. Selection of animals that were superior for a given productive characteristic and breeding them together tended to concentrate the genes governing this trait, with resulting improvement. This selection automatically caused them to become more alike genetically than nonselected animals; that is, more homozygous than animals bred randomly. With the formation of the breed societies, which record the ancestry of animals, the matings of more closely related animals could be controlled and the process of standardization of the animals within the group accelerated. When the genes controlling characteristics are few in number and their inheritance is simple, the animals become alike very quickly because a larger proportion of the animals become more homozygous for the characteristic. However, when a large number of genes control the characteristic, the standardization of a group of animals is more difficult and the process requires a longer time. All of our present-day breeds are still heterozygous or "mixed" with respect to the genes controlling size and productive characteristics.

Blood Types

The general heterozygosity of the different breeds has been demonstrated clearly by the blood typing of cattle during recent years. Neimann-Sørensen et al. (1956) reported 47 alleles of the B group blood type in three Danish breeds of cattle. In the five American dairy breeds, 89 alleles have been reported for the same system. On the other hand, the Jersey breed in Denmark has the same B alleles, except for two, that are found in Jerseys in the United States. Thus the Jersey breed in Denmark is more closely related to the Jersey breed in the United States than to other breeds of cattle. Stormont (1958) compared the frequencies of alleles between Guernseys, Herefords, Holsteins, Jerseys, and Shorthorns. He found differences in frequencies of the alleles between the breeds and between strains within the breeds. The genetic differences present in individuals within the present-day breeds allow selection for higher production to be effective. If a breed should become homozygous, then improvement by selection would not be possible within the breed because all of the animals would be alike. Many genes control most of the productive traits and their random distribution in the offspring suggests that the production of a homozygous group or breed of animals is unlikely. If, however, some easily identified traits, for example, certain blood groups, can be associated with a productive characteristic, more rapid selection for that productive characteristic would be possible and selection would be more effective.

Body Size

A wide variation exists between breeds with respect to size. The minimum weights for cows and bulls of the five major dairy breeds, as published in the Unified Score Card of the Purebred Dairy Cattle Association, are listed in Table 7-1. Average weights for animals of the various breeds are not available but minimum weights have been suggested by the Purebred Dairy Cattle Association (Table 7-1). In recent years the tendency has been for animals in all breeds to be larger. Many of the animals holding the production records for their respective breeds are large animals.

Composition of Milk

As indicated in Table 3-2, the breeds differ with respect to the composition of their milk. In general, the milk from the Guernsey and Jersey breeds is high in fat and solids-not-fat, that from the Ayrshire and Brown Swiss is intermediate, and that from Holsteins is lowest. The variation between breeds is greatest for percentage fat, less for percentage solids-not-fat, and least for percentage ash. There is a good correlation between the percentage fat and the percentage solids-not-fat, so that in general the breeds and individuals with high content of fat also contain greater amounts of other solids in the milk. Individual cows within a breed, however, show marked differences in the percentage of each constituent. Within the Holstein breed, for example, milk from individual cows ranges from 2.6–6.0% fat, 2.4–6.5% protein, 3.9–5.7% lactose, 0.56–0.87% ash, and 10.7–17.6% total solids (Overman *et al.*, 1939). In spite of the wide individual differences, the breed differences in milk composition are real and are characteristic for the breed. They are genetically determined to a certain degree, but very little information is available concerning the manner in which they are inherited. In the future, selection of breeding animals will probably be based on the solids-not-fat in the milk as well as total milk and fat production.

There is a breed difference in the ability to convert carotene to vitamin A. Holsteins, Ayrshires, and Brown Swiss convert more carotene to vitamin A than Guernseys and Jerseys. The yellow color of the milk from the Guernsey and Jersey is due to the secretion of carotene instead of vitamin A into the milk. On similar rations that are adequate in carotene, the vitamin A value (carotene plus vitamin A) per unit of fat is the same in the different breeds but more is present as carotene in the milk with the yellow color. The carotene and vitamin A is secreted in conjunction with the fat; therefore the total amount secreted per unit of milk is greater in the milk with a high fat content even though the concentration per unit of fat is the same. The carotene is also stored in the body fat and secreted by the glands in the skin, giving the fat and glandular secretions a yellow color.

Factors other than breed affect the composition of milk. For example, high environmental temperatures decrease the solids-not-fat in milk, and finely ground hay when fed as the only source of roughage depresses the percentage of milk fat. Therefore, selection for changes in milk composition should be conducted on animals under similar environmental conditions and should be based on samples collected over the entire lactation period.

Quantity of Milk

Breeds also vary in the total amount of milk and fat produced. An estimate of the potential of the better animals within the different breeds may be obtained from the production of the daughters of proved bulls used in artificial breeding organizations (Table 7-2).

TABLE 7-2. | *Production of daughters of proved bulls used in artificial insemination studs.* 2X-305 day M.E. Records.*

Breed	No. of sires proved	Milk (lb)	% Fat	Fat (lb)
Ayrshire	48	10,650	4.2	448
Brown Swiss	75	11,554	4.2	482
Guernsey	202	9,337	4.9	459
Holstein	457	13,542	3.7	503
Jersey	162	8,921	5.4	477
Shorthorn	17	8,853	3.9	349
Red Poll	1	11,387	3.7	427
Red Dane	1	9,992	4.5	447

* From Dairy Herd Improvement Letter, ARS 44-58, July 1959.

As shown in Table 7-2, the greatest difference between the breeds with respect to production is the amount of milk they produce. In general the breeds producing less milk have a higher content of fat so that fat production per lactation shows less breed variation. A cow's milk-producing ability, when measured under standard conditions, depends on her maximum daily yield at the peak of lactation and ability to maintain this yield. Normally daily production of milk rises up to four to six weeks following parturition and then declines slowly until she is dried off. Persistency is the term used to describe the ability of the cow to continue to produce at a high level throughout her lactation and is very important as far as total production is concerned. Cows with the same productive rate at the peak of lactation may vary as much as 50% for total production per lactation because of differences in persistency. The few data available indicate very little difference in persistency between the Holstein, Jersey, and Guernsey breeds, with more variability between offspring of sires within each breed than between the breeds.

Color

Coat color is one trait distinguishing the different breeds. As compared to productive characteristics its inheritance is simple, and it affords an easy method for the identification of an animal as belonging to a given breed. The preferred colors for the different breeds are listed in Table 7-1. Many breeds have color standards for registration of animals. Color markings which prevent registry in Holsteins are solid black, solid white, black in the switch, black from the hoof to the knee or hock, black encircling the leg touching the hoof head, black belly, black and white intermixed to give color other than black and white, and red and white. These rigid color standards are hard to maintain and result in the loss of a few valuable productive animals to the purebred breeders. Black color is dominant to red, but in spite of continued selection against the red color, occasionally red and white animals are born from black and white parents. In these animals the genetic factor for red is present but is masked by the black. In the Brown Swiss breed, cows with any white or off-color markings above the underside of the belly or with a white core in the switch do not meet the color standards, and these markings must be recorded at the time of registration. White or off-colored spots, pink noses, and light streaks on the side of the face are objectionable. Black or brindle colors are objectionable in Ayrshires and a golden yellow skin pigmentation and clear muzzle are favored in Guernseys. As discussed in an earlier section, the yellow skin and fat found in the Guernsey and Jersey breeds are due to the storage of carotene in the fat and fatlike materials. It is related to the lowered ability to convert carotene to vitamin A, which suggests that their requirement for this vitamin might be higher than in other breeds. Some data suggest they do have a higher requirement but it does not appear to be much greater; critical experiments have not been done to establish the magnitude of the difference.

Heat Tolerance

Preliminary data suggest that differences exist in the popular dairy breeds with respect to heat tolerance—that is, the ability to produce milk when the environmental temperature is high. However, very few animals within each breed have been tested and no definite conclusions can be made as to whether these differences are associated with breed or with individuals within the breed. The limited data available indicate that the Brown Swiss is more heat tolerant than the Jersey and that the Jersey is slightly more resistant than the Holstein. However, many factors—level of milk production, body size, surface area, and the number and activity of sweat glands— affect the heat tolerance of the individual animal. Many animals will have to be tested to establish if a true breed difference exists.

Reproductive Efficiency

There are indications that breeds may differ in reproductive efficiency but experimental evidence is not available to verify this possibility.

Milk Fever

According to three different investigators (Metzger, 1936; Henderson, 1938; and Hibbs, 1946), Jerseys are more susceptible to milk fever than the other breeds. The incidence of milk fever in the different breeds as reported by Henderson is Ayrshire 6.0%, Brown Swiss 15.3%, Guernsey 8.6%, Holstein 5.6%, and Jersey 29.2%. These percentages are based upon the total number of calvings exclusive of the first calf in a large herd. The number of cows in each breed is not given and the level of production of milk by the animals having milk fever and those not having milk fever is not reported. The author states that the high-producing cows are more susceptible. These data indicate a breed difference in the susceptibility to milk fever. Other factors play a role in causing milk fever and their relative importance with respect to breed differences in susceptibility has not been evaluated.

In summary, the present-day dairy breeds differ in blood types, size, color, milk composition, and total milk production. Data also suggest that heat tolerance, breeding efficiency, and susceptibility to milk fever are breed characteristics. However, more information on larger numbers of animals is needed to establish these as breed characteristics. Most of these differences are controlled genetically but many of the traits are also modified by environment. The breeds are relatively "pure" or homozygous for those breed characteristics that are controlled by a few genes that are easily identified and inherited in a simple manner. However, they are still quite "mixed" or heterozygous for characteristics like milk production and milk composition that are controlled by a large number of factors that may be inherited in a complex way. Many of the productive characteristics are also modified by environmental factors and this increases the complexity of selecting for the genetic factors controlling them.

7-5. TYPE

One of the earlier references between the relation of type and production is found in Youatt's book, *Cattle, Their Breeds, Management and Diseases,* written in 1838. He quotes an earlier description of the Suffolk cow: "A clean throat, with little dewlap, a snake head, thin short legs, the ribs springing well from the center of the back, the carcase large, the belly heavy, the backbone ridged, the chine thin and hollow, the loin narrow, the udder square, large, loose, and creased when empty, the milk veins remarkably large and rising in knotted puffs; and this so general, that I scarcely ever saw a famous milker that did not possess this point, a general habit of leanness, hip bones high and ill covered, and scarcely any part of the carcase so formed and covered as to please the eye that is accustomed to fat beasts of the finer breeds." In many ways the above fits the description of dairy type as described by the Unified Score Card. Understandingly, these animals were not pleasing to the eye accustomed to selecting cattle primarily on the basis of their merit for meat.

Type may be defined as the presumed relationship between the animal's body conformation and its ability to perform a given function. For example, in cattle we speak of dairy type and beef type for animals whose primary function is milk production and meat production respectively. An animal's type may be expressed by giving it a numerical score, in comparison with the "ideal type" animal. In dairy cattle the ideal type and method for scoring have been standardized and published by the Purebred Dairy Cattle Association. Except for size and color markings there is a striking similarity in the general conformation of the ideal type animal in the breeds of American dairy cattle. The score card is shown in Fig. 7-6 for dairy cows. In order for an individual to be able to place a correct type score on a cow it is essential that he know the parts of the animal, as shown in the same figure.

Although type is not highly related to the production of dairy cattle, it is important to breeders. For example, a weakly attached udder in a high producing cow may break down and shorten her productive life. Pendulous udders are more subject to injury. Crooked feet and legs may restrict the animal's ability to move about. The breed associations have a type classifica-

DAIRY COW UNIFIED SCORE CARD

Copyrighted by The Purebred Dairy Cattle Association, 1943. Revised, and Copyrighted 1957
Approved — The American Dairy Science Association, 1957

	Perfect Score
Breed characteristics should be considered in the application of this score card	
Order of observation	
1. GENERAL APPEARANCE	**30**
(Attractive individuality with, feminity, vigor, stretch, scale, harmonious blending of all parts, and impressive style and carriage. All parts of a cow should be considered in evaluating a cow's general appearance)	10
BREED CHARACTERISTICS — (see reverse side)	
HEAD — clean cut, proportionate to body; broad muzzle with large, open nostrils; strong jaws; large, bright eyes; forehead, broad and moderately dished; bridge of nose straight; ears medium size and alertly carried	
SHOULDER BLADES — set smoothly and tightly against the body	10
BACK — straight and strong; loin, broad and nearly level	
RUMP — long, wide and nearly level from **HOOK BONES** to **PIN BONES**; clean cut and free from patchiness; **THURLS**, high and wide apart; **TAIL HEAD**, set level with backline and free from coarseness; **TAIL**, slender	
LEGS AND FEET — bone flat and strong, pasterns short and strong, hocks cleanly moulded. **FEET**, short, compact and well rounded with deep heel and level sole. **FORE LEGS**, medium in length, straight, wide apart, and squarely placed. **HIND LEGS**, nearly perpendicular from hock to pastern, from the side view, and straight from the rear view	10
2. DAIRY CHARACTER	**20**
(Evidence of milking ability, angularity, and general openness, without weakness; freedom from coarseness, giving due regard to period of lactation)	20
NECK — long, lean, and blending smoothly into shoulders; clean cut throat, dewlap, and brisket. **WITHERS**, sharp. **RIBS**, wide apart, rib bones wide, flat, and long. **FLANKS**, deep and refined. **THIGHS**, incurving to flat, and wide apart from the rear view, providing ample room for the udder and its rear attachment. **SKIN**, loose, and pliable	
3. BODY CAPACITY	**20**
(Relatively large in proportion to size of animal, providing ample capacity, strength, and vigor)	
BARREL — strongly supported, long and deep; ribs highly and widely sprung; depth and width of barrel tending to increase toward rear	10
HEART GIRTH — large and deep, with well sprung fore ribs blending into the shoulders; full crops; full at elbows; wide chest floor	10
4. MAMMARY SYSTEM	**30**
(A strongly attached, well balanced, capacious udder of fine texture indicating heavy production and a long period of usefulness)	
UDDER — symmetrical, moderately long, wide and deep, strongly attached, showing moderate cleavage between halves, no quartering on sides; soft, pliable, and well collapsed after milking; quarters evenly balanced	10
FORE UDDER — moderate length, uniform width from front to rear and strongly attached	6
REAR UDDER — high, wide, slightly rounded, fairly uniform width from top to floor, and strongly attached	7
TEATS — uniform size, of medium length and diameter, cylindrical, squarely placed under each quarter, plumb, and well spaced from side and rear views	5
MAMMARY VEINS — large, long, tortuous, branching	2
"Because of the natural undeveloped mammary system in heifer calves and yearlings, less emphasis is placed on mammary system and more on general appearance, dairy character, and body capacity. A slight to serious discrimination applies to overdeveloped, fatty udders in heifer calves and yearlings."	
Subscores are not used in breed type classification.	
TOTAL	**100**

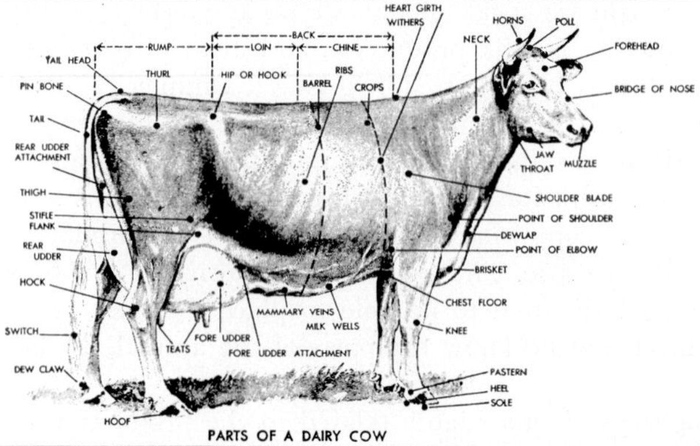

PARTS OF A DAIRY COW

Fig. 7-6. Dairy Cow Unified Score Card. [Courtesy Purebred Dairy Cattle Association.]

EVALUATION OF DEFECTS

In a show ring, disqualification means that the animal is not eligible to win a prize. Any disqualified animal is not eligible to be shown in the group classes. In slight to serious discrimination, the degree of seriousness shall be determined by the judge.

EYES
1. Total blindness: *Disqualification.*
2. Blindness in one eye: *Slight discrimination.*
3. Cross-eyes: *Slight discrimination.*

WRY FACE
Slight to serious discrimination.

CROPPED EARS
Slight discrimination.

PARROT JAW
Slight to serious discrimination.

SHOULDERS
Winged: *Slight to serious discrimination.*

TAIL SETTING
Wry tail or other abnormal tail settings: *Slight to serious discrimination.*

LEGS AND FEET
1. Lameness — apparently permanent and interfering with normal function: *Disqualification.*
— apparently temporary and not affecting normal function: *Slight discrimination.*

2. Bucked knees: *Slight to serious discrimination.*
3. Evidence of arthritis, crampy hind leg: *Serious discrimination.*
4. Boggy hocks: *Slight to serious discrimination.*

ABSENCE OF HORNS
No discrimination.

LACK OF SIZE
Slight to serious discrimination.

UDDER
1. Blind quarter: *Disqualification.*
2. Abnormal milk (bloody, clotted, watery): *Possible disqualification.*
3. Udder definitely broken away in attachment: *Serious discrimination.*
4. A weak udder attachment: *Slight to serious discrimination.*
5. One or more light quarters, hard spots in udder, obstruction in teat (spider): *Slight to serious discrimination.*
6. Side leak: *Slight discrimination.*

DRY COWS
Among cows of apparently equal merit: *Give strong preference to cows in milk.*

FREEMARTIN HEIFERS
Disqualification unless proved pregnant.

OVERCONDITIONED
Slight to serious discrimination.

TEMPORARY OR MINOR INJURIES
Blemishes or injuries of a temporary character not affecting animal's usefulness: *Slight discrimination.*

EVIDENCE OF SHARP PRACTICE
1. Animals showing signs of having been operated upon or tampered with for the purpose of concealing faults in conformation, or with intent to deceive relative to the animal's soundness: *Disqualification.*
2. Uncalved heifers showing evidence of having been milked: *Serious discrimination.*

Fig. 7-6. Dairy Cow Unified Score Card (continued).

tion program in which the cows of the individual breeder are compared with the breed ideal. When animals are classified by this method the components of type are scored individually and can be used as a basis for the selection of future breeding animals to strengthen weak points prevalent in the breeding herd. If a breeder's herd scores low on udder attachments or on feet and legs the breeder should select his next herd sire from families within the breed that are outstanding in these respects. Comparative judging, as practiced at Dairy Cattle Shows, is based on type indirectly. Type also has an economic value to the breeder. When he is selling breeding animals with similar productive capacity the better type animals are in greater demand and usually sell for a better price.

7-6. BREED ASSOCIATIONS

Many of the dairy cattle breed associations were formed in the last quarter of the nineteenth century. They were organized for the recording of animals which were distinctive in their breeding and for protecting the importers of cattle from unethical practices by some of the exporters. This was done primarily by requiring pedigrees of the animals, and the original herd books were primarily used for recording pedigrees. The present associations perform several functions for their members. They are responsible for the registration of animals, they promote their breed, they conduct production testing and type classification programs. Most of them have selective registration programs.

Several testing programs are supervised by the breed organizations. The broad aspects of the testing programs are the same for all the breeds but they differ in specific ways. These programs are discussed in chapter 32.

The breed associations also conduct the type classification programs. In addition, most of them have selective registration programs based on production records and type classification. Any animal that is the offspring of registered parents may be registered by the breed association, provided it is normal and meets the color standards. Selective registration is a method which is used to give recognition to outstanding animals within the breed. Programs are available for the recognition of outstanding productive ability, superior type, and superior transmitting ability for milk and fat production and type classification.

With the continued improvement in the productive characteristics of grade cattle, selective registration and continued selection for better production in the purebred cattle will be more important and the selection standards will be higher. For example, the lactations completed under the HIR testing program of the Holstein breed during 1959 averaged 13,612 lb. of milk, 3.69% fat, and 502 lb. of fat on a 305-day, 2 ×, mature equivalent basis. These averages are practically identical with those reported for grade and purebred progeny of Holstein bulls used in artificial insemination (Table 7-2). Both of these groups are selected but with the continued use of bulls transmitting the high production, the population of cows that are both grade and purebred will increase in productivity, and fewer bulls will have the ability to transmit increased milk and fat production above the average of the breed.

REFERENCES AND SELECTED READINGS

References marked with an asterisk are of general interest.

*Bowling, G. A., 1942. The introduction of cattle into Colonial North America. *J. Dairy Sci.*, 25:129–154.

*Caldwell, W. H., *The Guernsey*. American Guernsey Cattle Club, Peterborough, N.H.

*Gow, R. N., 1936. *The Jersey*. American Jersey Cattle Club, New York.

Henderson, J. A., 1938. Observations on reproduction and associated conditions in a herd of dairy cattle. *Cornell Vet.*, 28: 173–195.

Hibbs, J. W., W. E. Krauss, C. F. Monroe and T. S. Sutton. Studies on milk fever in dairy cows. I. The possible role of vitamin D in milk fever. *J. Dairy Sci.*, 29:617–624.

Metzger, H. J. and H. B. Morrison, 1936. The occurrence of milk fever in the Ken-

tucky Station over a period of 20 years. *Proc. Am. Soc. Animal Prod.*, pp. 48–52.

Neimann-Sørensen, A., P. H. Sørensen, E. Anderson and J. Moustgaard, 1956. Danish investigations on blood groups of cattle and pigs. Seventh International Congress of Animal Husbandry, Madrid, pp. 87–111.

Overman, O. R., O. F. Garrett, K. E. Wright and E. P. Sanman, 1939. Composition of Brown Swiss milk with summary of data on composition of milk from cows of other dairy breeds. Illinois Agr. Expt. Sta. Bull. 457.

*Prentice, E. P., 1942. *American Dairy Cattle*. Harper, New York.

*Prescott, F. S. and F. T. Price, 1930. *Holstein Friesian History*. Holstein-Friesian World Inc., Lacona.

*Sanders, A. H., 1925. The taurine world. *National Geographic Magazine.* 48:591–710.

Stormont, C., 1958. On the applications of blood groups in animal breeding. *Proc.*

Tenth International Genetics Congress, 1:206–224.

*Youatt, W., 1838. *Cattle, Their Breeds, Management and Diseases.* Baldwin and Cradock, p. 174.

Chapter 8

Breeds of Swine

8-1. INTRODUCTION

Swine have long been an important animal on American farms. They have been traditionally called the "mortgage lifter" in the corn belt. Swine have gone through more numerous type changes than other classes of livestock. One facet of swine production has remained constant during this century: the corn belt has served as the hub of the industry.

The listing below shows the leading states in hog production in 1959. Iowa produces more hogs yearly than the next two states combined, and this is in spite of the fact that Illinois occasionally produces more corn than Iowa.

State	No. on farms in 1959*
Iowa	12,533,000
Illinois	7,106,000
Indiana	4,848,000
Missouri	3,956,000
Minnesota	3,815,000
Ohio	2,628,000
Nebraska	2,453,000
Wisconsin	1,801,000
Georgia	1,780,000
South Dakota	1,591,000

* From USDA, Agricultural Statistics, 1959.

The per capita consumption of pork has slipped somewhat in relation to that of beef and poultry. This loss in popularity of pork products has been the principal incentive to the swine breeders to improve their breeds; some have made great effort; others have lagged.

Beginning about 1880, according to Vaughn (1941), there was a trend toward what was called the "cob-roller" type. This was a small-framed, quick-fattening type further characterized by small litter size and a slow rate of gain. Because commercial swine producers found it to be uneconomical, purebred breeders shifted about 1908 to the other extreme of very tall "stiltlike" hogs. Ranginess was stressed to the point that judges used their canes to measure height. Great arch of back was also encouraged. These animals did not reach a proper degree of finish until they weighed well over 200 lb. In the 1930's, therefore, another change in emphasis toward a smaller type took place, but at first no special attention was given to back-fat thickness and per cent lean. Since World War II, all the breed associations have initiated programs to develop swine which would have a minimum of wastiness and a maximum percentage of the lean cuts—ham, loin, picnic, and Boston butt.

Swine have a rapid rate of reproduction and a short generation interval. It has therefore been easy to make marked changes in type within the breeds, and these changes have tended to follow the demands for fat or meat. Thus during the war years the great demand for fats stimulated production of fat hogs. The current trend is toward a lean or so-called "meat type" hog. The discussion here will center principally on the current state of the breeds. There is little to be gained from studying the history of swine breeds, other than learning some things not to do.

Swine breeds at one time were classified into "lard" or "bacon" breeds. Most of the American breeds were classified as lard hogs, and the British and Scandinavian breeds as bacon hogs. The basis of this classification was that American hogs were an important source of fat, whereas the English and Scandinavian breeds were used in the production of Wiltshire type bacon, made from the whole side of the hog. The current meat-type hog presumably grows somewhat faster and has a larger ham than representatives of the bacon breeds. Some of the new breeds represent an attempt to borrow the more desirable traits from both bacon and lard breeds.

Currently several of the American breeds are in good repute as being meaty and efficient. The degree to which they are held in esteem by packers tends to be related to the improvement efforts that the respective breed associations have made. Concerted work toward improving breeds of swine has now become a principal function of swine record associations, which in the past were largely just recording and promotion agents.

Any statement characterizing a breed of swine is likely to be out of date shortly. Individual herds also may deviate sharply from the breed average. The performance characterizations which follow are based on the current state of the breeds, as nearly as the writer can determine them from recent testing station and experiment station results.

Some associations will point to their Production Registry data as an indication that their litter size is good. However, litters of less than eight are not submitted for Production Registry. Hence any estimate based on these records is biased, since the small litters are not considered.

8-2. MODERN BREEDS AND THEIR TRAITS

A list of some of the more popular breeds of swine and a few of their traits are given in Table 8-1. Though the figures listed for the traits are the averages of fairly large groups, they may not represent true averages

TABLE 8-1. | *Some popular breeds of swine and their traits.*

Breed	Origin	Color	Litter size	No. of pigs raised to 154 days†	Rate of gain	Carcass merit‡
Hampshire	America	Black, white belt	8.66*		Average**	Good (heavy loin)
Duroc	America	Red	9.78* 9.31†	6.92	138.9‡ Excellent**	Poor (small loin eye)
Poland China	America	Black, white points	7.98* 7.84†	5.82	Below average** 132.6‡	Good (heavy ham)
Berkshire	England	Black, white points	7.74*		Average**	Excellent (good muscling)
Spotted Poland	America	Black and white spotted	8.70†	6.92	139.0‡	
Yorkshire	England	White	10.75*		Fair**	Average (long loin, small eye)
American Landrace	Denmark	White	9.74*		Excellent‡	Average (long loin, small eye)
Tamworth	England	Red	7.43*		Below average‡	Poor (lack muscling)
Chester White	America	White	9.33* 8.78†	6.56	136.1‡ Average**	Poor (too fat)

* Lush, J. L. and A. E. Molln, 1942. Litter size and weight as permanent characteristics, U.S.D.A. Technical Bul. 836.
† Bradford, G. E., A. B. Chapman, and R. H. Grummer, 1956. Performance of hogs of different breeds and from straightbred and crossbred dams on Wisconsin farms. *J. Animal Sci.*, 12:582–590.
** Hazel, L. N., 1959. Quoted by Dean C. Wolf in *Farm Journal*, May, 1959.
‡ Weight at 134 days as reported by Bradford *et al.*, cited above.

of the breeds. Note, however, the very close agreement with the data on litter size as reported by Lush and Molln (1942) with the data of Bradford *et al.* (1956).

Color

Color is one of several characteristics used in identifying the various breeds. It is considered of such importance that in the Hampshire, aberrations in color—including width of the white belt—prohibit approximately 25% of the animals from registration. Spotted Poland Chinas should have no more than 80% nor less than 20% white on body. The color red is recessive to black or white in crosses. Hence the Duroc cross is not as identifiable by color at the market place as some other breeds, such as the Hampshire. The ability of Hampshires to transmit their color pattern to their offspring has sometimes caused some undesirable crossbred hogs of the Hampshire color to lower the opinion of this breed. In the Chester White, American Landrace, and Yorkshire, white is dominant to black or red, except in the cross with Hampshires, where the body is often white with a bluish colored belt. Producers sometimes discriminate against white hogs in areas where sunburn is a problem.

Face Length

The deviation from the regular shaped head of swine is most prevalent in the Berkshires and Yorkshires. Extreme dish of face in Berkshires has limited their increase, since commercial hog producers found that these short-faced hogs have difficulty in eating from self-feeders and in drinking from automatic waterers. Breeders have partially corrected this abnormality, but it is still one factor limiting the popularity of the breed. Tendency to pug noses has been disadvantageous to Yorkshires, too. Hampshire and Tamworth hogs have longer snouts than other American breeds.

Body Size

The big type Poland China was an extremely large hog, with boars weighing in excess of 1100 pounds at maturity reported. The Tamworth and Yorkshire average length is 1 to 2 and 1 to $1\frac{1}{2}$ inches, respectively, greater than the average hog of the American breeds (Table 8-2). Landrace, used extensively for producing Wiltshire sides, has been selected for its length. The present trend is toward a medium weight at maturity in all breeds.

Meatiness

Meatiness is the term used to distinguish the animals that have a high proportion of muscle to fat. The ideal meat type hog has larger hams and greater cross area of loin than the conventional bacon type. As shown by

TABLE 8-2. | *Information on carcass characteristics of various swine breeds.*

Breed	Av. Back fat Thickness*	Av. Carcass Length*	Av. Loin Eye Size*
	inches	inches	sq. inches
Duroc	1.79(202)	28.7(278)	3.31(98)
Poland	1.54(167)	28.8(173)	4.20(124)
Spotted Poland	1.63(100)	29.0(84)	4.06(8)
Hampshire	1.52(238)	29.5(385)	4.13(185)
Berkshire	1.47(136)	29.2(206)	3.79(115)
Landrace	1.53(52)	31.1(49)	3.33(36)
Yorkshire	1.62(254)	30.5(239)	3.70(183)
Chester White	1.65(46)	29.3(48)	3.36(42)
Tamworth	1.59(46)	31.1(116)	3.35(40)

* Data compiled by students under Dr. H. L. Self, from carcass contests at livestock expositions, from Iowa and Ohio Swine Testing Stations, and from Wisconsin Experiment Station data. The numbers in parentheses give the number of animals used in computing the average.

Iowa Testing Station carcass cutouts results, the Hampshire is one of the meatier breeds. Much effort is now being placed on improving the carcasses of the Duroc, which for some time was losing favor on the market because breeders had been paying more attention to the Duroc's prolificness and rate of gain than to its meatiness. The Poland China is superior in loin eye size and ham development, as indicated by Iowa Testing Station data. With the advent of the meat type hog, many producers put the stigma of being "lardy" on the Spotted Poland and the Chester White. However, research at Iowa has shown that this criticism of the Spotted Poland is not justified; and there has been a concerted effort to improve the carcass merit of the Chester Whites.

Although the American Yorkshire is considered to be a lean breed, it is not especially heavily muscled. This might have been expected, since its principal use in both Canada and England

Fig. 8-1. Hampshire boar, Superman, bred by C. T. Keen and Son, Le Grande, Iowa. He was one of the boars tested in the first test at the Iowa Station; several littermates made outstanding records, and his sire, Automation, is a leading sire in the breed.

was for the production of Wiltshire sides. In recent years breeders have imported many English
Large Whites, which are a more
rugged, faster gaining pig than
the Canadian Yorkshires. But at
the same time the Large Whites
have a tendency to get fatter.
Breeders are making much effort
to improve Yorkshire meatiness,
and since meatiness is highly
heritable, this should be fairly
easily accomplished. The principal use of the Danish Landrace,
like the Yorkshire, is for producing Wiltshire sides. Hence they
have been selected for leanness
and length, rather than for heavy

Fig. 8-2. Duroc boar, Kayward Constructor,
bred by LaVerne Reitz, Gilman, Ill., owned
by Kayward Farm, Iowa City, Iowa. This
boar made an outstanding record in one of
the Illinois testing stations.

hams and big loins. The carcass cuts a good percentage of lean cuts, but the
loin eyes have often been small. In the early stages of the development of
the meat type hog, many thought the Tamworth was the answer because
of its lean look and great length. Iowa Testing Station results, however,
indicate that the Tamworth is among the fatter of the breeds.

Lean cut percentage has recently been increasing. Animals in the first
Iowa test in 1956 averaged 48.5%. The four closely trimmed cuts (ham, loin,
Boston butt, and picnic) now are averaging 52–54% of the carcass. The
range will run from 44% to as
high as 60%, but few are found
at the lower end of the scale.

Specific data on carcass traits
of swine breeds are given in
Table 8-2. The figures are averages of modest numbers and may
not accurately reflect averages for
the breeds as a whole.

*Prolificness and
Reproduction*

Yorkshires and Durocs are
considered superior among the
breeds in prolificness. Iowa tests
indicate that the Duroc is the
only American breed that has

Fig. 8-3. Poland China boar, Famous CMS,
owned by Harvey Richardson, Elmore City,
Okla. Member of high-testing litter in Ohio
Testing Station. His progeny have qualified
him for superior meat sire rating.

Fig. 8-4. Spotted Poland China boar, L. & M., bred by Carver and Byers, Nevada, Iowa, owned by Bill Hemm, Sheffield, Iowa. This boar was tested in the Iowa Swine Testing Station and subsequently made a remarkable record of siring both high testing and show pigs.

successfully competed with cross-breds in this trait. The chief criticism is incidence of blind or inverted nipples and lack of enough nipples for good commercial production of litters of 10 to 12. The improvement of prolificness has been receiving emphasis in breeding programs. According to experimental work, the Yorkshire is the superior breed from the standpoint of number of pigs farrowed. Bradford *et al.* (1956) found the spotted Poland China to compare favorably with the Durocs on the basis of number of young raised (Table 8-1).

The Hampshire, the Chester White, and the American Landrace are considered average to good for prolificness. Sows of the Chester White and Hampshire breeds are good mothers. The Chester White sows have excellent underlines. The Landrace produces very prolific sows when crossed with American breeds.

Poor litter size apparently contributed to the decline of the Poland China in popularity. Although tests indicate that crossbred gilts carrying half Poland genes perform satisfactorily as mothers, the stigma of poor litter size still dogs the breed. At present much effort is being put forth to improve the litter size, through breed-sponsored herd improvement programs. The Poland has been extensively used for crossing with the Scandinavian and British breeds. Such crossings, popular in the corn belt, seem to produce a combination of meatiness, prolificness, and mothering ability in the crossbred female. Like the Poland China, the Berkshire has long been considered by commercial producers to be poor in prolificness, especially in gilt litters.

Practically all commercially raised hogs are crossbred. The principal function of the breeds is to supply boars for use in cross-

Fig. 8-5. Chester white boar, bred by Burton Lofgren, St. James, Minn., owned by Parkison and Rodebaugh, Rensselaer, Ind. This boar's littermates made outstanding cutout records in the Minnesota Testing Station.

breeding programs. Thus it is important that breeders consider the highly heritable traits in their selection programs, since selection for traits of low heritability will avail them little. Traits low in heritability usually give the greatest increase in crosses.

It is recognized that some of the breeds will perform better in crosses for certain traits, particularly those involved with reproduction. Iowa swine records indicate that about 7 pigs per sow are now being raised throughout the state. Production registry has a minimum standard requirement of 8 raised. Sows have been known to raise 15 pigs, and of course, some raise only one. There is a wide range in this trait.

Fig. 8-6. Berkshire boar, Locust Creek Hallmark Flash CM. CMS., bred by John Randall Tucker, Newton, Mo., owned by Elmer Monson, Blair, Neb. This boar made a good record in the on-farm test conducted by the association.

Rate and Economy of Gain

Gains may vary from 1 pound or less per day after weaning to more than 2.5 pounds per day. Efficiencies as good as 240 pounds feed per 100 pounds gain have been reported. There have been a few testing station boars which weighed 200 pounds at 105 to 110 days of age.

Fig. 8-7. CMS Yorkshire boar, Crab Tree Toastmaster, bred by Cerny Brothers, Dorcester, Neb., owned by C. J. Cooper and Sons, Hartley, Iowa. This is a certified meat sire based on the performance of his offspring.

The Duroc was long popular with the commercial producer because of its ruggedness and gaining ability. Iowa tests indicate that it is the only American breed that has successfully competed with crossbreds in rate and economy of gain. Lack of meatiness, however, has curtailed its popularity somewhat. According to Bradford *et al.* (1956) the rate of gain of the Spotted Poland China compares favorably with the Duroc.

In growth rate and efficiency the Hampshires and Berkshires are average. The Yorkshire has suffered from the commercial

Fig. 8-8. Landrace boar, Rob Boe Samson, bred by Robert Boesch and Son, Woodburn, Ind. He was a high record boar at the National Landrace Testing Station.

Fig. 8-9. Tamworth boar, Retta Rays Pard Echo, bred by Retta Ray Farm, Bolling Green, Ky. This boar was tested at the National Tamworth Testing Station.

producers' attitude toward its poor gaining ability and lack of ruggedness under farm conditions. However, due to the breeding of imported English Large White Yorkshires with the American Yorkshire, recent Iowa Testing Station results have shown the breed to be good in rate of gain and excellent in efficiency. Chester White records in testing stations indicate that the breed has been average to poor in rate and economy of gain.

Two diverse breeds in rate and economy of gain are the Landrace and the Tamworth. Long selected under "hothouse" conditions, the Landrace has not proved rugged enough to stand the environment provided by many American farms. Testing station results at Iowa have shown it to be excellent in rate and efficiency of gain in the summer and average to good in the winter. In contrast, the Tamworth is a rugged hog capable of surviving rigorous conditions. The Tamworth Breed Association Testing Station data indicate that the breed is average to poor in gain and efficiency.

8-3. OTHER BREEDS

A few other breeds need to be mentioned. Most of these were developed at state and federal experiment stations. Among them are the Minnesota Nos. 1, 2, and 3; Beltsville No. 1; and Palouse. The Wessex Saddleback has been imported recently and is being produced in some areas. None of these breeds seems to have the overall excellence to crowd out the established breeds which experiments indicate are doing a satisfactory job. Establishing a new breed is difficult. Perhaps the principal result of the development of the new breeds is the resulting competition, which pushed improvement of breeds already well founded.

REFERENCES AND SELECTED READINGS

Reference marked with an asterisk is of general interest.

Biannual reports from the Iowa Swine Testing Station.

Bradford, G. E., A. B. Chapman, and R. H. Grummer, 1953. Performance of hogs of different breeds and from straightbred and crossbred dams on Wisconsin farms. *J. Animal Sci.,* 12:582–590.

Hazel, L. N., 1959. Quoted by Dean Wolf in *Farm Journal,* May, 1959.

Lush, J. L. and A. E. Molln, 1942. Litter size and weight as permanent characteristics. USDA Tech. Bull. 836.

*Vaughn, H. W., 1941. *Types and Market Classes of Livestock.* College Book Co., Columbus.

Chapter 9

Breeds of Sheep
and Goats

Ewes yearly by twinning, rich masters do make:
The lambs of such twinners for breeders go take.
W. YOUATT, Sheep (1837)

9-1. DOMESTICATION AND EARLY HISTORY

Sheep and goats were probably among the earliest animals to be domesticated—some six to eight thousand years ago, as shown by evidence reviewed by Reed (1959). The tractability of sheep, which can be observed in wild forms today, and the versatility of their products, including meat, milk, wool, and skins, were no doubt dominant factors leading to their early husbandry by man. Sheep are even used for work and for sport in rare cases.

Breeds of sheep have been developed in relatively isolated geographic areas where adaptation to peculiar environmental factors has been dominant. Thus the Merino of Spanish origin thrives in hot, dry climates and the herding or flocking instinct is well developed. These sheep have been accustomed through many centuries to long trails, and those which failed to stay with the flock probably did not leave descendants. On the other hand, the British breeds—usually kept in enclosed pastures in a more northern climate—do not band together as tightly as the Merino and also, like wild types, have retained the tendency to breed at a time to bring the lambs when spring temperatures and plant growth are favorable for survival. The

154

fat-tailed and fat-rumped sheep in the deserts of Asia store fat during the lush season which can be drawn on during the often long periods when plant growth is dormant. Fine-wool Merinos were developed in a dry climate while the coarse- and long-wool types, such as the Lincoln and Romney, were found in a more humid climate.

Breeds of sheep have also resulted from selection for specialization to fill the need for meat or for a particular kind of wool. Some breeds kept primarily for meat, such as the Blackhead Persian or the Wiltshire Horn, are called woolless although they produce some wool fibers which are shed. Some native breeds in Central and Southern Europe, such as the German East Friesian or the Italian Langhe, are kept primarily for milk; the world-famous Roquefort cheese is made from ewe's milk. The Navajo type, developed from unimproved Spanish sheep, produces a coarse hairy outer coat from which Navajo rugs and blankets are made.

The wild Rocky Mountain Bighorn Sheep has long been present in North America but it was never domesticated and all of our present domestic breeds of sheep or their ancestors have been imported. Domesticated sheep were first introduced on the American Continent by the Spanish conquerors, as described by Carmen *et al.* (1892); Columbus brought sheep on his second voyage in 1493. Sheep were brought into the English Colonies almost as soon as they were settled, beginning with Jamestown in 1609.

Important importations of Spanish Merino sheep into the United States began about 1801. Earlier importations probably came to the Southwest by way of Mexico. Others came by way of France, Silesia, Sweden, and Saxony, where they were further developed and improved. Of particular interest were the Merinos bred at Rambouillet, France, since 1786. Some of these were brought to the United States in 1840 but the large importations from both France and Germany were made in the 1890's. These Rambouillets and Merinos have been the foundation of the Western sheep industry, and they and their crossbred descendants constitute a large majority of the ewe flocks of this country today. This is especially true of the Western range states and Texas, but in many states of the Middle West and East the Western ewe is also the chief producer of lamb meat and wool for market.

The early English importations of sheep were not of the quality of modern English breeds, as was noted by Connor (1918), because they were made before the time of breeding improvements, which began in England in the eighteenth century. Up to this time the English sheep were relatively coarse, leggy, late-maturing animals, but with good foraging qualities. Long-wool types from the marsh regions of Kent, Leicestershire, and Lincolnshire, as well as the intermediate types such as the Ryeland, Dorset, and Southdown, were evident in the early American sheep. The rise in industrial development, with the influx of foreign labor accustomed to eating mutton and lamb, led to emphasis on mutton sheep. Continued importation of other medium-wool mutton breeds such as the Hampshire, Suffolk, Oxford, Shropshire, and Cheviot now account for most of the meat type breeds most common in the United States.

Wentworth, in *America's Sheep Trails* (1948), presents a comprehensive review of the history of sheep production from the early development in the Eastern Colonies, and the movements into the Middle West and Southwest in the early 1800's to the completion of the Westward movement at the close of the Civil War. In the following years sheep numbers have fluctuated from 35 to 50 million, to a peak of over 50 million head at the beginning of World War II. Numbers declined to about 26 million head at the end of the war. Since then numbers have increased slightly but have remained fairly constant at around 30 million head.

9-2. CLASSIFICATION OF BREEDS
AND TYPES OF SHEEP

Sheep breeds are classified as to origin and use and, particularly, according to fineness and length of wool. The fine-wool breeds such as the Rambouillet and Merino produce wool largely used in apparel manufacture. These breeds are characterized by their heavy dense fleeces with staple lengths ranging from 2 to 4 inches. Fine-wool breeds are angular in form, have relatively slow growth rates, and reach maturity slowly.

Meat breeds such as the Suffolk, Hampshire, and Southdown produce wool medium in fineness and length but often with fairly lightweight fleeces. These breeds are noted for their thick, blocky, low-set conformation, which is usually associated with meatiness and ability to fatten readily.

Sheep breeds are generally classified as wool, mutton, or other type according to special use, but most breeds in the United States are dual-purpose being valued for both meat and wool. Meat production generally accounts for 60–80% of the income from sheep, although in the Southwest wool production may almost equal meat production in economic returns to the producer. This has led to emphasis on both meat and wool in all domestic breeds, although the Western ewe leans toward the wool type. On the other hand, less attention is paid to wool in the meat breeds which provide sires for the bulk of slaughter lambs. The crossing of these types provides a convenient and efficient means for maximum production of meat and wool without the difficulty of attaining proficiency for both in the same breed.

Sheep breeds specialized for products other than meat and wool are uncommon in the United States, although milking of sheep is common in many countries of the world. These breeds are triple-purpose, being also kept for meat and wool. The production of fur pelts and skins from sheep are important in many parts of the world, particularly in the Soviet Countries and the Middle East. Specialized breeds for fur pelts such as the Karakul are found in the United States but have little economic importance here.

9-3. SHEEP BREEDS OF THE WORLD

Hundreds of breeds of sheep exist over the world today and include a wide variety of sizes, shapes, types, and colors. Mason (1951) lists most of these with information on their origin, characteristics, and uses. Wool type breeds have become most important in the Southern hemisphere, particularly in Australia, New Zealand, South Africa, and Argentina and Uruguay in South America, although both fine- and long-wool breeds are found all over the world. Fat-tailed and fat-rumped sheep are common in the desert and semidesert areas of the Near East, Asia, and Africa. They usually also produce carpet wool, although wool yields are generally low and the sheep are valued for many purposes. Dairy breeds of sheep are more common in Central and Southern Europe. Northern short-tailed varieties, noted for their prolificness, are found in the Scandinavian countries. Meat breeds originating from Britain, which are common there as well as in the United States and Canada, are also widely distributed over the world.

9-4. SHEEP BREEDS IN THE UNITED STATES

Information on breeds of sheep in the United States is tabulated in Tables 9-1 and 9-2. Quantitative traits vary widely, of course, according to environmental conditions, and are therefore given in general terms. There is considerable overlapping, and wide variations exist within most breeds. Briggs (1958) has discussed in detail the history, characteristics, distribution, and importance of sheep and goat breeds.

Fine-wool breeds, of which the Rambouillet is most common, are of predominantly Merino origin and are noted for their high yields of uniform wool. Rambouillets are large but lack the conformation and also grow and mature somewhat slower than the meat breeds. Their wool ranges in average fineness from 64's to 80's or finer, with staple lengths from 2 to $3\frac{1}{2}$ inches. Skin folds which were once common are now almost nonexistent. Classification into A, B, and C types according to size and number of folds is no longer necessary as present-day

Fig. 9-1. Fat-rumped sheep from U.S.S.R.

TABLE 9-1. *Information on breeds of sheep in the United States.*

Classification	Breed	Country of origin	Approximate date of origin	Approximate date of first importation	Fleece Fineness*	Fleece Length†	Fleece Weight**
Fine wool	Rambouillet	France	1786	1840	Fine	Medium	Heavy
	Merino	Spain	Early	1801	Fine	Medium	Heavy
	Debouillet	U.S.A.	1920		Fine	Medium	Heavy
	Suffolk	England	Early 19th century	1888	Medium	Short	Light
Meat, medium wool	Hampshire	England	Early 19th century	1881	Medium	Medium	Medium
	Shropshire	England	1860	1860	Medium	Medium	Medium
	Southdown	England	Late 18th century	1803	Medium	Short	Light
	Dorset	England	About 1815	1887	Medium coarse	Medium	Medium
	Cheviot	England	End of 18th century	1838	Medium	Medium	Medium
	Oxford	England	1836	1846	Medium coarse	Medium	Medium heavy
	Tunis	North Africa	Ancient	1799	Medium	Medium	Medium
Crossbred, dual-purpose	Corriedale	New Zealand	1880–1910	1914	Medium	Medium long	Heavy
	Columbia	U.S.A.	1912		Medium	Medium long	Heavy
	Panama	U.S.A.	1912		Medium	Medium long	Heavy
	Targhee	U.S.A.	1927		Medium fine	Medium	Heavy
	Romeldale	U.S.A.	1915		Medium	Medium	Heavy
	Montadale	U.S.A.	1933 on		Medium	Medium	Medium
Long-wool	Romney	England	Early	1904	Coarse	Long	Heavy
	Lincoln	England	Early	Late 16th century	Coarse	Long	Heavy
	Leicester	England	1755–90	Late 18th century	Coarse	Long	Heavy
	Cotswold	England	Early	1832	Coarse	Long	Heavy
	Scottish blackface	Scotland	Early	1861	Coarse	Long	Heavy
Carpet wool, mixed wool, fur	Navajo	U.S.A.	Early	1540, 1598	Coarse	Long	Medium
	Karakul	Asia	Ancient	1909	Coarse	Long	Medium

* In general, fine wool averages 64's and finer, medium wool from 50's to 62's, and coarse wool 48's and coarser in U.S. Numerical Grades.

† In approximate terms of one year's growth, long wool would be 6 in. and longer, medium wool from 2 to 6 in., and short wool under 2 in.

** Heavy fleeces generally average over 12 lb, medium fleeces from 8 to 12 lb, and light fleeces under 8 lb, for one year's growth from mature ewes producing lambs.

TABLE 9-2. | *Information on breeds of sheep in the United States.*

Classification	Breed	Body Size*	Body Type	Color traits	Horns	Number of registrations in 1960†
Fine wool	Rambouillet	Large	Angular-blocky	White	Rams only	10,302
	Merino	Medium	Angular	White	Rams only	618‡
	Debouillet	Medium	Angular	White	Rams only	
	Suffolk	Large	Blocky	Black face and legs	Polled	36,574**
	Hampshire	Large	Blocky	Black face and legs	Polled	30,099
	Shropshire	Medium	Blocky	Black face and legs	Polled	8,347
	Southdown	Small	Blocky, lowset	Brown face and legs	Polled	10,871
Meat, medium wool	Dorset	Medium	Blocky	White face and legs	Rams and ewes	5,437
	Cheviot	Medium-small	Blocky	White face and legs	Polled	4,831
	Oxford	Large	Blocky	Brown face and legs	Polled	1,912
	Tunis	Medium	Angular, blocky	Red or tan face	Polled	300
	Corriedale	Medium-large	Blocky	White	Polled	17,418
Crossbred, dual-purpose	Columbia	Large	Blocky	White	Polled	10,172
	Panama	Large	Blocky	White	Polled	
	Targhee	Medium-large	Blocky	White	Polled	2,064
	Romeldale	Medium-large	Blocky	White	Polled	
	Montadale	Medium-large	Blocky	White	Polled	3,164
	Romney	Medium-large	Blocky	White	Polled	2,000
Long wool	Lincoln	Large	Blocky	White	Polled	337
	Leicester	Large	Blocky	White	Polled	
	Cotswold	Large	Blocky	White	Polled	
Carpet wool, mixed wool, fur	Scottish blackface	Medium-large	Blocky	Blackface and legs	Rams and ewes	
	Navajo	Medium	Angular	Variable	Rams and ewes polled and horned	
	Karakul	Large	Angular	Black, brown	Rams only	62§

* Large mature ewes in good condition would generally average over 150 lb., medium ewes from 110 to 150 lb., and small ewes under 110 lb.
† Registration numbers were tabulated by the *American Livestock Journal*, April, 1961.
** Registration for the Suffolks are the total from two associations, although some dual registration occurs.
‡ Registrations are totaled for three Associations.
§ Registrations are totaled for two Associations.

Fig. 9-2. Rambouillet ram. [Courtesy USDA.]

sheep are all of the smooth or C type. Unfortunately, wool covering on the faces is still common although it has been amply demonstrated by Terrill (1949) and many others that openfaced sheep, free from wool blindness, produce more lambs and only slightly less wool. Polled Rambouillets are becoming more numerous and have definite economic advantages, as shown by Terrill (1953). This is particularly true where damage from screwworms and fleece maggots are common. Unfortunately the polled gene is sometimes linked with that for cryptorchidism. Rambouillets have provided the foundation stock for most Western range sheep, and relatively pure Rambouillets are common in Texas and the Southwest.

Merinos of the American and Delaine types are somewhat smaller and have more angular forms than Rambouillets. They produce extremely fine wool with relatively high grease content. They were once quite common in Ohio and Texas but are tending to be replaced by the larger Rambouillet in Texas and by crossbred breeds in Ohio and other areas. The Debouillet, a relatively new breed, has resulted from crossing the Rambouillet and Delaine Merino and is most common near its area of origin in New Mexico.

Medium-wool meat breeds are kept in purebred or high-grade flocks throughout the farm states in the Middle West and East. The larger black-faced Suffolk and Hampshire breeds are used all over the country as sires of slaughter meat lambs, particularly when mated to Western white-faced ranged ewes. These Western ewes or their crossbred ewe offspring are transported in large numbers to the Middle West, East, and Southeast for use as mothers of slaughter lambs. The fleeces of these black-faced breeds and their crosses often contain black fibers which restrict their use to darker fabrics. Shropshire and Southdown rams are used as sires of crossbred slaughter lambs to a much lesser

Fig 9-3. American Merino ewe. [Courtesy USDA.]

extent. Southdowns are valued for showing, particularly by youth clubs. Dorsets have a reputation for less restricted breeding seasons than the other meat breeds. The polled strain, originating in North Carolina, is increasing in numbers. Cheviots with fairly small body size and Oxfords with generally covered faces are somewhat less numerous than the other meat breeds. The Tunis breed is quite rare although they have an active breed registry organization.

Fig. 9-4.   Suffolk ram. [Courtesy USDA.]

Crossbred dual-purpose breeds have increased in popularity in all parts of the United States in recent years. Their heavy fleeces of medium wool, along with rapid growth rates, good meat conformation, open faces, and high lamb production, have made them both profitable and popular. These breeds all originated from crosses of long-wool and fine-wool breeds.

The Corriedale, the oldest of these breeds, resulted from crossing Leicester or Lincoln rams on Merino ewes and was imported from New Zealand in 1914. It was more common in the Western range states during the early years but in recent years has become much more numerous in the farm states of the Middle West.

The Columbia was developed by the United States Department of Agriculture by crossing Lincoln rams on Rambouillet ewes (Marshall, 1949). The crossbred offspring were then interbred. This, the first breed to be developed in the United States, is noted for its large size and heavy fleeces. The breed Association formed in 1941 has pioneered with an inspection system of registration which requires that animals meet a standard of excellence as determined by an Inspector of the Association, as well as being offspring of registered parents. A similar breed, the Panama, formed by crossing Rambouillet rams on Lincoln ewes, is most common near its area of origin in Idaho.

The Targhee was developed by the United States Department of Agriculture by crossing Rambouillet rams on Lincoln-Rambouillet, Corriedale-Lincoln-

Fig. 9-5.   Hampshire ram. [Courtesy USDA.]

Fig. 9-6. Shropshire ewe. [Courtesy USDA.]

Rambouillet, Corriedale, and Columbia ewes (Terrill, 1947). Some other breeding was used but the breed is made up practically of three-quarters fine-wool and one-quarter long-wool breeding. This breed also has an inspection system of registration and permits flock as well as individual registration. The Targhee is well established in the Western States. Crossbred types or strains of sheep similar to the Corriedale, Columbia, Panama, and Targhee are common throughout the Western ranges, particularly in the Intermountain and Northwest areas.

The Romeldale, developed by A. T. Spencer of California by crossing Romney rams on Rambouillet ewes, is not common outside of its area of origin.

The Montadale resulted from crossing the Cheviot and Columbia (Mattingly, 1945), and is found largely in the farm states.

A tailless or "No Tail" sheep has been bred by the South Dakota Agricultural Experiment Station, using fat-rumped sheep as foundation animals. This breed has not been released to private breeders.

The long-wool breeds, although extremely important in the formation of crossbred types or strains are bred pure in only small numbers. Breeds such as the Leicester and Cotswold have largely disappeared. The Romney is most numerous in the warm damp climate of the Willamette Valley in Oregon. This breed has not been as successful in crossing to produce range sheep as the Lincoln. The Lincoln breed, although small in number, is often in demand for crossing with Rambouillets or fine-wool range sheep to produce first-cross replacement ewes. These first-cross ewes are highly productive of both lambs and wool.

Carpet-wool, mixed-wool, and fur breeds of sheep are of little importance in the United States. Importation of duty-free carpet wools results in low prices for domestic wools of these types. Scottish Blackface sheep have largely disappeared and only a few Karakul flocks remain. Na-

Fig. 9-7. Southdown ram. [Courtesy USDA.]

vajo sheep of New Mexico (Blunn, 1940, 1943) have been used to produce wool for weaving into the famous Navajo blankets. However, Navajo sheep have been top-crossed with Rambouillet rams and only a small flock of relatively pure but improved Navajo sheep still exists at the Southwestern Range and Sheep Breeding Laboratory at Fort Wingate, New Mexico. Improved, coarse weaving-wool sheep have been developed by this laboratory.

Fig. 9-8. Dorset ewe. [Courtesy USDA.]

Purebred sheep are far more important to production than their numbers indicate because they provide sires for a large part of the sheep population. In 1920 there were almost 500,000 registered purebred sheep in the United States, which represented slightly over 1% of the total sheep and lambs (Spencer *et al.*, 1924). The proportion would seem to be similar today although data are unavailable.

Some of the prominent breeds of today were well established in the United States 40 years ago. In 1920 the Shropshire, Rambouillet, Merino, and Hampshire made up 86% of the registered purebred sheep (Spencer *et al.*, 1924). In 1959 these breeds made up 35% of the registrations; additional breeds absent or of minor importance in 1920, consisting of the Suffolk, Corriedale, and Columbia, now make up 44% of the registrations. The leading breeds based on number of registrations in 1960 consist of the Suffolk, Hampshire, Corriedale, Rambouillet, Southdown, Columbia, and Shropshire breeds, which account for 85% of the sheep registered (*American Livestock J.*, April, 1961).

Experimental breed comparisons have been uncommon with sheep. Cooper and Stoehr (1934) under range conditions found Columbias to be heaviest in body weight, followed by Rambouillets and Corriedales. Columbias and Rambouillets produced heavier fleeces than Corriedales while Columbias and Corriedales produced greater numbers and pounds of lamb per ewe than did Rambouillets. Losses from dead and missing sheep were lowest for Rambouillets and

Fig. 9-9. Cheviot ewe. [Courtesy USDA.]

Fig. 9-10. Corriedale ram. [Courtesy USDA.]

highest for Columbias. Terrill and Stoehr (1942), with the same breeds and conditions, found that Corriedales produced more pounds of lamb per pound of ewe than did Columbias or Rambouillets while Rambouillets produced more pounds of wool per pound of body weight than did Corriedales or Columbias.

Branaman (1940) compared Hampshires and Southdowns under farm conditions. Hampshires produced more lambs which reached market weight earlier. The estimated total digestible nutrients required for each hundred pounds of final feed-lot weight were practically the same for Southdown and Hampshire single lambs but the yield of lean meat was slightly higher for the Southdowns.

These studies are among the few cases in which controlled experiments have been used to compare breeds of sheep. Progress in sheep production may have been retarded by the paucity of such comparisons, from which producers could more adequately discriminate among breeds.

9-5. USEFULNESS OF PUREBRED SHEEP OF THE VARIOUS BREEDS

Purebred sheep are useful in providing relatively uniform types adapted to special uses or to unique climatic conditions, and they can be expected to breed true in their particular characteristics. Fine-wool breeds, such as the Rambouillet, are adapted to warm dry climates while coarse long-wool types, such as the Romney, are adapted to damp, humid climates. It seems especially important that the type of wool be suited to the climatic conditions. The crossbred intermediate type like the Columbia and Targhee thrive in cool and temperate climates under a wide variety of conditions. In general, breeds of medium to small size, such as the Merino, are better suited to sparse feed conditions while

Fig. 9-11. Columbia ram. [Courtesy USDA.]

larger breeds, such as the Columbia or Lincoln, do best under
lush feed conditions. White-faced
wool breeds, such as the Rambouillet, Columbia, and Targhee, are suited to Western range
conditions, probably because of
their Merino blood, while the
meat breeds are generally kept
pure for commercial production
only in the farm states. The
Western purebred meat breed
flocks are kept under more ideal

Fig. 9-12.   Targhee ram. [Courtesy USDA.]

nutritive conditions to produce sires of crossbred slaughter lambs.

The breeder can choose among about 15 to 20 common breeds of sheep
in the United States to find one which best fits his particular situation. A
safe guide for the beginner is to choose the breed which is already most
common in the area. Market demand for breeding stock is an important
consideration. Commercial flocks of high-grade or nearly purebred sheep
can be readily established by continually topcrossing with a particular breed
of sire. Three or four top crosses will generally produce sheep very similar
to purebreds while five or six top crosses can be expected to produce those
almost identical to purebreds.

The gain in production or hybrid vigor from crossing breeds is an important advantage made possible by pure breeds. Sheep breeders have long
recognized that crossbreeding generally leads to increased fertility and
growth rate of the lambs over the average of the purebred parents. Increased
wool production and milk production have also resulted from crossbreeding. The crossing of a third breed on two-breed cross ewes gives an added
advantage (ARS Special Report, 1956). In addition, improved meat type
of offspring of wool-type ewes is
obtained by crossing with the
meat breeds, thereby increasing
the efficiency of production of
both lambs and wool. Many
comparisons have been made of
sire breeds for production of
lambs for meat from a variety of
native ewes. These have been reviewed by Rae (1952). In general these comparisons show
Hampshire or Suffolk sires to be

Fig. 9-13.   Lincoln ram. [Courtesy USDA.]

superior in the United States.

Interbreeding of crossbred animals has not resulted in the marked increase in variability which is often cited as a disadvantage of crossbreeding (Rae, 1956). However, variability of wool fineness in the flock may increase, particularly where widely different wool types are crossed. In general, interbreeding of crossbred animals does not provide the predictability of characteristics in the offspring which is found with pure breeding. On the other hand two- and three-breed crosses may be quite predictable and the offspring may be as uniform as purebreds. Crossbreeding, particularly to produce the wool type mother of the market lamb, has not been as fully exploited in the United States as has the use of the meat breed sire on the wool type ewe. Experimentation is needed to develop and test patterns of crossbreeding to give maximum efficiency in production of high-quality lambs and wool.

Crossing of existing breeds to form still more new breeds continues. Present efforts seem to be aimed at the development of white-faced meat breeds and meat breeds which have less restricted breeding seasons than the British mutton breeds. Outcrossing to improve existing breeds, which is so common in the Soviet Union, is generally not practiced in this country. An exception is the use of a number of long-wool and medium-wool breeds to improve the Navajo sheep of New Mexico.

Constant improvement of breeds continues with selection, aided by performance and progeny testing (Terrill, 1958). Those breeds which are most successful in improving efficiency of production are apt to grow in popularity while those which continue to emphasize fancy points and uneconomic traits, such as wool covering on the face, small scurs, or color on the legs, can be expected to decline. Breeds are in competition with each other and survival in the long run will probably depend more on their relative productivity and efficiency of production than on promotion efforts or on show ring performance. Many breeds in other parts of the world, such as the Dormer, German Whiteheaded Mutton, Ile-de-France, Precoce, and Texel, could probably be used to advantage in the United States, either as pure breeds in crosses with present breeds to produce hybrid vigor or to produce additional new breeds. This has generally been prevented by restrictions on importation of sheep from most of the world to avoid the introduction of exotic diseases.

9-6. BREEDS OF GOATS

Goats are similar to sheep and are difficult to distinguish from sheep in some cases, although the tail of the goat is said to turn upward always, while that of the sheep turns downward. Crosses of sheep and goats are not certain to have produced viable offspring but fertilization and early embryonic growth do occur (Gray, 1954). Goats, as well as sheep, produce a wide variety of products; milk, mohair, meat, and skins are most important.

9-7. MILK GOATS

Milk goats are most frequent in the suburbs of large cities and in small towns. A good milk goat will supply sufficient milk for a large family and can be kept where it would be impossible to keep a cow. Goat dairies are also common near large cities. Goat's milk differs from cow's milk, particularly in the small size of the fat globules and the soft curd. These probably contribute to its ease of digestibility. It is often used for infants, invalids, and those allergic to cow's milk. It is estimated that approximately one million goats are kept for milk production in the United States. Much of the information on milk goats presented here is taken from Potts and Simmons (1955). Information on characteristics of breeds of milk goats are summarized in Table 9-3.

The Saanen and Toggenburg breeds are most prominent in the United States, followed by the Nubian and various Alpine breeds. The Murcian breed, introduced from Spain and adapted to hot temperatures, is of fairly minor importance. Another minor breed is the Norska, which was brought from Norway many years ago. Common American and Spanish goats are kept in many parts of the United States. These are sometimes used for milk as well as for meat and are valuable for the clearing of brush land. These common breeds can be graded up for milk goats by topcrossing with dairy breed bucks.

The Saanen is one of the leading breeds of dairy goats. During the years when the United States Department of Agriculture maintained a herd at Beltsville, Maryland, the grade and purebred Saanen does milked from 8 to 10 months after kidding and produced an average of 5.6 lb. of milk a day. The average butterfat content of the milk was approximately 3.5%. Mature Saanen does will average 120 lb. and bucks 185 lb. in body weight.

The Toggenburg breed, including many high-grade animals, probably leads the other goat breeds in numbers. Wattles or appendages from the neck are generally characteristic of this breed. Records from the United States Department of Agriculture herd at Beltsville, Maryland, show that grade and purebred Toggenburg does have milked from 7 to 10 months after kidding and produced an average of 4.1 lb. of milk a day. The milkfat content of the milk has averaged about 3%. The average weight of mature does over a three-year period was 96 lb.

The Nubian breed is charac-

Fig. 9-14. Saanen doe. [Courtesy USDA.]

T A B L E | *Information on breeds of milk goats in the United States.**
9-3.

Breed	Country of origin	Approximate date of first importation	Color markings	Horns	Size	High record of production for approximately 10 months†	
						Milk (lb.)	Fat (lb.)
Saanen	Switzerland	1904	Cream to white	Hornless, but some exceptions	Large	4905	182.8
Toggenburg	Switzerland	1893	Brown with white stripes on each side of face; white legs	Hornless, but exceptions common	Medium	5750	202.5
Nubian	Nubia (Upper Egypt, Ethiopia)	1896	Black, dark brown, or tan; with or without white markings	Hornless, but some horned males	Large	4248	191.6
French Alpine	France	1922	White to black; often with spotting	Hornless, but exceptions common	Large	4655	171.5
Swiss Alpine	Switzerland		Brown with black markings	Usually hornless		2016	128.0
Rock Alpine	America		White to black; often with spotting			2793	95.3

* Information taken from Potts and Simmons (1955), except for production records.
† From American Milk Goat Record Association Handbook (1960).

terized by large drooping ears
and a peculiarly shaped head.
Although a large breed, it appears to be less hardy than the
breeds of European origin. The
distinct odor so prevalent in the
male goat, particularly during
the breeding season, is somewhat
less pronounced in the Nubian.
The milk is especially high in
milkfat, yielding 5% in some
cases.

Fig. 9-15. Toggenburg doe. [Courtesy USDA.]

The French Alpine breed is
large and hardy, with heavy
bone, and shows a good capacity for milk production. It appears to be increasing in popularity. The Rock Alpine has resulted from a combination
of the Swiss and French Alpine. A few British Alpine goats have been imported. These have resulted from general crossbreeding, but with the Saanen
and Toggenburg predominating.

9-8. ANGORA GOATS

Angora goats appear to have originated before Biblical times, as a number of references are found in the Bible to the use of goats' hair (Thompson, 1901). The area of origin surrounding Ankara (Angora) in Asiatic
Turkey is a high plateau of about 3000 feet elevation, with mountains and
deep valleys. The climate is dry with extremes in temperatures. This climate
seemed favorable for the development of the long, lustrous mohair.

Angora goats were first imported into the United States in 1849. They
spread westward after the Civil War, particularly to Texas and California.

Fig. 9-16. Angora buck. [Courtesy Sheep and Goat Raiser.]

Texas has been the leading state
practically ever since. In recent
years, Texas, with over 3 million
head, has had about 94% of the
Angora goats in the United
States. Other leading states are
Arizona, New Mexico, Missouri,
Oregon, California, and Utah.

The Angora goat with its long
locks of mohair presents a distinctive appearance. The locks
are of different types such as
ringlet, flat, or web, as described
by Gray (1959). The mohair

locks grow at the rate of 6 to 12 inches per year, and the goats are normally clipped twice each year. Mohair becomes coarser with age and the fine kid mohair is most valuable. Quality, covering, weight of fleece, and freedom from kemp is emphasized in selection. The average mohair clip per goat has increased from about 5 lb. in the late 1940's to almost 6 lb. in the late 1950's. Both sexes have horns. Open faces are associated with higher kid production (Shelton, 1960). Size and weight for age are also emphasized in selection. A yearling buck should weigh at least 80 lb., while mature bucks will weigh from 125 to 175 lb. Yearling does should weigh at least 60 lb. and mature does should weigh 80 to 90 lb.

9-9. SUMMARY

A brief account has been given of the development of breeds of sheep and goats, especially in the United States. A variety of breeds have been described which are available and from which the producer may choose the one which best fits his particular needs, whether for pure breeding, for grading up to high-grade flocks, or to take advantage of hybrid vigor from crosses. Production traits are emphasized as breeds of sheep or goats are only useful as they contribute to efficient production of meat, milk, wool, and mohair.

REFERENCES AND SELECTED READINGS

References marked with an asterisk are of general interest.

*AMGRA Handbook, 1960. American Milk Goat Record Association.

Agricultural Research Service, 1956. Hybrid lambs. Special Report.

American Livestock Journal, 1961. Annual Purebred Review. April.

Blunn, Cecil T., 1940. Improvement of Navajo sheep. *J. of Heredity*, 31(3):99–112.

———, 1943. Characteristics and production of old type Navajo sheep. *J. of Heredity*, 34(5):141–152.

Branaman, G. A., 1940. Some factors in lamb production associated with size and type in mutton sheep. *J. Agr. Research*, 60(7):473–486.

*Briggs, Hilton M., 1958. *Modern Breeds of Livestock*. Revised ed. Macmillan, New York.

*Carmen, Ezra A., H. A. Heath, and J. Minto, 1892. Special report on the history and present condition of the sheep industry of the United States. USDA Bureau of Animal Ind., Washington, D.C.

*Connor, L. J., 1918. A brief history of the sheep industry in the United States. Annual Report of the American Historical Association.

Cooper, J. M. and J. A. Stoehr, 1934. Comparison of Rambouillet, Corriedale, and Columbia sheep under intermountain range conditions. USDA Circular 308.

Gray, A. P., 1954. Mammalian hybrids. Technical Communication No. 10 of the Commonwealth Bureau of Animal Breeding and Genetics, Edinburgh.

Gray, J. A., 1959. Texas Angora goat production. Texas Agricultural Extension Service B-926.

Marshall, F. R., 1949. The Making of Columbia Sheep. *National Wool Grower,* 39(4):9, 32.

*Mason, I. L., 1951. A world dictionary of breeds, types and varieties of livestock. Technical Communication No. 8 of the Commonwealth Bureau of Animal Breeding and Genetics, Edinburgh.

Mattingly, E. H., 1945. The Montadale. A new breed. *Sheep Breeder,* 65(3):4.

*Potts, C. G. and V. L. Simmons, 1955. Milk goats. USDA Farmers' Bulletin 920.

Rae, A. L., 1952. Crossbreeding of sheep. *Animal Breeding Abstracts,* 20(3):197–207 and (4):287–299.

————, 1956. The genetics of the sheep. *Advances in Genetics,* 8:189–265.

*Reed, Charles A., 1959. Animal domestication in the prehistoric Near East. *Science,* 130(3389):1629–1639.

Shelton, Maurice, 1960. The relation of face covering to fleece weight, body weight and kid production of Angora does. *J. Animal Sci.,* 19(1):302–308.

*Spencer, D. A., M. C. Hall, C. D. Marsh, J. S. Cotton, C. F. Gibbons, O. C. Stine, O. E. Baker, V. N. Valgren, R. D. Jennings, G. K. Holmes, W. B. Bell and Will C. Barnes, 1924. The sheep industry. United States Department of Agriculture Yearbook, 1923, pp. 229–310.

Terrill, C. E., 1947. Breed crosses used in the development of Targhee sheep. *J. Animal Sci.,* 6:83–92.

————, 1949. The relation of face covering to lamb and wool production in range Rambouillet ewes. *J. Animal Sci.,* 8(3):353–361.

————, 1953. The relation between sale price and merit in Columbia, Targhee and Rambouillet rams. *J. Animal Sci.,* 12(3):419–430.

*————, 1958. Fifty years of progress in sheep breeding. *J. Animal Sci.,* 17(4):944–959.

————, and J. A. Stoehr, 1942. The importance of body weight in selection of range ewes. *J. Animal Sci.,* 1(3):221–228.

Thompson, G. F., 1901. Information concerning the Angora goat. USDA Bull. 27.

*Wentworth, E. N., 1948. *America's Sheep Trails.* Iowa State College Press, Ames, Iowa.

Chapter 10

Breeds of Horses

See from the first yon high-bred colt a field,
His lofty step, his limbs' elastic tread:
Dauntless he leads the herd, still first to try
The threatening flood, or brave the unknown bridges
But no vain noise affrighted; lofty-necked,
With clean-cut head, short belly, and stout back;
His sprightly breast exuberant with brawn.
VIRGIL, Georgics, III

10-1. HISTORICAL ASPECTS AND SOME CHARACTERISTICS OF FORMATION OF BREEDS OF HORSES

Although early ancestral forms of the horse are known to have existed in both western and eastern hemispheres, it appears that evolution in the eastern hemisphere occurred along lines which ended in early extinction. Thus the evolution of the modern horse from primitive forms took place largely in the Americas from whence the more recent in line of descent migrated to Asia and Europe. At a later time, during the ice age, the horse became extinct in the Americas but survived in the eastern hemisphere (Riggs, 1932).

Primitive Forms and Their Relative Importance in Formation of Modern Breeds. There is confusion as to the nature of the immediate predecessors of the modern horse, but a widely accepted view is that three distinct primitive stocks have contributed to present-day breeds (Ridgeway, 1905).

172

The Celtic horse which was found in the Hebrides and a part of Ireland is thought to have been the progenitor of pony breeds. The ancient horse of Europe, the Near East, and Britain probably derived from another wild stock which was widely distributed in Europe and Asia. A third type is thought to have originated in the deserts of Northern Africa and to have given rise to the horses of the Barbary States, Egypt, Arabia, and Persia. There is some historical evidence that the horses of North Africa were introduced into Europe by invaders from North Africa as early as the third century B.C. and probably often thereafter, mainly by way of Spain. Thus there was probably some admixture of the stocks in this area, as well as in Asia Minor, from very early times. Usually, however, the North African type is given credit for having played the more important role in the formation of modern breeds of light horses; the European type is credited with having been the ancestor of draft breeds, as well as having played a lesser role in development of light horse breeds. In general, draft breeds are thought to have been developed directly from native horses in Western Europe and Britain, only the Percheron breed having been improved by the use of Arabian breeding.

Improved Stocks and Their Use in Breed Formation and Improvement

BARB, ARAB AND RELATED STRAINS. All of the important light horse breeds throughout the world have descended from or have been largely improved by descendants of the North African horse. These horses, the Barb of North Africa and the Arabian and related strains, the so-called Eastern or Oriental horses, were greatly improved over a number of centuries by intelligent selection and breeding practices. The earlier introduction of these horses to Spain, as well as during the years of the conquest and occupation by the Moorish invaders, resulted in the great improvement of native stocks so that horses of Spain became recognized as being of excellent quality. These were the horses, brought to America by Spanish conquerors and colonists, which provided the seed stock for the Western mustang and horses which eventually spread over the eastern part of the United States.

THOROUGHBRED. At a somewhat later time the Arabian and related horses were used in a more methodical program of improvement of horses native to Europe and Britain and in formation of new breeds including the English Thoroughbred. The Thoroughbred horse resulted from the breeding of Barb, Arabian, and Turk stallions to mares indigenous to the British Isles at that time (1660–1750) as well as to imported mares of breeding similar to their own. The primary impetus to develop this breed appears to have been the desire to breed a horse with great speed and stamina for use on the racecourse. By 1750 this aim had been realized to such a degree that the importation of more eastern sires failed to improve the stock greatly. The Thoroughbred has played a large and important role in the

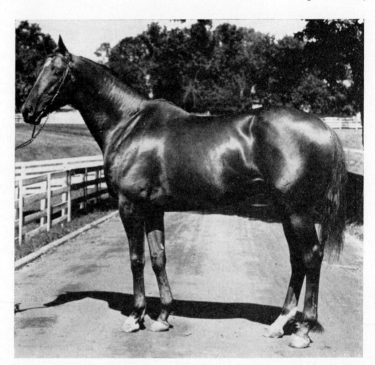

Fig. 10-1. Swaps, a fine example of the Thoroughbred horse, Kentucky Derby winner with earnings of over $800,000. Now at stud, he has sired the stakes winning filly Primonetta and the all-time yearling sales topping colt. [Courtesy Mr. John W. Galbreath.]

development of all modern breeds of light horses found in America except the Appaloosa and, of course, the Arabian.

Development of New Breeds

STIMULI FOR BREED FORMATION. It has been the case for most light horse breeds that they develop in response to fairly specific stimuli—for example, the requirement for speed and stamina on the racecourse for the formation of the Thoroughbred. Later the development of the Morgan breed occurred in response to the need for an all-round useful horse and road horse in America, at about the time of the American Revolution. As improved roads and demand for speed in harness—both for transportation and in racing—made themselves felt, the larger, faster American Standardbred was developed, drawing heavily upon the Thoroughbred for size, speed, and stamina. Similarly the American Saddle Horse breed was formed to meet the need for a good, smooth, and easy traveling horse under saddle. Impetus for the greatest development of the American Quarter Horse as a breed was furnished by the need for a horse suitable for working cattle. The character-

Fig. 10-2. Go Man Go, only recently displaced as top money-winning racing Quarter Horse. He was sired by the Thoroughbred horse Top Deck. Note heavy muscling of rear quarters, a desirable conformation trait for short distance racing. [Courtesy the American Quarter Horse Association.]

istics desired were at the same time compatible with tremendous speed for short distances. Often the requirements which were largely responsible for the formation of a breed have disappeared or have become relatively unimportant; for example, the need for horses solely for transportation, either on horseback or in horse-drawn vehicles, no longer exists. For this reason the Standardbred owes its continued existence to its use in harness racing and in the horse-show roadster classes. Principal uses of American Saddle Horses are now in the horse shows and as pleasure horses. In more recent years uses of the Quarter Horse have tended to become categorized so that most often they are bred for racing short distances or for stock-horse work, including showing at halter and in Western performance classes, rather than for both.

Fig. 10-3. Cuco Britches, a working Quarter Horse in action, is a good representative of the stock horse type with innate affinity for working with cattle.

Some of the more recently formed breeds and registries have been established not on the basis of functional requirements, but on the basis of characteristic color or color patterns. In some cases, for instance the palomino, these are in fact color registries only and horses registered in any of several other breed registries may also be listed in them. Thus they include an extremely heterogeneous genetic group. The Appaloosa registry, which also falls in this general category, lists three acceptable basic color patterns, but actually these cover a wide range. Likewise, an extreme range in conformational characters is permitted.

SELECTION OF SUITABLE FOUNDATION STOCK. In all cases where the need for a horse to perform a job has been a force for breed formation, the foundation stock has been selected from any suitable source available. For this reason all major breeds of horses developed in America have a number of other breeds and usually a considerable number of individuals of unknown breeding in their foundation stock. Usually the Thoroughbred or breeds tracing strongly to the Thoroughbred have provided the main basis for refinement, intelligence, speed, and stamina.

FORMATION OF BREED ORGANIZATIONS AND REGISTRIES. Breed organizations and registries have formed late in the developmental stages of the breeds in most instances, and selection and admission of so-called foundation stocks took place in an "after the fact" fashion. Subsequently these organizations have pursued various policies in order to attain the type of horse considered desirable for the breed. In the case of the Thoroughbred the registry has been closed for many years. A number of breed organizations have retained means for permitting continued admission of individuals of desirable nature into the registry. A system of graded registration and a combination of performance requirements and inspection for advancement in the registry has been used by the American Quarter Horse Association with satisfactory results. (See Briggs, 1958, for a summarization of this system.)

Examples of breed retaining procedures whereby desirable individuals may be admitted to registry are the Standardbred, the American Saddle Horse, and the American Quarter Horse. In practice relatively few such individuals are admitted to the Standardbred and American Saddle Horse registries; whereas the blood of other breeds, almost entirely Thoroughbred, is used freely in Quarter Horses. In 1959 approximately 30% of Quarter running horses which qualified for register of merit were sired by registered Thoroughbreds (*Quarter Horse J.,* 1960). Many more had at least one-half Thoroughbred blood by slightly earlier crosses. At the other end of the Quarter Horse spectrum, many halter and performance register of merit qualifiers have had no outcrosses for at least several generations. Thus the current status with regard to homogeneity of type and genetic constitution varies greatly from breed to breed. Generally it may be said that progress in this direction is greatest where performance is the basis for selection and especially when objective measures of performance are available.

Fig. 10-4. Plainview's Julia, winner of the $10,000 five-gaited stake at the Kentucky State Fair in 1960, shows the extreme refinement and elegance of the American Saddle Horse. The long, nicely sloping shoulders and pasterns, so important to a smooth, comfortable ride, are well demonstrated. [Courtesy the American Saddle Horse Breeder's Association.]

SUCCESS OF SOME BREED ORGANIZATIONS IN THE ATTAINMENT OF DESIRED TYPE AND HOMOGENEITY OF GENETIC BASE. The Thoroughbred by virtue of its long-closed stud book and selection for racing probably represents the most homogeneous genetic base of any breed. The American Standardbred and American Saddle Horse breeds, as well as the Tennessee Walking Horse, have been rigidly selected for specific purposes and it may be supposed that this has resulted in reasonable constancy of type, at least so far as the specialty of the breed is concerned. The conformation of Standardbred or the Tennessee Walking Horse is relatively less important to breeders than is performance; as a result there are wide variations in size and conformation in these breeds. Because it has long been, first and foremost, a show horse, conformation and quality of performance of varied gaits have been important in selection of breeding stock in the American Saddle Horse breed. Today this breed has no equal in the number and style of gaits it performs, nor does any breed equal it in elegance and refinement of conformation.

The American Quarter Horse breed must be considered still in its formative stage. While breeders of stock-horse types have relied to a great extent upon animals already in the registry for breeding stock for several generations, Quarter running horses are commonly not more than a generation or two removed from the Thoroughbred. No doubt if the stud books were closed to Thoroughbreds, dilution of racing Quarter Horse strains with stock horse strains would result in a slower breed. Thus, recently set track records might stand for a long time. The problem of fixing the breed type appears to be a serious one due to divergent ideas of members of the breed organization on just what the uses of the Quarter Horse should be.

10-2. CHARACTERISTICS DESIRED OR USEFUL IN HORSES

The primary uses of the horse as a source of power for the accomplishment of work or as a means of transportation—either for pleasure, for sport, or for facilitating performance of the riders' task—requires that horses be possessed of special traits suiting them to the particular job.

Draft Horse. The draft horse is almost a unique case in that the primary requirement is the development of a great deal of power. Some of the most important factors in fulfilling this requirement are relatively great weight, heavily muscled back, loin, and quarters, and—as in all horses—sound feet and legs. The chief means of developing the power required is the forward displacement of the center of gravity. This is achieved by the support of much of the weight of the forequarters by the muscles of the back, loin, and rear quarters and extension of the rear legs by muscles of the rear quarters. It may be seen that for efficient function the requirement for conformation of head, neck, and forequarters is such that a relatively larger proportion of the animal's total weight may rest upon the forelimbs than in light horses. For the same reason a little greater length of back may be tolerated in draft horses provided there is ample muscling in that region.

Since great power for relatively long periods is required, stamina is important. Most horsemen look for indications of this almost intangible qual-

Fig. 10-5. Fernand, an imported Percheron stallion which stood at the University of California, Davis, 1916 to 1918, when draft horses were the primary source of farm power.

TABLE 10-1. *Characteristics and uses of the more important modern breeds of horses.*

Breed	Approximate period of breed formation or most important development	Colors	Height (hands)	Weight (lb.)	Most important fields of use
Light horses, Arabian	1st–6th Cent AD	Bay, gray, chestnut, brown	14–2″ to 15–2″	850–1000	General pleasure
Thoroughbred	1660–1800	Bay, chestnut, brown, black, gray, roan	15–2″ to 17	1000–1300	Racing, hunting, polo, general pleasure, stock horse
Morgan	1790–1850	Bay, chestnut, black, brown	14–2″ to 15–2″	950–1150	General pleasure
Standardbred	1800–1875	Bay, chestnut, brown, black, gray, roan	14–2″ to 16–2″	850–1200	Harness racing, horse show roadsters
American Saddle Horse	1840–1890	Chestnut, bay, brown, black, other	15 to 15–3″	1000–1150	Gaited saddle and fine harness at horse shows, pleasure riding
Tennessee Walking Horse	1890–1935	Bay, chestnut, black, brown, roan, gray, sorrel, white, yellow	15 to 16	1000–1200	Horse show walking horse, pleasure riding
Hackney	1760–1885	Bay, chestnut, black, brown	15 to 16		Horse shows, heavy harness horse
American Quarter Horse	1850–to date	Bay, chestnut, brown, black, roan, gray, dun, palomino	14–2″ to 15–2″	1000–1250	Stock horses, rodeo, short racing, pleasure riding

TABLE 10-1. *Characteristics and uses of the more important modern breeds of horses (continued).*

Breed	Approximate period of breed formation or most important development	Colors	Height (hands)	Weight (lb.)	Most important fields of use
Appaloosa	1938–1949	Various patterns of spotting, speckling, mottling on various colors of background	14–2″ to 16	900–1200	General pleasure, parade, stock horse
Draft horses, Percheron	1800–1885	Black, gray, brown, chestnut, bay	15–2″ to 17	1600–2200	Draft
Clydesdale	1720–1880	Bay, brown, black, other	15–2″ to 17	1700–2000	Draft
Shire	1780–1880	Bay, brown, black, other	16–2″ to 17	1800–2200	Draft
Belgian	1850–1900	Chestnut, roan, bay, brown, gray	15–2″ to 17	1900–2400	Draft
Suffolk	1770–1880	Chestnut	15–2″ to 16–2″	1500–1900	Draft
Ponies, Shetland	1870 *et seq.*	Black, brown, bay, chestnut, mouse, spotted	9–2″ to 10	300–400	Child's mount, horse shows
Welsh	Unknown	Chestnut, bay, gray, black, roan	11 to 13	350–500	Child's mount, horse shows
Hackney	1760–1885	Bay, chestnut, black, brown	11–2″ to 14–2″	450–850	Heavy harness pony in horse shows

Fig. 10-6. Of historic interest, large hitches of draft horses and mules such as these were a common part of the agricultural scene in Western United States prior to their displacement by power machinery during the early part of the twentieth century.

ity in a deep heart girth and roomy middle. This seems reasonable in that such configuration is assumed to provide ample respiratory capacity, space for vital organs, and the ability to handle adequate amounts of nutrients.

While appearance is secondary to utility, most of today's few Purebred draft horses in this country are used for show. Where this is true, balance of conformation, refinement, and breed type are emphasized. Since strict utility, usually in teamwork, has always been demanded of draft types, a calm, tractable disposition and intelligence are essential.

Stock Horse. The stock horse of the kind found on Western cattle ranches and in rodeo competition and horse shows is required to perform a great variety of tasks. Some of the requirements for these tasks are the ability to start and stop quickly, to show a great deal of speed for short distances, to be extremely agile and capable of changing direction rapidly, and to have weight and strength enough to hold a steer on the end of a rope. Since he is usually expected to put in the day at these activities, he must have great stamina and must necessarily be of calm, even, and tractable disposition, yet alert and ready for action.

Probably most important in permitting rapid maneuvering, starting, stopping, turning, early speed, and so on, are powerfully muscled hindquarters and short, heavily muscled back and loins, since muscles of the rear quarters provide propulsive power and shortness and strength of the back maximize lightness and handiness of the forequarters. Good feet and legs are important. For maximum speed there should be considerable length of limb. However, it appears that most often sheer power makes up for a lack in this regard in horses used solely for stock-horse purposes.

The preferred appearance of stock horses results when the conformation requisite to desired characteristics is achieved— that is, a relatively short, compact, powerfully muscled but well-balanced horse with well-defined withers to hold a saddle, well-muscled, well-sloped shoulders for maximum support and absorption of concussion resulting from violent maneuvers, and with head carried moderately low to provide visibility and space for action of the rider and, incidentally, to enhance balance and speed.

Obviously the complexity of the tasks performed by stock horses makes a high degree of intelligence and learning ability a necessity. In practice the great majority of stock horses in use on ranches and in sports and shows are of American Quarter Horse breeding with a few Thoroughbreds, Arabians, Morgans, and Appaloosas comprising the small remainder.

Race Horses. The demands made by racing are undoubtedly among the most strenuous of any made upon the horse, especially on his feet and legs. Speed, great stamina, intelligence, and certainly feet and legs of the soundest kind are prerequisite. In general appearance there is considerable variation in conformation of horses used for racing; for instance, compare the Thoroughbred distance horse with the Quarter running horse or harness racing Standardbred. Nonetheless, certain characteristics are common to them when compared to other types of light horses. As a rule there is somewhat greater height for length in racing horses, due to the requirement for good length of legs. A good slope of shoulder is necessary for maximum length of stride as well as absorption of concussion at racing gaits. Flat smooth muscling without bulkiness of the shoulder is also essential for clean, unhampered action of the forelimb, and at the same time it reduces burdensome weight. Racing horses tend to have somewhat longer necks than other types but carried moderately low for best balance. Characteristically, muscling should be long, flat, and smooth in horses raced the longer distances. This tends to be true for Standardbred horses and for Thoroughbreds racing these distances. Muscling often tends to be heavier appearing, rounder, and thicker in Thoroughbreds used for sprinting the shorter distances, and this type of muscular development reaches a maximum in racing Quarter Horses, where extreme speed for distances up to a quarter of a mile is most important. Thoroughbreds, particularly sires, which have shown great speed as sprinters have been used extensively in the development of the racing Quarter Horse and thus they tend to have many characteristics in common.

Pleasure Horses. The category of pleasure horse today covers an extremely wide range of types, and in many instances pleasure types are synonymous with types whose only other value is in horse shows. The American Saddle Horse and the Tennessee Walking Horse breeds, for instance, probably find greater use in horse shows than in pleasure riding. The requirements for gaited saddle horses are an aptitude for certain acquired gaits and conformation which permits a smooth, comfortable ride. In addition, they should be of such a disposition as to appear animated and willing but very responsive to the rider's signal at all times. Conformation varies according to the breed. Points in common to the two breeds are their well-sloped shoulders, long-sloping pasterns, and long, well-shaped feet. These are all points which contribute to easy riding qualities and to animation and style of action.

There is much more emphasis on action than on conformation in the Tennessee Walking Horse; hence there is considerable variation in this regard. They are less refined generally than the American Saddle Horse, especially the head, neck, and topline. A fault of conformation often ascribed to them is that of excessive angle at the hock. In view of the gaits required and relatively little strenuous use, this is probably not as serious a fault in them as in some other breeds. On the other hand, quality and conformation are very important for the American Saddle Horse. Model classes for conformation and finish only are provided, and quality or fineness is important in judging all classes at major shows.

A large and important segment of the horse population can be classified as general pleasure horses. This group includes a majority of horses of a number of breeds: Morgan, Arabian, Appaloosa, and other purebreds, plus a large number of horses of more or less nondescript breeding. Desirable characteristics for such horses may vary according to specific use but in general a gentle tractable disposition would appear to be of primary importance. Obviously it could be said that all the points considered to constitute good conformation relative to soundness, action, and attractive appearance are desirable in pleasure horses. Unfortunately, the primary requirement imposed by many owners is that pleasure horses be the willing objects of considerable attention and devotion from owners. This laxity in standards is undoubtedly a deterrent to breed improvement to the extent that purebred horses are involved. Emotional attachment to horses, combined with ignorance of the real significance of pedigrees, results in overemphasis of the latter in many cases and precludes the culling of undesirable individuals from breeding operations.

Parade horses, which are chiefly of Palomino, Pinto, and Appaloosa types, are prized for spectacular appearance. While there are many excellent horses in these registries, their flashy and unusual colors are emphasized and thus other important qualities such as conformation, disposition, and action frequently receive too little emphasis. Fortunately many owners are good judges of horse flesh and require a well-conformed horse of manageable disposition as well as of unusual color.

Ponies. With the exception of the Hackney Pony, whose sole use is in horse shows as a heavy harness pony, the primary uses of ponies are for children's mounts and in horse shows. Characteristics desirable in a child's pony are about the same as those for general pleasure horses, with distinct emphasis on gentleness, tractability, and reliability. Since many of these ponies are shown in competition, they are also required to be attractive in appearance and to show breed characteristics. There has been a rather large upswing of interest in ponies recently with a resulting increase in numbers registered and, generally, improvement in quality.

REFERENCES AND SELECTED READINGS

References marked with an asterisk are of general interest.

*Briggs, H. M., 1958. *Modern Breeds of Livestock*. Macmillan, Revised Ed., p. 668.

*Ridgeway, W., 1905. *The Origin and Influence of the Thoroughbred Horse*. Cambridge University Press.

*Riggs, E. S., 1932. The geological history and evolution of the horse. Leaflet No. 13, Field Museum of Natural History, Chicago.

The Quarter Horse Journal, 1960, 12(10): 26.

Chapter 11

Types, Breeds, and Crosses of Poultry

The cock, astrologer in his own way,
Began to beat his breast and then to crow,
And Lucifer, the messenger of day,
Began to rise and forth her beams to throw
And eastward rose, as you perhaps may know.
CHAUCER, Troilus and Criseyde

11-1. CHICKENS

Origin and Domestication. Domestication of the fowl in India dates back at least to 1000 B.C., while records indicate that chickens were raised by the Chinese as far back as 1400 B.C.

Cockfighting has had as much to do with the domestication of the fowl as has its use as a source of food. The sport of cockfighting is many centuries old and is still popular in parts of Asia, in the Islands of Sumatra, Java, and the Philippines, as well as in Mexico and Puerto Rico. Cockfighting existed in England for many years and was especially popular during the reigns of James I and Charles II. By act of parliament cockfighting in England was declared unlawful in 1849.

Darwin believed that the wild jungle fowl of India (*Gallus gallus*) was the primary ancestor of all domesticated chickens. Because the Leghorn and other Mediterranean breeds closely resemble *Gallus gallus*, Darwin's theory would seem plausible. However, in the case of the Cochin and other Asiatic breeds which differ so markedly from the Mediterraneans, some authors believe that ancestors other than *Gallus gallus* were involved, especially a supposed wild species resembling the Aseel breed.

Breed Formation in America. Hutt defines a breed as "a group of fowls related by descent and breeding true to certain characteristics which the breeders agree to recognize as the ones distinguishing the breed." In general, body type or shape determines the breed, although there are some exceptions. Within each of the breeds there are different varieties as distinguished by different plumage colors, patterns, and comb shape.

The origin of recognized breeds and varieties is rather obscure except for those developed in England and America. However, enough information is available so that the influence of imported stocks on the poultry in the United States can be fairly well traced.

Poultry shows have played a very important part in the development of breeds in America. A poultry exhibit was first held in Boston in 1849 and this city has held a show each year since that time. Subsequently, other poultry shows have flourished in essentially all parts of the United States and Canada. Competition among exhibitors was an important stimulus to the perfection of older recognized breeds and in the creation of new ones.

The American Standard of Perfection. The American Poultry Association was organized in 1873 by representatives of different sections of the country, including Canada, with the primary objective of standardizing breeds and varieties of domestic fowl shown in exhibition. This organization sponsors the publication of the *American Standard of Perfection,* first printed in 1874 and now in its fifth edition. The *Standard* is principally a guide for judging the type and color characteristics of the breeds and varieties recognized by the Association. Breeds of fowl having common geographic origin are grouped together into *classes.* Thus we have breeds belonging to the Mediterranean, Asiatic, American, and English classes. However, some class designations are only for convenience, such as the class for Game Bantams.

In the 1955 edition of the *American Standard of Perfection* a total of 230 breeds and varieties of chickens, turkeys, ducks, geese, and guinea fowl are described. This includes 125 varieties of fowl belonging to 44 breeds. The problem of describing all these varieties is not as great as it might seem because there are relatively few standard color patterns. For example, the silver penciled plumage pattern is common to the Dark Brahma and to the Plymouth Rocks and Wyandottes of the silver penciled variety. Likewise, the columbian pattern is similar for the Light Brahma and Columbian Rock. Figure 11-1 illustrates some of the common plumage patterns.

In the poultry industry there are no flock registry associations such as are common in the case of purebred large farm animals. In a sense, the *Ameri-*

Fig. 11-1. Various forms of feather markings as found in the plumage of the domestic fowl. Numbers 1 to 7—laced feather patterns; 8–10—crescentric form of penciling; 11–12—mottled; 13–14—spangled; 15, 17 to 21 —barring or horizontal penciling; 16—diagonal spangling. [Courtesy American Poultry Journal, Chicago, Ill.]

can Standard of Perfection serves in lieu of such registry associations by recognizing only those individuals which show characteristics conforming to the *Standard of Perfection*. However, no attempt is made to guarantee the blood purity of breeds of poultry.

Important Breeds and Varieties. Of the 125 breeds and varieties of fowl described in the *American Standard of Perfection,* only 6 or 7 are of real economic importance. Table 11-1 gives the distribution of breeds and crosses participating in the National Poultry Improvement Plan in 1959, according to different regions in the United States. Commercially, pure breeds—or more correctly speaking, pure strains of pure breeds—are markedly declining in numbers. At the same time, the number of strain crosses, crossbreds, and incrossbreds have greatly increased in number. Almost all our commercial broilers come from cross-mated flocks of different breeds. Furthermore, Leghorn strain crosses, although qualifying as a "pure breed," are generally classified by the National Plan as arising from cross-mated flocks.

LEGHORN. The Single Comb White Leghorn is by far the most important breed kept for egg production in America, as well as in most countries of Europe. The Leghorn is characterized by an active and flighty disposition, early sexual maturity, excellent laying ability, and a relatively small body size. They are well adapted to the extremes in the climate of North America. The Leghorn lays white eggs, is nonbroody, and the chicks are early feathering and grow rapidly.

A greater total effort has gone into breeding high-production strains of Leghorns than any other breed. Leghorns were first imported into America about 1835 from Italy, and since then many outstanding egg-laying strains have been developed in this country.

The relatively small size of the Leghorn is an advantage from the standpoint of early maturity and rate of egg production. Leghorns commence laying considerably earlier than other breeds such as the Rhode Island Red or Plymouth Rock. Small size birds tend to be more economically efficient egg producers because less feed is required for body maintenance. The Leghorn, however, is inferior as a meat bird and most of the hens after completing their production year are utilized in the manufacture of chicken soup and other prepared foods.

BARRED PLYMOUTH ROCK. The Barred Plymouth Rock was developed as one of the first dual-purpose breeds in America, mainly from crosses of the Black Java and the Black Cochin with the American Dominique. Plymouth Rocks have single combs and lay brown-shelled eggs. Body type and plumage color was fixed by inbreeding selected families from the Essex strain, traced as far back as 1878. Since the Barred Rock carries the sex-linked barring gene, this variety is used to produce chicks with sexes distinguishable at hatching.

Much of the early development of the poultry industry in America can

TABLE 11-1. | *Breed distribution (percent of each breed or of crosses) of chickens participating in the National Poultry Improvement Plan.**

Region	New Hampshire	White Leghorn	White Plymouth Rock	Barred Plymouth Rock	Rhode Island Red	Cross Mated	Incross Mated	Other
North Atlantic	0.9	20.3	12.2	1.8	1.8	57.5	3.7	1.8
E. North Central	3.3	24.1	10.6	0.7	1.0	44.9	13.0	2.4
W. North Central	1.4	26.3	3.6	0.3	1.0	47.1	18.7	1.6
South Atlantic	1.2	5.9	4.5	0.03	0.9	86.2	1.1	0.22
South Central	1.0	6.2	8.1	0.3	0.4	80.1	3.6	0.3
Western	5.4	30.5	5.2	0.1	0.9	50.7	6.7	0.5

* From ARS 44-2 leaflet (1960) of the USDA.

be credited to the Barred Rocks. As a dual-purpose breed they have been used extensively for both egg and meat production. Some strains have figured largely in the development of the broiler industry, while others have been selected primarily for egg production. The Barred Plymouth Rock was important for many years, but has declined in number recently.

Barred Rocks were introduced into England about 1879 and won widespread popularity in that country. They are also a major breed in the poultry industry of Japan.

RHODE ISLAND RED. The states of Rhode Island and Massachusetts were most prominent in the development of the Rhode Island Red. Importations of Cochins and Malays from the Orient were crossed with the native fowl in the formation of this breed. The Rhode Island Red was originally developed as a dual-purpose breed, as were all the other American breeds. They have yellow skin, and red ear lobes, lay a medium-brown colored egg, and have a quiet disposition. Through selection, broodiness has been largely eliminated and some strains with high egg production have been developed. They are relatively early in sexual maturity although later than most strains of White Leghorns. The breed was admitted to the *American Standard of Perfection* in 1905.

The Rhode Island Red has been a favorite dual-purpose fowl as well as a fancier's breed. It has been important for crossbreeding and in the formation of commercial inbred lines used in hybridization. During the last 15 or 20 years the Rhode Island Red has declined in numbers, as have all dual-purpose breeds.

THE NEW HAMPSHIRE. The New Hampshire is one of the newest breeds of the American class, having been admitted to the *American Standard of Perfection* in 1935. This breed was derived entirely from the older Rhode Island Red breed. There is no record of any other blood ever having been introduced into the New Hampshire. In color the New Hampshire is similar to but of a much lighter shade than the Rhode Island Red. The New Hampshire has been especially selected for early maturity, rapid feathering, and fast rate of growth. The most popular strains have been closely allied to the development of the broiler industry. During recent years, however, the New Hampshire has lost much of its popularity in favor of the White Plymouth Rock.

THE WHITE PLYMOUTH ROCK. The White Plymouth Rock, like the Barred Rock, was originally developed as a dual-purpose breed. It was probably developed from outcrossing to white birds, followed by successive backcrosses to the barred variety. Recently this breed has attained first importance in the broiler industry while it has been almost completely abandoned as a dual-purpose breed.

The modern White Plymouth Rock today has been selected very intensively for rapid growth, early feathering, and good feed conversion. Since mature body weight is correlated with early growth, modern broiler strains are large in body size. Hens frequently weigh as much as 8 lb. and the cockerels as much as 12 lb. Such strains are relatively poor egg producers.

The White Plymouth Rock is literally the mother of today's enormous broiler industry having largely replaced the New Hampshire as the female parent for the production of commercial broilers. The main reason for this change is the preference for white feathers. White birds dress out into a more desirable appearing carcass, without the black pin feathers found in the New Hampshire and the Barred Plymouth Rock.

AUSTRALORP. The Australorp, developed in Australia, was derived from the dual-purpose English breed, the Black Orpington. Australian breeders placed primary emphasis on high egg production. The Australorp is not of importance in this country as a pure breed but is of some importance in the production of crossbreds.

CORNISH. The Cornish fowl, generally known abroad as the Indian Game, originated in Cornwall, England, and appears to have been developed from a composite of several different breeds, including the Aseel, the Old English Game, and the Malay. Both sexes of the Cornish are similar in conformation. The Cornish is a closely feathered, very compact bird of a distinct shape (Fig. 11-2). The breast is extremely plump. The three varieties are the Dark, the White, and the White Laced Red.

The Cornish has become important in this country in the development of male lines used for crossbreeding in the broiler industry. Most such male lines probably contain 50% or more of Cornish blood. These strains closely resemble the original Cornish type and have white plumage.

NONSTANDARD BREEDS. Not all of our commercially important breeds of fowl have yet been officially recognized in the *American Standard of Perfection*. The California Grey is one such breed. This is an egg-laying strain widely used by hatcherymen for crossing purposes. Developed by the Dryden Poultry Farm of Modesto, California, from initial crosses of the White Leghorn and the Barred Plymouth Rock, the breed retains the barred plumage of the Plymouth Rock and the white-egg characteristic of the Leghorn parent. The California Grey crosses successfully with many White Leghorn strains and frequently has been used in such crosses by hatcherymen in preference to a Rhode Island Red or a Plymouth Rock. This is because the Grey-Leghorn cross progeny lay white eggs, while the other breed crosses produce tinted or cream-colored eggs to which some markets object.

Undoubtedly the California Grey would be eligible for recognition by the American Poultry Association if the developers of the strain were interested in this type of recognition. Because the breeding of male and female parent lines for the production of both egg-laying flocks and broilers is under the complete control of private breeding concerns, there has been little incentive to obtain recognition of such strains in the *American*

Fig. 11-2. Some breeds of chickens: (a) Single-combed White Leghorn hen; (b) Barred Plymouth Rock pullet; (c) Dark Cornish hen; (d) Single-combed Rhode Island Red hen; (e) Columbian Wyandotte cock. [Courtesy Robert F. Delancey, Poultry Press, York, Pa.]

Standard of Perfection. In fact, so called *Standard* breeds in the American poultry industry today are coming to be of less and less significance. As an example, in the formation of an inbred line the blood of one or more breeds may be used. Since such inbreds would be used in the production of commercial hybrid crosses there would be little advantage in recognizing any of these lines as new breeds.

Commercial Types of Chickens. Practically all chickens produced in the country today can be divided sharply into those bred for egg production and those bred for broiler meat production. In either case, the final product may be a pure strain, a strain cross, a breed cross, or an inbred hybrid combination.

PURE STRAINS. A strain of chickens generally takes the name of the breeder who developed it. A pure strain would not necessarily be any more "pure" genetically than a pure breed; however, if a strain has remained closed to outside blood over a period of years, then, in this sense, such a strain might be called pure. Pure strain breeding has been an important method for the production of both meat and eggs in the past. However, the last 10 to 15 years has witnessed marked changes in systems of producing commercial types of chickens. Pure strains are now used almost exclusively as parents of commercial crosses. In fact, today it is virtually impossible to buy breeding stock of any of the well-known pure strains of chickens developed in the United States.

STRAIN CROSSES. The progeny of the cross of two different strains of the same breed is called a strain cross. The majority of commercial chickens produced today for egg production are Leghorn strain crosses. At the same time these may still be classed as purebreds. If the strains used in crossing are somewhat inbred or if they differ in recent origin, the cross progeny may show some favorable hybrid vigor in egg production. Consequently, this method of breeding has an advantage over pure-line breeding for the production of commercial stock. Strain cross Leghorns are popular not only because of increased production resulting from hybridization but also because they retain the uniformity of white-shelled eggs, plumage color, and other characteristics ordinarily associated with a purebred. Commercial strain crosses usually involve only two strains but three or even more may be used.

BREED CROSSES. Progeny from crosses of strains representing different breeds are called crossbreds. Such crossbreds ordinarily show hybrid vigor or heterosis for egg production, rate of growth, and certain other characters. Some of the more important commercial types of crossbreds follow.

Sex-linked cross. When a Rhode Island Red or a New Hampshire male is mated to a Barred Plymouth Rock female, the male progeny are barred like their mothers while the females are nonbarred like their fathers. This cross has been used extensively, over the past years, especially in the New

England area, where cockerels are raised for meat production and the pullets are kept as layers. The crossbred pullets are usually black and carry a variable amount of red or gold in the terminal feathers of the neck hackle.

The reciprocal mating of this cross—that is, the Barred Rock male mated to a Rhode Island Red or New Hampshire female—produces all barred crossbred progeny. This was a popular cross for the production of broilers in the early days of the broiler industry.

Leghorn-Red cross. Crosses using the Leghorn male on a Rhode Island Red female have been used extensively in the Midwest for the production of medium-weight layers. This type of cross has proved to be an exceptionally good layer, and when the hens are marketed they will usually command a better price than Leghorns. However, the eggs are intermediate in color between the white of the Leghorn parent and the brown of the Rhode Island Red parent. Because certain markets discriminate against the cream-colored or tinted egg, this has limited the use of this cross.

An interesting fact is that the performance characteristics of the cross of a Leghorn male on a Rhode Island Red female is quite different from the reciprocal mating. In the former case the crossbreds show a tendency toward early sexual maturity and nonbroodiness, but frequently have rather high adult mortality. In contrast, the crossbreds from a Rhode Island Red male mated to a Leghorn female mature more slowly, are much more inclined to broodiness, but surprisingly they show less adult mortality. Table 11-2 illustrates this point from an Iowa 3-year experiment comparing reciprocal crosses of these two breeds. Whether the difference in adult mortality between the crosses is due to sex linkage or to a maternal effect transmitted through the female Rhode Island Red parent has not been definitely established.

Austra-white. This cross of an Australorp male and a White Leghorn female has proved to be extremely hardy and able to withstand the rugged farm conditions frequently encountered in the Midwest. The Austra-white

TABLE 11-2.	*Performance of reciprocal crosses of White Leghorns and Rhode Island Reds.* [*Iowa Agr. Expt. Sta., 1957.*]	
	White Leghorn male ✕ RI Red female	RI Red male ✕ White Leghorn female
Number of birds	244	242
Age at first egg (days)	178	188
Number broody hens	21	3
Percent broody hens	8.6	1.2
Number of deaths	95	43
Percent laying house mortality	38.9	17.8

is a good layer but tends toward excessive broodiness. Dark shank color of the pullets and tinted colored eggs are disadvantages of the cross where there may be a market discrimination against these.

Because it has greater resistance to respiratory infection than a strain-cross Leghorn, this cross has regained some popularity, especially in the Southern California area.

The White-Austra is a cross of a Leghorn male on an Australorp female. It does not exhibit the high broodiness of its counterpart, the Austra-white. Yet it apparently is quite resistant to respiratory diseases (see Fig. 11-3).

INBRED HYBRIDS. An inbred hybrid is defined as the progeny produced from a mating of two inbred lines or from a mating of first-generation inbred line crosses. However, the term hybrid is used in describing crosses between breeds and varieties. Because of the possible confusion that may be associated with the word hybrid, the United States Federal Trade Commission in its trade practice rules for the poultry industry recommends that the word hybrid should be qualified by stating, "in immediate conjunction therewith the type of cross used in the production of the industry product, such as 'inbred line-cross hybrid' or 'inbred hybrid,' 'cross-bred hybrid,' 'strain cross hybrid,' 'line-cross hybrid,' etc." The Federal Trade Commission also defines an inbred line as "A group of inbred chicks resulting from breeding closely related poultry and in which the individuals in question have an average coefficient of inbreeding of 37.5% (equivalent to two generations of brother-sister matings)."

Some of the outstanding commercial chickens in the country have been produced by methods similar to the system used in the development of commercial hybrid seed corn. The use of inbreeding as a tool for developing commercial egg-laying chickens attained considerable importance after World War II, particularly in the Midwest. Actual breeding details of commercial inbred hybrids are trade secrets of the companies producing them. Generally, hybrid varieties are sold by a number designation, and a description of the product is given in terms of plumage color, color of the eggs, and other characteristics of the hybrid.

The inbred hybridization method appeared to gain momentum through the 1940's but some of this seemed to be lost after random-sample egg-laying tests became popular about 1952. Results show that the best performing entries in random-sample tests are not necessarily inbred hybrids. Strain-cross entries frequently prove superior to some of the inbred-hybrid entries. Thus, whether intensive inbreeding, as used by hybrid seed-corn producers, is justified with chickens is still an issue not yet settled. The production of chickens bred like hybrid corn is being challenged by breeding systems using lesser amounts of inbreeding. Commercial breeders today are more concerned with the performance of their product rather than the system of breeding.

Fig. 11-3. (a) White leghorn ♂ × Australorp ♀ to produce White Austra
shown in (b). (c) and (d) Special broiler-type cross used to produce broiler
progeny (e). (*opposite*).

e

f

g

Neither male nor female parent lines can be identified to a particular breed, yet each has been especially bred for broiler qualities. (f) Leghorn-type hybrid. (g) Strain cross. Most commercial egg layers today are classified as either straincrosses or hybrids. [Acknowledgments: (a) and (b), courtesy Richardson's Poultry Farm, Redlands, Calif.; (c), courtesy Peterson Breeding Farm, Decatur, Ark.; (d) and (e), courtesy Ames In-Cross Inc., Des Moines, Iowa; (f) courtesy DeKalb Agricultural Association, De-Kalb, Ill.; (g), courtesy Welp's Breeding Farm, Bancroft, Iowa.

11-2. TURKEYS

Origin. The modern domesticated turkey is thought to be descended from two differing wild subspecies, one found in Mexico and Central America and the other found in the United States. The southern species is smaller, while the species native to the United States is larger and has a characteristic bronze plumage.

Darwin held to the view that the turkey was domesticated by the original inhabitants of America. He suggested that the wild forms found in Mexico and Central America were first domesticated. However, since the modern strains of Bronze turkeys correspond closely to the wild subspecies found in the United States, it is probable that the latter was used largely in the development of American varieties.

Varieties of Turkeys. Only one breed of turkeys is recognized by the *American Standard of Perfection* and hence we speak only of different varieties. The most important of these are the Bronze, White Holland, and the Beltsville Small White. Other varieties recognized by the *American Standard of Perfection* are the Narragansett, the Black, the Slate, and the Bourbon Red.

THE BRONZE. The Bronze is by far the most popular variety of turkeys in this country. It is also the largest. In recent years a subvariety, called the Broad-Breasted Bronze, has almost completely replaced the original Bronze variety. The Broad-Breasted Bronze has been especially selected for rapid growth, high feed conversion, and body conformation but is lacking in fertility, hatchability, and egg production. The adult plumage of the Bronze is basically black with the surface showing an iridescent sheen of red, green, bronze. There are distinct bands of copper bronze on the tail and back feathers. The wing feathers in this variety are black and white barred. The females may show white edging on the breast feathers.

WHITE HOLLAND. Just as there is a preference for broiler chickens with white plumage there is a trend to white plumage in market turkeys. The original White Holland was a smaller bird than the Bronze. The white variety has been made commercially more competitive by selecting for large size and broader breast development. At the same time breeders have tried to maintain better egg production than in the Broad-Breasted Bronze variety. Actually the improvement of the variety has mainly taken place by repeated backcrossing to the Broad-Breasted Bronze. The new type is known as the *Broad-Breasted White*. However, it is also deficient in hatchability and fertility. Essentially, the only difference between the Bronze and the White Broad-Breasted varieties is in color, although the former tends toward somewhat heavier weight and the latter shows slightly better fertility.

BELTSVILLE SMALL WHITE. This is a separate variety recognized by the *American Standard of Perfection* and developed by the United States Department of Agriculture at Beltsville, Maryland. The originators of this variety set out to develop a breed that would satisfy the demand for light-weight birds. The Beltsville has been used to produce turkey fryer-roasters of 6- to 8-lb. market weights dressed for the New York market. Because Belts-ville Whites are rather small when mature, they do not make as economical gains in attaining heavy market weight as do the larger varieties. For this reason they have not become popular. On the other hand, they are good egg producers and are superior in hatchability compared to the broad-breasted varieties.

11-3. WATERFOWL

Ducks. The major duck-raising industry in the United States is con-centrated on Long Island in the state of New York. This area produces the bulk of the young roasting ducks for the New York market. Ducks may also be kept principally for egg production, but duck egg production has never attained the importance in this country that it has in other parts of the world.

According to Jull, the wild mallard duck (*Anas boschas*) is the ancestor of all domestic breeds. The mallard must have been domesticated at a very early time since the Romans referred to them more than 2000 years ago. It is believed that duck raising on a commercial level has been practiced for a longer period of time in China than in any other country. Ducks are raised rather extensively in Belgium and the Netherlands, where farms are located along the canals. The most important breeds are the Pekin and the Khaki Campbell. Other well-known breeds are the Indian Runner, the Rouen, the Aylesbury, the Cayuga, and the Muscovy.

PEKIN. This breed, used exclusively in the Long Island duck industry, originated in China and was first imported into this country about 1873. The Pekin is noted for very rapid growth, pure white plumage, and yellow skin. It produces an attractive carcass. Ducks averaging 6 lb. at 8 weeks of age are not unusual.

THE KHAKI CAMPBELL. This is the most important egg-laying breed of ducks in Europe. They are especially popular in the Netherlands and in England. They were developed from crosses involving the Indian Runner and are similar to them. The Jansen strain of Khaki Campbells developed in Holland has shown some remarkable egg-production records. In fact, the question has been raised as to whether the chicken is really the best choice of species, after all, for the production of man's egg supply. Reports show that the Jansen strain of Khaki Campbell ducks far exceeds the best production obtainable in chickens. These ducks have averaged 320 eggs per bird per year and moreover they lay larger eggs. Adult mortality averages only about one-third that found in chickens.

MUSCOVY. The Muscovy (*Cairina mouschata*) belongs to a different species than the other breeds of ducks. The Muscovy is thought to have originated in Brazil. The females rarely quack and the drake does not have the curled tail feathers which is characteristic of drakes of all other breeds. The drake is about one-third larger than its mate.

Geese. With the possible exception of the chicken, the goose was probably the first bird domesticated and was regarded as a sacred bird in Egypt 4000 years ago. The Romans learned the value of goose liver as a delicacy and large numbers of geese were placed in pens to be fattened for the liver. The domestic goose became well distributed over all of Europe early in the Christian era. The Romans also learned to use the feathers for filling mattresses and cushions. Goose raising is still an important enterprise in many European countries, including France and Hungary.

a

b

c

Fig. 11-4. Some breeds of poultry: (a) Toulose gander; (b) White Emden gander; (c) Broad Breasted Bronze Turkey tom. [Courtesy Robert F. De Lancey, Poultry Press, York, Pa.]

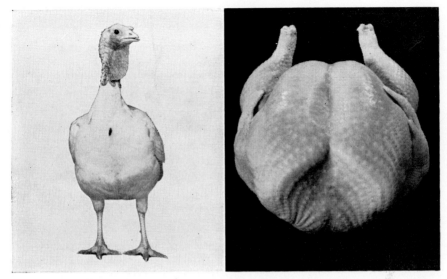

Fig. 11-5. Body conformation in a modern commercial strain of turkeys: (a) live turkey; (b) dressed turkey. [Courtesy Nicholas Turkey Breeding Farm, Sonoma, Calif.]

Geese have never been produced in concentrated areas in the United States as have other classes of poultry. They are raised in relatively small numbers on farms widely scattered throughout the United States and Canada. The total number of geese in the United States has consistently declined since about 1930. According to the 1950 census, there were only slightly more than 1 million geese raised in 1949. Geese were present on only 1.8% of the farms in the United States. Goose raising has limited opportunities because the demand for goose meat is largely restricted to city areas having a substantial foreign-born population.

Breeds most commonly found in this country are the Toulouse, Embden, and Chinese. Other breeds are the African, Roman, Pilgrim, and Sebastopol.

TOULOUSE. This breed originated in the south of France and was named after the French city of that name. It has a grayish plumage, being darker on the back and lighter in the fluff (see Fig. 11-4). The adult gander averages 26 lb. and the adult goose 20 lb. The Toulouse is the most common breed in the United States. They are not as good as the Embden in egg production, generally laying from 20 to 35 eggs per season. They are a hardy and vigorous breed but are somewhat slow in growth and not adapted for marketing at an early age.

EMBDEN. This is a white-plumaged breed originating in Germany. Standard weights are less than the Toulouse. Egg production averages from 30 to 50 eggs per season. Because of the white plumage the feathers of the Embden are more valuable than those of colored breeds.

11-4. GUINEA FOWL

The guinea fowl, native to Africa, was brought to Europe by the Portuguese toward the end of the Middle Ages.

There are three domestic varieties, the Pearl, the White, and the Lavender. The most common is the Pearl, which appears to be the original variety developed from the wild West African species. Guinea fowl are bred in very limited numbers in this country. They are valued most for the delicate and somewhat wild flavor of their meat.

REFERENCES AND SELECTED READINGS

American Poultry Association, 1953. *The American Standard of Perfection.* 1958 ed. Box 337, Great Falls, Montana.

Bateson, W. and R. C. Punnett, 1906. Experimental studies on the physiology of heredity. *Poultry Repts. Evol. Comm. Roy. Soc.,* 3:11–30.

Brown, E., 1906. Races of Domestic Poultry. Arnold, London.

Jull, M. A., 1927. The races of domestic fowl. *National Geographic Magazine,* 51: 379–452.

Inheritance of Livestock Traits and Livestock Selection

Chapter 12

Introduction to Modes of Inheritance

"Mendelian theory, it seems clear, was resisted from the time of its announcement, in 1865, until the end of the century, because Mendel's conception of the separate inheritance of characteristics ran counter to the predominant conception of joint and total inheritance of biological characteristics."

BARBER, B., *Science*, 134:596, 1961

12-1. INTRODUCTION

One of the most interesting characteristics of living things is their ability to reproduce themselves with reasonable accuracy. There is little difficulty in distinguishing between species, for example, a calf from a lamb. In most cases one has little difficulty distinguishing between breeds—a Hereford from an Aberdeen Angus calf, for instance. Each has inherited easily recognized color patterns from its parents. However, when we examine in detail the characteristics of a group of Angus calves of similar age, we are struck by the variation in certain traits, and the uniformity of others among individuals in the group. In a group of Angus calves, there is little variation in color, except that in a rare instance a red calf may be born; but weaning weights in a group of uniform age may vary 100 pounds or more. A group of Leghorn pullets may show little, if any, variation in color, but the age at the laying of the first egg may vary several months among the group.

Certain facts emerge when we study the reproduction of animals. One is the striking ability of species and breeds to reduplicate distinctive traits such as color. The other is that a great deal of variation in many characteristics occurs in groups which appear similar in general make-up. Genetics is the biological science concerned with the study of inheritance of traits. Geneticists seek to understand how these likenesses and variations are brought about, and so they must study the traits of offspring of controlled matings. They must take into account differences due to feeding, weather, and other outside factors on the development of offspring, and they must study the variation between more and less related animals.

The sources of likeness and variation may be broadly divided into two categories: heredity and environment. Most difficult but still the most important job of the geneticist and animal breeder is to learn to distinguish more accurately between the effects of these two factors in the development of animal characteristics so that he may interpret and properly use his breeding results. Seldom indeed do we have a situation where one factor is exerting an influence without the other. One such exceptional example is in the case of clones of plants which are propagated vegetatively by cuttings or graftings. All members of the clone of Bellflower apples, for instance, are identical in their heredity since in reality they are all parts of the same plant. Thus all of the differences we see among them as to tree size, shape, and so forth, must be due to differences in environmental factors such as soil, climate, and cultural methods. Another example of an exception—in animals—is identical twins, both of which are developed from the same fertilized egg cell. All differences between them are due to environmental factors. In almost all of the cases where we are observing and trying to use variation for improving animals, however, both heredity and environment are involved and are difficult to separate. Environment may have little effect on the coat color of cattle. Most of the differences we see are hereditary, but even here extreme environmental differences, such as fading of hair pigment in bright sun or certain nutritional conditions, may influence the variation observed.

Perhaps a working definition of the two sources of variation is needed at this point. *Heredity* shall be considered as all inborn tendencies and capabilities which are derived from the parents of an individual. *Environment* includes all those external conditions, including nutrition, which surround an animal and have an effect on its growth, development, and production.

12·2. THE BRIDGE BETWEEN GENERATIONS

Each animal grows entirely from one cell, a fertilized egg or zygote. This cell must divide and duplicate itself many, many times—until the daughter cells number many millions—in order to develop into an adult individual (see Fig. 12-1). During this time, no new living material is added to the organism. Nutrients are absorbed into the cells and converted to living

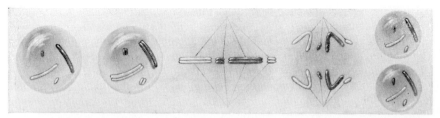

Fig. 12-1. Behavior of chromosomes in an ordinary growth division (mitotic division) of a body cell. Each and every chromosome duplicates itself so that each daughter cell has the same number as the parent cell. [From Srb and Owen, *General Genetics,* Freeman, San Francisco, 1952. Redrawn after Sharp, *Fundamentals of Cytology,* McGraw-Hill, New York, 1943.]

matter but no new living material is added from outside sources. Thus, the single cell from which the new individual grows is the only bridge between offspring and their parents. All inherited characteristics, tendencies, and abilities must be contained in the fertilized egg. The controlling mechanism for every trait of the offspring, including its ability to grow into a complicated set of organs and tissues, resembling its parents more or less closely, must be contained in some way in the single-celled zygote.

Let us examine this fertilized egg a little more closely. It is derived from the union of an egg from the female parent and a sperm from the male. The egg is a relatively large cell, and most of its mass is composed of cytoplasm. Embedded in the cytoplasm is the nucleus, which contains a set of rod-shaped structures called chromosomes. The sperm, on the other hand, is small, with very little cytoplasm, and the part which enters the egg at fertilization is composed mainly of chromosomes. Detailed microscopic studies of these cells have shown that the contribution of the sperm and egg to the fertilized egg or zygote, while very unequal in cytoplasm, is almost identical in chromosomes. With the exception of some species, such as the chicken, in which one half of the ova contains no sex chromosome, an equal and approximately identical set of chromosomes is contributed to the zygote by each parent cell. Painstaking work by many scientists in the last sixty years has shown conclusively that these chromosomes contain the real hereditary bridge between the generations. All of the factors necessary to direct the growth of an individual animal of the proper kind from the egg are carried from generation to generation in the material of the chromosomes. Like modern-day computers which have complicated directions for mathematical operations "memorized" or built in, the chromosomes carry myriad directions for growth, reactions to environmental forces, and the development of specific characters. In this way all the inherited characteristics are passed from parent to offspring, generation to generation down through the ages. The bridging of generations by chromosomes is illustrated in Figure 12-2.

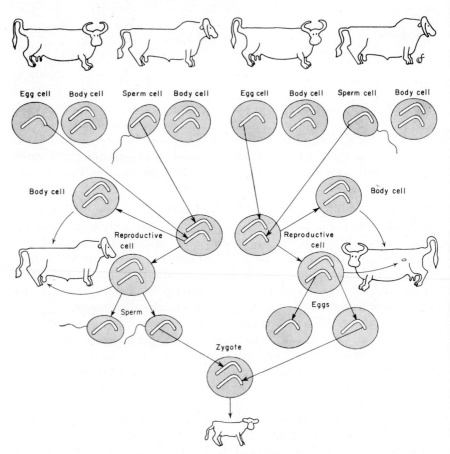

Fig. 12-2. How one pair of chromosomes acts as bridge of heredity between generations. One of each pair of chromosomes is in each sperm and egg. When the two come together to form the zygote which will grow into a new individual, they re-form each pair of chromosomes. Thus a sample of all the heredity of each pair of parents is transmitted to each offspring.

12-3. CHROMOSOMES IN INHERITANCE

One set of chromosomes comes to the fertilized egg from each of the two parents. In our domestic livestock, except domestic birds, the set from the female parent contains exactly the same number of chromosomes as that from the male parent. Each chromosome in a set is a little different in its shape, size, or composition from each other one. In other words, the chromosomes in the egg of a cow are 30 individual units, all slightly different from each other. For each individual chromosome in the egg, there is one like it in the sperm of the bull. Thus, when the two sets come together in the zygote, they make up 30 pairs of chromosomes. This pairing is very important since it accounts for the behavior of inherited characteristics in crosses.

In short, chromosomes come in pairs, one member of each pair coming from each of the parents of the individual. When the cells in the reproductive organs of the individual divide to produce sperm or eggs, the members of each pair of chromosomes separate and go to different sperm or egg cells. This results in sperm and eggs having only half the number of chromosomes that body cells contain. The type of cell division which occurs in sperm and egg formation is illustrated in Fig. 12-3. Geneticists designate

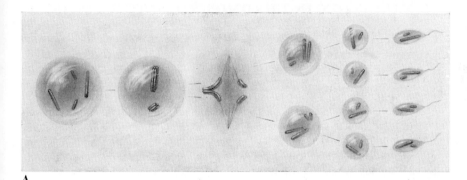

A

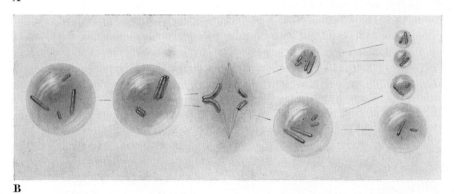

B

Fig. 12-3. Reduction division (meiosis) in the male (A) and female (B), showing the behavior of the chromosomes. Note that in both sexes, chromosomes undergo pairing and separation of the pairs to the daughter cells as well as a duplication, so that division of one mother cell results in four daughter cells, each with half the number of chromosomes of the mother cell. In the male, all four develop into sperm, whereas in the female three fail to develop and the result is only one functional egg cell. [From Srb and Owen, *General Genetics*, Freeman, San Francisco, 1952. Redrawn after Sharp, *Fundamentals of Cytology*, McGraw-Hill, New York, 1952.]

this half number as the "haploid" number. When the sperm and egg unite to form the zygote, pairs are made up again and the normal ("diploid") number of chromosomes is restored. In all cell divisions, during growth of the individual (see Fig. 12-1), each and every chromosome divides so that all body cells have diploid chromosome numbers and only the cells which are becoming sperm or eggs in the reproductive organs have haploid numbers. By this process a constant number of chromosomes is maintained in the species and at the same time hereditary material from the two parents is brought together so that both contribute equally to the hereditary traits of the new individual.

12-4. VARIATION IN CHROMOSOME SETS

It is often said that no two people are exactly alike. It is unlikely that any two individuals of any species of domestic animals have the same hereditary makeup (except identical twins). One reason for this may be seen when we consider the variety of combinations of chromosome sets which may be contributed by one animal to its offspring. Let us consider a female fruit fly, for instance, where there are four pairs of chromosomes in normal body cells. The fruit fly is used as an example because of the simplicity of its chromosome make-up. In the formation of an egg cell in the reproductive organs, the member of each pair which goes to this cell is entirely a matter of chance, and each member of a pair of chromosomes may contain slightly different hereditary material. The list in Table 12-1 shows that there are 16 possibilities for different combinations of chromosomes in the set which may be in a given egg or sperm.

In swine, with 19 chromosome pairs, there would be 524,288 combinations possible. In cattle, where there are 30 pairs of chromosomes, there are

TABLE 12-1.	*Possible chromosome combinations which may appear in ova of the fruit fly (Drosophila Melanogaster) according to the law of independent assortment of chromosomes. The somatic or body cells in this species have four pairs of chromosomes:* A_2A_1, B_2B_1, C_2C_1, D_2D_1.*

$A_1B_1C_1D_1$	$A_1B_2C_1D_1$	$A_2B_1C_1D_1$	$A_2B_2C_1D_1$
$A_1B_1C_1D_2$	$A_1B_2C_1D_2$	$A_2B_1C_1D_2$	$A_2B_2C_1D_2$
$A_1B_1C_2D_1$	$A_1B_2C_2D_1$	$A_2B_1C_2D_1$	$A_2B_2C_2D_1$
$A_1B_1C_2D_2$	$A_1B_2C_2D_2$	$A_2B_1C_2D_2$	$A_2B_2C_2D_2$

* Each letter stands for a chromosome; A_1 and A_2 are the two members of one chromosome pair. Since the two members of a pair of chromosomes almost always carry slightly different hereditary material, each combination shown would make a slightly different contribution to the inheritance of the offspring. The same number of possible combinations may appear in the male.

proportionally more combinations of chromosomes possible—1,073,741,824 different ones, to be exact. This great number of possible combinations of hereditary material gives us an idea how there can be much hereditary variation in the characteristics of animals. It also explains why there is so little chance of two individuals being exactly alike.

12-5. CROSSING OVER BETWEEN CHROMOSOMES

If we consider an individual pair of chromosomes, one member of the pair came from the sire and one from the dam. We might think then, that an individual chromosome is passed on intact from generation to generation from time immemorial. Things are not that simple, however. Due to a phenomenon called *crossing over,* material may be exchanged between the members of the chromosome pair in the formation of sperm and egg (Fig. 12-4). Thus, although a chromosome in an individual comes from its sire, it may or may not have come intact from the grandsire or granddam. Sometimes material is exchanged between chromosomes of a pair during forma-

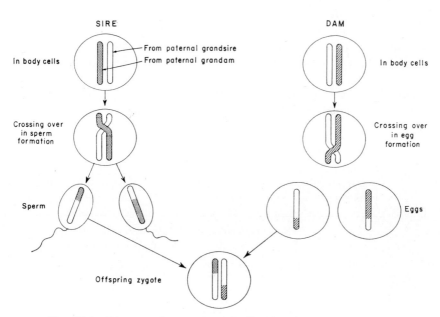

Fig. 12-4. Diagram shows schematically how material is exchanged between the members of a pair of chromosomes during the development of sperm or eggs from cells in the reproductive organs of the parents. Thus it is possible that some hereditary material from both of the grandparents may be passed on by a parent to its offspring, in a single chromosome.

tion of the egg or the sperm—in this instance part of the chromosome comes from one grandparent and part from the other.

Considering an individual's whole complement of chromosomal hereditary material, exactly half comes from the dam and half from the sire, because one member of each pair comes from each parent. Were it not for crossing over, a given chromosome in a given sperm would have come entirely from either the grandsire or granddam. As Fig. 12-4 shows, however, a portion of a chromosome in the sperm may be derived from each of the grandparents. It is thus extremely unlikely that a sire may transmit to any offspring only material from its sire or only material from its dam. This is important, when we are considering the influence of an outstanding animal in the pedigree of one we are considering for purchase or selection. If the outstanding ancestor is more than one or two generations back, we can see that its influence on the heredity of the individual is very much diluted.

12-6. NUMBER OF CHROMOSOMES

Different species of animals differ in the number of pairs of chromosomes in their normal body cells. How these differences arose in the evolution of the species is still not known. There are related groups of species of plants in which the chromosome numbers are multiples of each other, indicating that the number may somehow become double through some accident in development. Indeed, plant scientists have learned how to double chromosome numbers by treatment with chemicals such as the alkaloid colchicine,

| **TABLE 12-2.** | *Chromosome numbers in certain animals, including man. Considerable variation in the number of chromosomes is seen between different species. Owing to the difficulty of preparing cells in which chromosomes can be counted accurately in mammals and birds, different scientists have found slightly different numbers of chromosomes. [Most of the figures cited in this table were determined by Mathey, quoted by Makino, S., 1951, in* Chromosome Numbers in Animals, *Iowa State College Press, Ames, Iowa.]* |

Species	No. of chromosomes in body cells	No. of chromosomes in sperm and eggs
Man	46	23
Cattle	60	30
Sheep	54	27
Swine	40	20
Horse	66	33
Goat	60	30
Chickens		
male	78	39
female	77	38 or 39

thus producing new plant types with slightly different characteristics. So far this manipulation of hereditary material has not been achieved in animals. Chromosome numbers of our domestic species are listed in Table 12-2.

12-7. SEX

In domestic animals a difference in the composition of one pair of chromosomes is associated with sex determination. In all other pairs of chromosomes the two members of the pair are indistinguishable in their appearance, even though they differ in their content of hereditary material. In the sex chromosomes, however, there is often a difference in appearance in one sex. In mammals the two pair members are identical in the female but differ in the male. In birds, such as poultry, a different situation exists. The female has only one sex chromosome while the male has two, which are identical. The sex chromosomes are usually designated as X and Y (see Fig. 12-5). The following chromosome make-ups then appear:

	Male	Female
Mammals	XY	XX
Birds	XX	XO*

* Most workers have found no Y chromosome in the hen, thus leaving her with one less than the male.

In cattle, then, there can be only one kind of egg produced as regards the sex chromosome pair—that containing an X type chromosome. Males, on the other hand, may produce sperm containing either an X chromosome or a Y chromosome. Thus the male parent (female in birds) determines the sex of the offspring according to which type of sperm fertilizes the egg. Attempts by research workers to control the sex of offspring have centered on trying to find some way to separate X- and Y-bearing sperm. The most promising method to date involves the migration of the two types of sperm to different poles of an electrical field. Sex control, however, has not reached the stage of practical application.

12-8. GENES

Everyone talks of genes as being the things which govern hereditary characteristics. However, as yet no one really knows exactly what they are. We know a great deal about their location and behavior, but their actual description still escapes us.

Inference from studies on microorganisms indicates that the hereditary material is deoxyribonucleic acid (DNA). Among the most interesting studies of genetics is the determination of how much DNA constitutes the single gene. Many scientists are at work with electron microscopes and chemical techniques trying to solve this mystery.

A specific gene is located at a particular spot—which we call a locus—on a certain chromosome. Chromosomes are paired and, since there is a corresponding spot on each of the members of the chromosome pair, genes are paired also. Just as chromosomes duplicate themselves when cells divide, so genes also duplicate themselves. The members of each pair of genes, working together, influence a specific characteristic of the animal.

Considering all the animals of a species, there may be one or several types of genes available for a specific locus on a particular chromosome pair. If there is only one type of gene available, then all the animals of the species will be alike in the trait which this gene pair controls. Many such cases probably exist but unfortunately we can only recognize the existence of a gene when there are several genes located at a specific locus. All the genes located at a particular locus are called *alleles*. They all have some effect on the same characteristic, but their effects differ. In any individual they appear as a pair and the particular pair of genes which happen to be together will affect the resulting characteristic; that is, different alleles interact with each other. Their effects may have different strengths so that one will obscure the other (dominance), or the effects of two alleles may be simultaneously expressed (no dominance). Examples of these interactions follow.

Dominance. Probably the most familiar type of gene interaction is that called dominance. A well-known example is that of eye color in humans. The allele for brown is dominant over the allele for blue. Conventionally, the dominant gene is indicated by a capital letter and the recessive gene by a small letter. Let us call the blue eye gene "b," and the brown eye gene "B." Since both alleles are available in various individuals within the population, the following genetic types of individuals can occur:

> BB—Brown eyes.
> bb—Blue eyes.
> Bb—Brown eyes.

Individuals carrying two genes for brown (BB) or two genes for blue (bb) are said to be "homozygous" for eye color. Gene interaction is evident in the third type (Bb). The B gene is dominant over b and covers its effect more or less completely in individuals where both genes are present. The b gene is said to be recessive and blue is said to be the recessive eye color. A person carrying genes for both brown and blue eyes (Bb) is described as "heterozygous" for eye color. Such a brown-eyed, heterozygous individual can be distinguished from a brown-eyed homozygous individual (BB) only if he or she has a blue-eyed child.

Of course, even though there might be many alleles or genes affecting eye color, the child has only those genes which are contained in the chromosomes of its particular parents. It must receive one of these genes on the chromosome which it receives from its father and the other on the chromosome which it receives from its mother. Fig. 12-6 illustrates a case of dominance in color inheritance in cattle.

Two genetic terms may be introduced at this point—genotype and phenotype. Genotype refers to the genes which an individual carries for a specific trait or traits. For eye color in humans, the genotypes are BB, Bb, and bb. The phenotype refers to the visible trait actually expressed in an individual. Thus, while the genotype of an individual heterozygous for eye color is Bb, the phenotype is "brown-eyed."

No Dominance. Sometimes there is no dominance between allelic genes, or dominance may be incomplete. An example is the roan color in Shorthorn cattle. Considering that there are genes N for white and n for

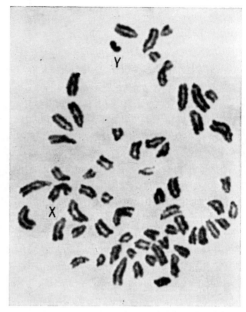

Fig. 12-5. Photomicrograph of chromosomes of a bull of the Swedish Lowland Breed. These 60 chromosomes are each dividing in an ordinary growth division of a body cell. The X and Y chromosomes are indicated. [Photo courtesy Dr. Yngve Melander, University of Lund, Sweden.]

nonroan (or solid color) in the population, there are three possible gene make-ups.

> NN—Animals' color will be white.
> Nn—These have white hairs mixed in with the colored
>   ones—roan color.
> nn—These animals will be solid colored. The usual color
>   with Shorthorns would be red.
> (In some crossbreds with black breeds, these genes could
> operate to produce "blue-roans," where black hairs instead
> of red are mixed with white in the Nn type.)

In the case of no dominance, neither gene covers up the effect of the other, but in the animal possessing both genes the effects are mixed.

More than Two Alleles. An example where three genes may be available for a given locus in the population is found in coat color in rabbits. Genes for full color (C), white with black points (Himalayan, c^h), and albino (c) are known. The C gene is dominant to both the others, and c^h is dominant to c. Genotypes and phenotypes which may be found are as follows:

CC —Full colored.
Cc^h —Full colored.
Cc —Full colored.
c^hc^h—White with black points (Himalayan pattern).
c^hc —White with black points (Himalayan pattern).
cc —Albino.

Crossing colored (CC) to Himalayan (c^hc^h) results in all colored offspring. Breeding these offspring together results in 3 colored and 1 Himalayan. Further, all offspring from Himalayan (c^hc^h) crossed with albino are Himalayan in color. If these offspring are bred together, the results are a ratio of 3 Himalayan to 1 albino offspring. Large numbers of offspring are necessary to obtain the mathematical ratios. These genes are termed an allelic series. A number of examples involving larger numbers of genes are known.

Interacton Between Different Pairs of Genes. The gene make-up of an individual at one chromosome locus may have an effect on the expression of the effect of genes at another locus. For instance, in sheep there is a color locus which has an overpowering effect on other color inheritance. In individuals which are WW or Ww the animal has a white fleece. However, if the gene make-up at this locus is ww, then other color genes at other locations or on other chromosomes may have an effect: the animal may be black or brown, depending on its gene makeup at another locus. However, when W is present, it suppresses the action of these other genes. Other types of interaction between different pairs of genes are known. In many cases genes at several chromosome locations may affect the same characteristic. Many pairs of genes at different chromosome locations affect milk production in dairy cattle. Since milk production is a complex process, genes affecting a number of different body processes influence it. Examples are body size, appetite, the secretion of hormones affecting udder development, lactation, and general metabolic level of the animal. For each locus the genes available may be considered as affecting production in a plus or minus way. The genetic potential for milk production, then, is the result of the net sum of all the plus and minus effects of all the genes present. This is called "additive gene action." There are probably additional gene pairs involved in this important character which involve some type of gene interaction such as dominance.

Genes, in general, interact with the environment in producing their effects. Stated differently, the effect produced by genes is influenced by the environment. Genes for high milk production or egg production are not able to make their effects appear in animals which are starved or subjected to other extremes of environment. Hereford calves which are genetically the usual white-face, red-body pattern, may become very yellow in color if they feed on grass or hay with a high content of the element molybdenum. Other less drastic environmental effects are also of great importance in the expression of the genetic potential of individuals.

Mutation. If genes are capable of reduplicating themselves accurately millions of times when cells divide, how then do different types get in the population? In other words, where did this variety of genes come from? Once in a great while, in the process of duplication of a gene, some accident occurs which changes the character of the gene so that it will affect the trait it conditions in a new way. This accidental change is called a mutation. Mutations are the source of all the genetic variation which exists in a population. Estimates of the frequency with which they occur in certain genes have been made. For most loci, these accidents occur only once in millions of gene duplications. This low frequency of change in the genetic material is necessary to the stability of the genetic system of a species. If mutations occurred often, a species would not be able to maintain its form and characteristics. The whole system of cell division and reproduction is geared to maintaining stability in a species. That mutations do not occur easily can be seen from the drastic treatments which are required to cause them artificially. Adequate X-ray treatment will produce an increased number of mutations. Chemical treatments with strong poisons, such as some of the war gases, will also increase mutations.

Probably most of the mutations which do occur are lost from the population of animals because their effect makes the animals less adapted to survival. Once in a while, however, one will occur which does not decrease adaptation or actually makes animals possessing it better fit to survive. This new gene then may become one of the available genes in the population of the species. By this process, new genetic variation may gradually come into the population.

Chance in Inheritance. The formation of the particular complex of inherited material of any new offspring from a mating is a matter of chance. For a particular chromosome locus, the two parents between them have twice as many genes for this locus as the offspring will have. Excluding mutation, the offspring can only have genes possessed by the parents. But which of the parental genes appears in the offspring is a matter of chance.

To illustrate the chance distribution of genes to the offspring, let us consider the inheritance of red color in Aberdeen Angus cattle. A single autosomal recessive gene (b) is involved. Black (B) is dominant to red (b). Figure 12-6 shows the type of gametes furnished by heterozygous parents, as well as the result of the mating. In the bull two types of sperm are formed: one carries the gene for black (B) and the other carries the gene for red (b). The two types of sperm are formed in equal numbers and it is equally likely

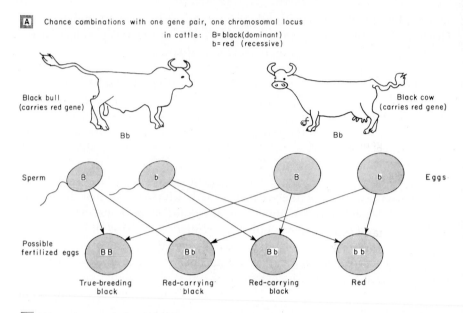

A Chance combinations with one gene pair, one chromosomal locus

in cattle: B= black(dominant)
b= red (recessive)

Black bull
(carries red gene)

Bb

Black cow
(carries red gene)

Bb

Sperm   B   b   B   b   Eggs

Possible
fertilized eggs   B B   B b   B b   b b

True-breeding
black

Red-carrying
black

Red-carrying
black

Red

B Other possible matings considering only this locus and same genes.

	Male parent		Female parent	Offspring	
I.	BB	×	BB	All BB	Black, non-carriers
2.	BB Bb	× ×	Bb BB	1/2 Bb 1/2 BB	Black, red carriers Black, non-carriers
3.	BB bb	× ×	bb BB	All Bb	Black, all non-carriers
4.	Bb bb	× ×	bb Bb	1/2 Bb 1/2 bb	Black, red carriers Red
5.	bb	×	bb	All bb	Red

Fig. 12-6. Part A shows possible chance gene combinations which may be formed in the mating of two black animals each carrying the recessive red gene. Each possibility is equally likely to occur. Part B gives the possible matings which can occur when these two genes are present in the population for this locus on the chromosome and the possible ratios of offspring which might occur if large numbers were produced.

that either type will fertilize the egg in a particular mating. The distribution of the B and b genes in the ova is the same as in the sperm. Thus there are four combinations of sperms and eggs and each is as likely to occur as the other. One of the four possible combinations will result in a red animal; in other words, the chance of obtaining a red Angus by this mating is one chance in four. The second part of the diagram (B) shows the other possible matings in a herd in which parents with all possible genotypes for this characteristic are present. For instance, the chance of obtaining a red animal from mating No. 4 is one chance in two.

More than One Locus. Consider Fig. 12-7, where the possibilities of a mating involving genes at two different chromosome loci are diagramed. If the two gene pairs are located on different chromosomes, then the distribution of one pair of genes to the offspring has no effect on the distribution of

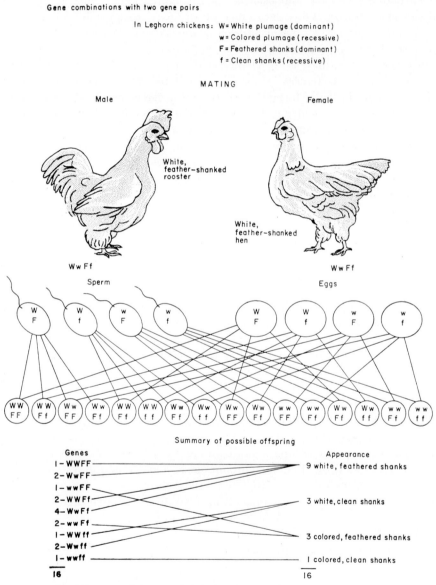

Fig. 12-7. Possible combinations of offspring when considering two pairs of genes which are independent of each other, and the ratio of different types of offspring which would be most likely to be produced if a large number were born to the mating shown.

the other pair. They are completely independent of each other. Since this is true, each of the parents produce four different types of sperm or eggs, when we consider genes for both pairs. There are sixteen ways in which the two sets of four types of sperm and four types of eggs may combine to form a particular offspring, and each of these combinations is just as likely to occur as any other. Thus the chance of any particular combination occurring is the number of times it appears in the sixteen possible combinations. The combinations are summarized at the bottom of the diagram. Considering gene make-up, there is one chance in 16 that any particular offspring will be WWFF, but 4 chances in 16 that it will be WwFf. We thus see how chance enters into the formation of the gene make-ups of offspring. Note that the chance for a given phenotype is not the same as for a given gene make-up. Where dominance is involved, as with the genes chosen for this diagram, several gene make-ups produce the same appearance in the offspring. Thus there are 9 chances in 16 that an offspring of this mating will be white with feathered shanks. Four of the different gene combinations produce this same appearance.

Of course there are many ways in which genes can interact to produce offspring which differ in appearance. Many ratios in the occurrence of a trait result from different matings. However, which gene from a parent goes to an offspring is purely a matter of chance, and this is the basis for the probability of any offspring combination occurring.

Linkage. When two pairs of genes are located on the same chromosome, they cannot be distributed independently, like those in the previous diagram. By being located on the same chromosome, one member of one gene pair is physically linked to one member of other gene pairs on this chromosome. If the locations of the two gene pairs are close together on the chromosome they are closely linked. If they are far apart on the chromosome, then there may be exchanges of material between the members of the chromosome pair in the formation of sperm or eggs. This is called crossing over, and the more it occurs the less close is the linkage. However, the chances of producing particular offspring combinations are different than if they were independent —that is, located on different chromosomes. This is important in animal breeding. If a desirable gene is closely linked to one which has an undesirable effect, they may be very difficult to separate in selective breeding.

Mendelian Genetics. Up to now the discussion has been concerned primarily with the laws and principles involved in inheritance controlled by one or a few pairs of genes, each having an effect which may be individually recognized. This part of the science of genetics is called classical or Mendelian genetics, after its founder. Gregor Mendel was a monk in what is now Brno, Czechoslovakia, who made experimental matings and observations on plants in the monastery gardens. He observed and reproduced the genetic ratios which have been discussed above, and summarized his work in a paper, in 1865. However, he received no recognition until his results were rediscovered in 1900. This was the beginning of the science of genetics—one of the younger scientific disciplines.

After the rediscovery of Mendel's work, many investigators expanded the knowledge of heredity. It was soon seen, however, that many complex characters, such as growth or milk production, could not be explained in simple ratios produced by a few genes. To deal with these problems, the branch of genetics known as quantitative or population genetics has developed.

Multiple Factor Inheritance. Most of the economic characters which we are interested in changing in selective breeding programs—milk production, egg production, growth, and feed efficiency—are apparently governed by the action of a large number of gene pairs, each having an effect too small to select out from the others. In a herd of dairy cattle, for example, the amount of milk produced may vary over a wide range with no separable classes. These quantitative traits are more susceptible to influence by environmental forces than is, for instance, coat color. This also makes it more difficult to identify individual gene effects.

We have seen that as we go from one pair of genes to two, the number of possible offspring combinations to consider goes from 4 to 16. If three gene pairs were involved, there would be 64 combinations. With the large numbers of genes which almost certainly are involved in determining traits such as milk production, there are probably millions of possible combinations and it becomes impractical to raise enough calves to identify all combinations. How, then, can we study and use the hereditary differences in these characteristics which are inherited in such a complicated way?

Though the individual genes involved cannot be identified, they no doubt follow the same rules as those which we can identify. Thus we know that the offspring receives one gene of each pair in its entire complement from each of its parents. That is, each parent is equally important in the inheritance of an offspring. This is true even in characteristics like milk production, where one of the parents does not exhibit the character—bulls have just as much influence on the milk production of their daughters as do the cows. One-half of the genes which a sire passes to an offspring came from his dam and half from his sire although, because of the way genes interact and recombine, the traits coming down from either parent or grandparent may be impossible to distinguish.

Generally, however, since we cannot work with the individual gene makeups and effects for these economic characters, we must use a statistical approach to breeding for them. We must study herd and population averages and the amount of variation from genetic and environmental sources in different groups in order to formulate good breeding programs.

12-9. THE ROLE OF ENVIRONMENT

Any characteristic observed in an animal is a result of the interaction of that animal's genetic make-up with the environment to which it is subjected. We can be safe in saying that if any animal had been raised in a different environment—hotter, colder, or with different feed or treatment—that it would have been different in many characteristics even though it had exactly the same gene make-up. In a breeding program we are constantly attempting to measure the true genetic worth of an animal. We wish to see through the masking effect of environmental differences.

Even such things as coat color may be changed by environmental extremes. If we remove some hair from the backs of Himalayan rabbits and place them in a cold room, the hair which grows back will be black, but if kept in a warm environment, it will usually grow in white. Black sheep which are maintained on a copper-deficient diet or one high in molybdenum will grow new wool of a steely gray color rather than black. When returned to a normal diet, they grow their usual black wool (see Fig. 29-6). Cattle on the same type of diet, that is an excess of molybdenum or deficiency of copper become yellowish in the hair if they are normally red and grayish if they are normally black (see Fig. 12-8). These are examples of extremes in

Fig. 12-8. Even with relatively stable inherited characters such as coat color, extremes of environment may cause modification. Both of these animals are genetically black and appeared like the one nearest the fence at weaning time. A diet high in the element molybdenum caused the color change you see in the nearer animal after a period of several months feeding. [Photo courtesy University of Nevada.]

environment. However, the more common differences we encounter in breeding programs are of more economic concern to us.

As an example, let us consider the selection of ewe lambs for flock replacements on the basis of the best hereditary ability to grow fast. One might think that it would be simple to select those that are largest at a given age. However, regardless of their gene make-up, lambs born as twins are smaller at an early age than those born as singles (Table 12-3). Likewise, those whose mothers are young will be smaller than those from mature dams, again without regard to their genetic makeup. In both instances smaller size is due to less milk being available to the

TABLE 12-3.	*Average weights at 120 days of age of Suffolk lambs raised under farm conditions.**

	Av. wt (lb.)	Difference between groups (lb.)
Av. all lambs in flock	92.4	
Av. all single lambs	98.7	
Av. all twin lambs	86.1	12.6
Av. lambs from 2-year-old ewes	83.8	
Av. lambs from 4-year-old ewes	94.5	10.7
Av. all male lambs	99.7 †	
Av. all female lambs	85.1 †	14.6

* University of California at Davis, 1952–1954.
† Sex is determined by heredity and thus this is not an environmental factor.

lamb while it is growing. This is an environmental effect and must be taken into account in trying to select the genetically best replacements.

Pullets which have been raised on high energy diets may begin to lay at a different age and to lay at a different rate than those raised on the range. Different light-control plans may cause pullets of exactly the same breeding to lay earlier or later and more or less heavily. These differences are due to environment and if we are attempting to pick the ones which are genetically best for breeders, allowances must be made for these environmental differences in order to distinguish genetic differences.

In considering inheritance, the animal breeder must constantly seek to remove, or evaluate, the effects of differences in environment in order to be successful in determining the true breeding value of his stock.

12-10. PROBLEMS AND OPPORTUNITIES

This discussion has taken a short look at the basic knowledge of heredity, which has been accumulated in the young science of genetics during the past sixty and odd years. This insight has enabled us to make progress in the solution of many important problems of heredity, for example the Rh factor in "blue" babies, the dwarf problem in cattle, and the production of hybrid corn. Many important problems remain to challenge the worker in this field.

Undoubtedly the improvement of productivity of livestock by selective breeding has barely started. Progress in the breeding of chickens for egg and meat production is showing what can be done.

The study of the heredity of bacteria and viruses provides leads, not only to the nature of the gene, but to the nature of life itself. The nature of cancer has received much attention from workers in this field.

Practical problems such as the control of sex, the development of methods for producing outstanding sires for use in artificial insemination, and the improvement of feed conversion and carcass qualities by selective breeding provide challenges to the animal geneticist.

In short, the potentials for contributions both to knowledge of living things and to the betterment of the human race by the science of genetics have barely begun to be realized.

REFERENCES AND SELECTED READINGS

Bogart, R., 1959. *Improvement of Livestock.* Macmillan, New York.

Castle, W. E., 1940. *Mammalian Genetics.* Harvard Univ. Press, New York.

Iltis, H., 1932. *Life of Mendel.* Translated by E. and C. Paul. Norton, New York.

Rice, V. A., F. N. Andrews, E. J. Warwick, and J. E. Legates, 1957. *Breeding and Im-* *provement of Livestock.* McGraw-Hill, New York.

Scheinfeld, A., 1950. *The New You and Heredity.* Lippincott, New York.

Sinnott, E. W., L. C. Dunn, and T. Dobzhansky, 1950. *Principles of Genetics.* McGraw-Hill, New York.

Srb, A. M. and R. D. Owen, 1955. *General Genetics.* Freeman, San Francisco.

Chapter 13

Selection and Mating Systems

13-1. INTRODUCTION

Powerful means for developing more efficient farm animals lie in the hands of the breeder. Just as the designer and engineer may blueprint and develop more efficient tools and machines, so may the breeder outline programs for developing improved animal tools—better equipped to produce food and fiber of higher quality and at less cost. Genetic "engineering" is a field of development barely tapped in the improvement of most farm animals.

Among the pioneer scientists who have developed theories and experimental testing of procedures most useful in applying the results of Mendelian genetics to animal improvement are Sewall Wright of the University of Wisconsin, R. A. Fisher of Cambridge University, and J. L. Lush of Iowa State University. They have developed and explained many of the concepts concerning selection and mating systems which apply to the genetics of herds and populations. George Harrison Shull and Edward M. East caused a genetic revolution in the breeding of plants, which has affected animal breeding as well, in their discoveries of the power of inbred lines when hybridized to produce increases in corn yields of as much as 20% or more (Kiesselbach, 1951).

Population genetics is the term used for this special area of genetics so important to animal improvement. While its biological soundness is rooted in Mendelian genetics, it differs from the classical studies of the effects of single genes in F_1 and F_2 generations. Population genetics is concerned with genetic changes in the total herd—the effect on the average of all animals and the variation found. The population approach was found necessary because early experiments indicated ratios of phenotypes such as 3:1 and 9:3:3:1 were not found for most of the economically important traits. Rather, a continuous distribution of phenotypes over a wide range was observed, which were best explained by the actions of many pairs of genes. For example, variations in milk production indicates involvement of 7 to 200 pairs of genes. With total estimates of 10,000 to 20,000 pairs of genes occurring in animals, it becomes obvious that the breeder is dealing with populations of great numbers of genes as well as populations of animals. Appraising individual actions of genes in these cases seems an impossible task. The most useful avenue, to date, has been to study the gross effects of the actions of many genes under effects of selection and mating systems.

13-2. HERITABILITY ESTIMATES

Further complexities in applying Mendelism to the improvement of economic traits result from the variation caused in these traits by environment as well as by inheritance. Even identical twins, animals which have the same genotypes, are found to differ. These differences illustrate conclusively the effect of environmental variation on the expression of traits. All of this background contributes to the popularly debated subject as to which is the more important—heredity or environment. "Which is more important" is generally interpreted to mean which contributes more to the individual's own deviation from the general average.

Population geneticists and animal breeders (Lush, 1948) have found mathematical and statistical tools which helped them appraise the relative amount of variation attributable to genes and to environment. The relative importance of heredity, they found, varied with the trait. In traits such as variations in the amount of white on Holsteins, 90–95% of the differences were found to be due to the heritable differences between animals. In traits such as litter size in pigs, heritability was only 10–15%. Heritability is the term coined to describe the degree of phenotypic resemblance among relatives, as between offspring and parents. It is a term now widely used and accepted in animal breeding. Heritability indicates the per cent response or improvement expected by the breeder from exerting a given amount of selection pressure on a trait in his herd. As an example, if a breeder's unselected sheep flock averages 8 lb. of wool and rams averaging 11 lb. are selected from the flock to mate with selected ewes averaging 9 lb., the average selection differential between that selected group and the overall average is $(11 + 9/2) - 8 = 2$ lb. If heritability were 100%, the progeny of the selected group would average 2 lb. above the mean of the progeny of an unselected flock. However, the offspring average is usually nearer the mean of the herd than is their parents' average. That is, heritability is less than

1.0 and the progeny of selected parents under the same conditions do not on an average produce as well as the selected parents. In observations in many experimental flocks, about .40 of the selection differential or "reach" in wool production has been reflected in the production of the selected group. The heritability then is .40 and we have, as well, one example of how heritability is computed. In this case it is the regression of each off-spring's record on the average of its parents. The selection differential must be multiplied by the heritability to estimate the progeny average. Since .40 × 2 = .8, .8 lb. improvement in wool yield in the next generation is expected, rather than 2 lb.

Much of this regression toward the mean is attributed to the selection of animals that have had, by chance, a better environment than the average within the herd. The environmental contribution to their superior pheno-type does not, of course, breed on.

Since, for a given amount of selection, more is gained by selecting for traits with high heritabilities than for those with low, the breeder might simply conclude that these are the traits to emphasize. This is true only if they have approximately the same economic worth, for the breeder is an applied economist as well as an applied geneticist and must combine these considerations into an overall selection program. In Hereford cattle, shade of red is highly heritable, about 70%, but variations in the trait have yet to be shown to be important in the production of beef. On the other hand, weaning weight is much less heritable but is one of the more economically important traits in beef cattle. The breeder might well decide to emphasize in selection the trait with only moderate or even low heritability.

In one study in which steers were individually fed to low choice grade, variations in several traits were correlated with the net income per 100 lb. live weight. Squaring these correlations gives an estimate of the variation in net income attributable to a given trait. This is one procedure by which relative economic importance of the traits can be estimated. The breeder must, in addition, consider the likely response to selection as estimated by the heritabilities of these traits; so that overall ranking of importance of single traits to the breeder depends upon both economic importance and heritability.

In addition, there are genetic situations which help explain some of the regression of offspring toward the mean. Offspring of hybrids are known to show some of this regression. Second-generation seed from hybrids yields only about 85% as much as first-generation seed (Kiesselbach, 1951).

Superior appearance or performance due to specific interactions between genes are not usually reproduced in the offspring at the average level of the selected parents.

Heritability values thus are not abstract or theoretically derived. They are based on actual observations from selection experiments or resemblances of relatives in herds.

TABLE | *Some average heritability estimates of farm animals.**
13-1.

Beef cattle		Chickens	
Weaning weight	0.21	Mortality	0.10
Feedlot gain	0.68	Egg production	0.22
Dairy cattle		Sheep	
Milkfat production	0.24	Fleece weight	0.33
Mastitis resistance	0.26	Type score	0.10
Services per conception	0.05	Face covering	0.53
		Swine	
		Litter size, 56 days	0.17
		Feed economy	0.27

* Averages of all estimates from Table 88, *Handbook of Biological Data*, W. B. Saunders, 1956. These estimates vary with the material from which the data are gathered. For example, earlier in this chapter, the heritability estimate for fleece weight (from another source) was given as 0.40 instead of 0.33. In Chapter 6, the heritability of feedlot gain is given as 0.45.

The ranking in Table 13-2 shows the situation in one experiment and thus may not be applicable in other situations. The example shows, however, that one trait may deserve 5 to 10 times more emphasis than another trait. While single-trait selection is not advocated as the most efficient procedure for overall improvement, emphasis on a trait or traits must take these factors into consideration when they are to be incorporated into a total score or selection index for an animal.

Selecting for one trait probably does not often leave other traits unaffected. This is explained by the fact that genes have been observed to influence more than one characteristic. For example, selecting for rate of

TABLE | *Estimated ranking of importance of single traits to the breeder based*
13-2. | *on economic worth* and heritability.*

Traits	Relative economic worth (r^2) †	Heritability (g^2)	Index of importance $(r^2 \times g^2)$
Weaning weight	0.64	0.30	0.19
Size of dam	0.10	0.70	0.07
Daily gain	0.14	0.45	0.06
Days to finish	0.21	0.25	0.05
Percent calf crop	0.64	0.07	0.04 (estimated)
Feed per pound of gain	0.04	0.39	0.01
Carcass cut-out value	0.08 (estimated)	0.25–0.50	0.02–0.04 (estimated)
Slaughter grade	0.21	0.00	0.00

* Lindholm, H. B. and H. H. Stonaker, 1957. Economic importance of traits and selection indexes for beef cattle. *J. Animal Sci.*, 16:998–1006.
† Correlation coefficient between each trait and net income.

gain in swine will cause a genetic improvement in efficiency of feed conversion, but also automatically slightly increases fatness. In dairy cattle high production is negatively correlated genetically with per cent fat solids in milk. In beef cattle, selection for daily gain increases efficiency and mature size; although selection for mature size does not increase efficiency very much.

These associations between traits have a bearing on overall results from selection as well as the heritabilities and economic considerations. A milestone in animal improvement was reached when L. N. Hazel in 1943 invented a selection index procedure which would maximize selection opportunities by appropriate weighting of traits according to heritability, economic worth, and the correlations between traits. An example of a selection index is provided in Chapter 16.

While it is difficult experimentally to appraise the increase in efficiency of selection by this method, estimates in sheep indicate at least a 20% to 50% increase. In some breeds or herds, undoubtedly even greater improvements have been or could be brought about by the use of a selection index.

13-3. PROGENY TESTING

Traits such as carcass characteristics or sex-limited ones such as milk production cannot be accurately predicted from the animal's appearance. In these instances evaluation of a breeding animal must be delayed until the progeny have been tested. On the other hand, several important economic traits in sheep, such as growth rate, fleece character, and face covering can be observed. Thus selecting breeding rams on the basis of phenotypes will result in a shorter generation interval and thereby hasten improvement. This point is discussed in Chapter 17.

The Danish system of progeny testing for carcass quality in swine (Clausen, 1953) offers a classic example of meat animal improvement by adherence, over an extended period of generations, to a consistent procedure of progeny testing swine litters. Systematic testing for back fat and belly thickness of the bacon for length of side and efficiency of feed over almost 60 years illustrates changes made in the direction desired. Estimations of changes through the years in the Danish Landrace are shown in Table 13-3.

In dairy cattle, progeny testing of sires based on the production of their daughters is an essential. Rapid advances in procedures have been made in recent years. The long-followed sire index—based on the comparison of daughters' records with their dams' records—has practically been discredited because of the confounding effects and important influence of changes in the herd environment for the dams' records vs. the daughters' records. More promising and accurate appraisal of sires' progenies are being made through the use of artificial insemination, for it is possible to breed to sev-

TABLE | *The improvement in carcass quality of the Danish Landrace pig.**
13-3.

		1926–27	1951–52
	Loss at slaughter (dressing %)	27.2	26.4
	Export bacon (Wiltshire sides) %	59.5	61.3
	Length of body (cm)	88.9	93.4
	Thickness of back fat (cm)	4.05	3.42
	Thickness of belly (cm)	3.06	3.30
Judged by points. Maximum score, 15 pts.	Firmness of back fat	12.7	13.6
	Shoulders	12.2	12.7
	Distribution of back fat		12.8
	Thickness & quality of belly	12.0	13.1
	Hams	12.3	12.5
	Fineness (heads, bone, skin)	12.5	13.1
	Amount of lean meat	12.4	12.9
	General bacon type	12.2	12.6
Percentage of pigs	Too lean	0	3
	Very good	50	83
	Too fat	28	12
	Much too fat	22	2
		1929–30	1951–52
	Feed units per pound live wt. gain	3.39	3.06

* Clausen, H., 1953. *The Improvement of Pigs.* Marjory Boyd, Belfast, Ireland.

eral different bulls within a given herd. Thus progenies which have more nearly the same environment may be compared. This new type of sire evaluation holds promise of a new era in dairy cattle improvement.

Progeny testing of sires based on sufficient numbers of offspring of randomly selected mates and raised concurrently under similar environmental conditions can theoretically reveal precisely the additive genotype of the parent. No other system can do this. The number of progeny required to reveal this varies with the heritability of the trait and relative sampling errors. Generally speaking, greater genetic gains can be expected by compromising accuracy of the sire's evaluation with opportunities to select among more sires. If 100 cows were available for the progeny testing of bulls, it would usually be better to mate a few cows to each of a relatively large number of bulls than many cows to few bulls.

These relationships are illustrated in Table 13-4. In the example, 100 cows are available for progeny testing and 2 progeny-tested bulls are ultimately needed. The 100 cows could be mated to only 2 bulls. This would give a very accurate appraisal of the 2 bulls, but 2 bulls are needed, so no selection on progeny test is possible, and a zero selection differential is obtained as shown in Column A. The greater selection differentials are ob-

TABLE | *An example of genetic progress as a result of using different numbers*
13-4. | *of sires in progeny tests with 100 females.*

Number of bulls to progeny test	Number of progeny per male	Percent of males to be retained	(A) * Selection differential on sires	(B) † Correlation between sire's genotype and daughters' av. performance	Relative expected progress (A × B)
2	50	100	0	1	0
4	25	50	0.8	0.82	0.66
8	12	25	1.3	0.73	0.95
16	6	12	1.6	0.60	0.96
32	3	6	2.2	0.47	1.05
100	1	2	2.4	0.30	0.73

* Lush, J. L., 1945. *Animal Breeding Plans*. Iowa State College Press.
† Lush, J. L., 1931. The number of daughters necessary to prove a sire. *J. Dairy Sci.*, 14:209–220.

tained by progeny testing more bulls, even though each individual progeny test is a less accurate appraisal of that particular bull's genotype.

Column B is an example of the expected correlations between a sire's genotype and the average of varying numbers of offspring. This illustrates for a trait of a given heritability the increasing reliability of a progeny test with increased numbers of progeny. The overall relative rates of progress from progeny testing is shown as the product of the selection differential and the correlation between sire's genotype and offspring average. As can be seen, a peak in rate of genetic improvement was achieved by using the test herd of cows so as to produce about 3 progeny per sire. There was not much difference in achievement between 3 and 12 progeny per sire but rate of improvement was decreased if we cut down on the number of sires tested so as to produce as many as 25 progeny per sire.

The B column in the table is influenced by the heritability of the trait. The correlations would be lower for traits with low heritabilities and higher for traits with high heritabilities.

13-4. PEDIGREES

Pedigrees are useful aids in selection but are limited in predictive value due to the sampling nature of inheritance, the influence of environmental factors on the traits, and, to a degree, the reliability of the pedigree itself.

Pedigrees are most useful for traits which are sex limited, low in heritability, or greatly influenced by inbreeding and hybridizing. In recent years they have been widely used in lowering the incidence of such undesired recessives as dwarfism in cattle. The probability of an animal being a heterozygote can be indicated from pedigree information as follows:

Relationship to a recessive dwarf	Probability of being a carrier
Parent	100%
Full brother or sister	67%
Half brother or sister	50% +
Son or daughter of a half sib*	30–40%
Average normal appearing animal in major beef breeds	15–25%

* Above 25% because of probability of obtaining recessive gene from other parent. (Mimeograph release "Dwarfism in Beef Cattle," J. L. Lush & L. N. Hazel, Iowa State University.)

From this table it is indicated that for dwarfism, a trait which has not been uncommon in occurrence, a breeder could better his chances of avoiding dwarfism if the trait had not been found "close up" in the pedigree. On the other hand, pedigrees thought to be clear of dwarf production have been worth a considerable premium.

Stressing ancestors many generations removed usually approaches faddism so far as the genetic contribution of that animal is concerned, because of the halving of relationships each generation. Exceptions are illustrated later under linebreeding, where relationships are held high even to rather remote ancestors by breeding systems devised for that purpose.

On cannot determine precisely the genotype of an offspring from a given mating regardless of how much is known about the animals in the pedigree. The genotype of that offspring is a sample of the parents, and this is the limiting biological factor in prediction.

13-5. MATING SYSTEMS

There are traits in which little or no response to selection is obtained. This might seem to be very discouraging to the breeder, but the fact that a trait has low heritability does not mean it offers little chance for genetic manipulation or control. In fact the greatest industrial commercialization of genetics in farm animals, thus far, has been with low heritability traits —egg production in chickens and litter size in swine. The reason is that in characteristics influencing fertility, there generally is a low heritability but a considerable amount of heterosis or hybrid vigor which results from crossing of breeds or inbred lines. *Hybrid vigor or heterosis is that extra performance obtained in the cross above the average of parents raised under a comparable environment.*

A study of mating systems has to do with an aspect of genetics and animal improvement quite apart from the selection process. There are many ways in which breeding animals may be paired for matings. They may be paired by relationship so as to produce progeny which are more inbred than average, for example brother to sister, sire to daughter, son to dam. They may be paired so as to be different genetically and to produce a hybrid or outbred, such as mating a Shorthorn bull to a Brahma cow. They may be paired so as to be unlike in appearance such as a racing-type Quarter Horse to a "bulldog" type. This tends to produce intermediate types of offspring; it is sometimes called corrective mating. They may be paired phenotypically alike; such pairs cause more extreme types in the overall population than is found otherwise. If tall men tend to select tall wives and if short men were to select short wives we would have an example of assortive mating or the mating of likes. It tends to create greater extremes among the offspring within the population than if mating were random with regard to the trait. Different mating systems are used to accomplish different ends. Under most situations a selection program is used in conjunction with a mating system.

Inbreeding and outbreeding or hybridizing are the best-known mating systems. They are the opposite of one another in pairing procedure and in their genetic effects, for inbreeding makes animals more homozygous, whereas outbreeding makes them more heterozygous. Tremendous incentive to investigate inbreeding vs. hybridizing effects in farm animals has resulted from the findings of Shull and East. Shull (1909) reported the phenomenon of hybridizing in using but 2 inbred strains of corn for crossing. Later, in noting results of crosses of 8 inbred strains, he found some crosses which markedly outproduced outbred, open pollinated corn. This phenomenon of hybrid vigor in corn has led to widespread experimentation with hybridization in most of the farm animals. Successful industry application has been achieved with chickens and swine. One West Coast chicken breeder, long noted for the excellence of his selected outbred birds now produces commercially nothing but hybrid chicks. Why should the hybrid be able to outproduce such rigidly selected outbred populations? This question has not been completely answered, but in lower forms of life such as in the molds and bacteria, clues are developing which indicate that the life processes are enhanced in instances by the biochemical action of different alleles, each contributing something to an increased efficiency of the organism's development. An example in man is the greater resistance to malaria of individuals heterozygous for the sickle-cell gene. This gene causes hemoglobin cells to have a distinctive sickle shape. In malarial ridden sections of Africa, these heterozygotes have a higher survival rate than individuals without the sickle-cell gene. Individuals that are homozygous for the sickle gene, however, are the least fit and have a high rate of death from anemia. Thus the heterozygote is more fit than either homozygote. Geneticists call this overdominance, or the extra performance of the hybrid due to heterozygosity at a given locus.

Another type of hybrid vigor results because favorable genes often have a degree of dominance and unfavorable genes are likely to be recessive.

Hybrids thus have a greater dosage of dominant genes at the many loci involved than do their more inbred parents. Thus, they have a greater dosage of dominant genes at many loci than the parents possessed. Both theories are important in explaining heterosis.

The tremendous commercial importance of hybrids in poultry and corn comes about as a result of the great economic importance of certain low-heritability traits influencing fertility or reproductive rate. Heritabilities of egg production and corn yields are known to be low and yet these are the most important production traits in those species. Should the economic importance of reproductive rate in swine, sheep, and cattle be found to be as great as in poultry and corn, there will be need to study applicability of similar methods. In beef cattle, reproductive rate and weaning weight already have been indicated by some to be the most important traits economically, and these traits also show a great amount of heterosis. The general rule is that traits high in heritability do not show as much heterosis as do traits of lower heritability. Nor do traits that show little heterosis show much inbreeding regression. We may then accept the general proposition that inbreeding and heterosis are opposite and exclusive of one another in their effects. They actually may be considered as gradation of the effects from much homozygosity to little homozygosity.

For traits in which considerable heterosis is necessary for their fullest expression, there is an increase in the amount of vigor found with a decrease in relationship between animals in the cross. Crosses between breeds give greater hybrid vigor than crosses between families within a breed. Crosses between inbred strains from different breeds give even greater heterosis than those previously mentioned. This is the usual picture until crosses are made between extremely unrelated animals, such as between different species or different genera. In the latter instances there are high rates of embryonic loss and other incompatibilities which limit the ability to cross. For example, in crossing bison bulls on domestic cows frequently there is hydramnios, the development of excessive amniotic fluid. Also, F_1 males from the cross often are sterile.

Various types of matings listed are shown in order of probable increasing heterozygosity produced in the progeny.

Inbred—The progeny resulting from the mating of closely related animals. Linebreds are inbred, but with a high relationship to a particularly admired animal.

Outcross—The mating of relatively unrelated animals within the same breed or variety.

Topcross—The mating of a male of a specified family to females of another family of the same breed.

Topincross—The progeny resulting from the mating of inbred sires with noninbred dams of the same breed.

Incross—The progeny resulting from the crossing of individuals of inbred lines within the same breed.

Crossbred—The progeny resulting from the mating of different breeds.

Topcrossbred—The progeny resulting from the mating of inbred sires with noninbred dams of different breeds.

Incrossbred—The progeny resulting from the crossing of individuals from inbred lines of different breeds.

The maintenance of a crossing system requires breeders of seed stock to maintain noninterbreeding stocks from which crosses can be made. This is how the purebred breeder and the registry society fulfill needs of the commercial producer. They serve to maintain a closed population which is not permitted to cross with other populations. While the degree of homozygosity obtained is not high—probably not more than 8 to 12% in many breeds—it does maintain a source of material making crossbreeding feasible in some areas of the livestock industry.

Many breeders obtain further control over the inheritance of their herds by linebreeding to the most admired animals within their herds. The idea here is not so much to inbreed purposely as it is to maintain high relationships to better animals. Homozygosity increases more than it would under usual purebreeding methods, but the prepotency of the breeding stock from that group of animals should be enhanced in the process. There are many instances in the history of many herds where linebred families have become famous for their breeding performance and individual excellence as well.

Robert Kleberg purposely linebred the King Ranch Quarter horses to Old Sorrel, a son of a Thoroughbred mare and Old Hickory. The pedigree of a Quarter horse colt bred by King Ranch illustrates the results of this long continued line breeding program. This has resulted in holding a high degree of relationship to Old Sorrel (.45) without greatly increasing the inbreeding of the colt (F = .09).

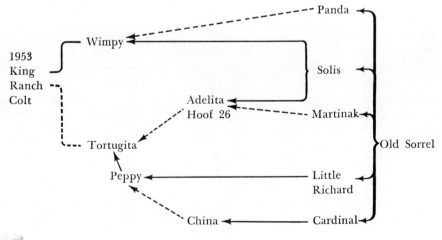

The development of inbred families within the breed serves to increase or maintain the genetic uniformity within the strain and to increase the breeding predictability of that strain within itself and in crosses with other strains (Fig. 13-1). Experiments indicate that the conformation and producing ability within such inbred strains is hurt by the inbreeding. In chickens, and to a lesser degree in swine, there has been considerable application of the development of inbred lines to be used in crossing for producing useful hybrids. Brother-sister, sire-daughter, and son-dam matings are the closest that can be made in livestock. These cause a decrease in heterozygosity of 25% per generation in contrast to the 50% reduction that can be made by selfing in corn. Sample inbreeding and relationships from matings of relatives are as follows:

Mating	*Inbreeding of Progeny*	*Relationship Between Mates*
Uncle-Niece	.062	.125
Half Brother-Sister	.125	.250
Full Brother-Sister	.250	.500
2 generations " " "	.375	.600
3 generations " " "	.50	.727

Today, if many systems of mating and selection are to be compared simultaneously, we rely largely on experimental evidence from laboratory animals. In Drosophila it has been found that "elite" hybrids have consistently outproduced carefully selected outbred populations in egg production, a trait low in heritability. For traits higher in heritability such as egg size, selection has been highly effective. Where both high and low heritability traits with both high and low heterosis are involved, a combination of selection and crossing seems indicated. In Table 13-5, the single crosses represent crosses of two inbred lines. Reciprocal crosses are between two large noninbred populations which have been selected to specifically com-

TABLE 13-5. *Relative performance in various selected traits after 16 generations of selection under 4 different methods.**

Methods of selection	n	Mean daily fecundity	Mean egg size	Performance index
Closed population	582	90.8	38.93	2309.2
Reciprocal cross	573	97.7	38.42	2314.5
Recurrent cross	544	102.1	39.16	2366.9
Single cross I	161	104.3	38.58	2346.0
Single cross II	164	101.3	38.38	2324.1

* Bell, A. E., C. H. Moore, and D. C. Warren, 1955. The evaluation of new methods for the improvement of quantitative characteristics. Cold Spring Harbor Symposia on Quantitative Biology XX. Biol. Lab. Cold Spring Harbor, N.Y.

Fig. 13-1. Inbred herd bulls from two distinct inbred families are the product of many years of inbreeding coupled with selection for heavy weaning weights and fast feedlot gains. (Top) Linecross sons of this bull were the fastest gaining cattle in a feed test involving 21 progeny groups. (Bottom) This bull, used through artificial insemination, increased weaning weights of calves in a commercial herd by 40 lb and sired high-gaining progeny in several feeding tests. For commercial beef production linecross daughters of one strain should be bred to bulls in the other strain. This results in the production of hybrid vigor within a breed. [Courtesy Colorado State University.]

bine well with each other. Recurrent crosses are crosses between two strains in which the one strain is selected to cross well with a specific inbred tester strain.

13-6. SUMMARY

It becomes obvious that breeding techniques useful under one set of circumstances cannot be considered necessarily as appropriate for another objective. In general, selection for desired traits is applicable for all breeders. In order to maintain reasonably high selection differentials, they must restrict the number of traits selected. They should select animals raised in about the kind of environment under which they expect their commercial progeny to perform. Due to the differences between herds in environmental conditions, the animals generally should be ranked on a "within herd basis." Usually the breeder of commercial animals should follow a different mating system from that of the purebred breeder, in order to maintain a greater degree of hybrid vigor in his market animals. The commercial breeder generally should outcross whereas the purebred breeder should linebreed to hold high relationships to his best animals; in some cases the purebred breeder will actually form closely inbred families in order to supply the commercial breeder with the inbred lines needed for greatest opportunities for exploiting hybrid vigor through crossing.

REFERENCES AND SELECTED READINGS

References marked with an asterisk are of general interest.

*Clausen, H., 1953. *The Improvement of Pigs.* Marjory Boyd, Belfast.

*Kiesselbach, T. A., 1951. A half-century of corn research. *Am. Scientist,* 39:629–655.

Lindholm, H. B. and H. H. Stonaker, 1957. Economic importance of traits and selection indexes for beef cattle. *J. Animal Sci.,* 16:998–1006.

Lush, J. L., 1931. The number of daughters necessary to prove a sire. *J. Dairy Sci.,* 14:209–220.

*———, 1945. *Animal Breeding Plans.* Iowa State Univ. Press.

———, 1948. Genetics of populations. Iowa State Univ. Mimeograph, pp. 271–284.

——— and L. N. Hazel. Dwarfism in beef cattle (Unpublished). Iowa State Univ. Mimeograph.

Shull, G. H., 1909. A pure line method in corn breeding. *J. Am. Breeders' Assn.,* 5:51–59.

Spector, W. S., 1956. *Handbook of Biological Data.* Saunders, Philadelphia, pp. 111–113.

high. An individual should therefore ordinarily be average or above in individuality to warrant trial as a breeder.

The third basis for selection is progeny performance. In theory this is the best method of selection, since animals with superior progeny have demonstrated their transmitting ability. In practice with beef cattle there are, however, limitations on the usefulness of progeny testing. First, only a limited number of sires can be progeny tested and these must be selected on the basis of individuality or pedigree so that much of the possible selection pressure has already been applied before progeny-test information is available. Second, cows will be well along in years before they can have produced enough offspring for an accurate appraisal of transmitting ability. Third, generation interval is lengthened by progeny-test procedures. For rate of gain, a reasonably highly hereditary trait, about one of every three or four bulls selected for high gains failed to produce above average calves (Kincaid and Carter, 1958). Thus every breeder should use progeny performance to an extent to weed out breeding animals whose offspring fail to live up to expectations. Progeny testing becomes of increasing usefulness in artificial insemination programs in which extensive use is made of those sires proved superior on the basis of progeny (Warwick, 1960).

14-2. SELECTION FOR CHARACTERS RELATED TO ECONOMICAL PRODUCTION OF BEEF

Fertility and Longevity. Specific, simply inherited defects leading to sterility or lowered fertility (Eriksson, 1943) and hereditary tendencies toward the development of cystic ovaries and other conditions which produce at least temporary sterility (Erb *et al.,* 1959) have been found in dairy cattle. Presumably, hereditary low fertility in certain strains of Bates-bred Shorthorn cattle contributed to their loss of popularity in the 1870's. For a time low fertility was considered a desirable trait, however, since it kept numbers low in certain lines of popular pedigrees and thus kept the prices per head high!

In spite of these examples, however, the studies made to date (Table 14-1) in beef cattle, as well as more numerous studies in dairy cattle, have usually found the apparent influence of heredity on reproductive efficiency to be small. There is, and presumably has been from time immemorial, automatic selection for fertility. Infertile animals leave fewer offspring to propagate the next generation. Conceivably, under normal management conditions an hereditary equilibrium has been reached in which further intentional selection will be ineffective or nearly so. Under these circumstances, much emphasis beyond what is automatic on reproductive records of sires and dams in selecting animals for breeding purposes will probably slow total progress, since it will not improve reproductive rates and will decrease selection intensity for traits which will respond to selection,

TABLE 14-1. | *Heritability estimates for beef cattle characters.**

Character	No. of estimates	Av. of estimates
Calving interval	3	8
Birth weight	15	41
Weaning weight	29	29
Cow maternal ability	2	40
Postweaning feed lot gain	19 †	47
Efficiency of feed lot gain	8 †	40
Final feed lot weight	9	69
Postweaning pasture gain	9 †	34
Cancer eye susceptibility	2	32
Live animal scores:		
Weaning	18	27
18 months off grass	7	27
Slaughter	7	44
Carcass traits:		
Dressing percent	2	71
Carcass grade	6	32
Rib eye area	3	69
Tenderness	5	58

* From data in literature as presented with references by Warwick (1960).
† A few unreasonably high or low estimates omitted.

The foregoing may require modification for those breeds or strains which have recently been taken from unfavorable to improved environments and possibly for breeds based on crosses of such breeds. Under conditions of inadequate feed supplies, low reproductive rates may have survival value. Perhaps the cow that calves annually under such conditions will be unable to survive for very long while the every-other-year calver will be able to build up body reserves between calves and survive longer. Cattle with this type of background, when brought into an improved environment, may require several generations to reach a new equilibrium and during this period selection for fertility might well be effective. This possibility has not been experimentally tested.

No studies are available on the effects of heredity on length of life in beef cattle. Studies in dairy cattle have given conflicting results but a recent analysis (Parker *et al.*, 1960) does not indicate heredity to be an important factor. Here again there is natural selection, for animals with a long productive life leave more offspring and hence contribute more genes on the average to the next generation. Whether breeders can afford to put additional intentional selection pressure on longevity is presently uncertain,

Preweaning Growth and Factors Affecting It. The beef cow has two functions to perform: (1) to calve regularly, preferably each year, and (2) to
raise her calf to weaning age. The overhead of maintaining a cow—both
fixed costs and feed—are relatively little affected by whether she calves or
not nor by the size of the calf weaned. It takes the equivalent of about
$3-3\frac{1}{2}$ tons of dry roughage to maintain the average beef cow a year. She
must raise a heavy calf each year if efficient production is to be achieved.

Weaning weight is affected by both inherent growing ability of the calf
and the maternal qualities of its dam. Weaning weights are correlated with
milk production of dams (Gifford, 1953) to a considerable degree but probably other less obvious characters of cows also affect growth of their calves.

Heritability of calf weaning weight based on individual calf performance
and the maternal qualities of cows as evaluated by weights of their calves
are both moderately high (Table 14-1), and selection should be effective in
improvement.

Calf weights are rather highly repeatable. Cows in the lower $\frac{1}{10}$ to $\frac{1}{4}$ of
a herd on the basis of one or two records can be safely culled. Only rarely
would they rank in the upper half of the herd with subsequent calves
(Botkin and Whatley, 1953).

Evaluation of weaning weight presents some problems since it is affected
by several nonhereditary factors. Bull calves gain faster than heifers. Mature
cows in the age range of 5 or 6 to 8 or 9 years raise heavier calves than those
either younger or older. Thus adjustments of records are necessary if selection of calves or culling of cows is to be based on true genetic merit. Unfortunately, the sizes of the adjustments necessary apparently vary from
area to area and even from herd to herd in the same general region. The
adjustment factors given in Table 14-2 are based on a large body of data

TABLE 14-2. | *Examples of factors used to adjust preweaning daily gains of calves.**

	Sex of calf		
Age of dam	Bull	Heifer	Steer
2 years	1.15	1.29	1.20
3 years	1.06	1.19	1.10
4 years	1.02	1.14	1.06
5 years	0.99	1.11	1.03
6 to 10 years	0.96	1.08	1.00
11 to 13 years	1.01	1.13	1.05
14 years & over	1.10	1.24	1.15

* From Marlowe *et al.*, 1958. Factors given are for spring-born, non-creep-fed calves. To adjust
calf gains to basis of steer calves from mature dams (6 to 10 years of age), multiply actual daily
gain of each calf by the factor given.

from Virginia (Marlowe *et al.*, 1958). They are illustrative of general trends but should not be applied directly without collateral information indicating they are applicable to the herd in question.

Growth to weaning age can be expressed either as average daily gain from birth to weaning or as weight at a standard age such as 210 days. Either is satisfactory and personal preference and convenience should determine the choice.

Postweaning Gaining Ability. Carcasses most in demand in the United States come from cattle in the 900 to 1200 lb. range in live weight. This means that the average slaughter animal makes half or more of its total weight gain after weaning. Rapid gains during this period are desirable because the length of time cattle must be grazed or fed is reduced, with resulting reductions in labor and overhead. In the case of year-round feed-lot operations, rapid gains permit feeding more total cattle in the course of a year. A more important reason for desiring rapid gains is the apparent relation between rate and efficiency of gain (to be discussed in the next section).

Extensive studies have shown rate of gain in the feed lot to be one of the more highly hereditary traits in beef cattle (Table 14-1). Direct selection for gaining ability in both high and low directions has been shown to be effective (Kincaid and Carter, 1958; Shelton *et al.*, 1957). Heritability of gain on pasture is somewhat lower but is still high enough for selection to be effective. Apparently heritability tends to be higher if nutritional levels are high, allowing full expression of inherent differences.

Evaluation of postweaning gaining ability in beef cattle is complicated by the questions of when to test, length of test period, and influence of pretest environment on gains. Much research has been done on these questions but final answers are not available; indeed, there may not be single answers to fit all conditions.

Various proposals have called for feed tests: during fixed age periods (age-constant), during certain fixed time periods irrespective of age (time-constant), during fixed weight periods (weight-constant), to a certain final weight or to a certain final degree of finish.

If environmental conditions are uniform, gains vary greatly between animals, but individual beef cattle of conventional types will gain at a reasonably constant rate to at least 1000 to 1200 lb., after which gains will decrease as maturity is approached. Under constant environmental conditions, then, any of the above proposals will give a good evaluation of inherent gaining ability. Variations in weather make it impossible to maintain uniform environmental conditions over long periods. In time-constant tests which begin on a given date and end on a given date, all animals on test are exposed to the same environment. Time-constant tests are also the simplest to conduct because all animals go on and off test on the same dates.

In all other tests, animals go on and off test individually as they reach given ages, weights, or degrees of finish. For these reasons time-constant tests have to date been the most popular if evaluation of gaining ability is the only objective. They are satisfactory if the length of test period is adequate, if the animals tested have only a relatively small initial variation in age and weight, and if they are conducted while the animals are in the age and weight ranges in which gains of individual animals tend to be linear.

Research workers have not reached agreement on the preferable length of time-constant postweaning gain tests. Knapp and Clark (1947) found heritability of gain increased during consecutive 84-day periods of a 252-day feeding test. On the other hand, in the direct selection experiments referred to above, tests of 140 and 196 days proved satisfactory.

Of greater importance than type of test or exact length of test is the problem of effect of pretest environment on gains. The phenomenon of "compensatory gains" has long been recognized. Cattle held for a period of time on restricted nutritional levels will gain at rates above their long-time inherent potential when later put on adequate rations. Thus, if a period of undernutrition precedes a gain test, an erroneously inflated appraisal of an animal's gaining ability will be obtained.

This problem of variation in pretest environment can never be completely eliminated. Prior to weaning some cows will have given enough milk for their calves to have gained at a near maximum rate while other calves will have been on suboptimal nutritional levels. Even if put on gain evaluation tests immediately after weaning, compensatory gain may result in less accurate estimates of inherited gaining ability than desired. The problem is greatly magnified, however, if gain tests are delayed and a period of undernutrition occurs between weaning and the test. This is not particularly serious if all animals in the test groups are treated alike and test gains are compared only within the group. Results may not be too meaningful if these two conditions are not met.

The use of lifetime gains to the end of postweaning gain tests is a means of reducing error and is now being widely used. Limited evidence indicates that heritability of this final weight may be higher than either weaning weight or postweaning gain alone.

The foregoing discussion applies primarily to young bulls being tested to aid in determining which will be used for breeding purposes, and to steers being fed out for slaughter to progeny test their sires.

Although by no means conclusive, some research results (Chambers *et al.,* 1960) suggest that heavy feeding of young heifers damages their future milking and perhaps their reproductive abilities. This possibility, together with the cost of feed-lot testing which puts on more condition than needed for normal growth, strongly suggests that gaining ability in heifers should be evaluated by weight at a standard age of 14 to 18 months under normal herd management rather than in feed-lot tests.

Efficiency of Gain. Accurate direct evaluation of efficiency of gain, defined here as amount of feed consumed per pound of gain, is difficult in beef cattle. Individual feeding must be practiced and this may influence feed consumption. It is a different feeding procedure than used in industry and it may possibly rank cattle differently than would be the case under normal feed-lot conditions (Fig. 14-3).

Feed required for maintenance is thought to increase according to about the three-fourths power of live weight. Thus, as animals get heavier a higher proportion of the feed consumed is required for maintenance and apparent efficiency is reduced.

More feed energy is required to produce fat than other body tissue. As an animal puts on fat, gain in relation to feed intake is reduced.

On the assumption that individual feeding is a satisfactory evaluation method, the ideal method of evaluating efficiency would be to individually feed beef animals of comparable body composition through a fixed weight range under constant environmental conditions. Unfortunately this is a physical impossibility, since some animals finish at lighter weights than others. Further, since animals would go on and off test at various times, it

Fig. 14-1. A productive 3-year-old Angus cow and her first calf raised without creep feeding. This calf graded high choice and on a mature-dam basis had a daily gain of 2.09 lb. Productive cows such as this are money-makers. [Photo courtesy Tennessee Agricultural Experiment Station.]

would be impossible for them all to be exposed to exactly the same environment.

In view of the foregoing, any system of direct evaluation of efficiency yet devised involves some compromises. Animals must be individually fed under all proposed systems. One of the earlier proposals (Knapp and Black, 1936) was to feed from 500 to 900 lb., ignoring differences in finish. Guilbert and Gregory (1944) recommended feeding to a constant degree of finish. This proposal suffers from the drawbacks of (1) difficulty of evaluating finish accurately in live animals, and (2) the possibility of some animals being either lighter or heavier than markets prefer when the specified degree of finish is reached.

Others have recommended feeding through a time-constant or age-constant period and adjusting feed consumption figures statistically for differences in live weight, ignoring degree of final finish.

None of these procedures is ideal. It is uncertain whether any of them are superior to the more generally used system of basing selection on rate of gain of group-fed animals. There is a rather high correlation between rate and efficiency of gain (Knapp and Baker, 1944) so that selecting for rate of gain results in considerable indirect selection for economy of gain. In one study there was a saving of about 8% in feed per unit of gain for each $\frac{1}{4}$ lb. increase in average daily gain.

There is, however, considerable disagreement among research workers on this point. At present, few breeders can afford to feed individually, but they should select for efficiency indirectly through selection for rate of gain. If future research develops better methods of estimating efficiency this general statement will be subject to modification.

Hereditary Defects. Any hereditary defect will reduce efficiency of beef production. Some of these are simply inherited (Gilmore, 1950), usually as recessives. Dwarfism (Pahnish *et al.*, 1955) is the trait which has been of greatest concern to the beef industry in recent years. In general, the frequency of such defects can be reduced in a commercial herd by eliminating all animals which have produced defective calves. In purebred herds more drastic measures—including elimination of animals related to those producing defective calves and using cows previously producing defective calves to progeny test bulls introduced to a herd—are necessary since the purebred breeder, in addition to stopping the birth of defective calves in his own herd, has the obligation to eliminate the gene so that he will not be selling carrier animals to his future customers. When suspected hereditary abnormalities occur, a breeder should get the best professional advice available on its mode of inheritance and apply known genetic principles to its elimination.

Other traits, of which cancer eye (Anderson *et al.*, 1957) is a good example,

Fig. 14-2. Hereditary differences are economically important. When bred to comparable groups of cows the bull on the left sired calves worth an average of $10.49 more at weaning (210 days of age) and his steer calves had a $10.08 greater net return in the feedlot when full fed for six months as compared to progeny of bull on the right. [Photo courtesy Oklahoma Agricultural Experiment Station and Animal Husbandry Research Division, USDA.]

are partially hereditary and partially dependent upon environment. Selection against them in much the same manner used for other quantitative traits should reduce their frequency.

Cattlemen believe that some types of feet and legs which can be observed in young animals are likely to become unsound later in life. There is little or no scientific evidence on this point.

14-3. SELECTION FOR QUALITY BEEF

Kinds of Beef in Greatest Demand by Consumers. Surveys have almost always shown that American consumers want beef with a high percentage of lean, a minimum of waste fat, sufficient marbling, and a high degree of tenderness. Since fat may be associated to some degree with tenderness and flavor, this is a difficult order to fill. Within the carcass some cuts—the rib, loin, and round—are preferred by consumers, and it would be desirable to produce cattle with as high a percentage of these as possible.

It is only in very recent years that serious attention has been given to the possibility of using scientific approaches in attempts to breed for improved carcass qualities in beef cattle. Inevitably, under these circumstances research has exposed fallacies in traditional standards without developing evidence which will permit clear-cut recommendations on improved procedures. It is, however, a fast-developing field and the alert student will give careful consideration to new developments.

Conformation in Beef Cattle Selection

HISTORICAL ASPECTS. Until very recently most beef cattle improvement was based upon visual appraisal of animals, with those deemed superior being selected for breeding purposes. History tells us that Robert Bakewell and other pioneer beef cattle improvers nearly 200 years ago were conscious of carcass quality problems. Bakewell is said to have pickled the joints of certain animals in order to have them for future reference. We cannot more than guess at this late date as to the influence objective or semiobjective estimates of beef quality may have had on their selections. Since objective methods of evaluating beef quality were not then available, it seems probable that ideas of what constituted desirable beef types developed more from observation than from objective evidence. Further, there is every reason to assume that ideas then (just as has been true to an extent in the recent past) developed in part at least on the basis of what seemed logical rather than on exact measures.

As is probably true of every procedure which develops as an art rather than a science, certain things about conformation in beef cattle long ago were suggested as probabilities and after being repeated many times came to be accepted as fact when they were actually untrue or only partially true. For example, it was generally believed that animals of what was considered superior beef type—wide, deep, compact, and low-set—were more efficient in use of feed than other kinds. Actually, it was shown at the Iowa Station as long ago as 1893 that dairy steers made as efficient gains as beef steers (Wilson and Curtiss, 1893); other experiments since then have shown little or no relationship between conformation and efficiency of gains. Judging lore is full of ideas about the relationships of such things as head shape, thickness of hide, fineness of hair, and so forth, to gaining ability and efficiency. Without exception, controlled experiments have shown little or no relationship.

It is thus a mistake to expect that conformation evaluation can serve as a substitute for objective measures of production abilities. It is an equally serious mistake to jump to the conclusion, as some have done, that because it has limitations, conformation evaluation is of no value or consequence in beef production. There can be no reasonable doubt that beef cuts from beef-type cattle are of a superior thickness of lean and shape or that modern beef cattle have a far more even fat distribution than animals of dairy or unimproved breeding. These differences and others have resulted from generations of selection for conformation.

RELATION OF CONFORMATION TO YIELD. The term yield in beef cattle usually refers to dressing per cent or the weight of the dressed carcass in relation to live weight. We shall also use it in relation to the per cent of the most valuable cuts—rib, loin, and round—in relation to carcass weight.

Dressing per cent is greatly influenced by finish, with fatter animals usually having higher yields. Its relationship to conformation is less clear although beef animals with width and thickness and minimal development of the middle are usually thought to dress higher.

Fig. 14-3. Calves being individually fed to determine both rate of gain and efficiency of gain. Either tie-in feeders of this general kind or stalls for each calf are necessary to determine individual feed consumption and efficiency. [Photo courtesy Nebraska Agricultural Experiment Station and Animal Husbandry Research Division, USDA.]

Conformation was long thought to be related to the percentage of preferred cuts in the carcass and the belief was general that the more thickness, depth, and shortness of body and low-setness an animal exhibited, the better its carcass would be. During the late 1930's, extra short, low-set types (variously known as Comprests or Compacts) appeared in at least two breeds of beef cattle and for a time were thought by many to represent the ultimate so far as beef type was concerned. Research showed, however, that when fed to the same degree of finish, cattle of this kind had no higher percentage of preferred wholesale cuts (Stonaker *et al.,* 1952). Since they also had several production disadvantages they soon disappeared from the scene.

Other work has also indicated that conformation by previously accepted standards is not a good indication of yield of preferred wholesale cuts (Casida *et al.,* 1957). There are indications, however, that animals which are wide at shoulders, loin, and hooks, and round and deep in the twist, tend to be superior in yield of preferred cuts (Green, 1954). Thus there appears to be a definite possibility of visually selecting for improvement in this regard if proper standards are developed.

RELATION OF CONFORMATION TO EATING QUALITY OF BEEF. Flavor, tenderness, and juiciness are the factors usually considered to be important in determining palatability of beef to consumers. Apparently, tenderness may be the thing a majority of consumers want above all else. Tenderness appears to be rather highly heritable (Table 14-1) but has little or no relation to conformation. Recent experiments have shown that the lean tissues of even such extremes as beef and dairy steers fed for equal lengths of time do

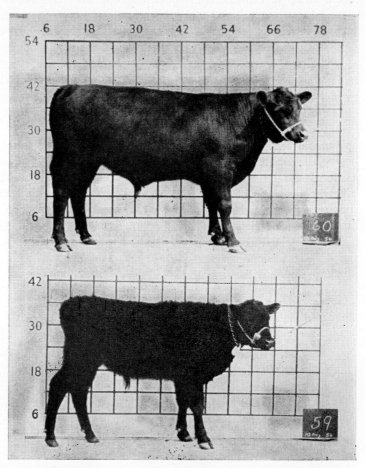

Fig. 14-4. A pair of identical (monozygotic) twins illustrate how differences in fat influence apparent conformation. Twin above had been on liberal ration for six months while his twin below had been on a submaintenance diet. Had they been fed same ration, appearance would have been nearly identical. [Photo courtesy Animal Husbandry Research Division, USDA.]

not differ appreciably in eating quality. Therefore in selecting for eating quality we must use criteria other than conformation.

EVALUATION OF CONFORMATION AND ITS IMPORTANCE TO CATTLE BREEDERS. From the foregoing it is apparent that selection of cattle on the basis of conformation with standards used in the past leaves much to be desired. However, conformation is a very important factor in marketing purebred, feeder, and slaughter cattle today. Changes in preferences tend to evolve slowly—that is, by evolution rather than revolution—so that cattlemen cannot depart far from accepted standards without running the risk of severe financial loss. Today it definitely appears that beef cattle can have greater length of legs and body than previously preferred and still produce superior carcasses, and that the extreme depth of chest and middle sometimes favored in the past are not necessary for economical production and probably result in increases of brisket and other cheap cuts of meat. Width of body, particularly near the top line and in the region of the rump and round, is desirable and should receive emphasis. Indications are that these facts are being applied in industry and that the types favored in the 1940's would not be popular today.

The old Scottish saying that "fat is a good color" is a succinct way of posing the greatest problem in evaluating conformation of beef cattle. Fat cattle always look better and it is very difficult from visual appraisal to differentiate those cattle with an abundance of natural lean tissue from those which are merely well covered with fat. The problem can be minimized by raising all animals to be compared under the same environmental conditions and systems of management. Fatter animals will then tend to be those which have done best and differences in finish will tend to favor cattle also superior in other regards.

Systematic conformation evaluation of animals in a herd is desirable at weaning and again at the time they approach market weights at some standard age of 12 to 18 months. Several scoring systems are in use, differing primarily in the numbers or letters used to designate the various grades. (See Albaugh *et al.*, 1956, and Marlowe *et al.*, 1958, for two widely used grading systems as well as discussion of other aspects of performance testing.)

Methods of Selecting for Improved Carcass Merit. The reader may get the impression that improvement of carcass quality is an impossibility. It is true that carcass quality is unrelated—or nearly so—to items important in economical production of beef and that visual appraisal of conformation is of only limited usefulness for effecting further improvement. But this is not to imply that selection for conformation was not effective in years past, when average merit was lower.

Admittedly, carcass improvement will not be easy, and very little has been done using new techniques. It presently appears that the best approach is that of making initial selections of breeding animals for traits important in economical production on the basis of their own performance and whatever family information may be available. Attention can also be paid to conformation with emphasis on those factors having at least some relation to carcass quality. The most promising sires can be progeny tested on randomly selected groups of cows, and a sample of at least six steer progeny fed out to normal market weights, slaughtered, and their carcasses evaluated. The sires whose progeny had the best combination of productive traits and carcass characters could be used extensively. Emphasis in carcass evaluation should be on animals producing the highest percentages of lean meat of satisfactory eating quality, the least waste fat, and cuts of satisfactory shape.

Little has been done along this line in the beef industry to date and procedures are not well standardized. Some breeders are taking initial steps in programs of this kind. The general procedure outlined may well be the next important development in beef cattle breeding.

It is estimated that progress per year in changing carcass characteristics can be only $\frac{1}{5}$ to $\frac{1}{4}$ as rapid as would be feasible if it were possible to estimate accurately the carcass characteristics of living animals and to use the superior ones for breeding without having to wait for progeny test information. Research is active in this area (see Chapter 2). Techniques include the use of ultrahigh-frequency sound devices to estimate thickness of fat and lean in living animals, use of small biopsy samples of tissue on which chemical determinations of potential tenderness can be made, and refinements of methods of taking live animal measurements and conformation scores in hopes some can be found which will more accurately predict carcass composition. None of these are ready for use in industry as yet and breeders can only hope that some of them, or other new techniques as yet untried, will be useful in the future. Until this happens breeders should use the progeny-test technique to make as much progress as possible.

REFERENCES AND SELECTED READINGS

References marked with an asterisk are of general interest.

Albaugh, R., H. T. Strong, and F. D. Carroll, 1956. A guide for beef cattle improvement programs. Calif. Agr. Ext. Serv. Cir. 451.

Anderson, D. E. and D. Chambers, 1957. Genetic aspects of cancer eye in cattle. Okla. Agr. Expt. Sta. Misc. Pub. MP-48, pp. 28–33.

Black, W. H. and B. Knapp, Jr., 1936. A comparison of several methods of measuring performance in beef cattle. *Proc. Amer. Society Animal Prod.*, pp. 103–107.

Botkin, M. P. and J. A. Whatley, Jr., 1953. Repeatability of production in range beef cows. *J. Animal Sci.*, 12:552–560.

Casida, L. E., O. B. Butler, D. E. Brady, and J. H. Knox, 1957. Symposium: The meat type steer. *J. Animal Sci.*, 16:224–248.

Chambers, D., J. Armstrong, and D. F. Stephens, 1960. Development of replacement heifers for expression of maternal traits. Rpt. Okla. Agr. Expt. Sta. 34th. Annual Feeders Day, pp. 89–94.

Erb, R. E., P. M. Hinze, and E. M. Gildow, 1959. Factors influencing prolificacy of cattle. II. Some evidence that certain reproductive traits are additively inherited. Wash. Agr. Expt. Sta. Tech. Bull. 30.

*Eriksson, Karl, 1943. *Hereditary Forms of Sterility in Cattle.* Hakan Ohlossons Boktyckeri, Lund, Sweden.

Grifford, W., 1953. Records-of-performance tests for beef cattle in breeding herds. Milk production of dams and growth of calves. Ark. Agr. Expt. Sta. Bull. 531.

*Gilmore, L. O., 1950. Inherited non-lethal anatomical characters in cattle—a review. *J. Dairy Sci.*, 33:147–165.

Green, W. W., 1954. Relationships of measurements of live animals to weights of grouped significant wholesale cuts and dressing percent of beef steers. *J. Animal Sci.*, 13:61–73.

Guilbert, H. R. and P. W. Gregory, 1944. Feed utilization tests with cattle. *J. Animal Sci.*, 3:143–153.

Kincaid, C. M. and R. C. Carter, 1958. Estimates of genetic and phenotypic parameters in beef cattle. I. Heritability of growth rate estimated from response to sire selection. *J. Animal Sci.*, 17:675–683.

Knapp, Bradford, Jr. and A. L. Baker, 1944. Correlations between rate and efficiency of gain in steers. *J. Animal Sci.*, 3:219–224.

―――― and R. T. Clark, 1947. Genetic and environmental correlations between growth rates of beef cattle at different ages. *J. Animal Sci.*, 6:174–181.

Lush, Jay L., 1947. Family merit and individual merit as bases for selection. Amer. Natur., 81:241–261, 362–379.

Marlowe, T. J., C. M. Kincaid, and G. W. Litton, 1958. Virginia beef cattle performance testing program. Va. Agr. Expt. Sta. Bull. 489.

Pahnish, O. F., E. B. Stanley, C. E. Safley, and C. B. Roubicek, 1955. Dwarfism in beef cattle. Ariz. Agr. Expt. Sta. Bull. 268.

Parker, J. B., N. D. Bayley, M. H. Fohrman, and R. D. Plowman, 1960. Factors influencing dairy cattle longevity. *J. Dairy Sci.*, 43:401–409.

Shelton, M., T. C. Cartwright, and W. T. Hardy, 1957. Relationships between performance tested bulls and the performance of their offspring. Tex. Agr. Expt. Sta. Prog. Report No. 1958.

Stonaker, H. H., M. H. Hazaleus, and S. S. Wheeler, 1952. Feedlot and carcass characteristics of individually fed comprest and conventional type Hereford steers. *J. Animal Sci.*, 11:17–25.

*Warwick, E. J., 1960. Genetic aspects of production efficiency in beef cattle. Proc. of Conf. "Beef for Tomorrow." Natl. Acad. Sci., Natl. Research Council Pub. 751, pp. 82–92.

Wilson, J. and C. F. Curtiss, 1893. Steer feeding. Iowa Agr. Expt. Sta. Bull. 20.

Chapter 15

Genetic Improvement in Dairy Cattle

The present discoveries in science are such as lie immediately beneath the surface of common notions.

FRANCIS BACON, *Advancement of Learning* (1605)

15-1. INTRODUCTION

The economic justification for specialized dairy cattle is their great proficiency in transforming feeds, mostly inedible by man, into one of man's most nutritious foods. The dairy cow vies closely with the hog in leading other classes of domestic animals in economy of production of human food. The dairy cow returns nearly four times as much edible food as the steer from an equivalent amount of feed consumed.

Constructive breeding should have for one of its goals the production of an animal that manufactures products for human consumption more economically over a long life span. This is a difficult problem with dairy cows because the genetic make-up responsible for a large flow of milk, including the constituents of milk, is not completely known.

The problem becomes even more difficult when trying to improve two or more characteristics simultaneously. Most dairy cattle breeders desire their animals to evidence the approved dairy type in addition to being high and profitable milk producers; this complicates selection since type and production are not highly correlated. The progress made when selecting for two or more characteristics depends primarily on the heritabilities of

255

these characteristics, the genetic correlation between them in the same individual, and the actual intensity of selection.

Most of our economically important characteristics are of the difficult or
complex type of inheritance called multifactor inheritance. They are controlled by many genes, and the individual effects of a single gene are seldom,
if ever, recognized. Milk production is a good example of multifactor inheritance. Many genes and many kinds of gene interactions are involved. In
addition to the genetic aspects, environment also plays an important role
in milk production. Feeding and management practices as well as herd
health can cause great variation in total milk yield. In spite of the difficulties, enormous progress has been made in increasing the production and
improving the conformation of dairy animals. The earliest cows produced
only enough milk to nourish their calves, whereas today many thousands of
cows average over 10,000 lb. of milk in a 305-day lactation. The production
record of one outstanding cow is almost 43,000 lb. of milk in 365 days.

The dairy cattle breeder striving for genetic improvement in his animals
has two basic tools at his disposal—selection and mating systems. Selection
is choosing the animals that will have an opportunity to reproduce and
consequently pass their genes on to future generations. The basic problem
of selection, which is the same for all farm animals, is estimating as accurately as possible the genotype of the animals. After the animals that
are to be the parents of the next generation are selected, the breeder must
decide which mating system (outcrossing, linebreeding, or inbreeding) will
be most apt to result in maximum improvement in the next generation.

Dairy cattle breeders are usually trying to improve several qualities in
their cattle—high production, persistency, regularity of breeding, longevity,
disease resistance, good conformation, easy milking, and good disposition.
Even though individual qualities are considered in the selection of breeding
animals, each animal must be rejected or retained on the basis of the sum
of all its qualities. Animals must be selected that have the best combination
of desired qualities, since only rarely is an individual best in more than one
or two traits. The relative emphasis to be given each of the traits is dependent on the amount of improvement that is likely to result from selection. Some traits may have such a low heritability that attempts at improvement by selection would be ineffective. Another point to be considered is
the increase in profit to be expected from improvement of a trait. In herds
where the sale of milk is the main source of income the dairyman should
concentrate on production, with emphasis on conformation only as it will
influence the productivity and usefulness of his cattle. But if the breeder
is selling breeding stock or exhibiting cattle he may pay more attention to
conformation and color markings.

There are three aids that the breeder can use to select his animals more
accurately. The first aid is the use of lifetime averages. The use of an

average of many repeated observations as a basis of selection is one of the most effective ways of overcoming mistakes and confusion that would otherwise result from the effects of temporary environmental conditions (Lush, 1945). This method requires the existence of records, so culling must be postponed until two or more observations have been made. Lifetime averages are most useful in helping to overcome temporary environmental effects, but do not keep the breeder from being deceived by permanent effects of environment.

The second aid to selection is the use of pedigrees. This means selecting an animal wholly or in part on the basis of performance of relatives. When pedigree selection is used the intensity of individual selection is reduced. The average individual merit of those selected is lowered when superior animals are rejected or inferior animals kept for breeding on the basis of their pedigree.

Because most of our economically important characteristics are controlled by many genes and these genes are heterozygous in most animals, the sampling nature of inheritance limits the accuracy of pedigree selection. It is generally agreed that pedigree selection should be used as an accessory to individual selection. It can best be used in making decisions on animals of similar individual merit. Pedigree selection is particularly useful when selecting young animals for traits that are sex-limited or that are exhibited only after sexual maturity. Udder shape and attachment is an example of such a trait; milk production is another.

The third aid to selection is progeny tests, which means estimating the individual's heredity by studying its offspring. The progeny test for quantitative characters is most valuable when (1) heritability is low and individual selection is therefore not very accurate, (2) the character is expressed in only one sex, (3) the time between generations is long, and (4) the number of offspring is low. Progeny tests are valuable when selecting for such quantitative characters as milk and milk constituent production. Because of the relatively large number of genes involved, very little is known about the mode of inheritance of these characteristics. When properly used, progeny tests make selection more accurate; they prevent the breeder from being deceived by the effects of environment, and dominance and epistasis as much as he might otherwise be. In practice, even for these characteristics, progeny testing should be used as a supplement to other types of selection rather than as the sole basis. Lush (1935) carefully investigated the theoretical accuracy of progeny testing as compared with individual selection. He concluded that when the likenesses between the performance of offspring (correlation between phenotypes) was not due to anything except the genes they received in common from their parents, and the heritability of the trait being considered was low, then at least five tested progeny were necessary to make the selection of these parents more accurate on a progeny test basis than selection on the basis of their own individuality. If there is a correlation as large as 0.25 within progeny due to nongenetic factors, progeny testing cannot possibly be as accurate as individual selection.

15-2. SELECTION FOR CHARACTERS RELATED TO ECONOMICAL PRODUCTION OF MILK

Milk and Milk Constituents. Since dairy cattle are maintained primarily for their production of milk, this character should be given major emphasis in breeding programs. In order to accurately evaluate their production merits, dairy cattle must be production tested. The tests can range from only periodic milk weights, if only milk production is to be considered, to monthly tests for milk, milk fat, solids-not-fat, and proteins, if the constituents of milk as well as milk production are to be considered.

Numerous studies have shown that the heritability values for production traits in dairy cattle are not high. Heritability estimates determined from intrasire daughter-dam regressions for milk and milk fat average near 0.20 to 0.30. For solids-not-fat and total milk solids, estimates of 0.34 and 0.36 have been reported (Johnson, 1957). These values for heritability indicate that selection for these individual production traits should bring about a gradual improvement in them. However, a negative genetic correlation exists between milk yield and milk fat test, which makes it difficult to simultaneously improve both of these traits (Johnson, 1957). The relationship between milk yield and solids-not-fat appears to be independent or slightly positive while for milk fat and solids-not-fat the relationship is not linear (Johnson et al., 1961).

In order to accurately compare production records of individual animals the records must be standardized to common conditions. Most records are converted to twice daily milking, 305 days in length, and to a mature age. Conversion tables are available (Rice et al., 1957) by which records can be standardized. On the average a cow milked three times daily will produce 17–20% more milk than if she is milked twice daily. Since most records are now made on twice daily milking, conversion tables will not be listed. Conversion tables are also available (Rice et al., 1957) to adjust records less than 305 days and more than 305 days to a 305-day basis. However, the merit of adjusting short records to a 305-day basis is very questionable and may greatly bias results. Since it is not possible to compare a large number of cows at any given age, age conversion factors are used to adjust production records to a mature basis. The age conversion factors given in Table 15-1 were developed by Kendrick for use in the DHIA Sire-proving Programs.

The production record of a cow results from genetic and environmental effects as well as their interaction. In order to evaluate more accurately a cow's genetic potential for production, environmental factors must be evalu-

TABLE 15-1.	*Age-conversion factors for 305-day production records. [Condensed from table developed by Kendrick for use in the D.H.I.A. Sire Program.]*

	Ayrshire	Brown Swiss	Guernsey	Holstein	Jersey
Age	Factor	Factor	Factor	Factor	Factor
2–0	1.30	1.45	1.24	1.31	1.27
3–0	1.18	1.23	1.12	1.10	1.15
4–0	1.10	1.10	1.06	1.08	1.06
5–0	1.03	1.04	1.02	1.02	1.02
6–0	1.00	1.00	1.00	1.00	1.00
8–0	1.00	1.00	1.01	1.00	1.01
9–0	1.02	1.01	1.02	1.02	1.02
10–0	1.03	1.02	1.04	1.04	1.04
11–0	1.04	1.04	1.06	1.06	1.06
12–0	1.06	1.06	1.08	1.09	1.08
13–0	1.07	1.08	1.10	1.12	1.10
14–0	1.09	1.10	1.12	1.15	1.12

ated. Some of the more important of these are age of cow at calving, length of gestation, length of lactation period, number of times milked daily, season of calving, length of preceding dry period, and health. Many of these environmental effects can be adjusted by statistical analysis; however, their effects cannot be entirely removed and production records are still the result of genetic and environmental effects. By the use of more than one record (lifetime averages) some of the effects of environment can be overcome.

Selection for Type. The type or conformation of an animal is given a great deal of emphasis in the show-ring and the various herd classification programs. How much selection pressure the breeder should devote to improving the conformation of his cattle will depend on his major goal. If he wishes to show cattle and sell breeding stock, type may receive considerable attention. On the other hand, if the primary goal is maximum milk production, only such components of type related to usefulness, such as conformation of feet and legs, body size, or udder size and attachment would usually be considered. An example of the components of type generally considered in dairy cattle classification is listed in Table 15-2, with the heredity and genetic correlation to butterfat production (Johnson and Fourt, 1961).

The breeder can improve the conformation of his animals by careful selection. However, overall conformation is the total of many single parts of conformation and the more of these single factors the breeder tries to improve simultaneously the less effective is his selection for any one factor.

TABLE 15-2. | Heritabilities* of type and the components of type of 3161 daughter-dam pairs of Brown Swiss cattle. [From Johnson and Fourt, 1960.]

Characteristic	Intrasire correlation†	Heritability on basis of intrasire correlation	Intrasire regression**	Heritability on basis of intrasire correlation	95% confidence limits‡	Genetic correlation to butterfat production
Type	0.187	0.37	0.176	0.35	±0.11	0.242
General appearance	0.175	0.35	0.167	0.33	±0.13	0.450
Dairy character	0.158	0.31	0.151	0.30	±0.16	0.410
Body capacity	0.124	0.24	0.116	0.23	±0.15	0.377
Rump	0.197	0.39	0.183	0.36	±0.16	0.210
Feet and legs	0.102	0.20	0.095	0.19	±0.14	0.237
Mammary system	0.122	0.24	0.116	0.23	±0.15	0.410
Fore udder	0.146	0.29	0.141	0.28	±0.14	0.461
Rear udder	0.179	0.35	0.175	0.35	±0.13	0.480
Milk fat	0.115	0.23	0.142	0.28	±0.15	

* This term is an expression of the degree of likeness between daughters and dams grouped by sires.
† This term expresses the change in type rating of the daughters per unit of change in that of their dams. The data, again, are grouped by sires, each group of daughters of a particular sire being considered a unit in the analysis.
** These are the limits within which the heritability lies unless a 1 in 20 error has occurred. Example: The chances are 95 out of 100 that the heritability of type lies between 0.24 and 0.46 (0.35 − 0.11 and 0.35 + 0.11).

Then, too, most dairy cattle are of little value unless they are high milk producers regardless of how outstanding their conformation is. The dairy cattle breeder usually desires to increase or at least maintain the present level of milk production in his herd while improving conformation of the cattle.

Estimates of genetic correlation between type and production have been quite variable: −0.52 (Freeman and Dunbar, 1955), 0.18 (Harvey and Lush, 1952), and 0.24 (Johnson and Fourt, 1960). The high negative correlation of −0.52 means it would be impossible to improve type and production simultaneously. If the 0.24 correlation were correct, selection for type alone would require approximately four generations to obtain the genetic improvement in production that could be expected in one generation of selection for production alone.

Selection for Fertility and Longevity. Heritability studies of breeding efficiency have not given consistent results; estimates of from near zero to 0.32 have been reported. No significant differences were found in breeding efficiencies among 19 cow families for services per conception, days from calving to first breeding, or days from first breeding to conception (Tabler et al., 1951).

Since fertility, or more accurately lowered fertility, has many causes, it is difficult to determine which cause is responsible for infertility in specific instances. It is not easy to obtain heritability estimates. Two of the more common methods used to measure reproductive efficiency are: number of services required for each pregnancy and the length of time in months between calvings. Both of these methods are seriously affected by such things as purposely not breeding a female for a given length of time in order to change season of calving, breeding to older males of known low fertility, health of the animals, and feeding and management practices.

There are several inherited characters that cause sterility or reduce reproductive efficiency (Gilmore, 1952). Hereditary tendencies toward the development of cystic ovaries and other conditions which produce at least temporary sterility have been found in dairy cattle (Erb et al., 1959).

It is very doubtful if the breeder will gain much by trying to select for reproductive efficiency since the heritability at best is low. Rather he should use the selection pressure for traits that respond better to selection. Of course there will be some automatic selection for fertility and longevity since sterile animals do not reproduce and hence leave the herd—also animals of low fertility leave fewer offspring in the herd to propagate the next generation. Studies on the effect of heredity on longevity in dairy cattle have been quite variable but a recent analysis (Parker et al., 1960) did not indicate heredity to be an important factor.

The low heritability values point out that most of the variation in the commonly used measures of reproductive efficiency is nongenetic. At present it appears that application of genetic principles in selecting for improved breeding efficiency has little to offer dairy cattle breeders.

Disease Resistance. Little has been done in practical dairy husbandry to develop resistant lines. The use of preventive and therapeutic measures has been relied upon to control most of our cattle diseases. Mastitis in dairy cattle represents a serious disease problem that costs the dairymen of the United States more than all the rest of the diseases combined. It is a difficult disease to control since so many different bacteria can produce the disease. Special instances which indicate that the susceptibility to mastitis manifested by related animals may have a genetic bias have been pointed out. Other reports and common observations indicate that pendulous udders predispose to mastitis by permitting the udder and teats to be subjected to infection and injury. Udder size, the nature of the teat sphincter, and strength of udder attachment also appear to be genetically influenced and related to mastitis susceptibility.

The role of inheritance in most of the diseases of dairy cattle has not been given much consideration in the past. Increasing the frequency of genes for resistance to diseases to which dairy cattle are susceptible, however, would be of great practical importance. Future studies may justify more emphasis on disease resistance in dairy cattle.

Hereditary Defects. Hereditary defects can be listed as two types, lethal and nonlethal. Lethal characters are those inherited traits that result in premature death. There are a great many known lethals in dairy cattle (Gilmore, 1952). The economic importance of lethals can be great. The average cow produces only 1.3 females that reach milking age in a lifetime. Lethals that prevent the perpetuation of a particular line of breeding containing genes of desired characters could result in great economic loss. The total loss caused by inherited lethals is not known; but a realization of the importance of the problem of inherited lethals in dairy cattle has been accentuated by the rapid growth of artificial breeding. The use of frozen semen now makes it possible for a male to sire thousands of offspring in his lifetime. It is therefore of great concern to be sure he is not a carrier of lethal genes.

Nonlethal hereditary defects are those that do not cause death but do reduce the efficiency of an animal. Some of these are simply inherited, usually as a recessive (Gilmore, 1950). Dairy cattle do not have any one trait that is of greatest concern, such as dwarfism in beef cattle; however, there are many traits that are of concern—sickled hocks, flexed pasterns, winged shoulders, sloping rumps, udder shape and attachment. Selection against these traits in much the same manner used for other quantitative traits should reduce their frequency.

15-3. MATING SYSTEMS

The second basic tool the dairy cattle breeder has at his disposal, by which he can improve his cattle, is the mating system. In this class of livestock, crossbreeding is rarely used as a system of mating; advantages accruing from its use in other classes of livestock warrant exploration of its usefulness in dairy cattle.

There are three mating systems in common use by dairy cattle breeders —outcrossing, linebreeding, and inbreeding.

Outcrossing. This system of breeding has been used more extensively than any of the others in dairy cattle breeding. Outcrossing means mating of unrelated or distantly related animals. The usefulness of outcrossing depends almost wholly on the effectiveness of selection. More variation would be expected between the individual offspring because the mates would be more heterozygous than with linebreeding or inbreeding. Since it is unlikely that unrelated animals will carry the same genes, the chief "advantage" of this system of breeding is that it tends to cover up undesirable recessives. It is the mating system recommended for the average or below-average purebred herd. In herds of this type the owner has the problem of maintaining individual merit rather than of making undesirable genes homozygous.

The disadvantage of a continuous outcrossing program is that it is not likely to lead to any great improvement through the fixation of desirable genes.

Inbreeding. Inbreeding is defined as the mating of animals more closely related than the average of the population from which they came. The primary effect of inbreeding is to increase the probability that the offspring will inherit the same thing from sire and dam. This is accomplished by the increase in the percentage of gene pairs that are homozygous and a decrease in the percentage that are heterozygous. The speed with which this occurs is determined by the closeness of relationship between the individuals mated.

The general effect of inbreeding is a decline in vigor, as is shown by lowered yields of milk and fat, more disease, less growth, higher mortality during calfhood, and a greater percentage of calves born dead. These effects are the results of undesirable genes becoming homozygous. A decrease of 210 lb. of milk and 4.9 lb. of milk fat per 1% of inbreeding was reported by Laben *et al.* (1955) from a longtime California inbreeding experiment.

Although the general effects of continued inbreeding are usually undesirable, inbreeding has an important place in dairy cattle breeding. Some reasons for practicing inbreeding are: (1) it forms uniform and distinct families so that interfamily selection may be possible in a more effective way; (2) it is necessary if relationship to a desirable ancestor is to be kept high; (3) it increases prepotency. Prepotency is the power of an animal to stamp its own characters on the offspring to the exclusion of those of the other parent. Since prepotency depends upon homozygosity of dominant genes, inbreeding is the only known method of increasing it. Inbreeding is also necessary to hold together desirable gene combinations and their propagation through future generations. A good rule to remember when trying to determine if inbreeding should be practiced is this: inbreeding intensifies what is present; therefore never start an inbreeding program with poor or mediocre cattle.

Linebreeding. Linebreeding is very popular and is in common use among dairy cattle breeders. Linebreeding is a means of maintaining relationship in a herd to some ancestor regarded as unusually desirable. Since the only way to accomplish this is by intermating among that ancestor's descendants, some degree of inbreeding will become inevitable. The degree of inbreeding is kept down by using for parents animals which are both closely related to the admired ancestor but are little, if at all, related to each other through any other ancestor.

Linebreeding, more than any other breeding system, combines selection with breeding. A great deal of the success will depend on the breeder's ability to select the animals that were outstanding in his herd on which he is to base his program. The better the animals, the better the results from linebreeding.

Linebreeding tends to separate the herd into distinct families, between which effective selection can be practiced. It will also build up homozygosity and prepotency but usually not as fast as close inbreeding. Linebreeding should only be used in herds that are well above average for type and production. The herd should be large enough to permit rigid culling and to prevent inbreeding from occurring too rapidly.

Remarkable progress has been made through breeding, feeding, and management in developing the high-producing dairy cow of today, from an ancestor that produced only enough milk to nourish its young. In spite of the remarkable progress, much still remains to be done. Many of the problems that remain to be solved and understood are difficult ones—that is why they still remain unsolved. Some of these difficult problems that need the attention of the dairy cattle breeder and research worker are to increase resistance to disease, especially mastitis; to prolong the useful life of the dairy cow; to increase the percentage of certain constituents in milk, especially protein; to increase fertility and breeding efficiency; to increase the economy of production through better feed utilization; and to develop more accurate methods of evaluating sires. These are but a few of the many problems challenging the dairy cattle breeder and research worker.

REFERENCES AND SELECTED READINGS

Erb, R. E., P. M. Hinze, and E. M. Gildow, 1959. Factors influencing prolificacy of cattle. II. Some evidence that certain reproductive traits are additively inherited. Wash. Agr. Expt. Sta. Tech. Bull. 30.

Freeman, A. E. and R. S. Dunbar, 1955. Genetic analysis of the components of type, conformation, and production in Ayrshire cows. *J. Dairy Sci.*, 38:428.

Gilmore, L. C., 1950. Inherited non-lethal anatomical characters in cattle—A review. *J. Dairy Sci.*, 33:147.

————, 1952. Reproductive efficiency. *Dairy Cattle Breeding*, Chap. 7, Lippincott, Chicago.

————, 1952. Lethals. *Dairy Cattle Breeding*, Chap. 9, Lippincott, Chicago.

Harvey, W. R. and J. L. Lush, 1952. Genetic correlations between type and production in Jersey cattle. *J. Dairy Sci.*, 35:199.

Johnson, K. R., 1957. Heritability, genetic and phenotypic correlations of certain constituents of cow's milk. *J. Dairy Sci.*, 40:723.

Johnson, K. R. and D. L. Fourt, 1960. Heritability, genetic and phenotypic correlations of type, certain components of type, and production of Brown Swiss cattle. *J. Dairy Sci.*, 43:975.

Johnson, K. R., D. L. Fourt, R. A. Hibbs, and R. H. Ross, 1961. Effect of some environmental factors on the milk fat and solids-not-fat content of cow's milk. *J. Dairy Sci.*, 44:658.

Laben, R. C., P. T. Cupps, S. W. Mead, and W. M. Regan, 1955. Some effects of inbreeding and evidence of heterosis through outcrossing in a Holstein-Friesian herd. *J. Dairy Sci.*, 38:525.

Lush, J. L., 1945. Aids to selection—The use of lifetime averages. *Animal Breeding Plans*, Chap. 13, Iowa State College Press, Ames.

————, 1935. Progeny test and individual performance as indicators of an animal's breeding value. *J. Dairy Sci.*, 18:1.

Parker, J. B., N. D. Bayley, M. H. Fohrman, and R. D. Plowman, 1960. Factors influencing dairy cattle longevity. *J. Dairy Sci.*, 43:401.

Rice, V. A., F. N. Andrews, E. J. Warwick, and J. E. Legates, 1957. Selecting dairy cattle. *Breeding and Improvement of Farm Animals*, Chap. 19, McGraw-Hill, New York.

Tabler, K. A., W. J. Tyler, and G. Hyatt, Jr., 1951. Type, body size and breeding efficiency of Ayrshire cow families. *J. Dairy Sci.*, 34:95.

Chapter 16

Genetic Improvement in Swine

.

Epitaph on a Prize Pig

Here Lies
All That was Eatable
Of a Prize Pig.

He was Born
On February 1, 1845:

He was Fed
On Milk, Potatoes, and
Barley-Meal:

He was slaughtered
On December 24, 1846,
Weighing 80st. 9lbs.

Stop, Travellor!

And Reflect How Small a Portion
Of This Vast Pig
Was Pork Suitable
For Human Food.

YOUATT, *Punch* (1855)

16-1. INTRODUCTION

Swine differ from the other farm animals in several respects which must be considered in devising methods of genetic improvement. Let us look at some of these differences:

1) Swine are polyovulatory (litter-bearing) animals; that is, several eggs are released at each estrus and several offspring are produced at each parturition rather than one as in cattle and horses and one or two as in sheep.

2) Meat is their sole product. They do not perform work or produce fiber, milk, or eggs for human use.

3) Their suckling period is much shorter and less important in total weight gain than it is in cattle and sheep.

4) Swine are concentrate eaters. Their digestive tract is not adapted to utilize large amounts of roughage.

5) They have a greater tendency to produce overfat carcasses than do other classes of meat animals. Fat in excess of the amount desired is becoming more of a problem with all meat animals, because of changes in eating habits of people in many countries, particularly in the United States. Nevertheless, beef cattle and sheep commonly require a finishing period on a high-energy ration in order to have enough finish for desired meat quality, whereas with swine it may be necessary not only to select for "meatiness" but also to modify feeding during the finishing period to reduce the amount of fat in the carcass.

These unique qualities suggest that plans for improvement through breeding will differ in some respects from those for other animals.

16-2. DEFINITION OF TRAITS

Swine traits can be classified in a general way into three groups: (1) productive, (2) reproductive, and (3) structural.

The productive group includes such things as rate of gain, efficiency of feed utilization, and milk production. Research experience has indicated that the *productive* traits in swine have intermediate heritability. Thus, these traits can be improved by selection, but they will also show some response in crosses.

The reproductive group includes number farrowed per litter and number weaned per litter. Number farrowed is influenced by the number of eggs shed and the survival rate of the embryos during development. *Reproductive* traits have low heritability. However, they show the greatest response of any of the groups to crossing. The response in crossing is particularly strong where the sow is herself a crossbred.

The *structural* traits include carcass characteristics such as fatness and leanness, muscle size, and mature body size. These structural traits are highly heritable and can be improved by selection. Their response to crossbreeding is less than for either reproductive or productive traits.

Table 16-1 contains heritability estimates from many studies, as summarized by Craft (1958).

16-3. SELECTION

Selection is simply keeping some animals and culling others, and is effective in improving traits in proportion to their heritability. One can ex-

TABLE 16-1. | *Estimates of heritability of swine traits, based on reports of investigations from many breeds and several countries.**

	Heritability Percentage	
	Range	Approximate Av.
Productive Traits		
Weight of pig at 5–6 months	3–66	30
Growth rate (weaning to 180–200 lb.)	14–58	29
Economy of gain	8–72	31
Reproductive Traits		
Number of pigs farrowed	0–24	15 †
Number of pigs weaned	0–32	12 †
Conformation and Carcass Traits		
Length of legs	51–75	65
Number of vertebrae		74
Conformation scores	10–35	29
Type, within herds of similar type		38
Type, between herds of small, intermediate, and large type (Poland China)		92
Length of carcass	40–81	59
Loin eye area	16–79	48
Thickness of backfat	12–80	49
Thickness of belly	39–72	52
% of carcass weight		
loin	51–65	58
shoulder	38–56	47
fat cuts	52–69	63
lean cuts	14–76	31 **

* From Craft, W. A., 1958. Fifty years of progress in swine breeding. *J. Animal Sci.*, 17:960.
† Probably high.
** Probably low.

pect fairly rapid improvement to result from selection of animals superior in conformation and carcass traits (provided they are accurately measured), moderate improvement from selection for rate and efficiency of gain, and very slow improvement from selection for larger litters.

There are three systems of selection which a breeder may use, either separately or in combination. These three (previously discussed in Chapter 13) are (1) index, (2) independent culling levels, and (3) tandem. Some practical illustrations of their use in swine improvement follow.

At the Iowa Swine Testing Station an index was developed which provided for half of the selection emphasis on backfat probe, one-fourth on rate of gain, and one-fourth on efficiency. The greatest emphasis was placed on the trait with the highest heritability—backfat thickness—but some emphasis was also placed on the other two traits. The Iowa Index, as originally used, was:

$$260 + (35 \times \text{gain}) - (75 \times \text{BF}) - (40 \times \text{EFF}) = \text{Index}.$$

The 260 is a constant, chosen so as to give an average index of about 100. The other figures used as multipliers are weighting figures for the items included in the index. Rapid growth rate, low back fat, and efficiency (a small number of pounds of feed used per pound gained) will contribute to a high index. To illustrate the use of the index, suppose a choice is to be made between two boars with the following records:

No. 1—2.0 lb. gain/day, 1.2 in. backfat, 3.2 lb. feed/lb. gain.

No. 2—1.8 lb. gain/day, 1.0 in. backfat, 3.0 lb. feed/lb. gain.

No. 1 has an index of 112 and No. 2 an index of 128, indicating that the leanness and efficiency of No. 2 more than compensate for his lower rate of gain. Thus the index removes the guesswork from combining information on different traits and makes selection decisions easier. Of course, some common sense must be used in the application of any index, and the presence of a serious defect in conformation, or some unsoundness, will eliminate a few animals regardless of index. Generally, such animals will be eliminated at an early stage, before the indexes are computed.

In the application of the Iowa Index cited, it was felt that some pigs were passed which were too fat or too slow in growth rate, even though they met the standard of 100. A system of *independent culling levels,* in addition to the index, was therefore established. All pigs with less than 1.6 lb. daily gain, more than 1.45 inches back fat, or more than 3.25 lb. feed per lb. of gain, would fail the test. Thus the index gave a general description of the pig, weighted according to the importance and heritability of the traits concerned, but the independent culling levels eliminated some high-indexing pigs which were badly deficient in one of the three traits.

The principal advantage of the index in selection is that it allows a particularly good score in one trait to compensate for a deficiency in another. The use of culling levels curtails this advantage, and is a less efficient system than the index method. It is true, of course, that certain traits may be of more importance to one breeder than to another, due to the level of performance of the herd for that trait, and there is therefore justification in some cases for considering individual traits as well as the index. For example, a breeder whose herd has an excellent average for gain and efficiency but in which the hogs are much fatter than desired will wish to select boars that are especially lean.

A summary of the first four years' tests at the Iowa Swine Testing Station is given in Table 16-2. The general testing procedure has been to test a set

TABLE 16-2. | *Rate and efficiency of gain and carcass traits of pigs for successive years. [Iowa Swine Testing Station, Ames, Iowa.] L, Carcass length in inches; BF, Backfat in inches; LC, Percent lean cuts, chilled carcass; LE, Loin eye area in square inches; H&L%, Percent ham and loin; S, spring; F, fall.*

| | Pen average | | Boar average | | Season comparison | | | | |
| | Gain | Eff. | Probe | Index | L | BF | LC | H&L% | LE |
					Barrow cutout				
56S	1.89	292	1.46	101	29.1	1.64	48.5		3.22
56F	1.95	303	1.31	109	28.9	1.61	49.8		3.50
57S	1.80	294	1.24	113	29.2	1.60	50.3		3.40
57F	1.79	319	1.11	112	29.1	1.51	51.7		3.80
58S	1.80	285	1.22	118	29.4	1.51	51.4		3.62
58F	1.76	323	1.19	106	29.1	1.50	52.3		3.81
59S	1.80	296	1.25	119	29.5	1.50	53.0*	35.3	3.63
59F	1.87	297	1.17	125	29.1	1.48	54.3*	36.2	3.94

* Estimated on basis of 1.5 times (H&L%).

of February and March farrowed pigs in the spring and summer and a set of August and September farrowed pigs in the winter.

Inspection of the table points up at least two pertinent facts:

1) A marked change has occurred in the meatiness of the tested pigs in the four years of testing, but little improvement has been shown in either rate or efficiency of gain.

2) Winter pigs have generally been somewhat meatier and less efficient than summer pigs farrowed in the same year.

Thus the index, designed to cause more improvement in meatiness, has apparently been effective. As meatiness has improved, the index has been changed to give less emphasis to the backfat probe and more to the other traits. Standards have also been raised, and adjusted to accommodate the poorer winter efficiency.

The original index was weighted to give most emphasis to backfat probe. If all the emphasis had been placed on this trait until the desired level of performance was reached and then selection attention directed toward a second trait, such as gain, this would have been *tandem* selection. This method of selection has the advantage in that more rapid improvement in a specific trait occurs, but it is the least efficient method of improving total merit and is not recommended. It has the further disadvantage that if any desired performance traits are genetically negatively correlated with the trait under selection, they will decline while the selected trait is being improved.

16-4. MATING SYSTEMS

Under mating systems we consider the degree of relationship of the sows and boars mated. This can range from close inbreeding, where the sows and boars are close relatives such as brother and sister, to the mating of unrelated individuals within a breed, and to crossbreeding, in which boars of one breed are bred to sows of another breed or cross.

The effects of inbreeding and crossbreeding have been investigated in many experiments, and although it would be desirable to have more information on how specific breeds combine in crosses, in general the effects of these different mating systems are well known in swine. Much of the available information in this area, particularly with respect to the effects of inbreeding and of crossing inbred lines, has come from the Regional Swine Breeding Laboratory, a cooperative research project between the USDA and several state experiment stations set up in 1937 to investigate swine-breeding methods.

In general, inbreeding decreases performance traits, with the greatest decrease coming in litter size and survival, followed in order by rate of gain, feed efficiency, and carcass characteristics, the last being scarcely if at all affected. It may be noted that this is in inverse relationship to the heritability of the traits, those of high heritability showing little inbreeding effect and those of low heritability being seriously affected. It has been found that inbreeding the equivalent of one generation of full brother-sister mating decreases litter size raised by about 1.1 pigs per litter (Dickerson *et al.*, 1954; Bradford *et al.*, 1958). The effect seems to be greater in first-litter gilts than in mature sows. Inbreeding does lead to greater genetic uniformity than outbreeding systems, but because of its effect on performance is not generally recommended.

Crossing inbred lines leads to a recovery of the vigor lost through inbreeding and possibly some additional gain, but because of the cost of developing inbred lines and their poor performance, the use of inbred lines to produce hybrid hogs, according to the system used to produce hybrid corn, has not become widespread. Swine producers can and do utilize hybrid vigor, however, by crossing animals of different breeds; in fact, most commercially raised hogs in the United States are crossbreds of one kind or another.

Crossbreds may be two-breed crosses, produced by mating purebred boars of one breed to purebred sows of another breed, three-breed crosses, produced by breeding purebred boars of one breed to crossbred sows representing two other breeds, or more complex crosses. The advantages of crossbreeding are greatest in reproductive traits, and because of this the crossing program should involve the use of crossbred females, such as in the three-breed cross described above. Two other crossbreeding systems which permit the use of crossbred females are crisscrossing, in which boars of two breeds are used alternately, and rotational crossbreeding, in which boars of three or more breeds are used in rotation, in each case the females from the previous cross constituting the sow herd.

Examples of specific crossbreeding plans for swine, with comments on these plans, are given in Table 16-3. The contributions of the breeds involved (expressed as percentages) to the different kinds of crosses are summarized in Table 16-4.

Rate of gain also exhibits some hybrid vigor but feed efficiency is only very slightly affected. Carcass characteristics usually are intermediate between those of the parents, emphasizing the importance of careful selection of the breeding animals used for crossing.

In spite of the many experiments on crossbreeding, the actual effect of crossbreeding, in terms of percentage increase of crossbred over purebred performance, is difficult to arrive at accurately. This is because the experiments have differed in such things as breeds used, experimental conditions, characteristics measured, and whether purebreds of both parent breeds were

TABLE 16-3. | *Examples of crossbreeding plans for commercial hog production.*

Plan	Example	Comments
2-Breed repeat crossing	Breed Hampshire sows to Yorkshire boars. Market all crossbred pigs. Buy Hampshire replacement gilts and Yorkshire boars.	2-Breed crossing is the starting point for all crossing schemes. It is not recommended as a terminal program because it does not use crossbred females.
Crisscrossing	Breed Duroc sows to Landrace boars; breed Landrace X Duroc sows to Duroc boars; breed $\frac{3}{4}$ Duroc, $\frac{1}{4}$ Landrace sows to Landrace boars; continue alternate use of boars of these two breeds.	Uses crossbred females, therefore is preferred to 2-breed repeat crossing. Recommended where only two suitable breeds are available.
3-Breed crossing	Breed Hampshire sows to Landrace boars; breed Landrace X Hampshire sows to spotted Poland China boars. Market all 3-breed cross pigs and repeat cycle, starting with Hampshire gilts again.	Should give slightly more hybrid vigor than crisscrossing, since boars are always of completely different breed than sows.
3-Breed rotational crossing	Same as 3-breed crossing, except that 3-breed cross gilts are kept and bred to boars of one of the original breeds (Hampshire or Landrace in the above example).	About the same amount of hybrid vigor as 3-breed crossing. Preferred, because purchase of females is not required after first cross. Recommended where three suitable breeds are available.

TABLE 16-4. *Outline of various methods of crossbreeding, with the percentage contribution of the parent breeds.*

Crossbreeding scheme	Breeding of original sows	Breeding of sows after 1st generation	Breeding of boars	Percentage contribution of parent breeds to crossbred offspring (A:B:C)			
				1st generation	2nd generation	3rd generation	4th & later generations
2-Breed repeat crossing	Purebred	Purebred (probably purchased)	Purebred	50:50	50:50	50:50	50:50
Crisscrossing	Purebred	Crossbred (raised)	Purebred	50:50	75:25	37.5:62.5	67:33 (approx)
3-Breed crossing	Purebred	Alternately crossbred & purebred (or purchased crossbred)	Purebred	50:50	25:25:50	50:50	25:25:50 or 50:50
3-Breed rotational	Purebred	Crossbred (raised)	Purebred	50:50	25:25:50	62.5:12.5:25	57:29:14 (approx)

TABLE 16-5. | *Results of crossbreeding experiments summarized by Carroll and Roberts (1942).*

Factors of production	No. of experiments	Mean of two pure breeds	Mean of crossbreds	Relative performance of crossbreds with purebreds = 100
No. pigs per litter	12	9.74	9.48	97.3
Birth weight of pigs (lb.)	6	2.77	2.79	100.6
Survival (%)	15	76.3	80.2	105.1
Weaning wt of pigs (lb.)	15	32.5	33.12	101.8
Weaning wt of litters (lb.) *	13	235.6	254.1	107.9
Av. daily gain (lb.)	9	1.38	1.44	104.0
Feed for 100 lb. gain (lb.)	6	374.1	368.6	101.5
Danish pig-testing stations:				
Av. daily gain	32	1.3	1.38	101.5
Feed per 100 lb. gain (lb.)	32	345.4	344.3	99.7

* From the original publications of these experiments.

available for comparison. A summary by Carroll and Roberts (1942), as presented by Dickerson (1952), is shown in Table 16-5.

Note that the increase in total litter weight weaned is larger than that for any of the other traits listed. Both components of litter weight—number of pigs in the litter and individual pig weight—are increased. Litter weight at 5 to 6 months of age would show an even greater effect, since postweaning gain increased more than preweaning gain.

The data in Table 16-5 do not show the effect of crossbreeding of the sow or her litter production. In a study of data from commercial herds, Bradford *et al.* (1953) found that 3005 straightbred gilts raised an average of 6.53 pigs per litter, while 836 crossbred gilts raised an average of 7.20 pigs per litter. It would take many generations of selection to increase litter size by this amount, illustrating the importance of crossbreeding in improving productivity.

A sound crossbreeding program involves selection of the best breeds and individual representatives of those breeds available as foundation stock. Since breeds differ in different traits and no one breed is outstanding in all traits, breeds should be selected so that the strong points of one parent breed compensate for the weaknesses of the other parent breed or cross. In the initial cross it is wise to select the more prolific breed as the female parent.

There is a belief, once very common among stockmen and still strongly held by some, that crossbreeding leads to increased variability and eventual degeneration of the stock. While indiscriminate crossing of inferior stocks will lead to poor results (just as will the breeding of inferior purebreds), a systematic crossbreeding program based on carefully selected purebred boars produces pigs which are superior in overall production potential to pure-breds, and no more variable in performance traits than straightbred commercial hogs. Some variability in such things as color pattern and shape and size of ear do occur, but there is no evidence of increased variability in rate of gain, litter size, or carcass traits. The general acceptance of crossbreeding by swine producers is undoubtedly an advantage to this industry as compared to the beef-cattle industry, where this practice is as yet much less widely used.

Summarizing the discussion on selection and mating systems: selection is effective in improving carcass traits, but relatively ineffective for reproductive traits; selection is moderately effective in improving rate of gain and efficiency of feed utilization; and crossbreeding is effective in improving litter size, and moderately effective in improving rate of gain. It has little effect on carcass traits or feed conversion.

To illustrate, the gains which might be expected from one generation of selection, and from crossing unselected representatives of different breeds are presented for three traits in Table 16-6. This shows that crossbreeding might be expected to result in about the same increase in 5-month pig weight (or average daily gain) as one generation of selection, and that using crossbred sows will result in an increase in litter size which would take several generations to achieve by selection.

Crossbreeding combined with selection—that is, the crossing of stocks selected as carefully as assumed here for the calculation of expected gains from selection alone—would be expected to result in improvement equal to the sum of the expected improvements shown for selection and for crossbreeding.

TABLE 16-6. | *Gains to be expected in three traits from one generation of selection, and from crossing unselected representatives of different breeds.*

		Increase over straightbreds of:	
Trait	Expected gain from selection*	Crossbred from purebred dam	Crossbred from crossbred dam
No. pigs raised per litter	0.06 pig	.035 pig†	.67 pig**
5-month pig weight	6.9 lb.	6.6 lb.†	Probably similar to value for 2-breed cross
Backfat probe	0.14 in.	‡	‡

* Assuming: (a) Top 20% of gilts and 2% of boars raised are selected. (b) Standard deviation of 2.0 pigs, 24.0 lb. and 0.3 in. for litter size, 5-month pig weight and backfat probe, respectively. (c) Heritability values as given in Table 16-1. (d) Selection is based on 4 traits, that is, these three and one other, such as conformation score.
† Based on an increase of 5% in survival and 4% in postweaning rate of gain, as given in Table 16-5.
** From comparison of litters from crossbred and straightbred gilts, as reported by Bradford, G. E., A. B. Chapman, and R. H. Grummer, 1953. *J. Animal Sci.*, 12:582.
‡ No data available. Little or no difference expected between crossbreds and straightbreds in this trait.

Selection as intense as that shown would be possible only in a large closed herd where all boars and gilts born were available for selection. In actual practice in the industry, where most boar pigs are castrated and the boars used are produced in a relatively small number of herds, selection would, on the average, be less intense than has been assumed for this example. Thus these estimates of progress from selection are probably optimistic.

16-5. IMPROVEMENT PROGRAMS

Systematic swine improvement programs designed to measure and select for performance traits are a relatively recent innovation in the United States. One of the first—certainly the first where a selection index was used in the selection of commercially raised livestock—was the Wisconsin Swine Selection Cooperative, started in 1947 under the direction of Dr. A. B. Chapman of the University of Wisconsin. In this program, replacement gilts are selected on the basis of an index combining number of pigs farrowed, number raised, and litter and pig weight at five months. Backfat probe information has recently been added to the index. Both commercial and purebred herds use this program, with the majority being commercial herds.

Several other countries have had improvement programs for many years. Denmark initiated a progeny-testing plan in 1907 which has been in continuous operation since, except for the years of the two world wars. In this program, pigs submitted by breeders throughout the country are raised at central test stations under uniform conditions. The pigs are evaluated as to rate of gain, feed conversion, and carcass quality, and breeding animals are selected on the basis of performance of their offspring or litter mates at the test station. Changes in mean performance for all pigs tested in Denmark from 1923 to 1935, as reported by Lush (1936), were as follows:

Item	Approx. 1923 mean	Approx. 1935 mean
Average daily gain	1.2 lb.	1.4 lb.
Feed/lb. gain	3.6 lb.	3.3 lb.
Body length	89.5 cm.	92.0 cm.
Backfat thickness	4.2 cm.	3.6 cm.

Since feeding and management were quite uniform over this period, all or nearly all of this improvement must have been genetic improvement resulting from the selection practiced. Improvement has continued in most of these traits, so that levels of performance today are well ahead of those for 1935.

A program patterned closely after the Danish system has also been in operation in Canada for more than two decades.

The Danish and Canadian systems are based on the progeny test which, while accurate, is slow, since the breeder must wait until a boar or sow has several progeny evaluated before deciding whether that animal is good enough to add to the breeding herd. The development of the backfat probe by Dr. L. N. Hazel of Iowa State College, about 1950, has provided an important impetus to performance programs in the United States. It was known from earlier research on carcasses that thickness of backfat is a good indication of lean cut yield of the carcass. The probe provides a simple, accurate measurement of backfat in the live animal, providing a good estimate of potential carcass quality of an animal which can then be used for breeding.

The first organized swine testing station in modern times in the United States was established in 1954 by a group of breeders at Forrest, Illinois. The station was operated by the breeders. It tested boar and barrow litter mate pairs, the boar being probed and the barrow slaughtered.

The Ohio Agricultural Experiment Station established a Swine Evaluation Station in 1954, in which all the test animals were slaughtered. In this station all data were coded, and no information identified with breed or breeder was released to the public. The Iowa Boar Testing Station was established in 1955 and tested its first pigs in 1956. Here the test unit was, at first, two boars and one barrow per pen. Later it was changed to three boars and one barrow per pen. This was the first station to use an index as a system for classifying the tested animals, and also the first to castrate animals not meeting the standard set by the board of directors. All animals meeting the standard were sold at auction, and all information was published.

Many stations have been established since that time, among which are the two operated by a private concern in Iowa. Figure 16-1 shows a picture of the station at Eagle Grove, Iowa.

The testing stations have served two functions: education and direct improvement. Education has probably been the more important function, as many hog raisers have developed a working knowledge of the principles of

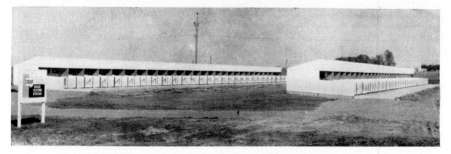

Fig. 16-1.   View of Eagle Grove, Iowa Swine Testing Station.

swine breeding through their work with the stations. Many breeders have set up their own facilities for on-the-farm testing, patterned after the large testing stations.

Concurrent with the development of central stations was the instigation in several states of such on-the-farm tests. Here the breeder either weighs and probes his pigs himself, or joins with his neighbor to hire someone to do the work. Many commercial producers use this on-the-farm program to aid in correct selection of sow herds.

Another program which has received considerable attention in recent years is the Swine Certification Program. Sponsored by the purebred swine breed associations, it was implemented largely through the efforts of the late Rollie Pemberton, formerly secretary of the Hampshire Swine Record Association.

For pigs to qualify for certification, they must meet certain standards for number farrowed and weaned, and weaning weight of litter. They also must meet certain growth rate standards and, upon slaughter, meet certain carcass standards. The first hurdle is in number farrowed, number weaned, and weaning weight. The last item varies between breeds, depending on

Fig. 16-2. Weighing time at the Ida-Grove, Iowa Swine Testing Station. [Photo courtesy Bob Casey, Station Manager.]

whether they use birth weight, 21-day weight, 35-day weight, or 56-day weight.

Growth and carcass standards are fairly uniform for all breeds as follows:

Weight—200 lb. at not more than 180 days.
The animal must be slaughtered between 180 and 220 lb.
Carcass specifications: Backfat—1.6 in. maximum
Loin eye—4.0 sq. in. minimum
Length—29 in. minimum

The program has been widely publicized and is extensively used by breeders in advertising. It has several advantages: (1) It is relatively simple for the breeder to keep the necessary records. (2) It has the wholehearted support of the breed secretaries. (3) It gives some unity to testing programs. Its disadvantages are: (1) The standards are too low for rate of gain; thus, a breeder could restrict food intake to make them lean enough to meet the carcass standards. (2) The best pigs in a litter may be slaughtered, as a basis for certifying litter mates which may not be as good. (3) The considerable emphasis on sow productivity traits is probably not warranted; the low heritability of these traits is likely to prevent much improvement in them. Thus, emphasizing such traits may result in reducing emphasis on other more highly heritable ones. The more traits considered, the less the attention which can be given to each. Those which are capable of being improved by selection should be emphasized.

Some selection for litter size will occur whether or not the breeder makes an effort to select pigs from large litters, because of the fact that there are more pigs available for selection from large litters than from smaller ones. This may be regarded as natural selection, and in fact its occurrence throughout the history of the species is the most probable explanation for the low heritability of this trait. Those genes acting in an additive fashion which contribute to large litter size in each breed have been fixed by this natural selection, leaving only those genes not readily fixed as a cause of genetic variation in the trait. On the other hand, some attention to litter size in a selection program may be justified on the basis that litter size and weight, at least weight at early ages, are negatively associated. That is, pigs from larger litters tend to be smaller because of less uterine space and/or nutrients and less milk per pig during the suckling period. Selection of the heaviest pigs without respect to the size of the litter in which they were raised could lead to selection of animals from smaller than average litters, which should probably be avoided.

Largely as a result of one or all of these improvement programs, thousands of swine breeders and commercial swine raisers today have some understanding of swine breeding principles. A perusal of a modern swine association journal indicates the emphasis being placed on records, as contrasted to the late 1940 period when the emphasis was almost altogether on show ring winnings. Swine breeders have adopted some objective methods of improving their stock. Much improvement has been made, and more will be made in the quality of pork available to the consumer and in the economy with which it is produced.

REFERENCES AND SELECTED READINGS

References marked with an asterisk are of general interest.

Bradford, G. E., A. B. Chapman, and R. H. Grummer, 1953. Performance of hogs of different breeds from straightbred and crossbred dams on Wisconsin farms. *J. Animal Sci.*, 12:582.

―――, 1958. Effect of inbreeding, selection, linecrossing and topcrossing. 1. Inbreeding and selection. *J. Animal Sci.*, 17:426.

Dickerson, G. E., J. L. Lush, and C. C. Culbertson, 1946. Hybrid vigor in single crosses between inbred lines of Poland China swine. *J. Animal Sci.*, 5:16.

Dickerson, G. E., 1951. Effectiveness of selection for economic characters in swine. *J. Animal Sci.*, 10:12.

*―――, 1952. Inbred lines for heterosis tests. *Heterosis*. Edited by J. W. Gowen. Iowa State College Press, Chap. 21.

*Dickerson, G. E., C. T. Blunn, A. B. Chapman, R. M. Kottman, J. L. Krider, E. J. Warwick, and J. A. Whatley, 1954. Evaluation of selection in developing inbred lines of swine. Mo. Research Bull. 551. (North Central Regional Publ. No. 38.)

Durham, R. M., A. B. Chapman, and R. H. Grummer, 1952. Inbred versus non-inbred boars used in two sire herds on Wisconsin farms. *J. Animal Sci.*, 11:134.

*Lush, J. L., 1936. Genetic aspects of the Danish system of progeny-testing swine. Iowa Agr. Expt. Sta. Res. Bull. No. 204.

Chapter 17

Genetic Improvement in Sheep and Goats

While the pride of man is humbled by the reflection, that the most profound works of art are but feeble imitations of nature, he will derive some consolation from the consideration, that God has condescended in some sort to render him his agent, and to give him extensive powers over the animal and vegetable creation; not only in subjecting them to his control, but even in enabling him, within certain limits, to change and alter their natures, so as better to adapt them to his own use, without subjecting them too far to his whims.
ROBERT R. LIVINGSTON, *"Essay on Sheep"* (1813)

17-1. INTRODUCTION

Sheep and goats are undoubtedly much more useful creatures to man than when our ancestors first tamed them some seven to eight thousand years ago. Tremendous improvement has even been made since they were first brought to this continent less than 500 years ago. In fact, in 1810 the average wool clip was reported as 2 lb. per head (Connor, 1918). USDA statistics show that this had increased to 7 lb. near the beginning of this century, and now approaches 9 lb. Gains in fleece weight have certainly been accompanied by improvement in staple length and clean yield for respective grades. Similar gains in mohair production by Angora goats are indicated by increases from 4 lb. clip per goat in the 1930's to 4.5–5.0 lb. in the 1940's and up to well over 6 lb. in the late 1950's. The reduction of cryptorchidism by selection in an Angora goat flock has been shown by Warwick (1961).

Lamb production has shown an upward trend from 83–89 lambs saved per 100 ewes, one year of age and older in the 1920's to 88–97 lambs saved per 100 ewes in the 1950's. Slaughter weights of lambs have increased also. Market lambs now may weigh as much as 10–20 lb. more at the same age than they did some 20 years ago. Improvements in production of milk goats are shown by higher records of production in more recent years; see the review of the American Milk Goat Record Association, 1960.

Average values for Rambouillet rams in the Sonora, Texas, ram tests show definite gains over a 12-year period in average daily gain, clean wool weight, staple length, and skin folds (Campbell, 1960). Only face covering showed no evidence of improvement.

Improvements in efficiency of production have also resulted from increased production per animal, as many costs are on a per head basis. These gains in productivity and in efficiency of production can be attributed to better feeding and management practices, including better control of parasites and diseases, as well as to gains from genetic improvement, although the latter has certainly been important. Notwithstanding these gains in efficiency of production further improvements can and must be made if the sheep and goat industries in the United States are to survive and grow.

17-2. SYSTEMS OF BREEDING

Pure breeding is practiced by most professional animal breeders. Pure breeds of sheep and goats provide the foundation and continuity through which most genetic improvements from selection are made. The presence of these purebred stocks also permit further gains from crossbreeding. Pure breeds of sheep and goats are almost entirely closed to outside breeding and therefore some breeding of relatives or inbreeding occurs. In fact, most purebreeders linebreed to concentrate the blood of outstanding sires. At the same time they usually avoid close or continued inbreeding. Studies of inbreeding in the Rambouillet and Hampshire breeds have shown that a slow increase in inbreeding has occurred in these breeds of 0.7–0.9% per generation (Dickson and Lush, 1933; Carter, 1940). A slightly higher increase was found for Toggenburg goats in Britain (Mason, 1954). It appears from these studies that a little separation into families within breeds was taking place, although this was probably more due to a geographic separation than to a deliberate attempt to form distinct families.

Inbreeding is usually avoided by practical breeders because of its detrimental effects on most productive traits. A review by Rae (1956) shows a decline in merit in most traits, the decline being most precipitous for body weight, type, and condition. Fleece traits were less affected than body traits. Inbreeding had little effect on staple length, face covering, and skin folds. Inbreeding generally results in a reduction in vigor and viability, as the more inbred animals grow at a slower rate and are more susceptible to death from conception on. The inbreeding effects remain fairly constant throughout life (Terrill *et al.*, 1948). The lost vigor is generally regained by crosses among inbred lines or by top crosses on noninbred stock. Recessive traits such as black color, overshot jaws, and cryptorchidism are more likely to be revealed with inbreeding.

Sheep breeders have long been concerned with the possibility of improving sheep through developing and crossing inbred lines. Such concern has been stimulated by successes with hybrid corn. During and since the 1930's relatively large numbers of inbred lines of sheep have been developed by state and federal agencies. Many of these were started at the U.S. Sheep Experiment Station, Dubois, Idaho. Testing of these lines through linecrossing and topcrossing to unrelated stock is still far from complete. It seems possible that crosses among the better crossing lines or topcrosses from some lines may excel selected outbred groups. Gains from crossing lines are most important for traits such as lamb production, growth rate, and viability. However, it is not yet clear how inbred lines of sheep can best be utilized in practical breeding procedures.

Outcrossing within pure breeds is a much more common breeding practice than inbreeding. This probably tends to counteract the effects of any inbreeding which does occur and also to maintain heterosis at a relatively high level. Heterosis cannot be measured directly and therefore one can only speculate as to its importance.

The beneficial effects of heterosis can be obtained by crossing breeds as well as by crossing inbred lines and crossbreeding is widely used in commercial sheep production (Rae, 1952). Crossbreeding of sheep generally leads to increases in fertility, milk production, growth rate of the lambs, body weight, and wool production (Terrill, 1958b).

17-3. INHERITANCE OF TRAITS IN SHEEP AND GOATS

Many traits have been identified in sheep which are inherited in simple Mendelian fashion. These have been reviewed by Rae (1956) and Terrill (1958b). These include color and pattern, horns, ear length, multinipples, lethals or sublethals, various abnormalities, chalk face, entropion, jaw defects, birth coat and fleece structure, skin folds, and blood traits. The knowledge of the mode of inheritance of these traits aids the breeder in eliminating those which are undesirable, such as black color and various other defects, and in fixing those which are desirable, such as the polled trait. Of course a variety of colors and color patterns have been studied. Recessive black is of interest where all important breeds of sheep in the United States are white. It appears that at least two pairs of recessive genes for black exist in domestic breeds. A dominant black gene is in evidence in the black marker sheep used in Western range bands. This gene may have been derived from the Karakul breed. Furthermore, there is evidence that several dominant genes can produce black.

The inheritance of horns is of interest in the Rambouillet and Dorset breeds although horns, particularly scurs, may appear in polled breeds. This is especially true of breeds with Rambouillet blood, such as the Columbia and Targhee. Horns are apparently recessive to the polled trait in both Rambouillets and Dorsets although Rambouillet ewes homozygous for the horned gene have horn knobs and those carrying the polled gene have depressions in the skull in place of the horn knobs. The inheritance of scurs has not been well defined.

Lethal and semilethal traits, which usually result in early death, are generally inherited as simple recessives and include muscle contracture, earlessness, cleft palate, paralysis, rigid fetlocks, dwarfism, nervous incoordination, congenital photosensitivity, and blindness.

Cryptorchidism, or failure of descent of one or both testicles, appears to be due to recessive genes, although it is sometimes linked with the polled trait. Entropion or turned-in eyelids is inherited, although not as a simple recessive. Wattles which appear in Navajo sheep and in Toggenburg goats appear to be inherited as a dominant. Jaw inequalities, particularly a short lower jaw, appear to be due to several pairs of genes. Hermaphroditism in milk goats appears to be inherited as a single recessive character (Eaton and Simmons, 1939).

Blood antigens and other blood traits in sheep have received increased attention in recent years. These studies are laying a foundation for identifying parentage, for determining relationship of blood traits to merit, and for providing a check on changes in homozygosity with traits which are not evident to the practical breeders.

Chromosome number seems established as 54 for the diploid number for sheep and 60 for goats (Makino, 1951).

Early genetic studies with sheep involved attempts to work out the mode of inheritance of many economic traits in a simple Mendelian manner. The F_1 and F_2 generations following breed crosses were studied. Particular interest was shown in twinning or in number of lambs born from single and twin mothers. Gradually the efforts to explain the inheritance of all traits in a simple manner were abandoned upon the realization that many production traits were dependent on many genes and that special statistical methods aided the study of these traits. The results of such studies have found useful application in selection for genetic improvement.

17-4. IMPROVEMENT THROUGH
SELECTION OF SHEEP

Selection is the most important way in which the sheep breeder can improve his products and in which he can improve efficiency of production

(Terrill, 1958a). It has been repeatedly demonstrated that effective selection methods will lead to permanent gains, not only in quantity but also in quality of lamb and wool produced. The amount of selection which can be practiced for any one trait is limited. Therefore it is important that traits for which the greatest progress can be made and which are most valuable are emphasized in selection.

Estimates of heritability, which estimate the proportion of gain made in selection of parents which is passed on to the offspring, are useful in determining the relative progress which can be made in selection to improve various traits. Thus, emphasis can be given to the traits with which the most progress can be made. In sheep, estimates of heritability have usually been obtained from relationships among relatives. Estimates are available for a large number of sheep traits but many are based on relatively small numbers under varying conditions, and therefore considerable variability among estimates is expected. Nevertheless, rough groupings of the various traits can be made according to their relative heritability (Terrill, 1958b). These are presented in Table 17-1. In general, heritability estimates over 40% have been classified as high, those from 20–40% as moderate, and those under 20% as low. It is noted that most economic traits are moderately or highly heritable.

Traits important to income must be emphasized if selection is to be effective in producing more profitable sheep. Lamb production is most important. Selection gains for more open faces will increase number and pounds of lamb per ewe with only slight loss in fleece weight (Terrill, 1949b). Larger ewes will produce more and heavier lambs. In fact for each pound increase in the weight of a yearling ewe, she may produce about one-half pound more of lamb per year (Terrill and Stoehr, 1942). Market weights of lambs have generally increased over the years and probably should be increased

TABLE 17-1. *Relative estimates of heritability of traits in sheep.*

High	Moderate			Low
Face covering	Body weight at birth	Clean fleece weight	Color on legs	Twinning
Staple length	Body weight at weaning	Clean wool yield	Milk production	Type or conformation
Skin folds	Body weight at one year	Wool-processing traits	Date of lambing	Condition or fatness
Fiber diameter	Average daily gain	Index of overall merit	Resistance to parasites	
Birth coat	Grease fleece weight	Fur characteristics	Number of nipples	

still more. Further gains should also come from increasing the proportion of lambs marketed per ewe. Thus it will pay to increase production of twins. Ewes having twins can be expected to wean an average of about 40 lb. of lamb per ewe-year more than ewes of the same age having singles (Sidwell, 1956; Terrill, 1949a, 1957). Twinning has low heritability but small improvements may be worthwhile. To select for twin production, favor the young ewe having twins and rams born as twins from young mothers. Twinning at first lambing is less frequent than in older animals; thus, mothers having twins at an early age are more likely to transmit this trait.

Quality and quantity of lamb meat deserves consideration in selection, but unfortunately we know little about how to measure these, particularly in the live animal where selection can be applied. Thickness through the

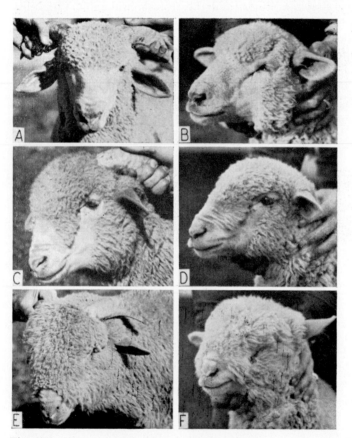

Fig. 17-1. Face covering of weanling Rambouillet lambs. A and B, open face with score of 3 for ram and ewe lamb; C and D, partially covered face with score of 4 for ram and ewe lamb; E and F, covered face with score of 5 for ram and ewe lamb. [Courtesy USDA.]

Fig. 17-2. Neale's device for estimating clean fleece weight by measuring volume of fleece under constant pressure. [Courtesy USDA.]

hind legs may offer promise. More facts are needed on the relation of various conformation traits to carcass value.

Clean fleece weight is the most valuable wool trait to consider in selection. Neale's device (Neale *et al.*, 1958) for estimating clean fleece weight provides a quick easy method for identifying high-producing sheep (Fig. 17-2). Improvements in staple length, fleece density, and uniformity of length and fineness will also probably lead to economic gains. Improvement in fleece quality will no doubt be given more emphasis by producers when prices paid for wool are more commensurate to quality.

Any selection program should include the culling of unsound and unthrifty as well as low-producing animals. The elimination of such animals may not lead to much genetic progress as they may tend to leave few offspring. However, the remaining animals will give higher average production and there will be less risk of transmitting defects.

17-5. SYSTEMS OF SELECTION

After decisions have been made as to which traits are to be emphasized in selection there are various systems which may be followed in determining which animals are best for these traits. The use of records on relatives are often useful, particularly where selection must be practiced before the trait can be measured in the offspring. When pertinent records become available

Fig. 17-3. Measuring staple length on mature Rambouillet ram. [Courtesy USDA.]

on the lambs these should receive more attention than any information from their pedigree. Consideration may be given to full sisters or brothers where traits such as milk production, lambing rate, or semen production cannot be measured in both sexes. Progress from selection is generally slower where selection must be based on the records of relatives than where the trait can be measured directly in the animals to be selected.

One of the most commonly used methods of selection on records of relatives is that based on records of the progeny or progeny testing. This method is usually more accurate than selection on the animal's own phenotype because a measure of the animal's breeding worth is obtained before selection is practiced. However, it is slower because decisions cannot be made until after progeny are produced, and a part of the flock must be reserved for producing these progeny (Dickerson and Hazel, 1944). Breeders, selecting within their own flocks, can use progeny tests on outside sires to compare them with sires of their own breeding before using them extensively.

Selection of superior animals usually involves the use of an index of some kind because one must combine the values of various important traits simultaneously or balance the strong points against the weak points in order to rank the animals from best to poorest. A calculated index combining objective measures will, generally, be more accurate and effective than any mental combining of values while ranking animals under observation.

The use of an index, as shown by Hazel and Lush (1942), is a more efficient way of selecting for several traits at the same time than the use of independent culling levels or tandem selection for one trait at a time. An index permits a constant and objective degree of emphasis on each trait considered in selection. Without an index, ideals are more apt to shift from year to year. Also, one is likely to overemphasize more obvious traits like body type or color and to underemphasize traits of greater economic importance, such as average daily gain or milk production.

Lush (1945) has presented an objective basis for determining emphasis on each of several traits in an index by giving weight to these characters in proportion to their heritability times economic importance (see Chapter 13).

Fig. 17-4. Weighing weanling lamb on Wisconsin farm. [Courtesy V. L. Felts, University of Wisconsin.]

The use of an index on Rambouillet lambs at Dubois, Idaho, was responsible for increasing over-all selection pressure by about 28% for weanling traits. The primary change brought about by index selection was to shift attention from neck folds to face covering and weaning weight. The use of an index on Wisconsin farm sheep based on weaning weight and staple

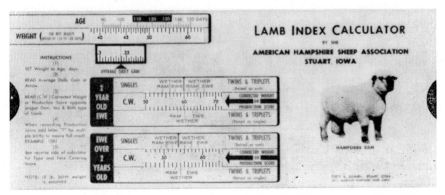

Fig. 17-5. Lamb index calculator or slide rule. [Courtesy American Hampshire Sheep Association.]

length has been accompanied by improvements in these traits (Felts *et al.,* 1957; Chapman, 1958).

17-6. FACTORS INFLUENCING RATE OF PROGRESS

Progress from selection for improvement of sheep and goats may not be as rapid as with animals which reproduce at a faster rate, such as poultry or swine. However, improvements can be made, especially if factors which influence the rate of progress are optimum. Factors which may influence progress are an optimal environment which allows a high proportion of a generation to reach breeding age and genetic factors such as intensity of culling for a specific trait or the heritability of the trait. Selection ideals must remain constant over a period of years for selection to be effective. The exhibition of sheep at fairs and shows has not only stimulated interest in sheep breeding but also serves to set breed ideals and standards. Unfortunately, the show ring has sometimes led to emphasis on uneconomic traits such as head shape, scurs, or complete face covering or on traits of low heritability, such as conformation and fatness. Greater emphasis on production traits which cannot be assessed in the show ring would be desirable.

Progress in improving individual traits may depend in part on the accuracy with which the trait can be measured, although the rapidity and cheapness of the measure are also important. Attention is being given to develop better measures for surface area, body form, carcass traits, semen production, wool fiber length and fineness, and celan wool yield. The device for estimating clean fleece weight developed by Neale *et al.* (1958) illustrates a significant gain in this area.

17-7. PERFORMANCE TESTING

Performance testing offers another means of increasing the accuracy of records on which selections are made, especially for stud sires. Ram tests such as are conducted in Texas and Utah permit the breeder to compare his rams with those of other breeders under standard conditions. Of course, such tests of the breeder's own rams may be conducted by on-the-farm tests, as is done in Wisconsin, Ohio, and other states. Ideally, performance tests should include, under standard conditions, information on the ram's own performance, such as daily gain, efficiency of feed use, clean fleece weight, staple length, and grade of wool, as well as similar information on his progeny. This could be done by mating the rams as lambs to sample groups of ewes at the start of the test and then to evaluate both the ram and his offspring about 9 or 10 months later. Such a test could include carcass information on the offspring. Such tests would be costly, but they might be worthwhile, particularly on important stud rams.

If adjustments are not made for age, type of birth, and age of dam, these factors tend to confuse nongenetic with hereditary effects. Single lambs generally weigh 8 to 10 lb. more at weaning than twins, and lambs from mature dams excel those from young dams by 6 to 8 lb. When lambs are gaining over 0.5 lb. per day at weaning, a few days difference in age can make an appreciable difference in weight. If single lambs are favored because they are bigger it is probable that no progress will be made in improving weaning weight because the twins, even though smaller, might still be better genetically than the singles.

Age has important effects on body weight, fleece weight, staple length, fineness, and pounds of lamb raised per ewe. Thus, when comparing dams of different ages, one should take into account the fact that body weights, fleece weights, and lamb production increase up to 3 to 5 years of age or older, Generally, staple length decreases and fleeces become coarser with age. The mohair of Angora goats markedly increases in coarseness with age. Effects of age on phenotype are fully as important for sires as dams. Lack of adjustment for age will favor 3- to 5-year-old rams over those 1 and 2 years of age. Younger rams of the next generation will generally be genetically superior if rapid improvement is being made.

If these nongenetic effects are not taken into account, the selected sheep may owe their advantage to favorable environmental factors and thus no genetic improvement will result. Years may make quite a difference. There is very little genetic difference from year to year with sheep because only a part of the parents can be changed each year but there may be large environmental yearly changes. Clean fleece weight can vary as much as $1\frac{1}{2}$ to 2 lb. in different years simply because feed or other environmental conditions are better in one year than another.

One way to minimize these environmental effects is to select within groups of the same age or within singles or twins by saving the same proportion of each. Statistical adjustments are more precise and can easily be applied to an index.

Generations should be turned rapidly for greatest gain, as genetic progress is made only from one generation to the next. Length of generation is defined as the average age of the parents when the offspring are born. This average is about 4 years in sheep. Ram generation length can be reduced to 2 years by using only the best yearling rams each year. Reducing generation length by one half would double the genetic gain per year. If improvement is being made and a reasonably large number of offspring are produced, the best son should be better than his sire. The quicker the change is made the more rapidly you take advantage of this gain. Thus, in many circumstances more rapid progress can be made by selecting solely on the basis of phenotype than by the slower progeny-test procedure. The breeder also often tends to make repeated use of an outstanding sire when a quicker change to his best son might give greater improvement.

The sheep or goat breeder must often choose between the frequent selection of outstanding young rams on their own merit and the slower procedure of selecting sires on the performance of their progeny. Progeny testing is most effective in selecting for lowly heritable traits such as conformation or fattening ability. It is usually unnecessary in selecting for highly heritable traits, such as face covering or staple length, where the offspring simply confirm what has already been observed in the parents. Progeny testing is usually desirable when selecting among rams whose records were made in different herds or farms. Adjustment for environmental herd differences in production records is difficult. Selection for crossing ability between lines or breeds necessitates the use of progeny tests. Likewise, progeny testing is important when a trait cannot be observed in both sexes, such as milk production, or where it can only be observed in a group of offspring, such as lamb mortality. Artificial insemination is safer with progeny-tested sires, as the greater accuracy in appraisal

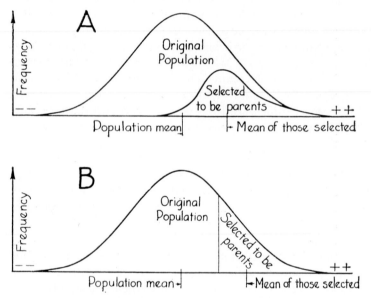

Fig. 17-6. Two ways in which the merits of those chosen to be parents by rather intense selection might be distributed with respect to the merit of the original population from which they were taken. The better individuals are to the right, the poorer to the left. *A* indicates the usual kind of selection where at least a few mistakes are made and where some attention must be paid to characteristics other than the one for which merit is indicated here. *B* is the most extreme form of selection conceivable. No mistakes are made and selection is entirely for the characteristic for which degrees of merit are indicated along the horizontal scale. [From Lush, *Animal Breeding Plans,* Iowa State Univ. Press, Ames, Iowa, 1945.]

of individual sires is more justified where sires are to be used so widely. The selection of inferior rams, which sire large numbers of lambs (as from artificial insemination), can be very costly. On the other hand, when selecting among relatively large numbers of rams for natural mating within a closed flock for moderately or highly heritable traits, more rapid progress can usually be made by mating only the best yearling rams each year. Only a few if any rams with the very best progeny can be expected to excel the best yearling rams available in the next year.

17-8. FACTORS AFFECTING SELECTION DIFFERENTIALS

The aspect of selection which can be most influenced by the breeder is the selection differential. Selection differential represents the difference in a trait or group of traits between the herd average and the average of the animals selected for producing the next generation. Any progress made is always a fraction of the selection differential. Much of the effort in selection is aimed at obtaining as large a selection differential as possible for the important traits. One measure of the effectiveness of a selection index is the size of the selection differentials for the respective traits resulting from its use, as compared with alternative methods of selection. In comparing selection differentials in terms of pounds of wool or inches of staple length it may be desirable to convert the selection differential to some standard unit of measure such as a percentage of the mean or a multiple of the standard deviation.

The amount of selection which can be practiced is limited by the size of the flock. For example, at least 3 rams usually need to be used within a closed flock to avoid close inbreeding. As each ram can be mated to 50 to 75 ewes the total flock size must be in the range of 150 to 225 ewes, or a lower selection differential for rams will result. Of course, selection takes advantage of genetic variation and the larger the breeding group the larger will be the total range of variation. Furthermore, in large flocks the best rams can be mated to the best ewes to produce rams for the entire flock. However, this superflock should be sufficiently large that considerable selection can be practiced among the rams produced.

The higher the reproductive rate the greater are the selection differentials which can be obtained, as the number of replacement animals needed remains constant. Feeding and management practices which increase the lambing rate are therefore usually an aid to greater gains from selection.

It pays to select on as few traits as possible. Opportunity for selection is definitely limited and attention to unimportant traits such as color on the legs or shape of head can reduce the attention to important traits such as pounds of lamb or wool produced. Progress for any one trait decreases as the number of traits selected for increases. The decrease is equal to one divided by the square root of the number of traits involved (Lush, 1945). For example, if you select for four traits you make only one-half as much progress in each one as if you selected for only one trait; selection for nine traits gives only one-third as much progress in any one trait as if only one was considered. It does not pay to select for fancy points or for things for which the lamb or wool producer is not paid.

It is also important to select under the feed and environmental conditions under which the sheep are going to produce. Unfortunately, conditions under which purebred rams are generally raised are usually better than the range or farm conditions under which their offspring will be raised. Thus they may be selected for characteristics which are not most desirable in the poorer or ordinary environment where most market lambs and wool are produced.

The use of accurate and objective records will increase the effectiveness of selection. Some of the most important records are those of lambing, weaning weight, staple length, and fleece weight. Neale's fleece-squeezing machine gives an accurate estimate of clean fleece weight very quickly. With this machine it is feasible to obtain clean fleece weight estimates on every sheep shorn. Certainly it would pay to obtain this measure—or at least grease fleece weight—on every ram fleece.

Demanding accuracy in records can be carried too far. As accuracy is increased, generally the cost becomes higher also. A cheap, objective, approximate measure may be far better than an expensive, highly accurate one. This is especially true if the cheaper measure is used more widely and consistently.

To be most effective, maximum selection pressure should be applied to both rams and ewes. However, selection of rams is of greater importance. About 80–90% of the gains which can be made in a flock closed to outside breeding comes from the selection of rams (Terrill, 1951). One ram can be mated to as many as 50 to 75 ewes in a limited breeding period, thereby requiring the use of only 3–4% of the rams produced to sire the next generation. Over half of the ewes produced must be retained to become mothers of the next generation. Thus, much larger selection differentials can be obtained for rams than for ewes. Therefore hereditary or permanent gains from selection come largely from the choice of rams to become sires.

The selection differentials for sires can be increased still further by the use of artificial insemination. In this way several thousand offspring may be obtained from each sire in one season. A record of up to 17,000 ewes mated to one ram over a 115-day period has been reported from the Soviet Union. Artificial insemination of sheep is advantageous chiefly because it permits more intense selection of outstanding sires (Terrill, 1960). Justification is difficult on any other basis. Any advantage of the breeding value of a sire can be extended to a much greater number of offspring by artificial insemination. There also may be disadvantages to the wide use of individual sires with artificial insemination. Rams which have not been thoroughly tested may spread undesirable traits far more widely by this method. This is especially true of recessive defects, which may not be revealed under ordinary use.

17-9. RATE OF PROGRESS FROM SELECTION

Rate of progress expected from selection on an annual basis can be estimated by multiplying heritability times the selection differential and then dividing by the generation length. As the last two generally differ for rams and ewes, it is convenient to calculate the expected progress per year separately for each sex and then to average them. These estimates cannot be very precise where a number of related traits are considered in selection, because exact estimates of heritabilities and phenotypic and genetic correlations among traits are not generally available for sheep. Even generation length may be difficult to calculate accurately. However, such estimates may still be very useful as guides to the best selection procedure to follow in any particular situation.

Actual progress from selection is usually determined by trends of values for each trait over a period of years. This is often unsatisfactory, as genetic trends are often confounded with environmental trends (Terrill, 1951). The use of unselected control groups or random repeat matings are thought to be essential for selection experiments (Terrill and Ercanbrack, 1960) to obtain estimates of annual environmental changes. Even such control groups may be subject to bias by natural selection and by genetic drift.

17-10. IMPROVEMENT THROUGH SELECTION OF DAIRY GOATS

The principles which have been emphasized for improvement of sheep through selection also hold true for dairy goats. Milk production should be emphasized. It would be expected to be moderately heritable as it is in sheep and dairy cattle. High milk production per day is not only desirable but persistency of production for 8 to 10 months or longer is also important. The udder should be large and the teats should be large enough to make milking easy.

Bucks should be selected from high-producing does and those who sire superior milking offspring should be retained for extensive use. Hornlessness is preferred by most breeders but this trait appears to be linked with the factor leading to intersexes (Eaton, 1945). Large size, high feed capacity, vigor, livability, and fertility are desirable in both sexes. Good dairy conformation is generally favored but direct selection for high milk production should receive the major emphasis.

17-11. IMPROVEMENT THROUGH SELECTION OF ANGORA GOATS

Again, the same principles which apply to improvement of sheep through selection also apply to Angora goats. Gray (1959) has outlined many important considerations in selecting Angora goats for mohair and kid production. Most of the income from Angora goats comes from the sale of mohair and therefore weight of fleece is the most important trait to emphasize in selection. Individual fleece weights should be kept by breeders —at least for the bucks. Length of staple contributes to fleece weight and thus is important. Mohair becomes coarser with age but the fine quality of the kid mohair is preferred and can be improved by selection. Goats with short staple and with fleeces which are light, kempy, or which contain any colored fibers should be discriminated against. The body and belly should be well covered and the covering should be dense. The web-lock or intermediate type of fleece holds up well in production and is often favored by commercial producers. Angora goats have more of a tendency to shed than sheep, and animals with this tendency should be culled.

Size, vigor, and fertility are important to efficient production and should be favored in both sexes. Open faces should be favored in selection as it is related to the production of both kids and mohair. Does with open faces are larger, produce heavier fleeces, and drop a much higher proportion of kids than does with covered faces (Shelton, 1960). Meat conformation should receive some attention in selection as many Angora goats, particularly the wethers, are sold for meat.

17-12. FUTURE NEEDS

While much is known regarding genetic improvement of sheep and goats, further advancements are urgently needed if these animals are to effectively compete with alternative sources of food and fiber. The rate of reproduction not only needs to be increased but more consistent methods of controlling it are needed. The artificial control or alteration of the sex ratio would be advantageous. Many advances in breeding and selection techniques would be facilitated by practical methods for storage, culture, and transfer of germ cells and gonadal tissues from both the sheep and the goat. The inability to store ram semen effectively either in the liquid or frozen state is a deterrent to more widespread use of artificial insemination as a selection aid.

Inbred lines of sheep show some promise but practical methods for their use in improvement programs need to be developed. Selection studies show promise of continued genetic gains but more rapid and effective methods of selection are required. Tremendous possibilities exist, not only from the improvement of present breeds of sheep and goats, but in the development of new and more useful breeds. Comprehensive comparisons of the productive ability of breeds and their crosses are particularly needed. With such results it is expected that much more effective and extensive use could be made of crossbreeding for more efficient commercial production of meat, fiber, and milk from sheep and goats.

17-13. SUMMARY

There is convincing evidence that large gains have been made in improving the productivity and efficiency of production of sheep and goats in recent years but that much more improvement is possible and desirable. The pure breeds and pure breeding provide the basis for continued gains. The production and crossing of inbred lines offer hope for the production of superior stock but tests are not yet conclusive. Crossbreeding offers a means for improved commercial production. A knowledge of the inheritance of many traits which depend on only one or two pairs of genes can aid the breeder in eliminating such traits which are undesirable and in fixing those which are desirable.

Selection procedures are mainly aimed at production traits which depend on many genes. The amount of selection which can be practiced is limited and therefore highly heritable traits and those which are most important to income should be emphasized in selection. These include lamb production, face covering, body weight, carcass quality, and clean fleece weight. Progress from selection can be maximized by the use of accurate records of production, by adequately accounting for environmental effects, by turning generations rapidly, by selecting consistently on only the most important traits, and by concentrating on the selection of males. Selection is the most important way in which the sheep and goat breeder can improve his products and in which he can improve efficiency of production.

REFERENCES AND SELECTED READINGS

References marked with an asterisk are of general interest.

AMGRA Handbook, 1960. American Milk Goat Record Association.

Campbell, Fred R., 1960. Improvement of sheep through the selection of performance-tested and progeny-tested breeding animals, 1959–60. Texas Agr. Expt. Sta. MP-422.

*Carter, R. C., 1940. A genetic history of the Hampshire sheep. *J. Heredity,* 31:89–93.

Chapman, A. B., 1958. Unpublished data.

*Connor, J. J., 1918. A brief history of the sheep industry in the United States. Annual Report of the American Historical Association.

Dickerson, G. E. and L. N. Hazel, 1944. Effectiveness of selection on progeny performance as a supplement to earlier culling in livestock. *J. Agr. Research*, 69:459–476.

Dickson, W. F. and J. L. Lush, 1933. Inbreeding and the genetic history of the Rambouillet sheep in America. *J. Heredity*, 24:19–33.

Eaton, O. N., 1945. The relation between polled and hermaphroditic characters in dairy goats. *Genetics*, 30:51–61.

—— and V. L. Simmons, 1939. Hermaphrodism in milk goats. *J. Heredity*, 30(6):261–266.

Felts, V. L., A. B. Chapman, and A. L. Pope, 1957. Estimates of genetic and phenotypic parameters for use in a farm flock ewe selection index. *J. Animal Sci.*, 16(4):1048 (Abstract).

Gray, James A., 1959. Selecting Angora goats for increased mohair and kid Production. Texas Agr. Expt. Sta. MP-385.

Hazel, L. N., 1943. The genetic basis for constructing selection indexes. *Genetics*, 28:476–490.

—— and Jay L. Lush., 1942. The efficiency of three methods of selection. *J. Heredity*, 33(11):393–399.

*Lush, Jay L., 1945. *Animal Breeding Plans*. Collegiate Press, Ames, Iowa.

*Makino, S., 1951. *An Atlas of the Chromosome Numbers in Animals*. 2nd Ed. Iowa State College Press, Ames, Iowa, 290 pp.

Mason, I. L., 1954. A genetic analysis of the British Toggenburg breed of goats. *J. Heredity*, 45(3):129–133.

Neale, P. E., G. M. Sidwell, and J. L. Ruttle, 1958. A mechanical method for estimating clean fleece weight. New Mexico Agr. Expt. Sta. Bull. 417.

Rae, A. L., 1952. Crossbreeding of sheep. *Animal Breeding Abstracts*, 20:197–207, 287–299.

*——, 1956. The genetics of the sheep. *Advances in Genetics*, 8:189–265.

Shelton, M., 1960. The relation of face covering to fleece weight, body weight and kid production of Angora does. *J. Animal Sci.*, 19(1):302–308.

Sidwell, G. M., 1956. Some aspects of twin versus single lambs of Navajo and Navajo crossbred ewes. *J. Animal Sci.*, 15(1):202–210.

Terrill, C. E., 1949a. Selecting Rambouillet ewes for high lamb production. Presented at Western Section, Amer. Soc. of Animal Prod., Moscow, Idaho.

——, 1949b. The relation of face covering to lamb and wool production in range Rambouillet ewes. *J. Animal Sci.*, 8(3):353–361.

——, 1951. Effectiveness of selection for economically important traits of sheep. *J. Animal Sci.*, 10(1):17–18 (abstract).

——, 1957. Sheep improvement through selection. *National Wool Grower*, 47(5):14–17.

——, 1958a. Recent advances in sheep breeding. *California Livestock News*, October 14.

——, 1958b. Fifty years of progress in sheep breeding. *J. Animal Sci.*, 17(4):944–959.

*——, 1960. *The Artificial Insemination of Farm Animals*. Edited by E. J. Perry. Rutgers, New Brunswick. Third Revised Edition, Chap. 9.

—— and S. K. Ercanbrack, 1960. Operation and usefulness of a random bred control population of Rambouillet sheep. Presented at the Joint Meeting of the Beef Cattle Breeding Technical Committees, Stillwater, Oklahoma, July 25, 1960.

—— G. M. Sidwell, and L. N. Hazel, 1948. Effects of some environmental factors on traits of yearling and mature Rambouillet rams. *J. Animal Sci.*, 7(3):311–319.

—— and J. A. Stoehr, 1942. The importance of body weight in selection of range ewes. *J. Animal Sci.*, 1(3):221–228.

Warwick, B. L., 1961. Selection against cryptorchidism in Angora goats. *J. Animal Sci.*, 20(1):10–14.

Chapter 18

Genetic Improvement in Horses

Horses and chariots let us have,
and to our sports.
SHAKESPEARE, *Titus Andronicus*

18-1. THE MIGHTY ARAB

The majestic light horse of the Eastern Mediterranean Basin has come down from antiquity with little or no change. He is represented by the Arab, Turk, and Barb, all of which are commonly designated as Eastern Horses, Desert Horses, or merely as Arabs.

Improvement of European horses quite generally was related to the introduction of Eastern blood. Intelligence, speed, endurance, and elegance are never far removed from the Arab. Desert Horses are famous for a strong and shortly coupled back, good spring or rib, depth of chest, and good feet and legs. Contrary to popular opinion these horses do not have great speed but they do have great capacity to run long distances. They are courageous, good weight carriers, and highly maneuverable.

18-2. THOROUGHBRED, A WAR HORSE

The major derivative of the Arab is the Thoroughbred, which acquired breed status in the last decade of the eighteenth century. The major objective in the importation of Arabs into Italy, Spain, France, and the British Isles was for the purpose of breeding officers' mounts. Officers and other gentry of that day raced these Arabs and their crossbred progeny. Racing was a means of testing horses for military uses. Racing calendars provided the basic data for the compilations which gave rise to the General Stud Book, and the very breed that is now so fussy about purity of blood came into being on the basis of performance. Registration is not a requirement for racing on English tracks but it is in America.

Selective breeding for racing performance for more than two centuries has increased speed, ability to carry weight, and body size. Present-day Thoroughbreds stand about 16 hands (5' 4") high at the withers and are about 2 hands taller than their ancestors in the formative period. Crile (1941) interpreted progressive improvement in racing capacity not only to selection but also to orthogenesis. According to Dr. Crile, man has bred the Thoroughbred and the Greyhound for a large brain, a large heart, and a large adrenal-sympathetic system but not for a large thyroid gland. Changes in the energy-controlling organs made greater speed possible. The present emphasis on early speed and shorter racing may endanger the stamina for which the Thoroughbred is famous.

18-3. MALE AND FEMALE LINES

All Thoroughbreds trace from sire, to grandsire, to great grandsire, and so on, to three stallions: Matchem (1748), Herod (1758), and Eclipse (1764). Modern Thoroughbreds are some 16 generations removed from those progenitors. Even at this late date, annual summaries of racing invariably include the total earnings and number of stakes winners for each of the paternal lines. There is no genetic basis for attaching special significance to these sire lines.

Thoroughbreds are also classed, according to the Bruce Lowe system (1898) into maternal families on the basis of descent through the bottom line of the pedigree to some 50 foundation mares. Numbers were assigned to these families on the basis of standing in the production of winners of three classic races in England: Derby, Oaks, and St. Leger. Some families were identified as running families, others as sire-producing families, and certain others as both running and sire-producing. The preposterous assumption of maternal predominance was at the heart of the system. Pedigrees of successful horses were cited as guides to the proper manner of combining and blending various families. Critical studies of samples rather than a few successful cases have revealed fallacies of the Bruce Lowe system. It lingers on, however, and family numbers are still used in expanded pedigrees in many sources. All breeds of livestock have their esteemed paternal and maternal lines.

18-4. INBREEDING

Contrary to popular opinion, Thoroughbreds are not highly inbred. An analysis by Steele (1944) provided an index of inbreeding of about 9%. This was based on pedigrees traced to 1748, the foaling date of Matchem. The average increase in inbreeding per generation was 0.6%, which was about one-half that of Standardbreds and American Saddle Horses and well within the limits observed in similar studies of the major breeds of livestock. Allowing for two additional generations subsequent to study, a fair estimate of the present inbreeding of Thoroughbreds may be 10 or 11%. This index provides an estimate of the most likely reduction in genetic heterozygosity resulting from inbreeding. It is reasonable to suppose that greater reduction in heterozygosity has occurred through selection than through inbreeding. Further analysis of the data on Thoroughbreds, Standardbreds, and American Saddle Horses revealed no pronounced separation into distinct families. Comparable studies of Scotch Clydesdales by Calder (1927) and of American Quarter Horses by Fletcher (1945) demonstrated similar breeding patterns.

18-5. "BEST TO BEST" AND OTHER BREEDING PRACTICES

Horsebreeding is quite similar to the breeding of other livestock. The familiar "breeding the best to the best" has found wide application.

A system of considerable historical interest was proposed by Col. Vuillier (1927). The main feature of that system involved the mating of individuals whereby the "dosage" or percentage of blood of various esteemed ancestors would approximate the actual "dosage" of those ancestors in the pedigrees of superior Thoroughbreds. To some extent this system is practiced in all kinds of animal breeding. When this matter was checked by Steele (1944) for stakes-winning and for poor-performing Thoroughbreds, the dosage of various famous remote ancestors was essentially the same in both groups. Similarly, an analysis of two random samples and one show sample of the American Saddle Horse by Bywaters and Davis (Steele, 1944) revealed only minor differences in the contribution of famous ancestors in that breed. The statement is almost axiomatic that any Thoroughbred is royally bred by merely extending his pedigree. The major differences in the ancestry of good and poor Thoroughbreds are in the first two generations, all of which points to the fact that pedigree extensions beyond the third or fourth generations are relatively unimportant in the appraisal of an individual.

There are practical limitations to the testing of Thoroughbred fillies. Most of them come into peak racing form a little later than colts. The

| TABLE 18-1. | *Classification of 1181 Thoroughbred sires according to racing index of progeny. Sires include only stallions with at least 40-year starters in North America and with progeny still racing in 1959.* [Condensed from Estes and Baumohl, 1960.] |

Racing index of stallions

Progeny index	Unraced		0 to 4.9		5.0 to 9.9		10.0 to 14.9		15.0 to 19.9		20.0 Up		Total	
	No.	%	No.	%	No.	%	No.	%	No.	%	No.	%	No.	%
3 Up	1	1.7	1	0.2	1	0.6			3	5.4	12	7.5	18	1.5
2 to 2.9			4	0.6	3	1.7	8	9.5	8	14.3	30	18.9	53	4.5
1 to 1.9	8	13.6	108	6.7	83	46.6	51	60.0	34	60.7	81	50.9	365	30.9
0 to 0.9	50	84.7	532	82.5	91	51.1	25	29.8	11	19.6	36	22.6	745	63.1
Total	59		645		178		84		56		159		1181	

* The progeny index is based on the performance of both males and females and is much lower than if only male progeny are considered. It is clearly evident that stallions having a high racing index exert a tremendous influence in the production of superior Thoroughbreds. Their initial opportunities are also much greater.

number of filly races is also relatively small. These limitations, combined with lower average racing capacity, force them into claiming races. Owner-breeders are reluctant to risk the loss of promising fillies and for that reason usually race them only long enough to get a demonstration of their racing class before retiring them to breeding. Colts have greater racing opportunities and their potential value as future sires is increased with each racing success. Unraced stallions regardless of pedigree have little chance of acceptance by breeders. Stimulus and *Alibhai[1] were the only major exceptions in the last thirty years. Large turf earnings and fashionable breeding are the requisites of a popular young sire; and to these, add precocity—because modern owners demand much of their 2-year olds.

Standardbred fillies compete more successfully with colts. They also race with few or no changes in ownership. Quarter Horse fillies also give a good account of themselves in racing and in utility uses.

Turf performance of the first two crops of foals determines in large measure the future patronage of a sire. A sire's own racing record and pedigree decline in importance as soon as the progeny test reveals his transmitting capacity. Obviously, sires are more highly selected than broodmares and more is demanded of them. In a recent study of racing class and sire success, Estes and Baumohl (1960) observed a positive relationship between them, as shown in Table 18-1. There was a decided tendency for "like to produce like," but there was also considerable regression of the progeny

[1] An asterisk preceding the name of a Thoroughbred is a common means of denoting an imported animal.

toward the average of the breed. The odds against success for a young sire are surprisingly large.

Similar relationships between racing and breeding are also well established in mares. There is, however, considerable popular opinion to the effect that a vigorous racing career reduces a mare's transmitting capacity; individual failures are cited as evidence. Several studies by Estes have demonstrated that there is no basis for this wild assertion except for an obvious reduction of productive years and fewer foals to establish transmitting capacity.

18-6. APPRAISAL OF PERFORMANCE
VERY ARBITRARY

Performance in the Thoroughbred has been studied more fully than that of other breeds of horses. Running races are conducted irrespective of the weather, except in emergencies. In a few well-established events, horses of the same age race under the same weight and may be further restricted to the same sex, but conditions of most races are less uniform.

Since horses are so different in their racing capacities and may also change over a period of time, those better on the basis of past performance are usually handicapped by the assignment of extra weight whereby all are supposed to have the same chance of winning. There are numerous other weight allowances in particular races: filly competing with colts; age difference; earnings less than a specified amount; foaled or owned within a particular state; apprentice jockey; and so on. Distances vary widely and the same is true of purses. No other form of animal performance has such complications to limit genetic analysis.

Trainers study the variables of racing with a practical objective. Burch (1953) relates that when he looked over a condition book in order to pick spots for his horses he recalled the famous words attributed to Col. Phil Chinn: "I always put my horses in the worst company I can find for them and keep myself in the best company I can find."

Evaluation of turf performance is largely in terms of monies earned. Time, particular horses beaten, number of races won, stakes won (or placed in), ability to carry weight and to run a distance are also considered. Time and earnings are the major criteria in the rating of Standardbreds. American Saddle Horses, Hackneys, and other fancy horses are rated in terms of their successes in recognized horse shows. American Quarter Horses compete in short races, halter shows, and in rodeo events. On ranches they are also subjected to rigid selection relative to their distinctive uses.

When one observes superior performance in racing, polo, roping, cutting, jumping, dressage, or other equestrian skills it is easy to understand why the ancient Aztecs in their initial contacts with the Conquistadores considered the horse and rider one individual of a supernatural character.

18-7. EARNINGS INDEX

An earnings index of great usefulness was developed by Estes (1948). One of its virtues is its simplicity. It is the ratio of actual earnings to average expectancy. It is computed according to the following formula

$$\text{Earnings Index} = \text{Actual earnings} \div \left(\frac{\text{Total prize money}}{\text{No. of starters}}\right)$$

The actual average of North American Thoroughbreds is about 0.8 of their potential expectancy. An earnings index of 4 is equivalent to stakes class and 20 or above is very superior.

The index for a particular horse may be computed annually or on a cumulative basis. With simple arithmetic changes it can be computed for progeny of sires, progeny of dams, produce of a farm, and other groupings, in which case it is designated as an average earnings index. The scheme is useful in comparing performance of horses in different generations because monetary inflation does not change the index provided purses and inflation increase concomitantly. Furthermore, it can be used in comparing performance of horses in different countries with different monetary systems.

The most extensive application of this scheme thus far involves the ranking of Thoroughbred sires* according to the performance of their progeny. This has been done not only on American sires but also on several groups of foreign sires. A high average earnings index of a stallion's progeny is comparable to a favorable progeny test of a bull or other sire. It helps to increase his prestige, to maintain or raise his stud fee, and to bring mares of good breeding credentials to his court. Table 18-1 illustrates the usefulness of the earnings index in showing comparative breeding performance vs. racing performance in sires.

18-8. BIOLOGICAL PERFORMANCE

In his extensive analysis of racing capacity in Thoroughbreds, Laughlin (1934) developed an index of performance based on the mathematical interrelationships between distance run, weight carried, age, sex, and time. It was a serious attempt to measure racing performance more objectively. It stressed biological performance rather than order of finish or earnings. Since inheritance of racing capacity was the primary objective of the study, Laughlin also developed an elaborate mathematical scheme for predicting the probable racing capacity of progeny from particular matings. Unfor-

---

* Recent volumes of "American Race Horses" (1959, as an example), list the sires of horses that raced. In addition to the usual information concerning sires, the following are also included: the earnings index of each sire; the earnings index of each of his progeny started that year; the average earnings index of all his progeny started that year; and the cumulative average earnings index of all his starters to date. This is one of the most valuable sources now available on sires in the entire field of animal breeding.

tunately, some of the tables required in the application of his scheme were never published, and for that reason breeders have not been able to subject Laughlin's proposals to a practical test.

The prevalent concept is that a large number of quantitative genes are involved in racing capacity and also that the effects of environment are large. Horsemen quite commonly distinguish between environmental influences at the farm and those at the track.

18-9. HERITABILITY OF RACING CAPACITY

The relative influences of heredity and environment on racing performance of 3-year old Thoroughbreds were obtained by Pirri and Steele (1952) by means of intraclass correlation of the earnings of paternal half brothers. The estimate of heritability was 63%. This is a very high estimate and may be subject to reduction by the use of other statistical methods. That breeders are willing to pay exorbitant stud fees reveals that they believe in the inheritance of racing class irrespective of their familiarity with technical genetics.

18-10. AGE OF PARENTS AND PERFORMANCE OF PROGENY

There appears to be some relationship between the age of parents and racing performance of progeny in Thoroughbreds. In mares, according to Estes (1934, 1943, 1944), the performance of their progeny increases up to the third or fourth foal and then declines progressively.

Buell (Estes, 1960) analyzed the racing performance of 3-year old progeny of stallions 9 through 20 years of age. A slight decline was observed. There is also some unpublished evidence that the young years are the best years in the stud career of stallions.

Fortunately, these apparent declines are small and of little concern to breeders. The problem deserves further study because there is no known genetic basis for a decline in transmitting capacity.

18-11. CONFORMATION

Horsemen place much emphasis on conformation because serious deficiencies are interpreted as limitations to action or ability to withstand hard usage. Appraisal of conformation is largely by eye. Attempts to predict performance by physical measurements within a breed have been very disappointing. The same is true of attempts to relate variables in the blood and physiological observations to performance.

Good conformation is especially important in horses that compete in shows. Fancy points are of little concern in racing and utility stock. Trainers of race horses appreciate good conformation but have even greater respect for that indescribable "will to win" without which a "perfect" horse is worthless. Conformation is a very live topic among Quarter Horse breeders. Even though some divergent influences are involved, the fact remains that this breed is "taking form" very rapidly.

Serious faults in conformation, erratic behavior, and failure to perform the gaits correctly in any breed provide the "problem horses." Corrective shoes, shin boots, shadow rolls, blinkers, and special bits are some of the devices used on such horses. Unfortunately, there is little genetic information available on the common faults in horses, and the same is true of their vices such as weaving, stall walking, cribbing, and flank biting.

REFERENCES AND SELECTED READINGS

References marked with an asterisk are of general interest.

Anon., 1959. *American Race Horses.* The American Thoroughbred Breeders Association, Lexington, Kentucky. (Note: This annual was published, from 1936–1955, by the Sagamore Press, Inc., New York.)

Bruce, L. C., 1898. *Breeding Racehorses by the Figure System.* Edited by W. Allison. William R. Jenkins, New York. (An earlier edition was published in 1895.)

Burch, P. M., 1953. *Training Thoroughbred Horses.* The Blood-Horse, Lexington, Kentucky.

Calder, A., 1927. The role of inbreeding in the development of the Clydesdale breed of horses. *Proc. Roy. Soc. Edinburgh,* 47: 118–140.

Estes, J. A., 1934. First foals and others. *The Blood-Horse,* 22:603–604.

———, 1943. Birthrank and class. *The Blood-Horse,* 40:701–705.

———, 1944. Addendum on birthrank and class. *The Blood-Horse,* 41:56–57.

———, 1948. Statistics on prominent sires adjusted for changing dollar. *The Blood-Horse,* 52:470–471.

——— 1960. The age of the sire, quality of his produce. *The Blood-Horse,* 80:962, 964, 966, 968. (Based on the study by Dr. James Buell.)

——— and A. Baumohl, 1960. Racing class and sire success. *The Blood-Horse,* 80:48, 50, 52.

Fletcher, J. L., 1945. A genetic analysis of the American Quarter horse. *J. Heredity,* 36:346–352.

Laughlin, H. H., 1934. Racing capacity in the Thoroughbred horse. I. The measure of racing capacity. II. The inheritance of racing capacity. *Scientific Monthly,* 38: 210–222, 310–321.

Pirri, J., Jr. and D. G. Steele, 1952. The heritability of racing capacity. *The Blood-Horse,* 63:976–977, 990.

*Steele, D. G., 1944. A genetic analysis of recent Thoroughbreds, Standardbreds and American saddle horses. *Ky. Agr. Expt. Sta. Bull. 462,* pp. 1–27.

Vuillier, J. (Lottery, pseud.), 1927. Les Croisements Rationnels dans la Race Pure: Tome III, Traité des Principaux Étalons du Monde Entier. Societé Anonyme de L'Imprimerie Maulde et Renow. Paris.

Chapter 19

Genetic Improvement in Poultry

19-1. GOALS OF THE POULTRY BREEDER

Broad goals of the commercial breeder are to increase product output per animal, to increase the efficiency of producing a product, and to improve the quality of an existing product. Improvement in fertility, hatchability, growth rate, body conformation, egg yield, meat yield, feed conversion, egg quality, meat quality, and viability are all facets of these three broad goals.

Interest in breeding for type, for breed characteristics, and for freedom from defects and standard disqualifications is secondary to these more important goals of the commercial poultry breeder. The modern breeder realizes that undue emphasis on characteristics of questionable economic value slows down the possible rate of genetic improvement in important economic traits.

19-2. ECONOMIC ASPECTS OF MODERN POULTRY BREEDING

The poultry industry in the United States consists of three major segments—concerned separately with the production of eggs, broilers, and turkeys—and for each of these there is a special kind of breeding enterprise. The poultry industry has exploited the sciences of biology for the development of high-performing genetic stocks far greater than any other class of livestock. It has been quick to make applications of modern breeding schemes and concepts, including inbreeding and hybridization, reciprocal recurrent selection, and many aspects of the theory of quantitative in-

307

heritance and even blood-typing techniques, for the possible improvement of performance. As a result this has created a moderate demand for the employment of college-trained geneticists for commercial research and development.

The Foundation Breeder and the Franchise Hatcheryman. The breeding segment of the poultry industry involves the foundation breeder, concerned with genetic improvement, and the hatcheryman, who multiplies the stock supplied by the foundation breeder. The producer, or farmer, then buys his chicks or poults from the hatcheryman, which he grows out as commercial egg layers, broilers, or market turkeys.

Not more than fifteen years ago the foundation breeder and the hatcheryman were independent operators. Breeders produced typically "pure strains" or "pure lines." The hatcheryman was free to purchase pure-line

Fig. 19-1. A foundation White Leghorn breeder establishment: (*a*) aerial view showing layout of buildings—all birds are confined; (b) a windowless trapnest house; (c) inside a windowless trapnest house; (d) birds in trapnest. [Courtesy Heisdorf-Nelson Farms, Inc., Kirkland, Wash.]

stock from any breeder he chose. It was his problem to decide whether the final product he would put together for the farmer customer would be a pure strain, a strain cross, or crossbred.

Today, the foundation breeder and the hatcheryman are associated typically in a franchise arrangement. A contract is signed between the two parties, whereby the breeder provides the hatcheryman with the breeding stock for his hatchery supply flocks. Such supply flocks are commonly referred to as parent flocks because the hatcheryman uses such flocks as parents of the commercial chicks he sells. The males going into the parent-flock matings are usually of different breeding than the females, so that the commercial chicks produced are a strain cross, a crossbred, or an inbred hybrid.

Franchises are a relatively new innovation in the poultry breeding and hatchery business. This arrangement gives the breeder essentially complete control of the stock his associate hatcheries sell. Control is dependent on the use of a strain cross or a hybrid combination. The hatcheryman finds the franchise arrangement desirable because this allows him to sidestep the technical problems of breeding and to concentrate his efforts on chick multiplication and selling. On the other hand, since he must sign a contract with the foundation breeding farm, the hatcheryman sacrifices some of his business independence.

Coupled with the franchising arrangement the foundation breeder recognizes the importance of a trade name. Most large commercial breeding farms today have their trade name copyrighted so that competitors will not infringe upon it.

The franchising system of selling breeding stock to associate hatchery outlets has proved highly successful. In Iowa, for example, of the 260 hatcheries who are members of the Iowa Hatchery Association, 215 (or 83%) operate under a franchise arrangement.

The key to a successful franchise arrangement hinges on hybridization in one form or another. In this regard there are two kinds of breeders. One is the strain-cross breeder, who believes that intensive inbreeding is not prerequisite to hybrid vigor. The other is the inbred hybridizer, who believes that intensive inbreeding of the lines to be crossed is necessary to produce a commercial chicken with maximum hybrid vigor.

The modern foundation poultry breeding farm has many of the characteristics of a large business or corporation. The majority of such breeding farms are incorporated and, as is typical of a large corporation, they are departmentalized. Specially trained personnel have charge of separate departments of sales, advertising, office management, purchases and so forth. Most of the large poultry breeders have sales representatives in each important state or region of the country. Many breeding farms have foreign sales outlets with a production and sales staff stationed in different foreign countries.

The business of genetic improvement is channeled through a department of breeding and development. Such a department may be directed by a college-trained geneticist, with key personnel consisting of physiologists, pathologists, veterinarians, as well as additional geneticists. Important tools of the breeding department include data-processing equipment to handle the thousands of individual records of new breeding combinations tested for performance and to compare the new combinations with their current commercial product and perhaps samples of competitors' stocks.

Random Sample Performance Tests. Random sample performance tests are enjoying popularity in this country today. In 1960 there were 15 egg-laying tests, 10 meat-production tests for broilers, and 8 turkey performance tests. Random sample performance tests are largely a development of the 1950–1960 decade, the first having been started in California in 1947.

The purpose of the tests is to provide information on the performance of commercial chicks and poults under uniform testing conditions. Test information serves as a guide for the relative performance of commercial stocks offered for sale. The random sample aspect of the test provides assurance that biases are eliminated in comparing different commercial varieties. Random sample tests have largely replaced the old "standard" egg-laying test for which the breeder hatched, selected, and reared his stock under conditions different from those of his competitors.

The typical random sample egg-laying test consists of 50 chicks or poults per entry, which are reared to maturity and then kept separate in a laying pen until about 500 days of age, at which time the entries are ranked in over-all net income based on the entire test period.

Fig. 19-2. A chicken house of the California Random Sample Poultry Test. [Courtesy California Poultry Improvement Commission, Modesto, Calif.]

A new kind of random sampling is the *Multiple Unit Poultry Test*, in which testing is carried out at more than one farm or location. Such tests are conducted in Iowa and New Hampshire; in Iowa each entry of 100 or more pullets is placed on four typical farms. By testing on several farms, differences in performance indicate more reliably the performance that poultry raisers can expect from a strain under average farm conditions.

There seems little doubt that the random sample performance test, particularly with reference to the egg-laying phases of the poultry industry, has acted as a powerful stimulas to breeders in developing high genetic merit of commercially sold poultry. The outstanding performance of the average chicken today compared with the chicken of 15 or even 10 years ago can be credited, in part, to the interest of breeders and hatcherymen in official random sample performance tests.

Not everything about the random sample test is on the favorable side of the ledger. Since success breeds success, winners of random sample tests naturally have expanded and have become larger. At the same time many breeders, some large and some small, have been forced out of business as a result of mediocre or poor performance in random sample tests. Thus, this type of official comparison of commercial products has tended toward monopolistic aspects. Some breeders are becoming larger but the total number of breeders is fewer. Just where this will ultimately lead remains to be seen.

19-3. CHARACTERS SHOWING SIMPLE MENDELIAN BEHAVIOR IN THE FOWL

It is interesting to note that some of the classic Mendelian principles were first applied to poultry after the rediscovery of Mendel's laws, about 1900. Simple monohybrid and dihybrid ratios illustrating Mendel's laws were reported by Bateson and Punnett. The classic examples of sex-linked inheritance and complementary gene effects also were very early illustrated with examples from the fowl.

Recent evidence indicates that the fowl has 6 pairs of chromosomes, including the sex chromosome. This agrees with the fact that only 6 linkage groups have so far been discovered in the fowl. In all avian species the female has a single sex chromosome (the heterogametic sex) and the male has two sex chromosomes. The turkey is thought to have 9 pairs of chromosomes. However, existing evidence is not yet conclusive as to the true number in either the chicken or the turkey.

Inheritance of Plumage Color. Only those color characteristics which have some economic significance are discussed in this section.

WHITE. Genetically, there are two kinds of pure white plumage—a dominant white and a recessive white. In addition, there is a Columbian

plumage, which is mostly white with some black feathers. White plumage
has become the favored color in all segments of the poultry industry. The
White Leghorn or crosses involving the White Leghorn are preferred for egg
production; the White Rock and specially developed "dominant white"
meat-type male lines are favored for broiler production. Even in the case
of turkeys and ducks the preferred color is white. In the Long Island duck
industry all ducks belong to one breed—the White Pekin. The trend in turkeys is to replace the bronze plumage with white.

Dominant White. This plumage color is represented typically by the
White Leghorn and is determined by the gene *I*. When a homozygous
White Leghorn (II) is crossed to a Black Australorp (ii), the resulting
progeny (Ii) are predominantly white with varying amounts of black
flecking. This shows that *I* is incompletely dominant in the F_1 genetic
background of half-Leghorn and half-Australorp. However, if the F_1 is
backcrossed to the Leghorn in successive generations, leading to a genetic
background of Leghorn blood, then the heterozygous Ii individuals are
indistinguishable from the II individuals. On the other hand, if the F_1 is
successively backcrossed to the Australorp, the heterozygotes (Ii) show a
large amount of nonwhite, proving that in the genetic background of the
Australorp *I* no longer behaves as a dominant (see Fig. 19-3).

Recessive White. White Wyandottes and the original White Plymouth
Rocks represent a white recessive plumage determined by a pair of genes (cc).
Crosses of these two breeds with colored varieties yield colored progeny, as
expected.

Columbian plumage. This plumage color is represented by the Columbian
Plymouth Rock, the Light Brahma, the Delaware, and other breeds. Plumage
color in these breeds is white, with some black in the hackle feathers, wing
primaries, and tail.

Two pairs of genes are responsible for the Columbian pattern, a restrictor
for extension of black (e) and a gene for white, called silver (S). The
restrictor is the allele of black plumage (E) and limits black to the areas
indicated. Silver (S) is sex-linked and dominant to its recessive allele gold (s).

Since the female is the heterogametic sex, a Columbian hen would have the
genotype eeS- and the cock would be eeSS or eeSs.

BLACK. Black plumage is considered due to a single autosomal gene, E
(extension of black), which is dominant to restriction of black, e. In addition, black plumage requires the gene for color, C, which is the allele of
the recessive white (cc) gene. Examples of breeds with black plumage are
the Australorp and the Black Minorca.

BARRING. The common form of barred plumage is due to a sex-linked
dominant gene, B. This gene acts as a restrictor on black, giving rise to the
black-and-white barred pattern in the feathers. The Barred Plymouth Rock
is the best known variety carrying this gene. The genotype is represented as
BBSSEE (male) and B-S-EE (female). The silver gene (S) determines the

Fig. 19-3. Dominance in white plumage as influenced by genetic background. In White Leghorns (left column) I is completely dominant, but in the Spanish breed (right column) I is incompletely dominant. [From Poultry Department, Iowa State University, Ames, Iowa.]

white bars of the pattern. If gold (s) replaces silver, then the plumage is black-gold barring.

The barring gene may be used to produce sex-linked crosses distinquish-able at hatching time. The cockerel progeny of a cross between a New Hampshire male and a Barred Plymouth Rock female are barred like the female parent, while the pullet progeny are nonbarred like the male parent.

Inheritance of Skin and Shank Color. There are two skin pigments. The carotenoids produce the yellow color and melanin produces the dark color of the skin. Melanin is formed in special cells known as melanophores.

Presence or absence of carotenoids is determined by an autosomal pair of genes (W,w). The dominant gene (W) inhibits carotinoid deposition, giving rise to white skin and shanks, while the double recessive, (ww) permits yellow skin and shanks. Most breeds common in America have yellow skin and shanks—for example the White Leghorn, White Plymouth Rock, Barred

Fig. 19-4. Influence of sex-linked gene (K, k) on feathering. Cockerel (right) is homozygous for rapid feathering (kk). Cockerel (left) is heterozygous (Kk). [Courtesy Poultry Department, Kansas State University, Manhattan, Kansas.]

Plymouth Rock and the Rhode Island Red. The White Minorca, having the genotype WW, is a breed with white skin and shanks.

Melanin is considered to be controlled by a sex-linked partially dominant gene pair (D,d). D inhibits melanin in the dermis of the skin and shanks. The Black Australorp, therefore, has the genotype d- (female) and dd (male).

In some breeds and crosses green shanks are encountered. This is due to the presence of yellow pigment in the epidermis and melanin in the dermis. The genotype for males would therefore be wwdd.

Rate of Feather Development. Early feathering is due to a sex-linked recessive gene (k). Chicks showing early feathering can be easily identified at hatching by the relative length of the covert feathers of the wing to the length of the primary feathers. At 10 days of age, late-feathering chicks show a short tail while early-feathering chicks show a longer one (see Fig. 19-4).

All modern broiler strains now carry the sex-linked early feathering gene. This is essential in controlling pinfeathers on the dressed carcasses.

Since the (K,k) genes are sex-linked they may be used in determining sex at hatching. Early-feathering males (kk) mated to late-feathering females (K-) produce slow-feathering male progeny and early-feathering pullets. This has utility in the breeding of egg-laying chickens since the cost of vent sexing can be avoided. The late-feathering cockerels would ordinarily be discarded at hatching in this case.

19-4. INHERITANCE OF ECONOMICALLY IMPORTANT CHARACTERS

Characters of economic importance are egg yield, egg size, exterior and interior egg quality, hatchability, fertility, viability, and rate of growth. All these factors enter into the economics of poultry production and all have an hereditary basis. Hence the poultry breeder is concerned with them.

Studies from random sample egg-production tests show that about 90% of the variation among entries in income over feed and chick costs can be accounted for on the basis of variation in four traits. Listed in order of their importance, they are: (1) egg production, (2) viability, (3) body weight, and (4) egg size. Factors of egg quality, fertility, hatchability, and other traits would, under average circumstances, be less important. Of course any economic trait may assume major importance to a breeder if his strain or cross is markedly deficient in some respect.

All economic characters are quantitative in nature; that is, they are not classifiable into distinct categories. In studying their inheritance the statistical approach (quantitative genetics) is used, since geneticists have not been successful in identifying single-gene effects. For this reason the genetic basis of quantitative traits is assumed to be *polygenic*—that is, these traits are influenced by many genes each with small effects. Furthermore, differences between individuals of identical genotypes are obscured by variable factors of environment. An important concept in studying the inheritance of quantitative traits is heritability (see Chapter 13). The degree of heritability brings into proper perspective the relative importance of heredity and environment as they influence the observed variation in a particular trait.

Egg Production. For egg-type strains, rate of production is naturally the most important character. The fowl, through hundreds of years of domestication, has developed into the efficient egg-laying machine that it is today. An important factor of domestication affecting rate of egg production is that of removing the eggs regularly from the nest. Even wild birds such as the sparrow have the capacity to lay several times its ordinary egg output in a season if the eggs are removed from the nest. It is important to recognize that environmental influences such as proper care and feeding are responsible along with breeding for the high production records we find in the modern strains of chickens today.

Egg yield is the product of two factors: intensity or rate of lay and the time interval in the laying period. The interval between the first egg that a hen lays and the last one she lays before she goes into a molt is known as the "biological year." Factors tending to increase rate of production or length of the biological year result in greater total egg production.

COMPONENTS OF EGG PRODUCTION. Many attempts have been made to determine the mode of inheritance of egg production over the past 40 or more years. In 1919 Dr. Goodale of Massachusetts, working with Rhode Island Reds at the state experiment station, developed the theory that the inheritance of egg production can best be studied in terms of five different components of egg production: (1) age at sexual maturity, (2) intensity of production, (3) persistency of production, (4) winter pause, and (5) broodiness.

Goodale suggested that each of these five different traits was independently inherited, and that genetic improvement in total egg production could be accomplished most effectively by separate consideration of the inheritance of each of these components.

There is some question as to whether or not winter pause is really a genetic entity. Also, breeders find difficulty in measuring persistency of production because many hens may continue laying through her fall molt period. For these reasons most commercial breeders today focus attention mainly on the other three.

Age of sexual maturity. A pullet is said to be sexually mature when she lays her first egg. The earlier the pullet commences laying the longer will be the biological year and the more eggs it will be possible for her to produce. On the average, Leghorns become sexually mature between 170 and 185 days. Dual-purpose breeds such as the Rhode Island Red and the Barred Plymouth Rock reach sexual maturity two weeks or more later. There are important differences between strains in age at sexual maturity.

Evidence from reciprocal crosses between early- and late-maturing strains indicates that some genes for maturity are sex-linked. For this reason, whenever a cross is planned between two strains differing in this trait it is wise to mate the males of the earlier-maturing strain to females of the late-maturing strain. The female progeny from such a cross would then carry the chromosome having early sexual maturity genes from the sire. Age at sexual maturity has been reported to be about 30% heritable (see Table 19-1). As one might anticipate, environmental factors exert an important influence on this trait. For example, early hatched chicks tend to mature earlier than those which are hatched late. This is explained by the difference in the amount of daylight during the growing period of early- and late-hatched chicks.

Intensity or rate of production. This factor is measured by the number of eggs laid by a hen over a standard time interval or by the percentage of eggs produced over a variable time interval. Rate of egg production is one of the most important factors determining the profitability of an egg-laying strain, but since this character is highly subject to environmental influence the heritability of this trait is low—perhaps no higher than 10%—although some studies indicate the heritability to be greater.

Broodiness. The Mediterranean breeds of fowl such as the Leghorn are characteristically nonbroody, while Asiatic breeds show a strong tendency toward broodiness. Strains of American breeds, having originated from crosses of Mediterranean and Asiatics, show variable amounts of broodiness. Since the hen takes time out from laying when she goes broody, this shortens the biological laying year and hence the total potential annual egg yield. At the same time, broody hens have considerable nuisance value because of their demands on the nests in a laying house.

Evidence exists that broodiness is determined by complementary effects of genes. Strains of Rhode Island Reds developed in Massachusetts during the period from 1920 to 1950 have been selected for freedom from broodiness.

TABLE 19-1.	*Broodiness in reciprocal crosses of White Leghorns and Rhode Island Reds. [Iowa Agr. Expt. Sta., 1956.]*			
	White Leghorn male × RI Red female		RI Red male × White Leghorn female	
	No. birds	% broody	No. birds	% broody
Test 1	37	0	44	18
Test 2	45	0	42	10

TABLE 19-2. | *Heritability of economic traits in chickens.**

Heritability	Percent
High	
Adult body weight	60
Average egg weight per hen	50
Intermediate	
Growth rate to broiler age	35
Sexual maturity	30
Annual egg production	20
Low	
Hatchability	12
Total mortality	8
Leucosis mortality	5
Fertility	5

* Estimates based in part on data from the *Handbook of Biological Data*, 1956. Saunders, Philadelphia, p. 111.

However, crossing these strains to Leghorns produces progeny showing an increase in broodiness compared to the parents. This suggests that gene interactions are involved. Furthermore, broodiness has a sex-linked basis. Thus, crossbred progeny of Rhode Island Red males mated to Leghorn females show higher broodiness than the reciprocal cross (see Table 19-1). Again, the high broodiness of the Austra-White (Australorp male X Leghorn female) is due to sex linkage.

MEASUREMENTS OF EGG PRODUCTION. Egg production may be measured on a flock basis or on an individual hen basis. In order to obtain individual hen records, trap-nesting is necessary. A few years ago almost all poultry breeders trap-nested seven days a week, each week in the year, in order to obtain a complete record for every hen. However, studies have shown that a satisfactory measure of the egg-producing ability of a hen is possible by trap-nesting less than seven days a week. Most breeders today trap-nest only two or three days per week. This reduces labor costs.

Viability. Although great progress has been made in the control of diseases of baby chicks and growing birds, mortality—especially of the laying flock—is still a top priority problem of the commercial poultry geneticist. It is not at all uncommon for flocks to show 30, 40, and even 50% mortality over the laying year without diagnosis of an epidemic disease such as Cholera or Newcastle. Instead, the diagnostic reports may show a high incidence of Leucosis and reproductive disorders. Since these do not respond to usual methods of disease control, they are of special concern to the commercial breeder. The most practical method of control seems to be in the development of genetically resistant strains and crosses.

Leucosis is a cancerlike disease of chickens recognized in several different forms. The most important are "Fowl Paralysis" or neurolymphomatosis, which affects the nerves of growing pullets and laying birds, and Visceral Lymphomatosis. In the latter, affected birds characteristically show an enlargement of the Liver; hence the common name, "Big Liver Disease."

Prolapsis of the oviduct is an important reproductive disorder. Poultry-men refer to afflicted birds as "pickouts," since the everted oviduct protruding through the vent is generally the focal point of cannibalism of pen mates. A heritable basis for this ailment is suggested by the breed differences shown in Table 19-3. The Fayoumi breed, native to Egypt, has consistently shown a higher incidence of prolapsis than Leghorns at the Iowa Station. However, the Fayoumi has a higher natural resistance to Leucosis.

Studies indicate that general laying-flock viability is heritable to a low degree, perhaps around 5%. This indicates that most effective genetic improvement requires an evaluation of average performance of sire progeny families. Many breeders deliberately expose chicks to mature birds to increase disease contamination in order to identify genetically resistant families.

The possibility of developing genetically resistant strains has been well demonstrated at Cornell University. Figure 19-5 shows the difference between strains selected for resistance and for susceptibility to Leucosis. In 1955 the resistant strains showed only 2–3% mortality from Leucosis, compared with over 25% for the susceptible strain.

A rather remarkable fact is that reciprocal crosses involving the Leghorn breed and the dual-purpose breeds (Plymouth Rocks, Rhode Island Reds,

TABLE 19-3. | *Breed differences in adult mortality due to prolapse of the oviduct.* [Data from the Iowa Agr. Expt. Sta.]

Year	Breed	Total birds	Total mortality	Number dead from prolapse	Percent prolapse of total mortality
1957	Leghorn	1380	269	1	0.4
	Fayoumi	629	64	16	25.0
1958	Leghorn	1731	208	0	0
	Fayoumi	1037	119	24	20.2
1959	Leghorn	1913	207	15	7.2
	Fayoumi	1467	173	29	16.8
All years	Leghorn	4024	684	16	2.3
	Fayoumi	3133	356	69	19.4

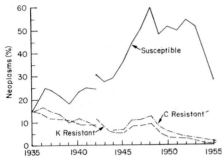

Fig. 19-5. Mortality from leucosis in White Leghorn lines selected for resistance and susceptibility. Break in curves 1942 represent two levels of exposure.) [From Hutt's *Genetic Resistance to Disease in Domestic Animals,* Cornell University Press, Ithaca, N.Y., 1958.]

Australorps, and others) show a striking difference in laying-house mortality. Table 19-4 gives the results of 2-year experiments conducted in Iowa which show that crossbred progeny produced in 1956 from Leghorn males mated to dual-purpose females had 24% mortality over a 9-month laying period, compared with 13% for the reciprocal crosses. Comparative figures were 39% and 18%, respectively, in 1957. Other workers have noted similar differential response is due either to a maternal influence of the dual-purpose female, perhaps in the form of disease transmission, or to a genetic effect associated with the sex chromosome of the Leghorn male parent.

Body Size, Conformation, and Growth Rate. One need not look far to discover evidence that body size and conformation are highly hereditary traits. Consider the size and shape differences between breeds, and contrast, for example, a Bantam, a Leghorn, and a Cochin.

BODY SIZE. Large body size is of primary importance to broiler and turkey breeders. This is mainly because mature body size is correlated with rate of growth. Also, broilers and turkeys produced from strains having large adult body size show the most efficient feed utilization.

On the other hand, in egg-laying strains of chickens small or intermediate body size is preferred. Such birds have lower body-maintenance cost but sufficient mature size is still necessary to insure the production of market eggs of satisfactory size.

Between individuals of the same breed and strain, differences in adult

TABLE 19-4.	*Laying-house mortality in reciprocal crosses of Leghorns and heavy breeds.** [Iowa Agr. Expt. Sta.]*			

Test year	No. birds	Leghorn male × heavy breed female	No. birds	Heavy breed male × Leghorn female
1956	246	24%	178	13%
1957	244	39%	242	18%

* Heavy breeds: New Hampshire, R.I. Red, B.P. Rock, W.P. Rock.

body size have been shown to be highly heritable. Most estimates indicate the heritability between 40 and 70% (see Table 19-1). This means that the breeder may effectively change body size within a strain by simple mass selection.

CONFORMATION. This is especially important in turkeys. The broad-breasted turkey common on the market today—but unknown twenty years ago—bears witness to the accomplishment of modern turkey breeders (see Fig. 11-5). However, whether this is all to the good is open to question. Many breeders now wonder whether the great emphasis on broad breasts is responsible for the poor reproductive performance found in many strains of turkeys today.

Body conformation in broiler chickens is of secondary importance because of the practice in marketing broiler meat in the cut-up and packaged form. In the case of egg-laying flocks, body conformation is essentially of no importance. Most of the egg-laying fowl when marketed are purchased by the canning industry and are used in the manufacture of chicken soup and other prepared foods.

GROWTH RATE. Rate of growth is of major importance in the breeding of meat chickens as well as turkeys. Rapid growth means a saving in time, labor, feed consumption, and overhead in the production of meat. Growth rate is apparently about 30% heritable in most strains of broilers and recent work suggests the same degree of heritability in the case of turkeys. This suggests that an important part of the high performance in growth rate and feed efficiency, attained by broilers and turkeys over the past two decades, can be credited to genetic improvement. However, this is not to underestimate the important contributions of modern rations to high performance.

For all animals, rate of growth is characterized by a period of acceleration followed by a period of deceleration. This gives rise to the typical growth curve illustrated in Fig. 19-6 for broilers and turkeys.

In broilers the periods of acceleration and deceleration are roughly divided at 12 weeks of age, while in turkeys the periods divide at about 16 weeks of age. The most economic growth takes place over the accelerated growth period. For this reason broilers marketed at 12 weeks or less, or turkey fryers grown to 16 weeks of age, can be produced on less feed per pound of gain than,

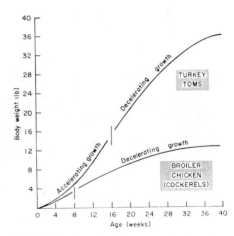

Fig. 19-6. Comparative growth of turkeys and broiler chickens.

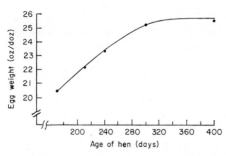

Fig. 19-7. Egg size increase in a laying flock. [Data from the Iowa Multiple Unit Poultry Test.]

say, more mature roasting chickens. Evidence has accumulated over the past 20 years that efficiency of feed utilization is hereditary. Breed differences, strain differences, and differences between sire progeny have been observed. For example, Jull (1952) found as much as 24% difference in feed consumed between two groups of progeny of different Barred Plymouth Rock sires. In general, feed efficiency is highly correlated with growth rate.

Egg Size. Figure 19-7 shows graphically how egg size increases to the maximum from the time that the first egg is laid. Weight of the first egg laid by the pullet represents about 75% of the maximum reached when the pullet is mature. The speed at which a pullet reaches mature egg size is influenced by hatch date and by age at maturity. Birds hatched in March and April reach maximum egg size in a shorter period of time than chickens hatched in October or November. Size of the first egg is closely associated with body growth, which in turn is influenced by time of hatching. The latter enters into the picture because of its relation to the amount of normal daylight during the growth of a bird.

A number of management factors may also influence egg size. For example, eggs from hens in cages may frequently be larger than those from hens under floor management; results reported by the California Random Sample Test show this to be true. A further example from the Iowa Multiple Unit Poultry Test is given in Table 19-5.

TABLE 19-5. *Egg size in floor vs. cage management (ounces per dozen) from 3 pairs of farms. [From the First Iowa Multiple Unit Poultry Test, 1958.]*

Test	Floor	Cage
1	24.8	26.8
2	25.7	25.8
3	25.5	26.6
Av.	25.3	26.4

19-5. CORRELATED RESPONSES TO
SELECTION IN POULTRY

The problem of the breeder would be much simpler if each of the economic traits were inherited independently. Then, if a strain is deficient, say, in egg size, a correction could be made by selection for larger eggs without worrying about the consequences to other traits of importance. Recent evidence leads to the point of view that all traits are genetically correlated —either in a positive or negative sense. This appears to be true, in the main, of populations which have been subjected to selection over many generations—for example, strains of chickens selected for egg production. In such populations most of the remaining genetic covariation would be caused by genes having pleiotropic effects. Over long periods of selection, genes favorable to each of two traits would have been fixed by selection. Then only those pleiotropic genes favorable to one trait but unfavorable to another would be unfixed. This accounts for the existence of negative genetic correlations.

From a practical standpoint, this means that the breeder wanting to select for improvement in one trait must see that no serious regression has occurred in important correlated traits. In some cases it appears that breeders have already encountered some difficulties. The relatively poor egg pro-

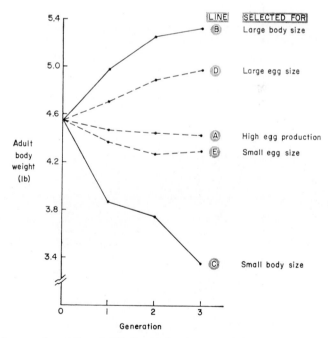

Fig. 19-8. Direct and correlated effects of selection on adult body weight. [Iowa Agricultural Experimental Station, 1961.]

duction of broiler strains appears to be a consequence of "all-out" selection for growth and feed efficiency. The poor fertility in broad-breasted strains of turkeys is probably a consequence of overemphasis on conformation.

As an example of correlated responses to selection for body size in White Leghorns, an experiment conducted at Iowa State University may be cited, in which lines were selected solely on the basis of body weight but in opposite directions. Figure 19-8 shows that these lines differed by two pounds after three generations of selection. The question now arises: what happened to the other important economic traits in these lines after selection only for body weight? If the traits are genetically uncorrelated then the two lines should have been the same. From results of this experiment we find that for each pound of body weight increase:

> Shank length increased .6 cm.
> Age to first egg increased 4.5 days.
> Egg weight increased by 2 oz/dozen.
> Rate of egg production decreased by 2%.
> Fertility and hatchability decreased by 4%.

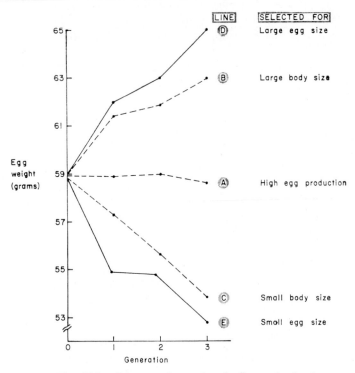

Fig. 19-9. Direct and correlated effects of selection on egg weight. [Iowa Agricultural Experimental Station, 1961.]

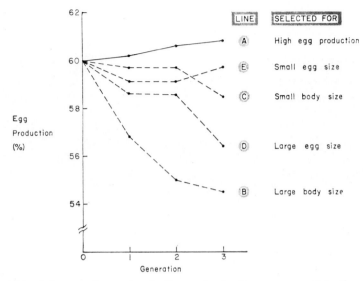

Fig. 19-10. Direct and correlated effects of selection on egg production. [Iowa Agricultural Experimental Station, 1961.]

It is clear, then, that such a simple trait as body weight cannot be changed without some alteration in other traits unless they are under selection. Commercial geneticists must be cautious in making genetic changes in their breeding stock—especially for highly heritable traits, since these are most apt to cause marked correlated responses.

As long as the genetic correlation between two traits is positive, simultaneous improvement in both traits is possible. However, the opportunity to advance genetically on both traits is decreased in proportion to the degree of negative correlation.

REFERENCES AND SELECTED READINGS

References marked with an asterisk are of general interest.

*Hagedoorn, A. L. and G. Sykes, 1953. *Poultry Breeding*. Crosby Lockwood and Son Ltd., London.

*Hutt, F. B., 1949. *Genetics of the Fowl*. McGraw-Hill, New York.

*———, 1958. *Genetic Resistance to Disease in Domestic Animals*. Comstock Publishing Associates, Ithaca.

*Jull, M. A., 1952. *Poultry Breeding*. 3rd ed. Wiley, New York.

Lerner, I. M., 1951. Principles of commercial poultry breeding. Agricultural Experiment Station and Extension Service Manual I. Univ. of California, Berkeley.

*Warren, D. C., 1953. *Practical Poultry Breeding*. Macmillan, New York.

———, 1958. A half century of advances in the genetics and breeding improvement of poultry. *Poultry Sci.*, 37:3–20.

Physiological Mechanisms and Livestock Production

Chapter 20

Nervous and Hormonal Controlling Mechanisms

The most important attributes of animals, whether common to all or peculiar to some, are, manifestly, attributes of soul and body, in conjunction, e.g. sensation, memory, passion, appetite and desire in general, and in addition, pleasure and pain.

ARISTOTLE, *On Sense and the Sensible*

20-1. INTRODUCTION

The nervous and endocrine systems are concerned with the adjustment of the animal body to external and internal changes. Certain changes in the external environment may be of little importance to the animal body, while others such as changes in food availability, temperature, light intensity, or impending physical danger, are of extreme importance—they are changes to which the animal must adjust in order to survive. A change in internal environment may be seen after violent exercise. The actively contracting muscles markedly increase the use of oxygen and nutrients and the production of carbon dioxide and other waste products. Since the greater mass of the active body is made up of contracting muscles, there very soon occur small but significant changes in blood composition in the body, changes in the internal environment. The change in internal environment sets into motion nervous and hormonal mechanisms which increase the heart rate and the blood flow to the lungs and active muscles, thereby renewing and tending to maintain a constant blood composition.

329

Rapid body adjustments to changes in the external or internal environment are for the most part initiated by the nervous system. The nervous system also provides in the cerebrum a center for storing and associating sensations, making possible the mental processes of memory, learning, and thought. The endocrine system is designed to regulate certain body functions, such as body growth, in which time is not the most important factor. The secretions of the endocrine organs, the hormones, although not directly concerned with higher mental processes, can modify them considerably; note the severe psychological disturbances that may be associated with the cessation of gonadal function during the menopause or climacteric in the human, conditions that are relieved by the administration of estrogens or androgens, the hormones normally secreted by the gonads. But the adjustment of body function by the nervous and endocrine systems is dependent upon the mechanisms which detect changes in the internal and external environment. Therefore, let us first consider the receptor organs of the nervous system.

20-2. THE NERVOUS SYSTEM

The Receptor Organs. Changes in the environment are of many types and must be sorted out or recognized; that is, the animal body must have receptor mechanisms capable of detecting the kinds of change and the degrees of change in the environment. The most complex receptors of the animal body are the eyes and ears, receptors sensitive to changes in the environment involving the intensity and quality of light and sound. There are, however, a multitude of receptors sensitive to changes in the external environment that are far simpler in structure and less evident. Receptors sensitive to chemical change (taste and smell), temperature, and pressure are located in discrete or diffuse areas of the body surface.

The internal environment has a multitude of receptors, located in the heart, arteries, muscles, hollow organs (digestive tract, reproductive tract, and bladder), the middle ear, and the brain, which are sensitive to changes in concentration of oxygen, carbon dioxide, and other chemicals in the blood and to the degree of stretching or contraction of muscles. Receptors, therefore, are strategically placed to detect changes in the external and internal environments, changes which constitute stimuli capable of exciting specific receptors. Excitations set up in the receptors by stimuli excite, in turn, nerve fibers attached to or in contact with the receptor. The excitation, propagated along the nerve fiber to the central nervous system at speeds up to 120 m/sec, is known as a nerve impulse.

The Neuron. Most of us are familiar with the nerves in the arms and legs. More precisely, they are really nerve trunks containing hundreds of extensions or processes of highly specialized body cells called neurons. Neurons are the units of the nervous system and are basically alike, whether concerned with highly involved functions of the nervous system, such as memory, learning, or thought, or the simpler functions of conduction to and from the central nervous system.

All the cells of the body possess the ability to react to stimuli and to conduct the excitation initiated by stimuli the length of their cells. The neuron exhibits this property of conduction to the highest degree. The extensive ramifications of neuron processes throughout the body and their multiple connections within the brain and spinal cord provide an excellent communication system between widely separated portions of the body as well as between the body and the external environment.

The neuron has a cell body and, typically, two types of cell projections —dendrites and axons (Fig. 20-1). Neurons conducting impulses from the body surface and from the various receptors to the spinal cord and brain are called afferent or sensory neurons. The afferent neurons have no dendrites but only long axons—extending in some cases from a receptor in the skin, running the length of a limb, past the neuron cell body just outside the spinal cord, and finally terminating within the gray matter of the spinal cord—a unique single cell approximately 3 feet long. Efferent or motoneu-

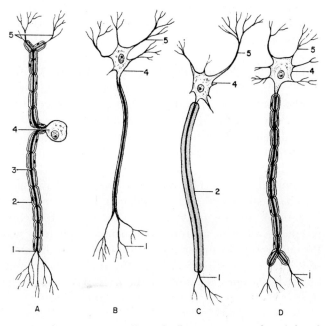

Fig. 20-1. Types of neurons: A, Myelinated afferent neuron of peripheral nerve; B, nonmyelinated interneuron of the gray matter of the spinal cord; C, multipolar myelinated motor neuron of the brain; D, myelinated motor neuron of peripheral nerve; 1, axon; 2, myelin sheath; 3, node of Ranvier; 4, neuron cell body; 5, dendrite.

rons, conducting impulses to muscles and other "effectors," originate in the spinal cord or brain, where the cell body of the neuron is located. The efferent neurons have short dendrites, and the axons emerging from the cord or brain vary in length according to the distance of the muscles and glands from the central nervous system.

A third type of neuron, the association or interneuron, makes connections between afferent and efferent neurons within the spinal cord and brain. Neurons are similar in that they have a cell body and cell processes but differ from each other in the number of dendrites, the length of their axons, and whether or not the processes are covered with a myelin sheath. Myelin is a lipoprotein material covering the axon and imparting a glistening white appearance to the nerve fiber. In peripheral neurons, as illustrated in Fig. 20-1 (a and d), the myelin sheath is interrupted at regular intervals by evenly spaced constrictions known as the nodes of Ranvier. The gray and white matter of the nervous system is dependent upon the distribution of nonmyelinated neuron cell bodies, dendrites, and axons (gray matter) and myelinated axons (white matter).

There are varied and extremely complicated connections of afferent, interneuron, and efferent neurons within the nervous system. The basic functional unit of the nervous system, however, the reflex arc, demonstrates the functional relationship between afferent neuron, integration center, and efferent neuron.

The Reflex Arc and the Basic Spinal Reflex. Many responses to changes in the external environment are protective mechanisms. This is exemplified by the abrupt withdrawal of a limb after contact with a sharp object. The body's reaction to this type of stimulus is very rapid and is usually accomplished before the individual is aware of the pain. The rapidity of response indicates that the nervous pathway from the stimulated receptor to the integrating center and back to the contracting muscles must be rather direct and uncomplicated. This type of response is a basic spinal reflex.

A basic spinal reflex is dependent upon the integrity of neurons present in a reflex arc. Figure 20-2 illustrates the components of the reflex arc— receptors, afferent neurons, interneurons, efferent neurons and effectors. Pressure receptors in the sole of the foot are stimulated by changes in pressure occurring during walking or by any localized pressure such as a sharp object. Sufficient excitation of the pressure receptors induces an excitatory state in a sensory nerve fiber, an excitation that is passed the entire length of the neuron as a nerve impulse. Fine endings of the axon of the sensory neuron terminate in close contact with the dendrites of an interneuron within the gray matter of the spinal cord, forming a synapse, or conjunction. The excitation is propagated across the synapse and is conducted in the interneuron to its synaptic connection with the cell body of an efferent neuron in the ventral horn of the gray matter of the spinal cord. The effer-

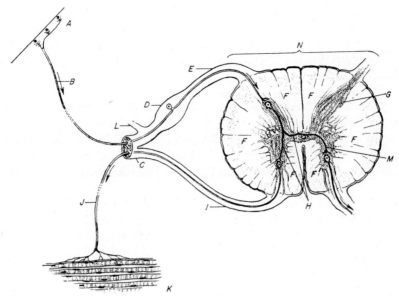

Fig. 20-2. The spinal cord, the spinal nerve, and the reflex arc. A, Pressure receptor in the foot; B, sensory neuron from the body surface; C, spinal nerve; D, afferent nerve cell bodies in dorsal nerve; E, dorsal root of spinal nerve; F, white matter of spinal cord; G, gray matter of spinal cord; H, interneuron in gray matter of spinal cord; I, ventral root of spinal nerve; J, motor neuron; K, muscle of leg; L, autonomic pathway to and from the spinal cord; M, interneuron connections with opposite side of spinal cord; N, spinal cord.

ent neuron, which leaves the spinal cord by the ventral root terminates in skeletal muscle and stimulates it to contract, thus removing the foot from the sharp object.

In view of the nervous conduction rate of 50–70 m/sec and the limited number of neurons involved, it is not surprising that the basic spinal reflex is almost instantaneous. The example given is certainly oversimplified; many receptors would be activated, several afferent, interneurons, and efferent neurons would be involved, and numerous skeletal muscles would contract in the removal of the foot. Nevertheless, the basic component of the reflex arc remains the same in all reflex actions of the body, although interneurons leading to other centers—as well as efferent neurons leading to other tissue —may be activated by the initial stimulation of afferent neurons.

As mentioned above, the excitation transmitted along the axon of the neuron is referred to as a nerve impulse. Space will not permit describing the nature of this impulse more than to say that it depends upon shifts in positive ion concentrations between the inside and outside of the axon. These changes result in a localized electrical current which in turn causes ionic shifts in adjoining portions of the axon. Thus the excitation or impulse is propagated along the axon much in the manner that a flame proceeds along a fuse—the conspicuous difference being that the changes in the fuse are irreversible whereas the nerve is restored to its resting condition in fractions of a second.

Parts of the Nervous System. Embryologically the central nervous system is a continuous tube extending from the anterior to the posterior portion of the body. Dilations, outgrowths, and considerable foldings of the anterior portion of the tube in the developing individual give rise to a prominent anterior portion, the brain, and a more posterior portion, the spinal cord (Fig. 20-3).

The spinal nerves leave the spinal cord at regular intervals—at each vertebra from the tail bone to the neck region—and supply afferent and efferent neurons to the tissues of the body. The reflex centers are located in the gray matter of the brain and spinal cord and communicate freely with each other by ascending and descending neurons in the white matter of the spinal cord (myelinated nerve fibers traveling in the outermost portion of the spinal cord). This intercommunication of the reflex centers makes possible the coordinated activities of skeletal muscle innervated by several spinal or cranial nerves. Furthermore, it is a means by which higher integrating centers in the brain are informed of changes controlled by lower spinal centers. This is why strong pressure applied to the sole of the foot would result in a contraction of several muscles in the leg to bring about

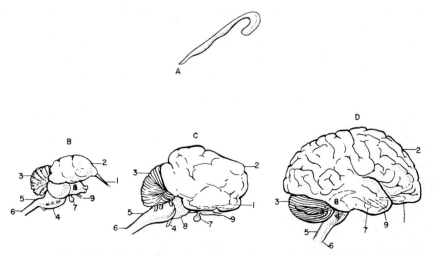

Fig. 20-3. Cerebral dominance in higher species. A, Undifferentiated neural tube in all embryos; B, pigeon brain; C, pig brain; D, human brain; 1, olfactory process; 2, cerebrum; 3, cerebellum; 4, pons; 5, medulla oblongata; 6, spinal cord; 7, pituitary gland; 8, mid-brain. 9, optic nerves.

withdrawal of the foot, a shifting of the body weight by the contraction of muscles in the hips, waist, and body trunk, and contraction of muscles in the opposite leg in order to maintain balance as the center of gravity of the body is shifted. There is also mental awareness of the stimuli, through afferent impulses in ascending neurons to higher brain centers.

The areas of the body supplied by neurons of each spinal segment can be mapped out, with the control of skeletal muscles in each area assigned to definite spinal nerves. Quite often, reflex testing by a practitioner can pinpoint damage to a particular level of the spinal cord, by testing the functional integrity of the various reflex arcs of the spinal cord.

The spinal reflex centers control the primitive movements of the animal body, including the contractions of skeletal muscles involved in protective responses. Spinal centers, with a minimal number of neurons involved in the reflex arc, are very well suited for rapid responses to external stimuli. Finer adjustments of reflexes are made by higher integrating centers, aware of the total sum of environmental changes impinging upon the body and influenced by the processes of experience, learning, and willful intent. The spinal reflex centers do not integrate the activities associated with several vital body functions such as respiration, circulation of blood, and regulation of heart beat.

The brain and the spinal cord cannot be considered as separate systems. Many of the functions of the brain are mediated through neurons descending the spinal cord and synapsing with spinal neurons, and all the functions of spinal reflex centers are influenced by brain centers. One of the greatest differences in the spinal cord and brain is in the amount and type of physiological activity that each controls. The spinal cord can be considered as a series of reflex centers concerned with skeletal muscle contraction. A spinal center on the right side of the spinal cord is duplicated by another on the left side; that is, there is a spinal center for each set of duplicate muscles. A portion of the brain is also made up of duplicating reflex centers controlling muscles in the head region. Other centers, however, control specific body functions and are not duplicated; there are, for example, several centers in the brain concerned with the flow of blood through the body. Each center has a definite role, controlling heart rate, the diameter of the arteries, or the shunting of blood flow from nonactive to active tissues, but their action is complementary or antagonistic.

The principle of the reflex arc applies to all reflex centers in the brain; that is, afferent neurons carry impulses to brain centers and efferent neurons carry impulses away from the brain centers. The main difference between brain and spinal centers is one of complexity, with extraordinarily complex connections, by means of association neurons, being evident between brain centers. A greater degree of complexity in neuron interaction is apparent from the lowest to the highest portion of the brain.

The afferent and efferent neurons of the brain do not necessarily travel together in one nerve as do many of the spinal neurons. The brain has 12 pairs of cranial nerves. The cranial nerves may be purely sensory (olfactory, optic, or acoustic nerves) or almost entirely motoneurons (oculomotor nerve —to muscles of the eye) or may be mixed nerves (facial nerve—sensory from the taste buds in the mouth and motor to the muscles of the scalp and salivary glands). The cell bodies of the neurons occupy the center of the spinal cord (the gray matter), but the reverse is true in brain tissue; that is, the outermost portion of the brain is made up of gray matter and the interior portions are made up of ascending, descending, and association myelinated nerve tracts. This is one reason why it is not too difficult to study the functions of some areas of the brain by placing electrodes directly on the skull and noting the responses obtained by electrical stimulation of specific neuron cell centers.

The medulla oblongata, the portion of the brain connecting with the spinal cord, contains reflex centers concerned with the regulation of breathing, the strength and rate of heartbeat, the flow of blood through body vessels, and the secretions of several glands, and centers controlling coughing, sneezing, vomiting, and the adjustment of posture.

The cerebellum, lying just anterior to the medulla oblongata, contains reflex centers involved in the maintenance of skeletal muscle tone. A state of partial contraction of skeletal muscles is necessary for reflex or voluntary contraction to avoid the jerkiness that would exist if the muscles contracted from a completely relaxed state; the contraction must be slightly opposed by antagonistic muscles. The cerebellum is also involved in the fine adjustment of skeletal muscle activity as seen in locomotion as well as in voluntary muscle activity requiring extreme dexterity. It is the coordinating center for many spinal reflexes in the body.

The midbrain has reflex centers controlling specific body functions and coordinating centers exhibiting considerable control over lower brain centers in the cerebellum and medulla oblongata. The anterior portion of the midbrain, the thalamus, is a relay center for the majority of sensory impulses to the cerebrum. It sorts the various sensory impulses to appropriate conscious areas of the brain and also initiates various body responses as a result of intense or extreme afferent stimulation. A large aggregation of neuron cell bodies make up the hypothalamus, which regulates extremely complicated body functions such as internal temperature, sleep, blood flow, heartbeat, and hunger, and controls the production or release of hormones from the anterior pituitary gland. Some of this regulation is indirect and is brought about by stimulation or inhibition of centers in the medulla oblongata.

The functions of the involuntary muscles and glands are controlled by the autonomic nervous system, which includes afferent and efferent neurons and reflex centers in the central nervous system, just like the somatic nervous system controlling the voluntary (skeletal) muscles. The smooth muscles and glands, contrary to the control of voluntary muscles, are in most instances under the control of two sets of motoneurons, the sympathetic and parasympathetic neurons. The parasympathetic neurons leave the central nervous system in certain of the cranial nerves and sacral spinal nerves in the posterior part of the body. The sympathetic motoneurons leave the central nervous system through spinal nerves in the thoracic and lumbar regions of the body. The parasympathetic system is mainly concerned with body functions of an animal in a resting state and regulates functions such as the secretion of salivary and digestive juices and the normal movement of the intestinal tract. The sympathetic system, on the other hand, is involved in what may be considered as emergency reactions; all the functions activated by stimulation of the sympathetic system are those which allow the animal to exhibit its greatest functional capacities. Sympathetic fibers also control the release of adrenaline from the adrenal gland. Adrenaline acts similarly to the tissue activators released by sympathetic neuron endings. The result of adrenaline release, therefore, is an intensification and reinforcement of all of the independent actions of the sympathetic system and a coordinated "alarm reaction." Body activities such as increased heart action, diversion of blood from nonactive to active tissues, mobilization of body energy sources, the secretion of sweat, maximal accommodation of the eyes for near vision, and the erection of hair or feathers are enhanced upon stimulation of the sympathetic system. Pain, fright, loud noise, or any intense afferent stimulation can result in the "alarm reaction," with stimulation of the sympathetic system and release of adrenaline.

For the most part, the sympathetic and parasympathetic systems act in antagonism to each other in the control of vital body functions, but together they complement general body welfare: vital body functions under their control are not allowed to come to a complete halt nor seriously to overfunction. A good example of this is seen in the control of the heartbeat. Both of the systems have afferent and efferent neurons to heart musculature, but the parasympathetic efferent neurons are inhibitory and sympathetic neurons stimulatory to heartbeat. In mammals, as contrasted to birds, there is considerable parasympathetic tone to the heart at all times; that is, the heart rate is always being depressed when an animal is in the resting state. One obvious result of this tone is that whereas the bird has an extremely high heart rate (very close to its maximal rate) even at rest, the mammal, when active, can triple the resting heart rate. Under conditions of extreme afferent stimulation of the midbrain—as in trauma, fright, loud noise, or willful physical exertion—the parasympathetic centers are depressed and heartbeat increases. Initially this alarm reaction is of short duration and the parasympathetic system renews the inhibitory role unless the emergency persists. If physical exertion is continued the parasympathetic system is inhibited through other brain centers aware of increased needs for a high blood pressure and increased blood flow.

The cerebrum, that portion of the brain reaching the highest development in birds and mammals, constitutes the major portion of the brain; in fact, it represents about three-quarters of the total mass of nervous tissue in the body. The high degree of intelligence found in man can doubtlessly be attributed to its relatively large size. The lower brain and spinal cord are mostly reflex centers that react predictably to impulses reaching them over sensory and motoneurons (from other brain centers). Functions of the cerebrum, however, which include learning, memory, thought, and purposeful action, cannot easily be explained on the basis of the reflex arc and reflex center, since the activities of the cerebrum are for the most part unpredictable and are based upon previous experiences of the animal. The cerebrum exerts considerable influence over the lower brain and spinal centers, not only in willful movement, but also in the perfect adjustment of lower brain and spinal cord reflex action. The cerebrum also makes possible modifications of basic reflex action.

Observations of animal activities demonstrate that there are considerable variations among animals in their responses to the same stimuli. This does not imply that basic reflex arcs are lacking or abolished in different animals and other responses substituted—we can assume, unless damage or developmental abnormalities are apparent, that all cattle, for example, are born with almost the same number and location of neurons. It does imply, however, that there are modifications of reflex responses in animals that are dependent upon experience (or, in the case of domestic animals, management). The conditioned reflex is a basic learning phenomenon. Once an animal has been exposed to certain situational stimuli, this exposure will influence the response to the same situation occurring at a later date. Conditioned reflexes can therefore be considered as all those reflexes that are gained by the animal in the course of their existence, and are modifications that contribute in large part to the personality or special activities of the animal.

The establishment of a conditioned reflex was early demonstrated by Pavlov in experiments on dogs. Certain chemical receptors in the tongue (taste buds) are stimulated by the presence of food in the mouth and, through a simple reflex, this results in the release of saliva. The normal stimulus for salivation, the placing of food in the mouth, is termed an unconditioned stimulus. If, when a dog is fed, a bell is rung, and if this association is made repeatedly (the bell rung each time the dog is fed), there comes a time when the ringing of the bell alone (the conditioned stimulus) will cause a secretion of saliva. The same response can be elicited if the conditioned stimulus is a particular sound, a light, or a tactile stimulus. In a conditioned response the efferent or motor side of the reflex arc remains the same; that is, in the dog experiment, the end result is the stimulation of the release of saliva, regardless of the conditioned stimulus. It is therefore obvious that the afferent side of the reflex arc can vary, and simply becomes integrated with the efferent side of the reflex arc already established. This is an uncomplicated example of a conditioned reflex, but much more complex relations dealing with the inhibition, reinforcement, and establishment of conditioned reflexes have been demonstrated.

Another conditioned reflex seen in domestic animals is the letting down of milk as the result of some repetitive conditioned stimulus associated with milking—the clanging of milk pails, the movement toward the milking shed, or any external stimuli (the conditioned stimuli) associated with the unconditioned stimulus, which is the manipulation of the teats at milking time. This reflex is considered in more detail in Chapter 23.

According to Pavlov, the formation and maintenance of conditioned reflexes are dependent upon an intact cerebral cortex. Theoretically there could be as many conditioned reflexes in an animal as there are separate reflex arcs. This would indicate, if conditioned reflexes can be established over the efferent limb of the many body reflexes, that neurons from the cerebral cortex must have direct or indirect synaptic connection with all of the lower brain and spinal cord reflex centers. This would indicate a tremendous amount of cerebral control of body function.

20-3. THE ENDOCRINE SYSTEM

Endocrine Glands and Their Hormones. There are available to the body cells many substances that modify their activities. Nervous excitation or inhibition of muscles or glands are brought about by the release of compounds from nerve endings close to the tissues. Various products of metabolism—carbon dioxide, for example—can inhibit metabolic activity in the majority of body cells but can stimulate activity in other cells—notably, the chemical receptors. However, the majority of the body's constituents supplied to the tissue fluids—minerals, amino acids, proteins, fats, and vitamins—although of immense importance to the normal function of the body cells, do not act as regulators of cell function.

One group of compounds in the animal body that regulate or direct the physiological activities of tissues are the hormones. They are "organic compounds produced by a tissue or tissues of the body, passed into the blood stream, exciting or inhibiting the physiological activity of some tissue and not as far as is known directly involved in metabolic processes." The term hormone means, "I excite," but it is known that a given hormone may stimulate one physiological activity and inhibit another. Hormones are believed to act either by increasing or decreasing the concentration of enzymes or the availability of substances necessary for normal cellular function within the stimulated or inhibited tissue.

The glands or tissues producing hormones, the endocrine glands, are not of any one type of tissue. The hormones also differ markedly in chemical structure. Figure 20-4 shows diagrammatically the location of the various endocrine organs in a sow. Notice that the hypothalamus and the pituitary glands, glands exhibiting a marked control over the function of the other endocrine glands, are located within the skull; that is, on the ventral surface of the midbrain. The hypothalmus is chiefly a nerve center composed of many neuron cell bodies, whereas the pituitary gland is a more typical endocrine organ—storing or producing the "tropic hormones," which control a large number of the other endocrine organs in the body. The hypothalamus, in addition to many other functions, controls the release of several of the hormones from the pituitary gland.

The endocrine tissues, their general locations in the body, the hormones they produce, and the type of tissue and responses they stimulate are listed in Table 20-1. The complementary and antagonistic action of the various hormones are too numerous to consider here. It should be pointed out, however, that the resultant physiological effect of endocrine control in the intact animal is due to the interaction of several endocrine glands and their hormones.

Hormones may be very specific as to the tissues they influence (their "tar-

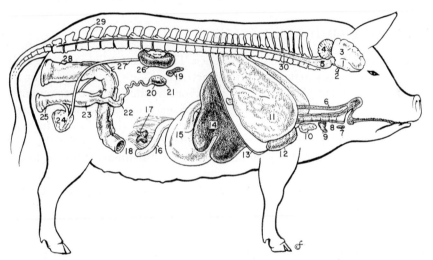

Fig. 20-4. The endocrine glands (marked with an asterisk) and other organs in a sow. 1, Hypothalamus*; 2, pituitary gland*; 3, cerebral cortex; 4, cerebellum; 5, medulla oblongata; 6, esophagus; 7, parathyroid gland*; 8, trachea; 9, lobe of thyroid gland*; 10, thymus gland; 11, lung; 12, heart; 13, diaphragm; 14, liver; 15, stomach; 16, small intestine; 17, islets of Langerhans in pancreas*; 18, approx. 55 ft of small and 12 ft of large intestine removed; 19, adrenal gland*; 20, ovulation bursa of oviduct; 21, ovary*; 22, right uterine horn; 23, cervix; 24, urinary bladder; 25, vagina; 26, kidney; 27, ureter; 28, rectum; 29, vertebral column; 30, spinal cord. Hormones are secreted by the gastric and intestinal mucosa—thus these tissues also are endocrine glands. [Drawn by C. A. Dick.]

get tissue") or they may influence all the tissues of the body. Growth hormone, the adrenal cortical hormones, thyroxin, and insulin influence most if not all the tissues of the body, whereas the gonadotropins—ACTH, TSH, estrogens, androgens, and progesterone—restrict their actions to a limited number of body tissues. These are, of course, generalizations, since it has been shown that androgens may influence protein metabolism in all cells of the body and that estrogens, at least in birds, strongly influence the mobilization and distribution of lipid during normal growth and egg production. As our knowledge of tissue functions expands we will, no doubt, find that all hormones are much less discrete in function than was at first supposed.

Means of Controlling Hormone Secretion. The secretion of certain hormones is believed to be a continuous process and the activities they support are of longer duration than the activities stimulated or inhibited by the nervous system. The exceptions to this generalization are apparent when one considers hormones involved in the development of the reproductive organs and mammary glands, tissues continually changing in patterns influenced by age, season, environmental conditions, and conception. The secretions of hormones are controlled by three means: (1) the nervous system, (2) other hormones reaching the glands through the blood, and (3) changes in the chemical composition of the blood supplying an endocrine organ.

NERVOUS CONTROL. An example of this type of control is the stimulation of ovulation in rabbits by the act of mating. The afferent neuron excitation brings about a release of gonadotropins from the anterior pituitary, and this in turn causes final maturation of eggs and ovulation about twelve hours after mating. Other examples of nervous control are considered in Chapters 21 and 23.

HORMONE CONTROL. The control of hormone secretion from an endocrine gland by hormonal means is noted in the case of the anterior pituitary thyrotropic, adrenocorticotropic, and gonadotropic hormones, which control the production and release of thyroxin, adrenal steroids, and estrogens and androgens, respectively, from their glands. Thyrotropin (TSH), from the anterior pituitary, stimulates the release of thyroxin from the thyroid glands, a hormone that increases the general metabolic rate of the cells of the body. The amount of thyroxin circulating in the blood in turn determines the amount of TSH secretion from the anterior pituitary; any drop in thyroxin stimulates further release of TSH, and any rise in thyroxin concentration inhibits further production of TSH. This feedback mechanism to the gland producing the tropic hormone is referred to as "reciprocal control" and represents an excellent mechanism for regulating the amounts of hormone in the blood stream. The feedback mechanism is illustrated as follows: if you place a normal animal on increased amounts of thyroxin you will, by supplying thyroxin to the blood, slowly shut off the release of TSH

TABLE 20·1. *The endocrine tissues in mammals, the hormones, and the tissues of the body directly influenced.*

Endocrine tissue	Hormones secreted	Tissues influenced	Major physiological actions
Hypothalamus	Neurohormones*	Posterior pituitary	Release of oxytocin and vasopressin.
		Anterior pituitary	Some control of tropic hormone secretion.†
Pituitary gland			
Anterior portion	Growth hormone (GH)	All tissues	Increases anabolic processes, growth of bone and muscle.
	Adrenocorticotropin (ACTH)	Adrenal cortex	Maintenance of functional adrenal glands and secretion of glucocorticoids.
	Follicle stimulating (FSH)	Ovaries	Germinative function (oogenesis).
		Testes	Germinative function (spermatogenesis).
	Luteinizing (ICSH or LH)	Ovaries	Maturation and ovulation of follicles (estrogen secretion) and establishment of corpora lutea.
		Testes	Secretion of androgens from Leydig cells.
	Lactogenic or luteotropin (LTH)	Ovary (corpus luteum)	Maintenance and progesterone secretion.
		Mammary gland	Formation of milk in alveoli.
		Crop gland (pigeon)	Formation of "crop milk."
	Thyrotropin (TSH)	Thyroid gland	Maintenance of thyroid gland and secretion of thyroxin and triiodothyronine.
Posterior portion	Oxytocin	Mammary gland	Alveolar smooth muscle contraction for letdown of milk into ducts and cisterns.
		Uterus	Contractions of estrogen primed uterus at estrus and parturition.
	Vasopressin or antidiuretic	Peripheral blood vessels	Constricts; increases blood pressure.
		Kidney tubules	Promotes water resorption.
Thyroid glands	Thyroxin and some triiodothyronine	All tissues	Increases rate of cellular metabolism.
Parathyroid glands**	Parathyroid hormone	Intestine, bone, kidney	Absorption and resorption of Ca and excretion of P; maintains normal blood calcium levels.
Adrenal glands			
Adrenal cortex	Glucocorticoids	All tissues	Antistress action hormones, anti-inflammatory; mobilizes energy sources; increases blood glucose.

Endocrine tissue	Hormones secreted	Tissues influenced†	Major physiological actions
Adrenal medulla	Electrocorticoids	Kidney, all tissue indirectly	Salt and water balance.
	Adrenaline	Muscles of cardiovascular system	Heart vessels dilate, heart muscle increases rate and strength of contraction. Increases blood supply to active tissues.
		Skeletal muscles	Mobilizes energy sources; increases strength of contraction.
		Liver	Glycogen mobilized for energy.
	Nor-adrenaline	Released at post ganglionic sympathetic nerve endings	Stimulates smooth muscle and glands.
Ovaries	Estrogens	Peripheral blood vessels	Functions in maintenance of blood pressure.
		Mammary glands	Development of duct system.
		Genital tract	Preparation of tract for reception of sperm and ova.
		Body conformation	Female fat distribution.
	Progesterone	Mammary glands	Development of alveolar system.
		Genital tract	Preparation of tract for fertilized ova, nutrition of zygotes, and maintenance of pregnancy.
	Relaxin	Cartilage and ligaments of pelvic girdle	Dissolution and relaxation of cartilage and ligaments to facilitate parturition.
Testes	Androgens	Accessory sex organs	Maturation, storage, and nutrition of sperm.
		Body conformation	Male muscle and fat distribution.
	Estrogens	Accessory sex organs	Action not obvious in normal male.
Placenta ‡	Gonadotropins, adrenocorticotropin, estrogens, progesterone	Ovaries and uterus and adrenals	Complements action of anterior pituitary and ovaries.
Gastrointestinal tract	Secretin	Pancreas	Alkaline secretions for digestion.
	Pancreozymin	Pancreas	Enzyme secretions for digestion.
	Cholecystokinin	Gallbladder	Evacuates bile into intestine.
	Enterogastrone	Stomach	Inhibits motility and acid secretions.
	Gastrin	Stomach	Stimulates acid secretion.

* Classification as endocrine organ questionable. Neurohormones are hormones passed through nerves and released at nerve endings.
† Tropic hormones are GH, ACTH, TSH, LTH, ICSH, LH, and FSH; the latter 3 are the gonadotropines—gonad stimulating hormones.
** The parathyroid glands vary in number and in species and may be located in or close to the thyroid gland or may be distributed throughout the neck and chest.
‡ The intimate attachment of fetal and maternal membranes for purposes of nutritive and excretory exchange. The hormones produced can therefore be of fetal or maternal origin.

from the anterior pituitary gland. When you feed an amount equal to or exceeding the amount of thyroxin the animal is normally producing the secretion of TSH from the anterior pituitary gland is almost completely shut off. If this thyroxin feeding is continued with a resulting deficit of TSH in the blood, the thyroid gland will atrophy and stay in a nonfunctional state, but the metabolic rate of the body is being maintained by the thyroxin. Sudden discontinuation of the thyroxin feeding will result in an animal completely unable to produce their normal complement of thyroxin and a hypothyroid state will result—that is, an abnormally low metabolic rate in all tissues of the body.

CONTROL BY CHANGING COMPOSITION OF THE BLOOD. Examples of endocrine glands which secrete by "chemical control" are the pancreas, controlled by the level of glucose in the blood, and the parathyroid glands, controlled by the level of calcium in the blood. Let us consider the control of insulin secretion by the pancreas. Increased amounts of sugar in the blood supplying the pancreas bring about a release of insulin, which stimulates the conversion of blood sugar to glycogen and to fat. This effect tends to lower blood sugar to normal levels. We can say, then, that the normal control of the release of insulin from the pancreas is dependent upon the level of sugar in the blood supplying this organ, any increase stimulating the secretion of insulin.

There are several other endocrine organs in the body—the adrenal gland, the anterior pituitary, and the pancreas itself—that secrete hormones tending to increase rather than lower the level of blood glucose, by the mobilization of glycogen in the liver and the conversion of fat and protein to blood glucose. It would seem that there is a delicate balance in the adjustment of proper blood glucose that is not readily apparent unless one of the antagonistic components becomes faulty. Certain conditions of pancreatic insufficiency result in diabetes mellitus. In this particular disease the functioning of the pancreas is faulty and it does not respond to high levels of blood glucose by the release of insulin. The antagonistic hormones which tend to increase blood glucose are therefore not opposed and blood glucose reaches levels two to three times that found in the normal individual. The amount of glucose in the blood reaching the kidney is far above the amount that the kidney can resorb. This leads to the pronounced symptoms of this disease—a tremendous increase in the volume of urine and a high amount of sugar in the urine. That the fault in this particular disease lies with the failure of the pancreas is indicated by the complete reversal of blood glucose levels and the disappearance of glucose from the urine following the injection of insulin. The regulation of the diet plus adequate insulin therapy in the diabetic results in normal metabolism and in the conversion of glucose to its storage compounds, glycogen and fat. With this method of therapy, however, extreme difficulties can be encountered with improper use of the insulin. Hypoglycemic shock can result in a diabetic either on normal levels of insulin with increased muscular activity or on too high levels of insulin alone. In either case the level of blood glucose is reduced below that level required for normal nervous activity, the end result being unconsciousness and death if glucose is not administered.

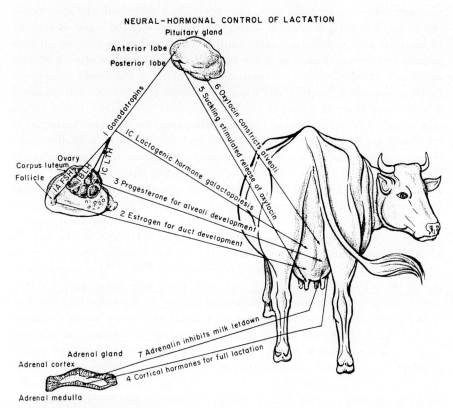

NEURAL–HORMONAL CONTROL OF LACTATION

Fig. 20-5. Neural-hormonal control of lactation. 1. Pituitary gonadotropins: (a) FSH—develops follicles; (b) LH—final maturation and ovulation of follicles and establishment of the corpus luteum; (c) LTH—luteotropin activity maintains corpus luteum and lactogenic activity stimulates milk formation in developed mammary gland. 2. Ovarian estrogens developes mammary duct system, slightly during normal cycle and markedly during pregnancy. 3. Progesterone develops mammary alveolar system, the milk secreting portion, by midpregnancy. 4. Adrenal glucocorticoid hormones necessary for normal lactation. 5. Suckling act or manipulation of teats, by nervous means, stimulates release of oxytocin from posterior pituitary. 6. Oxytocin, reaching the alveoli through the blood, constricts the smooth muscles surrounding them and lets down the milk. 7. Milk letdown can be inhibited by fright, by rough or poor management factors, or by release of adrenalin.

Hormone Action and Interaction. Although the exact mechanism of hormone action is not known, there are in general two types of body changes which follow endocrine gland activity or treatment with hormones. One change is the obvious increase or decrease in a specific type of metabolism within the body. Examples of such responses are the general increase in nitrogen retention in body cells, together with a decreased nitrogen loss in the urine, following treatment with growth hormone; the rapid conversion of body fat and protein to energy sources, expressed as an increase in non-protein nitrogen and glucose in the blood, following treatment with adrenal hormones; or the active resorption of calcium from the bones subsequent to treatment with parathyroid hormone. These changes are accomplished without any obvious increase in the functional size of the target tissues stimulated. The other type of response stimulated by hormone secretion or treatment is the increase in the number and size of the cells of the target tissues, a compensation which enables them to increase functional capacity. The action of the tropic hormones of the anterior pituitary (ACTH, TSH, FSH, LH, and LTH) stimulates this type of response. Adrenocorticotropin injection results in an increase in size of the adrenal gland and consequent increased production of adrenal hormones. The size and functional capacity of this endocrine organ are dependent upon ACTH, just as the thyroid gland is dependent upon TSH. Removal of the anterior pituitary gland (the source of the tropic hormones) is therefore followed by a regression in size of the adrenal and thyroid glands and a low functional state.

It is also possible in normal endocrine control to have one or more hormones stimulating the development of a tissue and other hormones maintaining the development and activity of the tissue. A response of this type is seen in the mammary gland: estrogens and progesterone from the ovaries develop the duct and alveolar systems of the gland; lactogenic hormone, from the anterior pituitary, can then induce the functional activity—that is, the formation of milk within the gland; and yet another hormone, oxytocin, is necessary for the squeezing out or the let-down of milk (Fig. 20-5).

REFERENCES AND SELECTED READINGS

Pace, D. M. and B. W. McCashland, 1960. *College Physiology*, Part 3, Nervous Coordination; Part 4, Receptors. Crowell, New York.

Pavlov, I., 1910. *The Work of the Digestive Glands.* Second English Translation by W. H. Thompson. C. Griffin and Co., London.

Scheer, B. T., 1953. *General Physiology.* Humoral Integration. Wiley, New York, Chapter 19.

Chapter 21

Reproduction

21-1. INTRODUCTION

The ultimate value of any farm animal depends upon its ability to reproduce. Our knowledge of the factors affecting reproductive efficiency is increasing through the accumulation of information on endocrine relationships and the interaction of nutritional and genetic factors on the reproductive process. The entire process is regulated by interlocking hormone systems which synchronize the function of the sex mechanism. The details differ in various species, but the problems in the rat and in the cow or chicken are basically the same. Eggs must be produced and shed by the female, and a mechanism must be present to ensure the presence of viable sperm. The rapid development of artificial insemination in domestic animals has stimulated much research on reproduction in recent years. Some knowledge of anatomy and physiology as well as endocrinology is important, if we are to take full advantage of advances in this area of husbandry.

21-2. ANATOMY OF THE MALE
REPRODUCTIVE ORGANS

In the male the primary organs of reproduction are the paired testes, where the sperm cells are produced. These organs are located in an outpocketing of the abdominal wall known as the scrotum. Other portions of the male reproductive system are the paired accessory glands, the duct system, and the penis (Fig. 21-1).

Testes. The testes develop from the sexually undifferentiated gonads and have a dual function: (1) production of spermatozoa in the seminiferous tubules, and (2) secretion of testosterone, the male sex hormone, by the

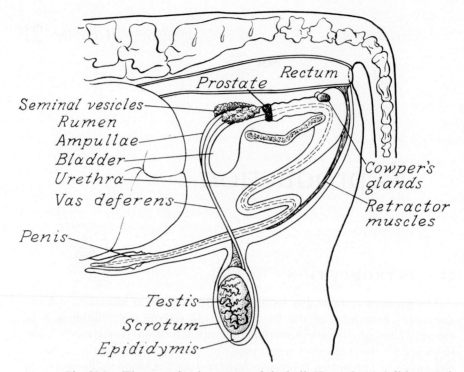

Fig. 21-1. The reproductive organs of the bull. [From G. W. Salisbury and
N. L. VanDemark, Physiology of Reproduction and Artificial Insemination
of Cattle, Freeman, San Francisco, 1961.]

interstitial cells which lie between the tubules. In adult domestic mammals
the testes are located in the scrotum; however, they develop in the dorsal
region of the abdominal cavity and migrate into the scrotum near the time
of birth. In birds the testes do not descend, but remain in the body cavity
near the kidneys. The scrotum is a thermoregulatory organ, and its principal function is to maintain the temperature of the testes below the body
temperature. In the ram normal body temperature is about 102°F, while
that of the testes averages 94°F. It has been known for a long time that
cryptorchids, animals whose testes remain inside the body, are sterile. This
condition occurs in all mammalian species and may be caused by hormonal
deficiencies or by anatomical obstructions in the inguinal canal that prevent the testes from descending into the scrotum.

Sperm cells are produced in the seminiferous tubules, which make up
most of the testicular mass. A mature sperm cell consists of the head, mid-
piece, and tail. Among mammalian cells, spermatozoa are unique because
of their mobility provided by the flagellate tail. The overall length of a
bovine sperm cell is about 70 microns (.07 mm), with the head being ap-

TABLE | *Average semen production and site of deposit in female.*
21-1.

Species	Volume per ejaculate (ml)	Sperm cell concentration (millions/ml)	Site of semen deposit in female
Boar	250	300	Uterus
Bull	5	800	Anterior vagina
Ram	1	2000	Anterior vagina
Stallion	75	200	Forced into uterus
Cock	1.5	4000	Everted vagina

proximately 9 microns in length. The head of the bull, boar, ram, and stallion sperm cell is oblong and flattened. The head of cock spermatozoa is cylindrical in shape.

Male Accessory Glands. The male accessory sex glands include the paired seminal vesicles, the prostate gland, and the paired bulbo-urethral or Cowper's glands. There is considerable variation in the relative size of the glands in different species. In the boar the seminal vesicles are greatly enlarged and contribute to the large volume of semen in this species. The male accessory organs contribute the seminal plasma of the ejaculate, which has two main functions: it serves as a suspending and activating medium and furnishes an energy source. Semen volume and sperm cell concentration vary according to the relative activity of the accessory organs in various species.

Removal of the testes, castration, effects significant changes in the male: (1) there is permanent sterility, (2) sexual desire or libido is greatly reduced or lacking, and (3) the secondary sexual characteristics or masculinity of body form are less prominent. Sterilization of a male without subsequent loss of libido and secondary sexual characteristics can be effected by removing a section from each vas deferens. In a vasectomized animal the cells which produce testosterone continue to function.

21-3. ANATOMY OF THE FEMALE REPRODUCTIVE SYSTEM

The female reproductive system consists of the ovaries and a duct system. The ovaries are homologous (having similar origin) to the testes in the male, and also have a dual function—that is, production of (1) eggs or ova, and (2) hormones.

The Ovaries. The ovaries are lobulated in structure in the sow and in birds. They are relatively smooth and almond- or bean-shaped in the cow,

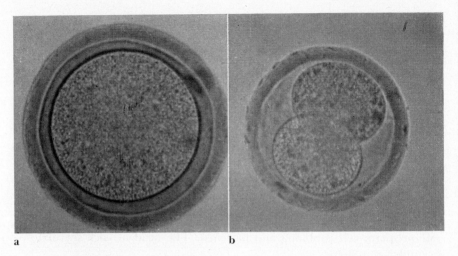

a　　　　　　　　　　　　　　　　　　　　b

Fig. 21-2. Photomicrographs of (a) an unfertilized sheep ovum, (b) a two-celled sheep ovum. Sperm heads can be seen in the zona pellucida of the fertilized ovum. (430 X.)

ewe, and mare. Prominent structures in the ovary are the follicles which produce the ova and corpora lutea, the solid bodies of tissue originating from the walls of ovulated follicles. The presence of a corpus luteum is necessary for initiation of pregnancy in all placental mammals and for successful maintenance of pregnancy in many of them. The diameter of a mature follicle in the cow is 1.8 cm; in the ewe and sow, 1.0 cm; and in the mare, 3.0 cm. The diameter of a fully developed corpus luteum or yellow body is similar to that of the mature follicle for the different species. Corpora lutea are not formed in the bird. The left ovary is functional; the right remains rudimentary.

There is very little difference in the size of ova produced by the various placental mammals; the rabbit and the cow are nearly equal in this respect. The diameter of the cow ovum is about 150 microns. Distinguishing features of the ovum are the cytoplasm enclosed by the vitelline membrane, which constitutes the ovum proper, and the surrounding thick, highly refractile membrane known as the zona pellucida. The presence of sperm cells in the zona pellucida after mating is suggestive that fertilization will occur, and normal cleavage of the ovum proper is strong evidence of fertilization. To get this information, however, ova must be obtained from the reproductive tract, following slaughter or by operative procedure, and examined microscopically. (See Fig. 21-2.)

The Duct System. The infundibulum is the funnel-shaped end of the oviduct near the ovaries. It picks up the ova and the oviduct transports them to the uterus. The latter is lined with a thick mucosal layer or endometrium, which contains many glands. The inner surface of the uterus in the cow, ewe, and other ruminants contains approximately 100 slightly projecting circular areas known as caruncles. During pregnancy these provide for the attachment of fetal membranes by interlocking with corresponding areas, known as cotyledons, on the surface of the chorion. Uterine glands are present only in the noncaruncular area. The sow uterus contains no caruncular areas. The uterine lining of the pregnant mare contains raised structures known as endometrial cups. These take no physical part in fetal membrane attachment, but secrete a hormone, equine gonadotropin. The uterus also contains a well-developed outer longitudinal and an inner circular layer of muscle, which assists in expelling the young at the termination of preg-

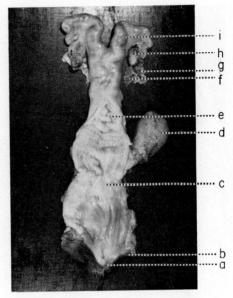

Fig. 21-3. The reproductive tract of a heifer. (a) clitoris; (b) vulva; (c) vagina; (d) bladder; (e) cervix; (f) uterine horn; (g) ovary; (h) oviduct; (i) infundibulum. ($\frac{1}{3}$ X.)

nancy. The cervix may be considered the neck of the uterus; it effectually closes the external opening and protects the uterine contents (Fig. 21-3).

The vagina is the posterior portion of the reproductive tract and serves as the female organ of copulation. The female duct system also receives the sperm cells and conveys them to the site of fertilization. The external genitalia are composed of the labia majora or vulva and the clitoris, which is a rudimentary organ located at the ventral junction of the vulva and is homologous to the glans penis of the male. The clitoris is capable of limited erection and the labia, because of an increased flow of blood, becomes turgid during estrus. The female genital tract is suspended from the dorsolateral wall of the pelvic canal by the broad ligament.

21-4. SEX DIFFERENTIATION AND DEVELOPMENT

Each individual is potentially bisexual; that is, the necessary primordia or rudimentary structures are present for the complete development of either the male or female reproductive system. The gonads and two sets of ducts are present. One set, the Mullerian ducts, will predominate and develop if the embryo is to become a female; another set, the Wolffian or mesonephric ducts, will develop if the embryo is to become a male. Genes

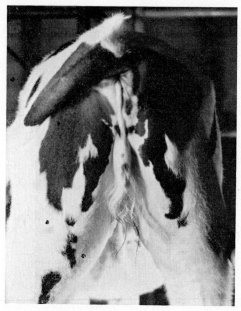

Fig. 21-4. A freemartin. The heifer was born twin to a bull. The vulva is modified into a sheathlike structure. Usually the external genitalia of the freemartin appear normal. The gonads of this heifer were located in the inguinal region. [Courtesy Dr. L. E. Casida, University of Wisconsin.]

for maleness or femaleness influence the differentiation of the gonads and the genital ducts into that of the male or female sex. If a gonad is to become a testis, chordlike masses of cells are formed which eventually become the seminiferous tubules. If the gonad is to become an ovary, these chordlike masses form the medulla of the ovary and additional primordial germ cells grow into the gonad, where they become differentiated into ova. Accidental interference with this embryological process can result in intersexuality.

The external genitalia and duct system, like the gonads, develop from a stage in which all of the rudimentary anatomic features of both sexes are present. Occasionally, however, developmental accidents happen, and the system intended to be rudimentary differentiates and gains considerable prominence. This may lead to aberrations in the duct system, which may be slight and harmless, or they may be great enough to cause complete sterility, as in the "freemartin" in cattle, described by Lillie (1917) (Fig. 21-4).

In cattle, when twins of opposite sex are produced, approximately 11 out of 12 genetic females have abnormal reproductive organs and are sterile; they are called freemartins. Placental membranes of cattle twins often join, resulting in a fusion of the blood vessels and in an intermixing of blood of the two fetuses. If they are of opposite sex, the male hormone has an arresting effect on the ovary and female genital tract and causes persistence in development of various portions of the male system in the female.

21-5. SEX RATIOS

In sexual reproduction the mechanism of reduction or meiotic division during formation of the reproductive cells should lead to the formation of equal numbers of male- and female-producing sperm cells. In mammals the male sex is heterogametic, producing two types of sperm cells so far as the sexual mechanism is concerned. Genetic sex of the young is thus determined by the type of sperm which unites with the egg. In chickens the opposite is true, since the female produces two types of ova. Sex ratios at birth based on large numbers of animals often show small discrepancies from equality. A summary of data shows that in horses, sheep, and chickens, there is a slight deficiency of males, while cattle and swine show an excess of males. If the x- and y-bearing sperm cells are produced in equal numbers, then lack of random fertilization or differential embryo mortality must be responsible for deviations from equality in sexes.

Many unsuccessful attempts have been made to control sex, including electrophoretic, mechanical, and chemical separation of the two types of sperm cells. Wide deviations from a fifty-fifty sex ratio can occur by chance alone; hence, we should view with considerable skepticism any method or theory which purports to give control over sex determination. Obviously, a solution of the problem of controlling the sex of offspring would have tremendous significance in the field of animal production.

21-6. HORMONES IN REPRODUCTION

Reproduction and lactation in domestic animals are regulated by hormones, which are chemical substances secreted by ductless or endocrine glands directly into the blood stream. The blood carries these chemical messengers to areas of the body—"target" organs—where they produce their effects.

Of the endocrine glands, the pituitary is the most important. In the cow it is about the size of an acorn and is located at the base of the brain. It has two main parts, the anterior and the posterior pituitary. If the pituitary gland is removed from young animals, the ovaries and testes fail to develop to normal size and do not produce eggs or sperm. If the gland is removed from mature animals that are producing eggs or sperm, these functions cease and the ovaries and testes degenerate. The growth of the ovaries and testes and their functions after sexual maturity or puberty are determined by the secretion of the gonadotropic hormones from the pituitary gland and by interaction with hormones produced by the ovary and the testis. Successful pregnancy is also largely a result of hormone activity.

Types of Hormones. Two types of hormones are concerned with reproduction: (1) gonadotropic hormones, which are complex proteins and affect the gonads, and (2) gonadal hormones, which are steroids, chemically, and are secreted by the gonads. Both types of hormones produce marked effects on the reproductive organs and on the behavior of the animal. Gonadotropins stimulate the accessory reproductive organs indirectly by stimulating the secretion of gonadal hormones.

Other hormones may modify the animal's metabolism so that normal re-

| TABLE 21-2. | | Reproductive traits in farm animals. | | | |

Species	Length cycle (days)	Duration of estrus	Time of ovulation	Length of gestation (days)	Age at puberty (months)
Cow	21	14 hr	14 hr after end of estrus	280	6–8
Sow	21	2–3 days	Usually before end of estrus	114	5–7
Ewe	16.5	1–2 days	Near end of estrus	146	Usually first autumn
Mare	22	5–7 days	1–2 days before end of estrus	336	12

productive function may be impaired. Of these hormones, thyroxin, secreted by the thyroid gland, has been most extensively studied. Hormones of the adrenal cortex are of vital importance to survival of the animal; however, their specific effect upon reproduction must await further study.

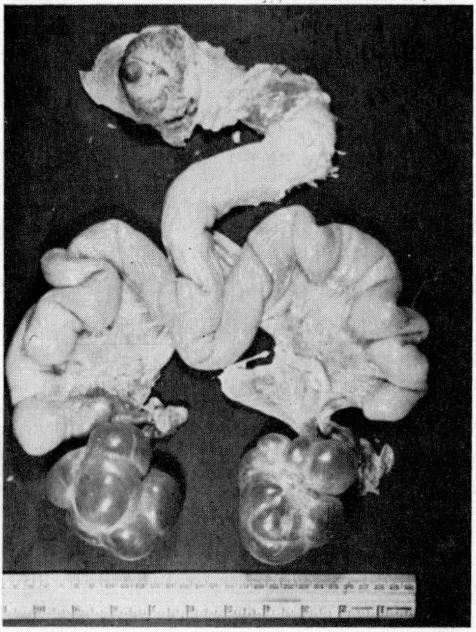

Conclusive evidence is lacking on the nature of the hormonal imbalance involved in the development of cystic ovaries (Fig. 21-5). Lack of luteinizing hormone is suggested because injection of pituitary extracts rich in this hormone has a beneficial effect in many instances.

Fig. 21-5. Reproductive tract of sow, showing cystic ovaries. The follicles have failed to ovulate and release an ovum, and many of them are enlarged to more than 1 inch in diameter.

21-7. THE SEXUAL SEASON

One of the striking characteristics of the manifestation of sex in animals is the rhythmic variation in intensity. In the nonpregnant female the secretion of the ovarian hormones, estrogen and progesterone, and the gonadotropins occurs in cycles rather than continuously. The secretions occur in a regular order and in varying amounts in such a manner that heat and ovulation occur at rather precise intervals. This sequence occurs because gonadotropins stimulate the secretion of gonadal hormones which, in turn, inhibit gonadotropin secretion.

In the majority of wild mammals and birds, both sexes have an alternating sexual and nonsexual season. At the time when reproductive function is quiescent, the animal is said to be in anestrus. In sheep the females of most breeds have a distinct sexual season, which in the northern hemisphere occurs in the fall and early winter. The mare also shows a tendency toward seasonal breeding, with short periods of anestrus and irregular cyclic patterns during fall and early winter. Species which exhibit this trait are said to be seasonally polyestrous in their reproductive behavior. Estrous cycles are repeated regularly throughout the year in the sow and in the cow, and they are known as polyestrous or continuous breeders.

The causes of seasonal reproduction are not fully known. There can be no doubt that light plays an important role in determining reproductive periodicity of animals. The pituitary itself has been shown to respond to varying lengths of daylight; in some species breeding activity is initiated by increasing, and in others by decreasing, the length of day. Nerve impulses resulting from the stimulation of the retina in the eye by light somehow influence the pituitary gland. Nalbandov (1958) has put forth the hypothesis that alteration in the kind of hormones secreted rather than secretory activity of the pituitary gland may be responsible for this ostensibly inconsistent pattern. Changing environmental temperature has also been shown to alter the time of onset of sexual activity in some breeds of sheep. It is important to point out that no single factor can explain the phenomenon of seasonal breeding activity in all species. Light, temperature, food supply, neural stimuli, and other factors may also be responsible.

21-8. THE ESTROUS CYCLE

As concerns the ovary, the estrous cycle consists of growth and maturation of the follicle, ovulation, development, and subsequent regression of the corpus luteum. The cycle may be divided into four phases: (1) proestrus—the interval between cessation of functional activity of the corpus luteum and the onset of estrus, (2) estrus—the period during which the female will accept the male, (3) metestrus—the interval between end of estrus and the time when the corpus luteum becomes secretory, and (4) diestrus—the longest phase of the cycle and the period during which the corpus luteum is functional.

One tentative explanation of the control of the estrous cycle is as follows. When estrogen is produced by the ovary under the stimulus of the follicle-stimulating hormone (FSH), its concentration in the blood increases to the point where it causes the animal to exhibit heat, and, theoretically, it in-

TABLE 21-3.   *Glands and hormones affecting reproduction.*

Gland	Hormone	Function
Pituitary		
Anterior	(1) Follicle—stimulating	Growth of follicles; stimulates spermatogenesis.
	(2) Luteinizing	Causes ovulation, growth of corpora lutea.
	(3) Luteotrophic or lactogenic	Maintains corpora lutea, secretion of milk.
Posterior	(1) Oxytocin or pitocin	Milk "let-down"; contracts uterine muscles.
Ovary	(1) Estrogen	Causes heat; development of female sex characteristics; growth of uterine glands; sensitizes uterine muscles; development of mammary-duct system.
	(2) Progesterone	Inhibits release of luteinizing hormone; maintains pregnancy; causes uterine and mammary glands to become secretory.
Testis	(1) Testosterone	Causes male libido or sex drive; development and secretory action of accessory sex glands; development of male sex characteristics.

hibits the secretion of FSH by the pituitary gland. The pituitary then produces the luteinizing hormone (LH), which causes ovulation and growth of the corpus luteum. When the corpus luteum is present and producing progesterone, this hormone affects the pituitary gland and prevents it from secreting LH, thus inhibiting ovulation. Upon regression or cessation of secretory activity of the corpus luteum, the follicles again begin to enlarge, under the synergistic action of FSH and LH, and produce estrogen in sufficient amounts to cause onset of the estrous period. The cyclic nature of reproductive phenomena depends on a delicate balance in the amounts of hormones that are secreted at various times.

21-9. OVULATION AND FERTILIZATION

After the ovum is discharged from the ovarian follicle, it enters the infundibulum and begins to travel down the oviduct toward the uterus. If sperm cells are present, fertilization will occur in the upper portion of the oviduct. Spermatozoa deposited in the female travel up the reproductive tract by means of uterine movement, as well as by means of their own motility. Billions of sperm cells may be deposited within the female at the time of breeding, and many may penetrate the outer shell or zona pellucida of the ovum. However, only one spermatozoon unites with the egg nucleus in fertilization.

After ovulation the ovum is capable of being fertilized for a period of five to ten hours. On the other hand, sperm cells are capable of retaining fertilizability for a day or two in the female tract. Fertilization has been reported in the hen up to 32 days after mating, but the sperm cells of mammals—with the possible exception of bats—do not remain viable in the female tract beyond a day or two. The relationship of time of breeding to ovulation is important in view of the short life of the ovulated ovum and sperm cells. It has recently been demonstrated that spermatozoa placed in the cervix reach the upper end of the oviduct in the cow a few minutes later. Trimberger and Davis (1943) reported that cows bred artificially at intervals from onset of estrus to 48 hours after end of estrus were most fertile when bred during mid-estrus. Fertility in cows bred 6 hours or later after the end of estrus was decidedly lower, and none conceived when bred later than 36 hours after the end of estrus.

21-10. PREGNANCY

As the fertilized egg passes down the oviduct, it continues to divide with no increase in size. By the fourth day the fertilized egg or zygote enters the uterine horns or the uterus proper. The stage of development during which the zygote is enclosed in the zona pellucida is called the period of the ovum. After the tenth day the zona pellucida disappears and the membranes of the developing embryo enlarge rapidly. Attachment of the placental membranes to the endometrium of the uterus is a gradual process in all farm animals. Amoroso (1952) has described fusion between the embryonic and maternal tissues as being practically completed by 22 days in the sheep, 24 days in the pig, 28 days in the cow, and only partially complete by 63 days in the mare.

During pregnancy much larger amounts of certain hormones may be produced. These additional amounts of hormones are not formed in the pituitary gland or in the ovaries, but in structures associated with the developing fetus. The blood of mares at 50–140 days of pregnancy contains large quantities of a gonadotropic hormone called equine gonadotropin or pregnant mare serum (PMS). The presence of gonadotropic hormones in the blood or urine in some species is the basis for the biological test for pregnancy.

During pregnancy the uterus is closed by a cervical plug, which protects its contents against infection from external sources.

21-11. FETAL MEMBRANES AND PLACENTA

The young zygote exists for a short time by absorbing nutrients contained in the fluids of the uterus, but as the embryo increases in size it is imperative that it establish a more adequate source of nutrition. Extra-embryonic membranes develop for this purpose, and they also serve as surrounding membranes which protect the embryo. Fetal membranes are made up of the

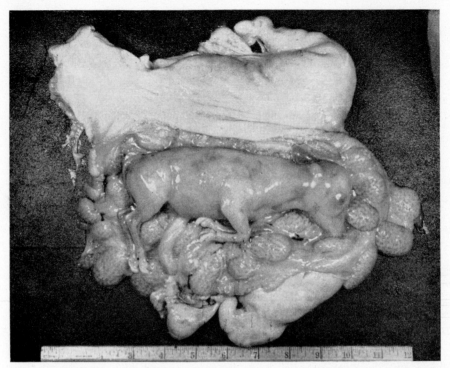

Fig. 21-6. A 100-day calf fetus. The placental membranes have been cut open to show the fetus and the umbilical cord. The areas resembling peanut shells are cotyledons.

amnion, allantois, and the chorion. The umbilical cord joins the embryo to the fetal membranes and is composed mainly of the umbilical veins and arteries.

The amnion is the inner, fluid-filled sac which surrounds the embryo, forming a protective cushion against external shocks; the fluid also prevents adhesions between the surface of the embryo and surrounding tissues. At parturition the amnion acts as a wedge in opening the cervix. This is commonly known as the "water bag." The allantois is an outgrowth of the hind-gut. In mammals its principal function is to carry the fetal circulatory system into the chorion to form the fetal placenta. The outer tissue covering the fetus is the chorion or the allantochorionic membrane. Through this membrane gaseous and nutrient exchange between the fetal and the maternal blood systems occurs.

Attachment of the fetal placenta to the uterus varies according to species. The mare and sow have a diffused type of placenta, in which the entire chorionic surface contains ridges which fit into corresponding folds in the endometrium of the uterus. The cow and the ewe have a cotyledonary type placenta. In this type, attachment to the uterine wall occurs only in localized regions on the surface of the chorion known as cotyledons. The cotyledonary type of attachment is considered more intimate than the diffused type, since fewer layers of tissues separate the maternal and fetal blood systems (Fig. 21-6).

21-12. PARTURITION

Maintenance of pregnancy is dependent upon the presence of functional corpora lutea—except in the mare, where the corpus regresses at about 150 days of pregnancy. When the exact mechanisms concerned with parturition are analyzed, they involve complex events which are incompletely understood. However, a change in hormone balance is clearly associated with the onset of parturition. Near the end of gestation the corpus luteum recedes and progesterone secretion is reduced. Actually, pregnancy can be prolonged and parturition delayed by injecting progesterone. The hormone relaxin, secreted by the uterus in some forms and apparently by the ovary in others, causes relaxation of the cervix and softening of the connective tissues of the pelvic region, which allows expansion to create a passageway for the fetus. With the decline in progesterone the active estrogen in the body increases and, at some point in this sequence, the uterine muscles become sensitive to the action of pituitrin or oxytocin. A series of uterine muscular contractions aided by abdominal muscles finally result in expulsion of the fetus.

A diffuse placenta may pull away from the uterus more rapidly than the cotyledonary type, resulting in cessation of gaseous exchange. For this reason, once the birth act has begun it should be fairly rapid in the mare and in the sow, while it may take somewhat longer in the ewe and in the cow without endangering the life of the newborn by suffocation. In the mare the amniotic and chorionic membranes do not fuse, and as a result of this the foal may be born enclosed in the amniotic sac. The presence of an attendant to free the newborn from this membrane so that it does not suffocate is advisable. In the ewe and cow the amnion fuses later in pregnancy with the chorion, and the young in these species are usually born free of any membrane covering.

21-13. FACTORS AFFECTING REPRODUCTIVE EFFICIENCY

Fertility of farm livestock is one of the major problems facing the breeder. Reproductive rate is determined by (1) litter size, and (2) length of the interval from parturition to the next successful conception. The number of young born depends upon (1) number of eggs ovulated, (2) number of eggs fertilized, and (3) number of fertile eggs that implant and survive through gestation to be born as living young.

In the broad sense fertility cannot be considered with respect to one sex without considering the other. In the male anorchidism (absence of testes) or cryptorchidism may prevent the formation of sperm. Anatomical sterility in the male may also result from deformities or complete absence of part of the reproductive tract. High environmental temperatures result in low fertility or temporary sterility in rams. Exposure to high temperature also has a detrimental effect on fertility and early embryo survival in ewes.

In the female various conditions involving the reproductive tract may interfere with or prevent conception. Cystic follicles or persistent corpora lutea may prevent follicles from maturing and result in temporary sterility. Nutritional deficiencies may delay onset of puberty and retard growth in general and affect ovulation rate in some forms. A review of current research by Reid (1960) shows that restricted feeding does not have an adverse effect on reproduction in cattle and swine. Full feeding to the extent that animals become overly fat is definitely detrimental to their reproductive performance. Wallace (1948) has shown that certain fetal tissues, notably nervous tissue and the skeleton, are less affected than other tissues by undernutrition in the dam. Hammond (1944) has put forth the theory that the fetus can exercise a demand for nutrients on the maternal organism and is not entirely at the mercy of its environment. This whole concept is extremely important in relation to maternal nutritional level and reproductive efficiency.

Pathological disorders may also interfere with fertility through inflammation of various parts of the reproductive system, resulting in blockage of tubes. Disease organisms such as *Brucella abortis, Vibrio fetus, Trichomonas fetus,* and *Leptospira pomona* interfere with gestation and result in abortion of the fetus. Initiation of the estrous cycles are often indications of early termination of pregnancy, even though an aborted fetus is not evident.

Occasionally cows will ovulate without showing estrous behavior. The cause of these "silent heats" is not clearly understood, but evidence points to incomplete regression of luteal tissue in the ovaries as a possible factor. Practically, this condition results in delaying the interval to breeding.

Recently much attention has been given to the hard-to-settle or "repeat-breeder" animal. These individuals require two, three, or more services before they conceive. Normal estrous cycles occur, and a large percentage of such females are apparently free of any abnormality of the tract which would preclude fertilization. The reasons for their inability to conceive are unknown; however, failure of fertilization and high embryonic mortality have been observed in studies involving repeat-breeding sows and cows (Casida, 1953).

For maximum fertility it is recommended that cattle not be bred earlier than 60 days following parturition, even though they may exhibit heat earlier. A disturbing problem among beef cattle is excessively long postpartum intervals to heat, since the problem of getting a calf crop yearly becomes more difficult if the interval is longer than 90 days. Mares usually have a heat period 5 to 10 days following foaling. Even though some mares will settle when bred during "foal heat," many breeders feel that it is advantageous to delay breeding until the second heat after foaling. Except for the postpartum heat which occurs about 3 to 7 days after farrowing, sows fail to exhibit estrus while nursing a litter. Breeding sows at the postpartum or 3-day heat is not successful, because ovulation usually fails to take place.

21-14. ARTIFICIAL INSEMINATION

Artificial insemination is the deposit of male reproductive cells in the female reproductive tract by mechanical means rather than by natural mating. The first research in artificial insemination of domestic animals was conducted by an Italian physiologist in 1780. The primary advantage of artificial insemination is that of speeding up the rate of livestock improvement. This can be accomplished, because the number of sperm cells required for insemination is less than that provided in natural mating. Bull semen can be routinely diluted 1:100 without any significant drop in fertility. With an accepted volume of 1 ml of diluted semen per insemination, it is possible to breed 500 cows from one ejaculate. Other advantages are continued use of superior sires which are unable to serve naturally, long-distance breeding, and with the development of techniques for freezing semen a sire can be used long after his death. Techniques of insemination are well established for cattle, but information on problems of spermatozoa storage, dilution rate, and number of sperm necessary for insemination is limited for other species (Fig. 21-7).

21-15. HORMONAL CONTROL OF THE REPRODUCTIVE PROCESS

The phenomenal success of artificial insemination for exploiting the reproductive powers of the bull in the dairy industry has stimulated interest in possible ways of similar exploitation in the female in order to obtain more offspring. Superovulation, the act of ovulating more than the normal number of ova during one heat period, and ova transplantation or inovulation have been suggested as means to this end (Willett, 1953). Synchronization of estrous periods by appropriate injections of progesterone to facilitate ova transplantation or mass insemination has been investigated. Recent development of orally effective progestational compounds may simplify this problem. Injection of gonadotropic hormones has been employed to increase twinning rate in sheep and in dairy cattle producing veal or feeder calves. An alteration in light-dark ratio will cause a reversal in the breeding season in sheep. Hormones have also been employed to induce conception in anestrous ewes, but results have not been uniformly successful. Possibly the

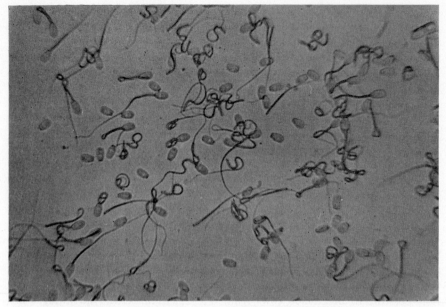

Fig. 21-7. Sperm cells of a ram showing damaging effects of high summer temperature—tailless heads and bent and coiled tails. This ram was temporarily infertile. (430 X.)

greatest benefit derived from these studies would be the use of these techniques as a tool for research in physiology of reproduction and in genetic studies of domestic animals.

REFERENCES AND SELECTED READINGS

References marked with an asterisk are of general interest.

*Amoroso, E. C., 1952. *Marshall's Physiology of Reproduction*, Vol. 2. Edited by A. S. Parkes. London.

*Asdell, S. A., 1946. *Patterns of Mammalian Reproduction*. Comstock Pub. Co., Ithaca.

Casida, L. E., 1953. Prenatal death as a factor in the fertility of farm animals. *Iowa State College J. Sci.*, 28:119–126.

*Cole, H. H. and P. T. Cupp (Editors), 1959. *Reproduction in Domestic Animals*. Vol. I and II. Academic, New York.

*Corner, G. W., 1946. *The Hormones in Human Reproduction*. Princeton Univ. Press.

Hammond, J., 1944. Physiological factors affecting birth weight. *Proc. Nutrition Soc.*, 2:8–14.

*———— (Editor), 1957. *Progress in the Physiology of Farm Animals*. Vol. 2 and 3. Butterworth's Scientific Publications, London.

Lillie, F. R., 1917. The free-martin; a study of the action of sex hormones in the foetal life of cattle. *J. Exp. Zoology*, 23:371–452.

*Marshall, F. H. A., 1952. *Physiology of Reproduction*. 3rd Ed. Vol. 2. Edited by A. S. Parkes. Longmans, Green and Co., London.

*Nalbandov, A. V., 1958. *Reproductive Physiology*. Freeman, San Francisco.

Reid, J. T., 1960. Effect of energy intake upon reproduction in farm animals. Supp. to *J. Dairy Sci.*, 43:103–122.

*Robson, J. M., 1947. *Recent Advances in Sex Reproduction Physiology*. Blakiston, Philadelphia.

*Sisson, S. and J. D. Grossman, 1938. The Anatomy of Domestic Animals. 3rd Ed. Saunders, Philadelphia.

Trimberger, G. W. and H. P. Davis, 1943. Conception rate in dairy cattle by artificial insemination at various stages of estrus. Nebr. Agr. Expt. Sta. Research Bull. 129.

Wallace, L. R., 1948. The growth of lambs before and after birth in relation to the level of nutrition. *J. Agr. Sci.*, 38:93, 242, 367.

Willett, E. L., 1953. Egg transfer and superovulation in farm animals. *Iowa State College J. Sci.*, 28:83–100.

Chapter 22

Egg Laying

We, however, commence with the history of the hen's egg . . . for as eggs cost little, and are always to be had, we have an opportunity from them of observing the first clear and unquestionable commencements of generation, how nature proceeds in the process, and with what admirable foresight she governs every part of the work.
WILLIAM HARVEY, *On Animal Generation*

22-1. INTRODUCTION

Success or failure of a species is measured by its ability to preserve itself and undergo some numerical expansion. The success of birds as a species is largely due to the fact that they have evolved physiological mechanisms which cause them to lay eggs at a time of season when such factors as weather and food supply are optimal and when maximal survival of the young can be expected. The numbers of eggs laid and incubated are commensurate with the physical capabilities of the hen for brooding the eggs and caring for the chicks; those species are most successful which tax these capabilities to the utmost and allow for the highest reproductive rate. There are mechanisms which cause the hen to *want* to brood eggs and care for chicks; and, finally, provisions are made for the return of the ability of hens to lay eggs after a cycle of mothering chores has been completed. Obviously such a complex situation requires a system of signaling mechanisms which tell a bird what time of the year it is, when it has laid enough eggs to start brooding them, and when the chicks no longer need parental protection so that the hen can again start the cycle of laying eggs. Such a signaling system can not be simple, and in both mammals and birds neuroendocrine feedback mechanisms have evolved. The nervous system maintains communications among parts of the animal body, while the endocrine system, using hormones as messengers and as local organ representatives, sees to it that this or that part is stimulated to the right degree at the right time. The neuroendocrine control systems have the task of synchronizing events within the body as well as relating the internal events to the external environment in which the population lives. Unfortunately, it will not be possible to treat in detail the many elegant methods which have evolved to permit optimal functioning of animal organisms, but a brief synopsis should encourage the interested student to go deeper into the most fascinating problems of reproductive physiology.

The eyes of birds serve as receptors of light intensity. Birds can thus tell the difference between seasons because increasing intensity and duration of light foretell spring, while decreasing light signals approaching fall and winter. In either event, excitations resulting are transmitted via the optic nerve to the hypothalamus, one of the major control centers of the neuroendocrine system (Fig. 22-1). From the hypothalamus, chemical substances are released and eventually reach the anterior lobe of the pituitary gland. If the amounts of light are increasing, then the anterior lobe responds by increased secretion of the hormones responsible for gonadal growth.

Many interrelated events occur in the reproductive cycle of hens, and there are many different messages received by and transmitted from the hypothalamus. For instance, in the wild ancestor of the hen, which laid about twelve eggs in a nest, the pressure of the eggs against the breast initiates a message to the effect that about as many eggs have been laid as a hen can hatch—that is, cover with her body. These messages, when properly decoded and relayed, cause the pituitary gland to switch from secretion of gonad-stimulating hormones to the secretion of the hormone prolactin, which is responsible for the manifestation of the maternal instinct. The flow of prolactin is at first maintained by the continued tactile messages caused by the pressure of eggs against the breast, and later by the presence of the hatched chicks. As the chicks become more independent, the chirping and crowding around the mother for shel-

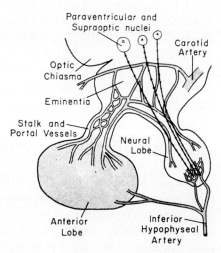

Fig. 22-1. The hypothalamo-hypophyseal system in birds. Note that the neural lobe is separate from the anterior lobe, that both lobes are connected to the hypothalamic nuclei by blood vessels, but that only the posterior lobe is innervated.

ter diminishes, and the signal for continued secretion of prolactin weakens. The hen's pituitary gland may now go back to secreting gonad-stimulating hormones and the laying of another set of eggs, *provided* messages from the outside still tell her that enough time remains to raise a second brood; that is, provided there has been no marked decrease in amount of light. If the brood becomes self-sufficient at a time of decrease when less light impinges on the eye, then the pituitary gland is not sufficiently stimulated to cause secretion of adequate amounts of gonadotropic hormone; the ovary remains regressed until the following spring, when the whole cycle begins again.

While the only connection between the hypothalamus and the anterior lobe of the pituitary gland is humoral, the connection between the hypothalamus and the posterior lobe of the pituitary gland is neural (Fig. 22-1). Thus, the nerves connecting the shell gland (or uterus) with the hypothalamus may carry the message that the shell gland contains a hard-shelled egg which is ready to be expelled. This information is transmitted directly via the connecting nervous system from the hypothalamus to the posterior lobe, which instantly responds by releasing appropriate amounts of the hormone oxytocin. This hormone causes contraction of the muscles in the shell gland and, hence, expulsion of the egg.

In a very general and sketchy way, this short discussion should introduce the kinds of problems we will examine in the hope of understanding the physiology of egg production. We must, of course, keep in mind that the domesticated hen is a development from its ancestor, the Indian Jungle Fowl, which was modified extensively by man before it achieved its present commercial usefulness. In the concluding portion of this chapter we shall return to the problem of how this hen—whose ancestors laid at most 50 eggs a year—became an organism capable of producing as many as 366 eggs in 365 days.

22-2. THE OVARY AND THE LAYING CYCLE

Components of the Egg. The prime aim in life of mammals and birds alike is procreation, but the reproductive problems faced by birds are basically completely different from the problems faced by mammals. In the latter, one or more young not only begin their existence in the uterus, but must continue to develop and be nourished in it. Thus, the mammalian egg can be small since the developing fetus can obtain all of its nourishment from the maternal organism to which it becomes attached by means of a placenta. The avian embryo develops completely outside of the maternal organism and for this reason the bird egg must be sufficiently large to contain all the nutrients which will be needed by the growing embryo throughout its development. Avian eggs also must be enclosed by a shell rigid enough to withstand the vicissitudes of the incubation period. The nutrients

TABLE 22·1.	*Comparison of average length of parts of the chicken oviduct, their contribution to the egg, and the time spent by egg in each section.* [*From Nalbandov, A. V., 1958. In* Comparative Endocrinology, *Wiley, New York.*]

		Contribution			
Part of oviduct	Average length of part (cm)	Kind	Total amount (gm)	Percent solids	Time spent by egg in each part (hours)
Infundibulum	11.0	Chalaza	32.9	12.2	$\frac{1}{4}$
Magnum	33.6	Albumen			3
Isthmus	10.6	Shell membrane	0.3	80.0	$1\frac{1}{4}$
Shell gland	10.1	Calciferous shell	6.1	98.4	18–22
Vagina	6.9	Mucus	0.1		$\frac{1}{60}$

contained in the egg are the lipoproteins of the yolk, the protein of the egg white (albumen), and the calcium carbonate of the egg shell (Table 22-1). All these substances come from the maternal organism and birds have mechanisms by means of which the different building materials are made available to the proper organ at the proper time.

The chemical components of the yolk, the albumen, and the shell are mobilized either directly from the gut or from maternal body reserves such as the skeleton, the liver, or the fat depots. These components must be transformed into chemical compounds which can readily pass through cell membranes and which can be transported through the blood stream. After the precursors of yolk and albumen appear in the blood stream the big and mysterious tasks of logistics must be faced: how do the lipoprotein globules suspended in the blood stream know that they are destined for the growing follicles where they will be transformed into yolk and deposited into the ovum? Why is it that the precursors of egg albumen are selectively removed from the blood stream in the oviduct and nowhere else? Similarly, the calcium carbonate is filtered out by the shell gland and deposited around the finished egg. These problems remain, for the time being, without definite answers. Endocrinologists call the ovary, the oviduct, and all other hormone-supported structures, "genetically conditioned end organs," but this term is meaningless since it explains neither the physiology nor the biochemistry of these processes. At best, it simply calls attention to the fact that the ovary has the built-in ability to distinguish between yolk and calcium carbonate, to accept and to use the former and to reject the latter. In the same mysterious way the ovary can differentiate among the multitude of hormones which are carried by the blood stream. It responds only to those hormones which it somehow recognize as belonging to it, but remains completely un-affected by all the others which bathe it.

Processes of Egg Formation. Near the time of ovulation, the ovary of a mammal contains one or two ripe follicles if the female is monotocous (*tokos* is Greek for offspring), or several follicles of ovulatory size if the female is polytocous. In contrast, the ovary of the laying hen consists of a series of follicles (called the follicular size hierarchy), ranging from microscopic size to the size of the follicle which is destined to ovulate next. This follicle weighs about 15 g, the next member of the size hierarchy about 14 g, and the third one about 10 g. Below this size there may be several follicles of the same weight, the different weight classes ranging down to follicles weighing less than 1 mg, and eventually down to a multitude of follicles of microscopic size (Fig. 22-2).

The interesting and significant fact about this size hierarchy is that only one follicle reaches ovulatory size each day. Only after ovulation of the largest follicle do the smaller follicles move up one notch in size and re-establish the hierarchy as it existed just before ovulation (Fig. 22-2). The interval between the ovulation of two successive eggs is usually 24 to 28 hours. As a rule hens lay one egg a day on several successive days before a day intervenes on which no egg is laid. The uninterrupted series of successive eggs laid is called a clutch. The tendency of some hens to lay short clutches (1 to 3 eggs) and others to lay longer clutches (6 and up, to 100 or more) is a heritable characteristic, and each hen tends to repeat her

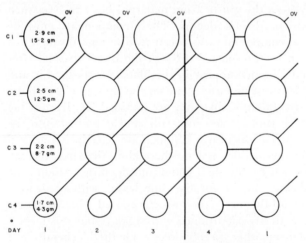

Fig. 22-2. Diagrammatic presentation of a hen's follicular hierarchy and clutch sequence. As the largest follicle leaves the hierarchy by ovulation, lower members move up one size notch. At the vertical line the clutch ends and the C4 follicle of the last clutch becomes the C1 follicle of the next one. [From Nalbandov, in *Comparative Endocrinology*, A. Gorbman (Ed.), Wiley, New York, 1959.]

typical clutch length throughout most of her productive life. The hens with the longest clutches will of course be able to produce the largest number of eggs each laying year, because they have the fewest number of nonproductive days; the hens with 1- or 2-egg clutches can not produce more than 180 or 240 eggs a year, even if there is no time off for molt or winter pause. In order to be able to produce 300 or more eggs annually the clutch length must be 5 or more eggs.

The laying cycle of the hen is, to some extent at least, related to light. Under normal day-night conditions, ovulations always occur early in the morning. The yolk then begins its trip down the oviduct, where it acquires the egg white, the soft shell membranes, and eventually the calciferous shell. This whole process from ovulation to oviposition (laying the egg) takes on the average 26 hours. Because in the majority of hens ovulations are held in abeyance until the previous egg has been laid, each subsequent ovulation and oviposition occurs a little later in the day than did the previous one, so that eventually the next scheduled ovulation would have to occur late in the afternoon. For unknown reasons, however, this ovulation does not take place and there is a break in the clutch of 24–36 hours. Hens with a very short interval between oviposition and ovulation lay longer clutches, while hens in which the interval between oviposition and ovulation is long —2 or more hours—tend to have short clutches and a lower total annual egg production.

These facts raise two very important and interesting problems. One is the problem of the mechanisms involved in establishing and maintaining the follicular size hierarchy for prolonged periods of time. The hen must be able to distribute the hypophyseal hormones circulating in the blood stream in such a way that some follicles get more hormones, which allow them to grow faster and attain larger size, while other follicles get proportionally less hormone. The net result of this rationing system is that there is established and maintained a follicular size hierarchy in which the position of the individual follicle is determined by the amount of hormone stimulating it. The second problem concerns the possible mechanisms involved in the timing of the intervals between ovulations.

We will now present the evidence which will be needed before we can try to provide answers to the problems raised.

22-3. ENDOCRINE CONTROL OF FOLLICULAR GROWTH AND OF OVULATION

Hormones Involved in Follicle Growth. The endocrine control of follicular growth and of ovulation is by no means simple and is not yet completely understood. Much of what will be said in this section can be documented by data, but such proofs are beyond the scope of this discussion and the interested student should consult recent symposia and textbooks if he wishes to separate scientific facts from educated guesses.

The neuroendocrine mechanisms governing reproduction in birds are very similar to those of mammals. In birds the anterior and posterior lobes of

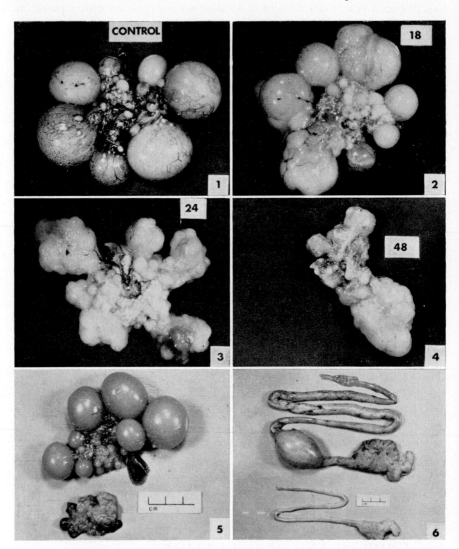

Fig. 22-3. Comparison of size and condition of normal ovary (1 and 5) with the effects of hypophysectomy. Note the rapidity with which the ovary degenerates 18, 24, and 48 hours after hypophysectomy. In 5 and 6 the ovaries and oviducts of normal and hypophysectomized chickens are shown 6 days after hypophysectomy. [From H. L. Open, Jr., Ph.D. Thesis, Univ. of Illinois, 1960.]

the pituitary gland are two anatomically distinct structures which are separated by a septum. Each of these lobes is connected by a separate stalk to the hypothalamus. Through the stalk of the posterior or neural lobe run nerve fibers connecting this lobe to the hypothalamic nuclei. The anterior lobe is not innervated and its only connection to the hypothalamic nuclei is through the vascular system—in which the blood flows only in one direction—from the hypothalamus to the anterior lobe of the pituitary gland. The posterior lobe serves as a storage reservoir for the posterior pituitary hormones (vasopressin and oxytocin), which are formed in the area of the hypothalamus and pass into the neural lobe along the nerve fibers connecting it to the hypothalamus.

The hormones of the anterior lobe are probably formed directly in the anterior lobe and released from it into the peripheral circulation. Although the anterior lobe secretes 5 or 6 different hormones—the somatotropic, adrenotropic, thyrotropic, gonadotropic, and lactogenic hormones—we will be concerned here mainly with the gonadotropic complex. Frequently this is subdivided into the follicle-stimulating hormone (FSH), associated predominantly with follicular growth, and the luteinizing hormone (LH), mainly responsible for causing ovulation. For the sake of simplicity we shall use the term "gonadotropic complex" (GTC) throughout most of this discussion.

Proofs of Hormonal Control of Follicular Growth. The gonadotropic complex from the pituitary gland is responsible for the growth and maturation of the ovarian follicle. That the ovary and its follicles depend for support upon the gonadotropic hormone is demonstrated by the fact that removal of the pituitary gland (hypophysectomy) leads to a rapid and complete degeneration of the ovarian follicles. This process of follicular degeneration is called atresia and is well illustrated in Fig. 22-3. Conversely, one can prevent follicular atresia in hypophysectomized hens by the injection of gonadotropic hormones (Fig. 22-4). Experiments of this type allow us to conclude that the rates at which hens lay eggs depend on the amount of the gonadotropic complex secreted by the pituitary gland.

The vascular networks covering the larger follicles (Fig. 22-5) are much more extensive and intricate than the networks supplying the smaller follicles. Ovulation of the largest follicle of the hierarchy results in an abrupt shutting down of the very extensive vascular network supplying that follicle. Thus, following ovulation, the amount of blood flowing through the vascular networks of smaller follicles of the hierarchy increases and more hormone becomes available for the lesser members of the hierarchy. How some follicles get a head start on their mates is not quite clear, but it is reasonable to think that this is a simple matter of chance and could depend on the initial proximity of some of the follicles to a larger blood vessel, allowing them to grow faster than some of their neighbors.

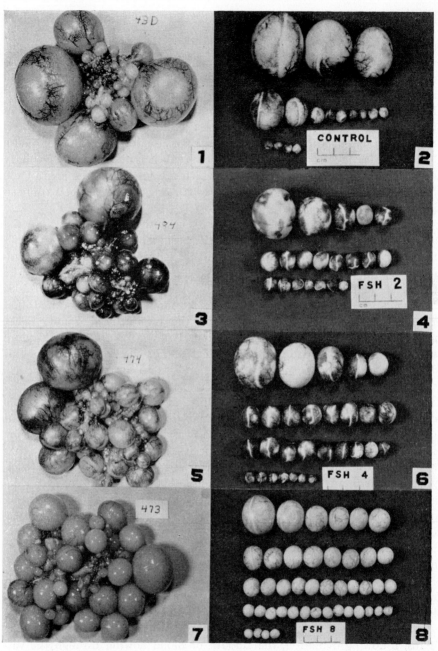

Fig. 22-4. Follicular atresia caused by hypophysectomy can be prevented. 1 shows the ovary of a normal hen. In 2 the size gradation of follicles (hierarchy) is well illustrated. Attempts to substitute for the hen's own pituitary by the injection of mammalian GTH (3 to 8) are only partly successful; atresia is prevented, total number of follicles is increased, but the hierarchical distribution of follicular sizes is different (compare 1 to 3, 5, and 7, and 2 to 4, 6, and 8). [From H. L. Opel, Jr., Ph.D. Thesis, Univ. of Illinois, 1960.]

Hormonal Control of Ovulation. Next we can examine the question of how ovulation is triggered and how the intervals between ovulation are kept at about 24 to 28 hours. We already know that the normal laying hen ovulates only one follicle each day, and that without hormonal support the follicles degenerate. We can study the mechanisms involved in follicular maturation and in ovulation either by injecting gonadotropic hormones (GTH) into normally laying hens, or by hypophysectomizing hens and then replacing the missing hormones by injection in an attempt to initiate the normal sequences of events involved in follicular maturation and in ovulation. If GTH is injected subcutaneously for several days into normally laying hens, the normal follicular size hierarchy is abolished—4 or even 10 and 12 follicles can be caused to reach ovulatory size simultaneously. (This fact is an excellent argument in favor of the assumption that normally the total amount of hormone available for the whole ovary as well as for the individual follicle is limited. When the ovary and the individual follicles are flooded with exogenous hormone—introduced artificially from the outside—one can increase the number of follicles reaching ovulatory size in accordance with the amount of hormone injected.) If hens pretreated with GTH are given an intravenous injection of this hormone, there will be ovulation of as many follicles as reached ovulatory size under the pretreatment. In laying hens with a normal follicular hierarchy, an intravenous injection of GTH usually hastens the ovulation of the largest follicle, which normally would have ruptured a few hours later; but it is never possible to cause the ovulation of the second- or third-largest follicles of the hierarchy. This demonstrates that follicles which have been nurtured to ovulatory size by proper endogenous or exogenous GTH can be made to ovulate if the organism is flooded by GTH at the proper time. Experimentally this can be done by the intravenous injection of GTH. This suggests that in the normal laying hen the anterior pituitary releases increased quantities of GTH at certain times during the maturation of the largest follicle, and that this causes ovulation of this follicle.

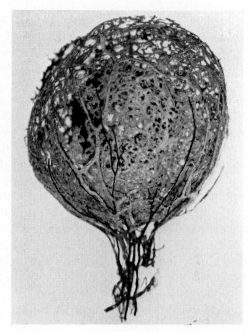

Fig. 22-5. Resin cast of a follicle of near-ovulatory size, showing the intricate venous system. The arterial system is shown in black. [From Nalbandov, *Reproductive Physiology*, Freeman, San Francisco, 1958.]

It has been established that the interval between release of endogenous GTH and ovulation (or the injection of exogenous GTH and ovulation) is between 8 and 12 hours. During this interval the hormone causes certain changes in the wall of the largest follicle, permitting it to break open and to release the ovum. What these changes are is not known, but a possible answer may be provided by the data presented in Table 22-2. These data were obtained from laying hens which were hypophysectomized and given a single injection of GTH at different intervals after the operation. It was found that when the GTH was injected fewer than 3 hours after hypophysectomy, the hens ovulated only 1 ovum; but when the GTH injection occurred 3 or more hours after the operation, an increasing number of hens ovulated 2 or more ova. In other words, the longer the ovary remains without support of GTH from its own pituitary gland, which was removed, the easier it is to cause multiple ovulations by exogenous GTH. By comparing (Table 22-2) the weights of the yolks, whose ovulation was induced by hormone injection (I_1 and I_2), with the weights of ova released prior to hypophysectomy (C_1 and C_2), it is found that in the absence of the hen's own pituitary gland not only the largest follicles, but also immature members of the follicular hierarchy, can be caused to ovulate. This is in distinct contrast to normal intact hens, in which injection of GTH can only hasten the ovulation of the largest follicle but can never cause the rupture of the second or third members of the follicular hierarchy. (On the basis of this information try to formulate a theory concerning the mechanism of ovulation before reading the explanation given below.)

These data suggest that the changes preceding follicular rupture occur more rapidly in the absence of the pituitary gland; that is, in the absence of follicular stimulation by GTH. Thus, ovulation may be normally an aging process which is initiated by the absence of GTH of hypophyseal

TABLE 22-2.	*Effect of increased interval between hypophysectomy and LH injection on ovulability of follicles. [Data from Opel, H. L., Jr., 1960. Factors affecting follicular growth and ovulation of hypophysectomized hens. University of Illinois. Ph.D. Thesis.]*

Interval (hours)	No. of hens	No. of single ovulations	No. of double ovulations	Average weight of ova (gm)			
				C_1	C_2	I_1	I_2
0	8	8	0	17.8	17.8	16.9	
2	8	8	0	18.4	17.7	16.3	
3	8	6	2	17.0	16.3	14.9	7.7
4	8	6	2	18.4	17.4	15.0	11.1
6	8	1	7	17.6	17.0	15.4	13.7
12	8	2	5	17.5	17.2	14.9	10.2

origin. This would mean that as long as a follicle is supported by some GTH it is incapable of ovulating. Therefore, in the normal hen, so long as the blood stream carries adequate amounts of GTH, the smaller follicles are stimulated to grow actively and are incapable of ovulating. The largest follicle approaching ovulatory size has the most extensive vascular system and gets the largest amount of hormone. As this follicle reaches its maximum size, the pressure of the accumulating yolk inside the follicular membranes partially squeezes shut some of the blood vessels supplying the follicle walls. This leads to diminishing blood flow, hence to diminishing hormone stimulation, hence to a breaking down of parts of the follicle wall, especially the stigma. All of these events finally culminate in ovulation. The smaller follicles of the hierarchy do not ovulate because their vascular systems carry enough GTH not only to maintain but to stimulate the follicle wall to further growth. So long as they receive such stimuli, the follicle wall cannot break down (or "age" or become ischemic) and ovulation cannot occur.

There remains the question of the mechanism involved in the timing of intervals between ovulation. We can at best present a plausible theory for which there is good evidence, but much additional work remains to be done before we can be certain of all the factors involved in the timing mechanism.

In the great majority of normal ovulations, the largest follicle ruptures within a few minutes, or at most a few hours, *after* the previous egg has been laid. We have learned earlier that the interval between release of ovulatory doses of hypophyseal GTH and ovulation is about 8 to 12 hours. If you look at the time sequences in Tables 22-1 and 22-2 you will see that this GTH release occurs during the time when the egg is in the process of acquiring the hard shell in the uterus.

There is experimental evidence to show that the oviducal nervous system participates in signaling the pituitary gland what to do, and that instructions *not* to release amounts of GTH adequate for ovulation may originate in the oviduct. We already know that such signaling systems are frequently involved in phenomena controlled by hormones and that they are part of the neuroendocrine feedback mechanism. In the hen it seems to operate, in brief, as follows. If a yolk is present in the albumen-secreting portion of the oviduct, a nerve-conducted signal goes from the oviduct to the hypothalamus, and from there to the pituitary gland, informing the latter that there is already one ovum in the oviduct and that no new ovulations should be permitted (that is, no ovulatory doses of GTH should be released) until the oviduct is ready for the next egg. Soon after the egg leaves the oviduct and enters the uterus or shell gland, these signals stop and the pituitary gland now releases the amounts of GTH needed to accomplish ovulation some 8 to 12 hours later; that is, after the hard-shelled egg is laid. As soon as the next ovum enters the oviduct, the ovulation-blocking signal again becomes effective and holds further ovulations in abeyance.

22-4. FUNCTION OF THE OVIDUCT

The oviduct consists of 5 anatomically distinct portions, 4 of which are also histologically different. The vital statistics of these areas, as well as their function, are summarized in Table 22-1. It is amazing that the magnum is able to contribute 32.9 g of a proteinaceous substance to the egg in just 3 hours. Even though the albumen is mostly water, the task of filtering this amount of albumen from the blood stream into the glands of the magnum, and from there into its lumen through which the yolk is passing, seems truly phenomenal. It is interesting that the magnum is incapable of distinguishing between a yolk and any other foreign body. Thus, it will deposit albumen around a cork or a wadded-up piece of paper, or, on one occasion, even around a cockroach which had somehow found its way into the magnum. The size of the laid egg is largely determined by the size of the ovum passing down the oviduct. Relatively less albumen will be deposited around a small yolk (as in the case of pullet eggs), and the resulting finished egg will weigh considerably less than the egg laid by a mature hen which tends to ovulate larger yolks. There is a slight tendency for successive eggs of a given clutch sequence to become smaller, because the yolks ovulated late in the clutch sequence are likely to be smaller than those ovulated earlier. This relationship holds statistically true for populations of birds, but individual hens may lay progressively larger eggs in a clutch.

The physiological function of the oviduct is controlled by the ovarian steroid hormones. The ovary normally secretes estrogen, androgen, and perhaps progesterone. Estrogen alone is able to cause the morphological enlargement of the oviduct, which is tremendously sensitive to estrogen. Even small doses of exogenous estrogenic hormone are capable of enlarging the oviduct of immature chicks several hundred per cent. This hormone alone, however, is incapable of stimulating the development of the oviducal glandular apparatus. To develop the glands—and to cause them to secrete albumen, or the shell membranes, or the calcareous shell—requires the interaction of at least two of the ovarian hormones. One of these is certainly estrogen, but it remains unclear whether the second cooperating hormone is androgen or progesterone. The ovary is known to secrete the male sex hormone, androgen, which is responsible, among other things, for comb size and its bright red color in laying hens. Because both androgen and estrogen are normally secreted by avian ovaries, it appears plausible that the interaction of these two hormones is normally responsible for the size of the oviduct, its glandular development, and its ability to secrete the various components of the completed egg. Under experimental conditions, even in sexually very immature female chicks, it is possible to substitute progesterone for androgen and to obtain oviduct growth and albumen secretion from either the estrogen-androgen or the estrogen-progesterone combination.

Having acquired the layers of albumen in the magnum, the egg is enclosed in the soft-shell membranes in the isthmus, while the calcareous shell is deposited around it in the shell gland or uterus. It is possible to cause the premature expulsion of the partially calcified egg from the uterus by the injection of the posterior pituitary hormone, oxytocin, which causes contractions of the musculature of the shell gland. It seems probable that this hormone is normally responsible for the expulsion of the finished egg and that uterine nerves are involved in signaling the posterior lobe of the pituitary that the egg is fully formed and can be laid. Whether it is the thickness of the hard shell or the time spent by the egg in the uterus that is responsible for the initiation of this neural signal, remains unknown. There is a striking similarity between the process of oviposition in birds and parturition in mammals: essentially the same hormones and the same mechanisms (uterine musculature) are involved in the expulsion of the fetus. In neither case is it known exactly how the signal for release of oxytocin is timed.

22-5. CONCLUDING REMARKS

This discussion began by pointing out that the ancestor of the domestic hen was content to lay some 25 to 50 eggs a season, to hatch them into chicks, and to take care of them as long as they needed protection. The enormous plasticity of the species, which could be converted by domestication from such primitive beginnings into an efficient egg-producing machine capable of producing up to 366 eggs a year, is astonishing. The physiologic principles underlying this transformation have been discussed earlier and need only be summarized. (It is suggested that the student attempt to make such a summary before reading what is to follow.)

When the chicken was taken into the household of early man, it was noticed that by removing the eggs from the nest of the hen, the onset of broodiness could be postponed and more prolonged periods of egg laying could be obtained. For a long time in the history of domestication of the hen, this was probably the only way in which an increase in productivity was obtained, but it is unlikely that the productivity of the individual hen could have been pushed much beyond 100 or at most 150 eggs per year. Within the present century, and especially since the advent of incubators, the maternal instinct became an unnecessary and even undesirable attribute of hens, because during the time of incubating eggs and caring for chicks, hens did not lay. It was noted that those hens which were better mothers, and which spent more time on being broody, consequently laid fewer eggs. By giving the hens with a poorly developed mothering instinct a greater opportunity for reproduction, it became possible to increase productivity of the population by gradually eliminating the broody instinct. Now we know that by eliminating the broody individuals, the early breeder was actually eliminating those hens and strains of hens which had genes which were

capable of causing the pituitary gland to secrete copious quantities of prolactin.

The ability of hens to lay the largest number of eggs is due to the presence or absence of at least four genetically controlled characteristics. High-
producing strains must be free from broodiness, they must have a short
winter molt, they must be persistent (that is, able to lay throughout most
of the year), and finally, they must have the ability to lay long clutches. The
intensity of the expression of these characteristics is determined by the rates
of production of certain hormones, which are more or less prominently concerned in determining the degree to which these characteristics are manifested. The early breeders, who were interested in improving domestic chickens, unknowingly selected individuals whose pituitary glands secreted less
prolactin, more gonadotropic hormone, and reduced amounts of thyroxine,
known to control rate and intensity of molt. In common with most quantitative characteristics, like milk production or growth rate, high egg production requires the complex interaction of a great number of genes, determining not only the rates at which glands secrete their hormones but
also the sensitivity with which end organs respond to the hormonal or
neural stimuli acting on them.

REFERENCES AND SELECTED READINGS

Breneman, W. R., 1955. Reproduction in
birds: the female. In *Comparative Physiology of Reproduction and the Effects of
Sex Hormones in Vertebrates*. Cambridge
Univ. Press.

Fraps, R. M., 1955. Egg production and
fertility in poultry. In *Progress in the
Physiology of Farm Animals*. Vol. 11.
Butterworth, London.

Nalbandov, A. V., 1958. *Reproductive Physiology*. Freeman, San Francisco.

Chapter 23

Lactation

Nor shall the brood-kine, as of yore, for thee
Brim high the snowy milking pail, but spend
Their udders' fullness on their own sweet young.
VIRGIL, *Georgics,* III

23-1. INTRODUCTION

Lactation or milk secretion is the sole physiological function of the mammary gland. By means of these glands, the young of these vertebrate animals we call mammals derive their first nutrients for the maintenance of life. In order to better understand the process of milk secretion, this chapter will consider first a brief discussion on the anatomy of the mammary gland, including the suspensory system of the udder, the milk-collecting system, teat structure, and the vascular, lymphatic, and nerve supply. Mammary gland development will be treated from the aspects of embryological and postnatal development. The subject of milk secretion itself will be divided into the neural and hormonal relationships of the initiation and maintenance of lactation, and milk expulsion (milk let-down) from the secretory and storage areas of the mammary gland. Since cows do not always secrete milk of constant composition, nor up to the level of their inherited capacity, the influence of various physiological and environmental factors on milk production will be considered.

The mammary gland is a *skin* gland because it originates from specialized cells (primordia) on the outside layer of the body surface during embryological development. Other skin glands are the sweat glands and the sebaceous glands, the latter being responsible for the oily secretions observed on the body surface. In their development, all three types of skin glands are similar.

The skin glands are *exocrine* in nature; that is, they pour their secretory products to the exterior, in contrast to the *endocrine* glands (see Chapter 20), which release their products into the blood stream.

23-2. ANATOMY OF THE MAMMARY GLAND

The number of mammary glands and their position on the external body surface is peculiar to the species concerned. In cattle there are 4 glands located in the inguinal region, each having 1 teat or passageway to the body surface. The mare also has 4 glands in the inguinal area, but only 2 teats; each teat contains 2 ducts, one from each gland served by the teat. Inguinal mammary glands are also present in sheep and goats. In the latter species, only 2 glands are present, each supplied with its own teat. The mammary glands of humans and elephants are located in the pectoral region. In the bitch, sow, rat, and others, the mammary glands number from 10 or more and are disposed on the ventral body surface, on either side of the midline from the pectoral region to the inguinal region. It is interesting to note that each mammary gland of humans and bitches has several ducts opening on the body surface rather than the single opening in the teats of cows and goats.

Gross Anatomy. It is beyond the scope of this chapter to pursue the individual features of the mammary glands of all the species of mammals. Since the production of milk by dairy cows is a major agricultural enter-

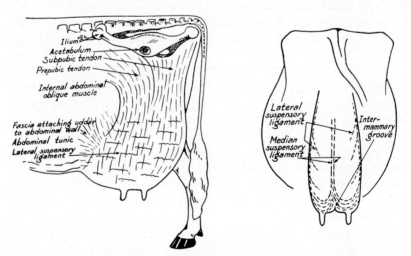

Fig. 23-1. Suspensory appartus of the udder. [From V. R. Smith, 1959.]

prise, the mammary system of the cow will serve as the model to be discussed.

The 4 mammary glands of the cow are grouped together as a unit and are referred to collectively as the *udder*. The udder is divided into *halves* with 2 glands or *quarters* present in each half. In high-producing cows, an udder just before milking may weigh as much as 150 lb. If the skin alone was responsible for suspending such a high-producing udder, it would hang far below the abdominal surface of the body. However, this does not usually happen because of the lateral *suspensory ligaments* and the *median suspensory ligament* (Fig. 23-1).

SUSPENSORY SYSTEM. When viewed from behind, the halves of the udder usually can be clearly distinguished because of the presence of a slight or marked groove between them, the *intermammary* groove (Fig. 23-1). The lateral suspensory ligaments, primarily composed of tough, strong, fibrous tissue, extend from the pelvic bones down the right and left sides and rear of the udder, and continue underneath the udder and up into the intermammary groove. The *median suspensory* ligament, which is firmly attached to the abdominal floor, is found between the two halves and is well supplied with elastic as well as fibrous tissue.

GLAND STRUCTURE. The four glands of the bovine udder are distinct, sepa-

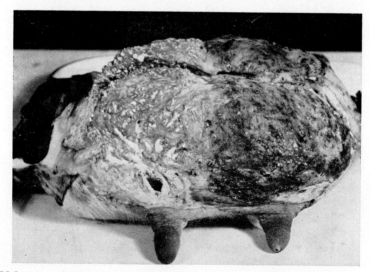

Fig. 23-2. A sagittal section of an udder half. The anterior quarter has been injected with white latex rubber and the posterior quarter with a darker colored latex. It is clear that there has been no diffusion of color from one quarter to the other, demonstrating that the glands are separate distinct secretory units. [From Yapp and Nevens, *Dairy Cattle, Selection, Feeding and Management,* Wiley, New York, 1955.]

rate units. In a cross section of the udder, the boundary between the two halves is clearly marked by the median suspensory ligament. However, between the glands of each half no clear line of demarcation is present. For gross examination it is necessary to inject one quarter of each half with a dye in order to show that the glands are not functionally connected (Fig. 23-2).

Each mammary gland is divided into *lobes* and each lobe into *lobules*. In this instance a mammary gland might be compared to a tree, where the entire tree would be equivalent to a complete mammary gland, the large branches comparable to the lobes, and the small branches to the lobules.

DUCT SYSTEM. The duct system not only conveys the milk from the secre-

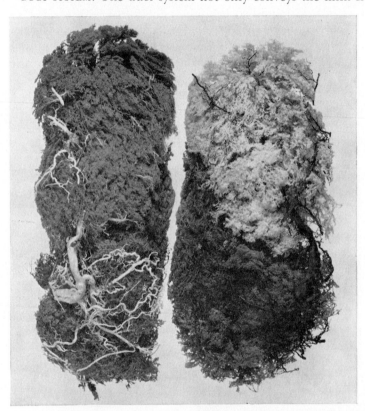

Fig. 23-3. A plastic cast on an udder showing the milk-collecting system. The quarters of the left half have been injected with vinyl acetate plastic of the same color, whereas the quarters of the right have been injected with different colors. The plastic was permitted to solidify and the mammary tissue dissolved away with concentrated hydrochloric acid. It can be seen clearly that each quarter is a distinct secretory unit. [From Yapp and Nevens, *Dairy Cattle, Selection, Feeding and Management,* Wiley, New York, 1955.]

tory units of the udder to the teat cistern where it can be removed, but it also stores a portion of the milk secreted during the milking interval.

Each secretory unit of the udder is connected to the remainder of its lobule by means of small intra-lobular ducts. The lobules in turn drain their contents into the large ducts present in each lobe, the in-tralobar ducts. Connecting all the lobes in each gland are the inter-lobar ducts which open into the large milk-collecting ducts leading to the gland and teat cisterns. The complexity of the milk collecting system can be seen in Fig. 23-3.

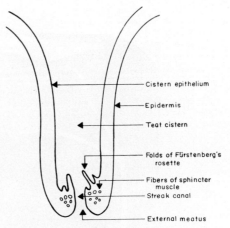

Fig. 23-4. A sagittal section of a teat, showing the important anatomical struc-tures.

THE TEAT. In the cow, each mammary gland is provided with a teat. It not only provides the means whereby the milk can be withdrawn from each gland, but it also has the unique functions of keeping the milk in and for-eign material out. These functions are accomplished by means of a strong sphincter muscle surrounding the teat opening (*external meatus*). Also aid-ing to keep the milk in are folds of tissue (Fürstenberg's rosette) at the top of the streak canal. These folds are so arranged that whenever pressure is applied to the teat the folds cover the streak canal like a cap. Figure 23-4 illustrates the main features of the bovine teat.

Vascular System of the Udder

ARTERIES. The synthesis of milk requires that a constant supply of nutri-ents be supplied to the udder. It has been estimated that for every pound of milk secreted, 150 to 500 lb. of blood must pass through the udder. This tremendous volume of blood reaches the udder primarily through the in-guinal ring (an opening through the abdominal wall, just dorsal to the udder, permitting communication between the udder and abdominal cavity) by way of the *external pudic arteries* (right and left). A secondary and almost incidental supply reaches the udder through the *perineal arteries* (right and left). All of these arteries are branches of large arteries leading from the *abdominal aorta,* the large vessel carrying oxygenated, nutrient-rich, arterial blood from the heart (Fig. 23-5).

VEINS. Actively metabolizing tissue produces a large volume of by-products which, in general, is waste. It is the function of the venous portion of the vascular system to carry these wastes to areas of the body where they can be discarded. The main venous drainage of the udder is by way of the *external*

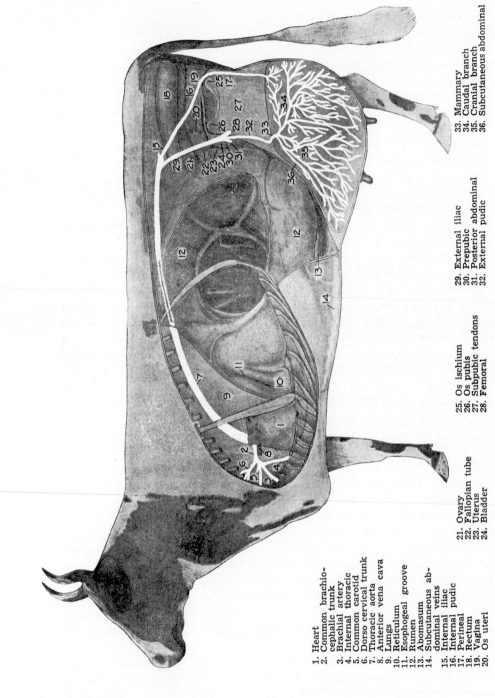

1. Heart
2. Common brachio-
   cephalic trunk
3. Brachial artery
4. Internal thoracic
5. Common caroid
6. Dorso cervical trunk
7. Thoracic aorta
8. Anterior vena cava
9. Lungs
10. Reticulum
11. Esophogeal groove
12. Rumen
13. Abomasum
14. Subcutaneous ab-
    dominal veins
15. Internal iliac
16. Internal pudic
17. Perineal
18. Rectum
19. Vagina
20. Os uteri

21. Ovary
22. Fallopian tube
23. Uterus
24. Bladder
25. Os ischium
26. Os pubis
27. Subpubic tendons
28. Femoral

29. External iliac
30. Prepubic
31. Posterior abdominal
32. External pudic
33. Mammary
34. Caudal branch
35. Cranial branch
36. Subcutaneous abdominal

Fig. 23-5.   Arterial circulation to the udder. [From V. R. Smith, 1959.]

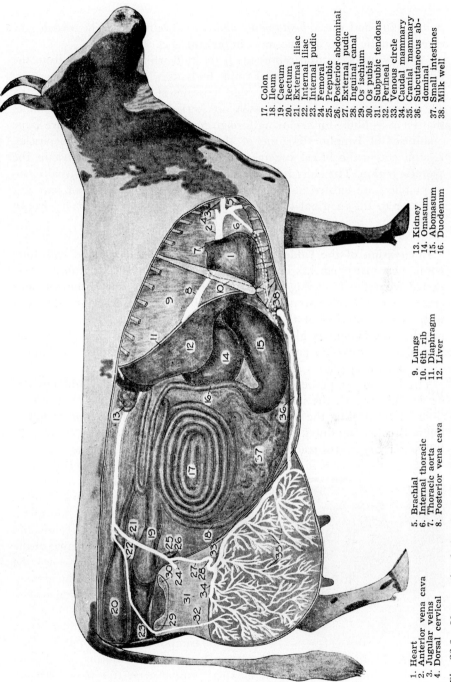

1. Heart
2. Anterior vena cava
3. Jugular veins
4. Dorsal cervical
5. Brachial
6. Internal thoracic
7. Thoracic aorta
8. Posterior vena cava
9. Lungs
10. 6th rib
11. Diaphragm
12. Liver
13. Kidney
14. Omasum
15. Abomasum
16. Duodenum
17. Colon
18. Ileum
19. Caecum
20. Rectum
21. External iliac
22. Internal iliac
23. Internal pudic
24. Femoral
25. Prepubic
26. Posterior abdominal
27. External pudic
28. Inguinal canal
29. Os ischium
30. Os pubis
31. Subpubic tendons
32. Perineal
33. Venous circle
34. Caudal mammary
35. Cranial mammary
36. Subcutaneous abdominal
37. Small intestines
38. Milk well

Fig. 23-6. Venous circulation from the udder. [From V. R. Smith, 1959.]

385

pudic veins and the *subcutaneous abdominal* veins. Of these vessels, the external pudic veins are the most important (Fig. 23-6).

LYMPH VESSELS. Lymph represents body fluid which has passed from the capillaries out into the tissues. Lymph finds its way back to the heart by the way of lymph vessels but, because it is almost colorless, the lymphatics are difficult to trace. Lymph vessels are periodically supplied with nodes that serve as filters for removing foreign materials; they also produce large quantities of lymphocytes, one of the types of white blood corpuscles. Lymph enters the blood stream through a duct in the vena cava in the thoracic region. The chief lymph nodes or glands in the udder, usually two in number, are located at the base, next to the abdominal floor and just posterior to the inguinal canal, and are called the *supramammary lymph nodes*.

Innervation of the Udder. A general outline of the somatic and autonomic nervous system has been considered in Chapter 20. It would be expected from the foregoing that tissues of the udder, like tissues of most organs, would receive contributions from both the sympathetic and parasympathetic branches of the autonomic nervous system. However, this is not the case. Mammary glands are skin glands, and it has been shown that skin glands receive no parasympathetic nerve fibers. Therefore the tissues of the mammary glands receive only sympathetic motor fibers.

The lumbar sympathetic plexus is responsible for all the udder motor nerves. They reach the udder through the inguinal nerve and are responsible for controlling the blood supply to the udder and for innervation of the milk-collecting ducts.

The sensory nerves reach the udder by three different pathways. (1) Sensory nerves to the anterior region of the udder have their origin in the first and second lumbar nerves, which leave the spinal cord in the lumbar region and reach the designated areas of the udder after following down the abdominal wall. (2) The glandular tissue, milk-collecting system, teats, and skin of the udder receive sensory nerve fibers from components of the lumbar spinal nerves contributing to the inguinal nerve that passes through the inguinal canal. (3) The posterior part of the udder receives its sensory nerves from the peri-

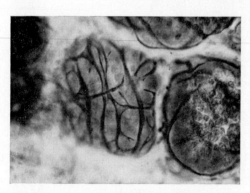

Fig. 23-7. Photograph of part of the surface of a small contracted alveolus (goat), showing a myoepithelial cell with nucleus and branching processes. [From C. K. Richardson, 1949.]

neal nerve, which originates from the sacral spinal nerves. The disposition of the nerve supply to the udder has been shown by St. Clair (1942).

Structure of Milk Secretory Units (Alveoli). Among the few structures of the bovine udder which cannot be seen without the assistance of a microscope are the milk-secreting alveoli and their tiny tubules, which lead to the intralobular milk-collecting ducts. In shape an alveolus is approximately spherical, and it is lined with the actual milk-secreting cells. Each alveolus is well endowed with capillaries, which furnish the raw materials for the various milk components.

Surrounding each alveolus is a basketlike network of strands of tissue called myoepithelium (*myo* denoting muscle) (Fig. 23-7). It is the contraction of these fibers that is believed to be responsible for the expulsion of milk from the alveoli at the time of milking.

23-3. MAMMARY GLAND DEVELOPMENT

Embryological Development. For an evaluation of the embryonic and fetal development of the bovine mammary gland, the student is referred to the excellent contributions of Turner (1930, 1931). In general, the work of Turner shows that by the time the heifer fetus is six months old, the gland cisterns, teat cisterns, and the groundwork for the duct system can be clearly differentiated. At birth all the nonsecretory structures of the udder are very near their mature form.

Postnatal Development

BIRTH TO PUBERTY. Until recently, it was generally believed that mammary glands undergo only slow change during this period of growth. Much of the increase in udder size up to the time of puberty has been attributed to

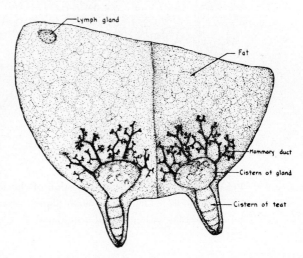

Fig. 23-8. Diagram of a cross section of the udder of a heifer before reaching sexual maturity. At this stage the glands consist of a small teat and milk cistern. The ducts leading out from the cistern are small and short, with few branches. [From C. W. Turner, 1934.]

the deposition of fat; however, the duct system appears to increase in magnitude, unquestionably contributing to the over-all size increase (Fig. 23-8).

Near the onset of puberty there appears to be a sudden increase in metabolic activity of the mammary gland, as shown by Cowie (1949) in his experiments with rats. He found that the growth of the mammary glands at this stage of development was three times that of general body growth. It was suggested that the increased activity of the anterior pituitary gland might be responsible for the increased rate of mammary growth. Whether the same situation exists in cattle remains to be shown.

EFFECT OF RECURRING ESTROUS CYCLES. The onset of puberty in cattle is associated with the periodic appearance of "heat" (estrous) symptoms. During this time, until the cow becomes pregnant, udder growth is confined to the extension of the duct or milk-collecting system (Fig. 23-9). It is believed that estrogen and possibly progesterone secreted by the ovary are responsible for this stage of udder growth.

EFFECT OF PREGNANCY. The state of pregnancy in the cow is associated with the presence of a functional *corpus luteum* in the ovarian tissue. During the first pregnancy, the first half of the gestation period is taken up with the completion of the duct system. The milk secreting units, the *alveoli,* develop during the last half of the gestation period (Fig. 23-10). Experimental evidence indicates that the final stage of the development of the

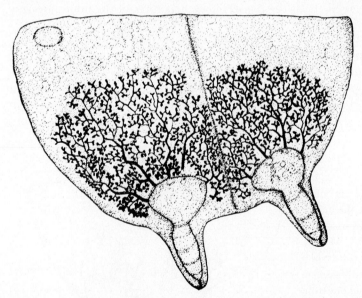

Fig. 23-9. Diagram of a cross section of the udder of a heifer after many "heat periods." The duct system shows extensive development but the lobule-alveolar system is not stimulated to growth. [From C. W. Turner, 1934.]

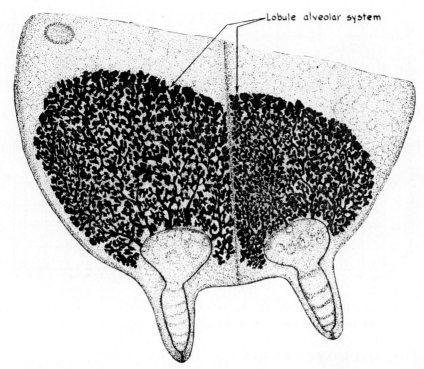

Lobule alveolar system

Fig. 23-10. Diagram of a cross section of the udder of a heifer at about the fifth month or the middle of pregnancy. The lobule-alveolar system has begun to develop. [From C. W. Turner, 1934.]

mammary glands of cattle during the first pregnancy is dependent upon the ratio of the two hormones estrogen and progesterone. Shortly before *parturition* (calving), the alveoli and ducts become distended with a fluid that only slightly resembles milk. The alveolar secretory product is called "milk" only after it has certain physicochemical properties.

In succeeding pregnancies the cow is lactating for most of the gestation period, and the mammary glands are nonfunctional for only a few weeks previous to parturition. The period of nonfunctioning of the mammary gland is commonly referred to as the "dry period."

EFFECT OF PARTURITION. Following parturition, the udder is stimulated into intensive secretory activity, and there is a gradual increase in milk production from the first to approximately the sixth week. After this time there is a gradual decline in milk production, until the cow is permitted to "dry up" for her ensuing parturition and next lactation period (Fig. 23-11).

INVOLUTION. The return of the udder to the nonfunctional state is called *involution*. When the udder is involuted, the milk-collecting system remains intact; however, it is impossible to differentiate the milk-secreting alveoli.

Fig. 23-11. Lactation curves illustrating the effect of frequency of milking on lactation persistency. [From Woodward, 1931.]

23-4. MILK SECRETION

It has been pointed out that a mammary gland is an exocrine skin gland; furthermore, it is an apocrine gland. In apocrine glands the larger secretory products accumulate at one end of the cells of which the gland is composed. The smaller, less complex molecules are secreted into the alveolar lumen. At some time, and for some reason unknown at present, the tips of the cells containing the secretory products rupture, and the products—as well as part of the cellular cytoplasm—escape into the alveolar lumen. Following this phase, the nucleus and cytoplasm begin again their activity of forming secretory products.

Physiological Considerations of the Secretory Process. The mechanisms whereby the constituents of milk are formed and pass into the lumen of the mammary alveoli have been the subject of much controversy. It appears that the formation of milk is best explained on the basis of filtration, selective absorption, synthesis, and secretion.

It first must be understood that before milk is formed there must be a source of raw materials for its formation. These materials can only come from the blood present in the capillaries adjacent to the alveoli.

Very uncomplicated molecules, such as water and mineral ions, can pass from the blood through the alveolar cells and into the alveolar lumen by simple filtration. More complex milk precursors are selectively taken from the blood by the alveolar cells and synthesized into substances more complex than the precursors. For example, the monosaccharide glucose is absorbed from the blood and formed into the disaccharide lactose.

After the characteristic milk constituents have been synthesized, they are secreted into the lumen of the alveoli by the method previously described for apocrine glands. The secretory activity continues until the pressure in the alveoli, resulting from the increased volume of fluids, exceeds the secretory pressure exerted by the alveolar cells.

The Initiation of Lactation. We have seen earlier that estrogen and progesterone are responsible for the growth and development of the mammary gland. Shortly before parturition, the secretion of milk begins—due to the action of another hormone, prolactin, secreted by the anterior pituitary. The cause for prolactin secretion at this moment is the subject of considerable debate. Suffice it to say that, according to most investigators in this field, changes in the levels of either (or both) estrogen and progesterone in the blood somehow influence prolactin secretion.

The importance of the anterior pituitary in the initiation of lactation cannot be overrated. For example, laboratory animals which have had their pituitary glands removed in late pregnancy deliver their young but do not lactate. Pituitary hormones other than prolactin that are important in lactation are *somatotropin* or *growth hormone* and *adrenocorticotropic hormone (ACTH)*.

Maintenance of Lactation

ANTERIOR PITUITARY GLAND. The integrity of the anterior pituitary appears essential for the maintenance of lactation. Experimentally, it is possible to cause the termination of lactation by surgical removal of the anterior pituitary. In animals which have undergone such surgery, it is possible to maintain approximately 50% of lactation by instituting a program of replacement therapy. At first thought, one might expect that the administration of prolactin alone would bring about normal secretory activity of the mammary gland, but this has not been found to be the case. As a matter of fact, crude extracts of the anterior pituitary gland have been found to be more efficient in maintaining milk secretion than purified prolactin. Using relatively pure substances, it was discovered that the secretory activity induced by crude pituitary extracts could be duplicated by simultaneous administration of prolactin, somatotropin (STH), and adrenocorticotropin (ACTH).

ADRENAL GLAND. Removal of the adrenal glands in experimental animals usually results in an immediate reduction of lactation, which can be returned almost to normal by the administration of the cortical hormones deoxycorticosterone and cortisone. The mechanism by which these hormones act in maintaining lactation is obscure at this time. However, it is believed that they are important in *gluconeogenesis* (the formation of glucose from noncarbohydrate sources) and *lipogenesis* (fat synthesis).

THYROID GLAND. The thyroid gland has the important function of assisting in the regulation of general body metabolism. It is doubly important to glands which are already functioning at a rapid rate. Since actively secreting mammary glands fall into this category, it is not surprising to discover that milk production may be depressed as much as 75% when the thyroid gland is removed. Milk secretion in thyroidectomized cows can be returned to normal by feeding or injecting thyroxine or other compounds having thyroxine-like activity.

Thyroxine is a *galactopoetic* material in that it is capable of causing increases in milk production over the normal when administered to intact cows. As a routine practice, it is not considered to be advantageous. For a more complete evaluation of this subject, the student is referred to an excellent review by Blaxter *et al.* (1949).

THE NEURAL ASPECT OF THE MAINTENANCE OF LACTATION. Up to this point, consideration has only been given to the hormonal influence on the maintenance of lactation—but this is not the complete story. Certain neurohumoral mechanisms are also important.

It was proposed by Selye (1934) that prolactin secretion is periodically stimulated by manipulation of the teats, and that, at the time of suckling receptors in the region of the teat are stimulated into activity. Impulses resulting from this stimulation are then carried centrally to areas of the brain responsible for the release of prolactin from the anterior pituitary gland. As evidence, he submitted that unsuckled rat mammary glands could be maintained in secretory activity for only as long as other mammary glands were routinely suckled. Furthermore, if all the teats of lactating mammary glands were tied off in order to prevent the removal of milk, the glands could be maintained in an active state by periodic suckling. Some time after Selye's experiments, another researcher contributed support to the theory by showing that even though lactating rat mammary glands were ligated and unsuckled, they could be maintained in functional condition by the injection of prolactin. It is quite probable that hormones other than prolactin are also liberated as a result of this sensory stimulation.

Milk Expulsion (Milk Ejection, Milk Let-Down). Milk expulsion involves all the processes whereby milk contained in the mammary gland at the time of suckling or milking is made available for withdrawal. It is a complex reflex and involves neuroendocrine mechanisms.

Though Gaines pioneered in the field, the modern concept of the reflex nature of milk expulsion was first proposed by Ely and Peterson (1941). In their experiments they denervated half an udder of a cow and found that no milk could be expressed from the denervated half until the intact half had been stimulated by suckling or manipulation of the teats. They theorized that manipulation of the teats stimulated sensory receptors in this region, which were in turn responsible for stimulating the release of oxytocin from the posterior pituitary. Oxytocin then traveled by means of the blood to the tissue of the udder responsible for expressing milk.

Since 1941 considerable effort has been expended in attempts to more fully understand milk expulsion. In general, the theory of Ely and Petersen (1941) has been confirmed many times. We now know that sensory impulses are sent to the brain by the receptors in the vicinity of the teat. The hypothalamic area of the brain is then responsible for causing the release of oxytocin from the posterior pituitary into the blood. When it reaches the udder, oxytocin stimulates the myoepithelial cells surrounding the alveoli to contract, with the result that the milk is squeezed into the ducts where it can easily be removed by proper milking procedure (Fig. 23-12).

Milk let-down can be easily developed into a conditioned reflex—the cow begins to associate the sights, sounds, and odors that occur just before

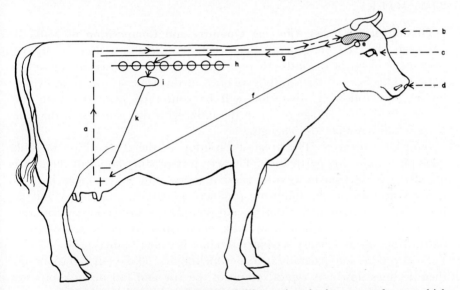

Fig. 23-12. A diagrammatic sketch illustrating the important factors which influence milk expulsion. Impulses resulting from tactile stimulation of the teats and udder (a), as well as impulses arising from auditory (b), visual (c), and olfactory (d), stimuli, cause the release of oxytocin from the posterior pituitary gland (e). Oxytocin is carried in the blood (f) to the udder, where it effects the expulsion of milk. Pain and other disagreeable sensations (fright, for example) result in impulses being sent to the adrenal gland (i), via the spinal cord (g) and sympathetic ganglia (h). Adrenalin from the adrenal medulla is carried to the udder in the blood (k), where it antagonizes the action of oxytocin. [After H. Ziegler and W. Mosimann, 1960.]

milking with the procedure itself. In other words, the stimuli arriving at the brain from the receptors in the eyes, ears, and nose at the time of milking are, after a period of training, just as efficient in eliciting the release of oxytocin from the posterior pituitary as are impulses which arrive as the result of teat manipulation (Fig. 23-12). As a matter of fact, milk frequently drips from the teats of cows as they enter the milking area.

A stimulus which is capable of causing pain or fear will result in the inhibition of milk expulsion, as will the injection of adrenaline. It is known that noxious stimuli (resulting in pain sensation) cause the release of adrenaline from the adrenal medulla in order that the animal can take action necessary to protect itself from the unfavorable circumstances. On the basis of this evidence it is believed that adrenaline is the substance in the blood responsible for the inhibition of milk let-down whenever noxious stimuli are present (Fig. 23-12).

23-5. MILK

Physiological Factors Affecting Quantity and Composition of Milk. It has been observed, in general, that whenever there is a decrease in the percentage of fat in the milk, there is a concomitant decrease in the solids-not-fat. This has not been fully explained at this time. In the light of this finding, the following discussion will be concerned primarily with the changes in the percentage of fat in the milk, with the assumption that the percent solids-not-fat also changes.

STAGE OF LACTATON. The greatest variation in the composition of milk takes place following parturition. The secretory product found in the udder at calving is referred to as *colostrum;* it is not milk as we know it. It is richer than milk in the following products: globulins, vitamins A and D, iron, calcium, magnesium, chlorine, and phosphorus. Conversely, it contains less lactose and potassium than milk does. Approximately 5 days after parturition, the mammary secretory product is called "milk."

Total production generally increases for the first 30 days of lactation and then declines slowly. A typical graph of the rise and fall of milk production over an entire lactation period is shown in Fig. 23-11.

During the lactation period, the fat per cent of the milk is usually inversely related to the amount produced. Whenever production is high, fat per cent is low, and vice versa.

PERSISTENCY. This term refers to the degree with which the rate of milk secretion is maintained as a lactation period progresses. It is an inherited characteristic that can be dramatically affected by environment, for example plane of nutrition. After the peak of production has been reached, each month's production should be approximately 90% of the preceding month if persistency is satisfactory.

EFFECT OF PREGNANCY. Carrying a calf in a normal pregnancy does not appear to influence the composition of milk. So far as total production is concerned, it has been estimated that the energy requirements of the fetus and the cost of pregnancy to the animal are equivalent to 400–600 lb. of milk. Expressed in other terms by another observer, the energy cost of pregnancy is approximately 3% of the total production.

Despite the strong stimulus for prolactin secretion by periodic removal of milk from the mammary glands of the cow, the hormones of pregnancy exert an inhibitory effect on milk production. On the other hand, most unbred lactating cows can be expected to lactate almost indefinitely, although at a much lower rate than that observed during earlier phases of a lactation period.

FIRST- AND LAST-DRAWN MILK. The percentage of fat is higher in the milk removed from the udder last. The reason for this is in doubt; however, it has been proposed that the fat and other large milk particles adhere closer to, or are actually in, the tips of the alveolar cells just previous to milk expulsion. Whenever the myoepithelial cells are stimulated by oxytocin, the water-soluble portion of the milk is readily forced into the large ducts. As this portion of the milk is removed from the udder, it is possible for the larger particles of milk to enter the lumen of the alveoli either as the result of reduced intra-alveolar pressure or because the tips of the cells are ruptured by the sudden contraction of the myoepithelium surrounding the alveoli. Perhaps both of these mechanisms are involved.

AGE. With advancing age there is a gradual increase in milk production until maturity is reached (6–8 years old). At this time production begins to decline but the rate is slower than the increase up to maturity. Conversion tables for the various breeds of dairy cattle are available for adjusting the records of immature cows to their expected mature production or *mature equivalent* (Kendrick, 1953). As a "rule of thumb" it is estimated that at 2 years a cow produces approximately 70% of her mature production, at 3 years, 80%; 4 years, 90%; 5 years, 95%; and at 6 years, her mature record.

After maturity there is a slight decrease in the percentage of fat and other major constituents of milk. Sodium chloride, albumin, and nonprotein nitrogen, on the other hand, gradually increase in concentration in the milk as the cow grows older. Presumably the latter reflects an increase in permeability of the alveolar cells for materials from the tissue fluid or a gradual reduction in the activity of the cell responsible for rejecting these products.

SIZE. Large cows within a breed usually produce more milk than small cows, but the increase in production is not in direct proportion to body weight. Brody (1945) found that for each 100-lb. increase in body weight, production only increased 70% of the proportional increase in body size. Of course, this increase applies only to animals which have the same efficiency of production.

BREED. The effect of breed on the average milk production and average composition is discussed under "Breeds of Dairy Cattle."

ESTRUS. The effect of estrus on milk production cannot be predicted for any individual cow; however, in the majority of cows, milk production drops slightly. Accompanying the drop in production is an increase in fat percentage.

Environmental Factors Affecting the Quantity and Composition of Milk.
It is only under the most favorable circumstances that a cow attains its inherited capacity for production. A purchased cow may produce more or less milk than she produced in her previous environment. Environmental conditions include, for example, milking techniques, nutrition, length of dry period, number of times milked daily, and disease.

LENGTH OF DRY PERIOD. The length of time that a cow is dry between lactation periods affects production in the ensuing lactation. A short dry period does not allow her to build up body reserves for the tremendous drain of the next lactation period. As a result, production usually suffers. Conversely, excessively long dry periods will lower her lifetime production record. A dry period of approximately 60 days is optimal.

NUTRITIONAL CONDITION AT THE TIME OF CALVING. It is only reasonable to expect cows in a poor nutritional condition at the time of calving to produce less milk than cows in good condition. On the other hand, excessive conditioning prior to calving has not regularly resulted in increased production.

PREPARTUM MILKING. The removal of mammary secretory products late in the dry period before parturition is called *prepartum milking*. It has been argued that prepartum milking is an aid in the relief of udder congestion; however, experimentally it has not been found to be a good general practice. When prepartum milking is performed, the composition of the mammary secretory product at the time of parturition is found to be similar to milk, especially if the cow is milked a week or so previous to calving. Prepartum milking can rob the newborn calf of the colostrum so important to its early well-being; therefore, if prepartum milking is found to be necessary, all of the secretory product should be saved and fed to the calf after it is born. The incidence or severity of milk fever has not been found to be reduced by prepartum milking.

THE INTERVAL BETWEEN MILKINGS. The recent reviews of Elliott (1959, 1959a) serve to indicate the controversial nature of this subject. In order to determine the true effect of "interval between milkings" one must rule out differences caused by the length of experimental periods, experimental design, management, age of cows, inherited level of production, and other unknown factors. Kendrick (1953) considered many of these variables when he reported: ". . . on the average, at two years of age a cow will produce approximately 20 per cent more milk if she is milked three times a day than if she is milked only twice a day; at three years of age she will produce approximately 17 per cent more; and at four years of age and over, she will produce approximately 15 per cent more. Similarly, at two years of age a cow will produce approximately 35 per cent more milk if she is milked four times daily than if she is milked only twice a day; at three years of age she will produce approximately 30 per cent more; at four years of age and over, she will produce approximately 20 per cent more." The increased production resulting from more frequent milking has been attributed to the more frequent reduction in intramammary pressure which has been shown to inhibit milk secretion. Therefore, by relieving the intramammary pressure more often, secretion continues for a greater proportion of time. Milking once a day reduces milk production approximately 50%.

ENVIRONMENTAL TEMPERATURE. Cows of breeds popular in this country produce most efficiently at an environmental temperature of about 50°F. When the temperature exceeds 80°F, most cows drop off in production; accompanying this is an increase in fat percentage. On the other hand, Holsteins can endure temperatures of 8°F with little or no effect on production. Cows of the Jersey breed exhibit a drop in production whenever the environmental temperature goes below 40°F. Once again fat percentage increases as the total production declines.

The decrease in production observed at temperatures exceeding 80°F is probably the result of decreased metabolic activity influenced possibly by a decreased activity of the thyroid gland; feed consumption is also decreased. Both of these mechanisms result in a net decrease in heat production. When the temperature is low, more energy is required to maintain body temperature and thus less is made available for milk production. Feed consumption is stimulated by low temperatures.

SEASON. It is difficult to separate such factors as management, nutrition, temperature, humidity, and exercise from a purely "seasonal effect" on milk production. The overall effect is, presumably, the result of a combination of all these factors. For example, cows usually drop off in milk production during the hot periods of late summer. This decline could be caused by the increased temperature or a decrease in nutrients from pastures—generally in poor condition this time of the year.

The time of year calving occurs also influences milk production with respect to the evaluation of seasonal effects on production. Cows that freshen in June usually have a higher average fat percentage for the year than cows that freshen at other times. On the other hand, cows freshening in fall and winter produce 10–20% more milk than cows that calve in spring or summer.

In general, cows get more exercise in the summer than they do in the winter, and animals exercising probably require more nutrients to maintain a level of production than do animals receiving little or no exercise. Thus, cows on poor pasture require feed supplementation to maintain milk production, not only because they take in less nutrients from such pasture but also because they expend large amounts of energy in searching the pasture for food.

It is clear that more research work is needed to evaluate the influence of season on milk and milk fat production.

DRUGS. Many types of compounds which exert a pharmacological effect have been used on cows in attempts to increase milk and milk fat production. Most have no effect. However, certain hormones such as thyroxine and oxytocin can temporarily increase yields of both milk and fat. Unfortunately, oxytocin must be administered just after each milking in order to get the *residual milk,* a procedure which is both expensive and time consuming. Tests have shown that even though thyroxine can temporarily increase production, increased nutrients are required to prevent the drain of milk precursors from the cow's body. Whenever thyroxine administration is ended, there is an immediate drop in production which counterbalances any temporary increase.

Recently research has been conducted on the use of stilbesterol and tranquilizers on milk production, but the results are not encouraging.

FEEDING. The adherence to the principles of good feeding practices is particularly important for the maximum production of milk of uniform composition. It will therefore be considered more completely in Chapter 32.

DISEASE. It is difficult to assess the effect of "disease" in general on milk secretion without considering the many manifestations of each individual disorder. In general, digestive disturbances and diseases that affect the entire cow reduce the yield of milk and elevate the fat percentage. Diseases of the udder, such as mastitis, not only reduce the yield of milk but drastically alter its composition.

REFERENCES AND SELECTED READINGS

References marked with an asterisk are of general interest.

Blaxter, K. L., E. P. Reineke, E. W. Crampton, and W. E. Petersen, 1949. The role of thyroidal materials and of synthetic goitrogens in animal production and an appraisal of their practical use. *J. Animal Sci.,* 8:307–352.

*Brody, S., 1945. *Bioenergetics and Growth.* Reinhold, New York.

Cowie, A. T., 1949. The relative growth of the mammary gland in normal, gonadectomized and adrenalectomized rats. *J. Endocrin.,* 6:145–147.

Elliott, G. M., 1959. The direct effect of milk accumulation in the udder of the dairy cow upon milk secretion rate. *Dairy Sci. Abstracts,* 21:435–439.

——— 1959a. The effect on milk yield of the length of milking intervals used in twice a day milking, twice and three times a day milking and incomplete milking. *Dairy Sci. Abstracts,* 21:481–490.

*Folly, S. J., 1956. *The Physiology and Biochemistry of Lactation.* Oliver and Boyd, London.

Ely, F. and W. E. Petersen, 1941. Factors involved in the ejection of milk. *J. Dairy Sci.,* 24:211–223.

Kendrick, J. F., 1953. Standardizing dairy-herd-improvement-association records on proving sires. USDA B.D.I. Inf. 162.

*Nevens, W. B., 1951. *Principles of Milk Production.* McGraw-Hill, New York.

*Petersen, W. E., 1950. *Dairy Science*. 2nd Ed. Lippincott, Philadelphia.

Richardson, K. C., 1949. Contractile tissues in the mammary gland, with special reference to myoepithelium in the goat. *Proc. Roy. Soc.* (London), B 136:30–45.

Selye, H., 1934. On the nervous control of lactation. *Am. J. Physiol.*, 107:535–538.

*Smith, V. R., 1959. *Physiology of Lactation*. 5th ed. Iowa State Univ. Press, Ames, Iowa.

St. Clair, L. E., 1942. The nerve supply to the bovine udder. *Am. J. Vet. Research*, 3:10–16.

*Turner, C. W., 1930. The anatomy of the mammary gland of cattle. I. Embryonic development. Mo. Agr. Expt. Sta. Research Bull. 140.

————, 1931. The anatomy of the mammary gland of cattle. II. Fetal development. Mo. Agr. Expt. Sta. Research Bull. 160.

————, 1934. The causes of the growth and function of the udder of cattle. Mo. Agr. Expt. Sta. Bull. 339.

*————, 1939. *The Comparative Anatomy of the Mammary Glands, with Special Reference to the Udder of Cattle*. Univ. Coop. Book Store, Columbia, Mo.

Woodward, T. E., 1931. The production of dairy cows as affected by frequency and regularity of milking and feeding. USDA Circ. 180.

*Ziegler, H. and W. Mosimann, 1960. *Anatomie und Physiologie der Rindermilchdrüse*. Paul Parey, Berlin.

Chapter 24

Growth

". . . new ideas need the more time for gaining general assent the more really original they are."

VON HELMHOLTZ

24-1. INTRODUCTION

Growth is a physiological activity of great practical importance in all classes of livestock but of special significance in meat-producing animals such as swine, beef cattle, and sheep. A fast rate of gain is the key to success. It is essential, therefore, that students in livestock production be introduced to the complexities of the phenomenon of growth.

Any definition of growth is almost certain to be inadequate since to be correct it must include all the intricate and complex processes and changes involved in this phenomenon. One definition by Brody (1945) describes growth as "relatively *irreversible* time change in magnitude of the measured dimension or function." Stating it more simply, growth is an increase in size during a specific period of a part or the whole of whatever is being measured. This concept is useful for purposes of quantitative analysis since it conveys the idea of an increase in population, an increase in cell numbers or size, an increase in linearity, or an increase in weight—all as a function of time. It excludes those irregularities occasioned by a changing food supply or different physiological states such as gestation or lactation.

This definition, however, is far too general since it is limited only to a measure with respect to some reference system, and tells us nothing about the types of changes or the processes which cause them.

"True" growth can be described as a composite of many diverse physio-

400

logical biochemical processes, and represents, in a restricted sense, a net accumulation of body substance in which protoplasmic reproduction exceeds destruction. Since the term "protoplasm" refers only to the "living" portion of the organism, this definition would rule out not only such things as food or water in the digestive tract and waste products not as yet excreted, but also such substances as glycogen stored in the liver, fat in the fat depots, and calcium in the bones. Thus, it is implied that "true" growth represents some permanent increase in the protoplasmic mass.

24-2. MEASURES OF ORGANISMIC GROWTH

Measurement of growth must depend upon the selection of a unit which best describes the type of physiological change being evaluated. When dealing with the organism as a whole, almost any unit chosen will represent the algebraic sum of many changes—reflecting loss as well as increase of body substance, and not necessarily indicating an accumulation of protoplasm per se. For example, much of the weight increase in mature beef cattle is in the form of stored fat rather than in protein or skeletal gain.

In spite of obvious discrepancies, the growth curve, showing rate of weight or linear increase, is a useful expression and deserves some analysis. The student, however, should continue to bear in mind the limitations imposed by the unit of measure selected.

The Growth Curve. If one plots the cumulative increase of the measured unit with time, in the general case, a sigmoid curve (S-shaped, Fig. 24-1) is obtained irrespective of whether the units are numbers of individuals, weight of an individual, or height of an individual.

The fact that these curves are similar in appearance might be anticipated. In a population, the unit is represented by an individual organism, and the shape of the curve reflects the changes in the numbers of these individuals or in the size of the population with time. Similarly, the change in size of a single individual or organism can be reflected by the number of individual cells existing at any time, although the unit chosen may be a weight or linear function. Accordingly, the rate of increase is essentially proportional to the number of units capable of duplicating themselves at any given time. Since this increase does not proceed indefinitely, the curves eventually show a rate decrease resulting from some inhibiting force. The student should realize, however, that the shape of the curve depends upon changes in growth processes throughout the entire lifetime of an individual or population. When the age of an individual or the size of a population is artificially limited, as is the case in domestic animals, the curve no longer has a characteristic S shape.

Growth can be represented and mathematically expressed in several ways: (1) as an average rate of increase in the measured dimension per unit of

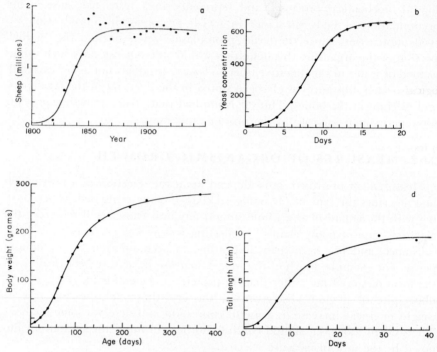

Fig. 24-1. Growth curves illustrating the similar S-shaped characteristic irrespective of the independent variable selected. (a) Sheep population of Tasmania. [Data from Davidson, *J. Tr. Roy. Soc. S. Australia*, **62**:342 (1938).] (b) Yeast growth. [Data from Carlson, *Biochem, Ztschr.*, **57**:313 (1913).] (c) Rate of body weight increase in the male white rat. [Data from Pearl, *The Biology of Population Growth*, Knopf, New York, 1925.] (d) Regeneration of tadpole tail. [Data from Durbin, *J. Exptl. Zool.*, **7**:397 (1909).]

time, (2) as a percentage increase of an initial dimension per unit of time, and (3) as a cumulative increase throughout a prescribed period of time.

The average rate of increase is the expression most commonly used by the animal husbandman, who speaks of the *average daily gain* made by an individual or group of animals. To obtain this value one need only subtract an initial weight (W_1) from a final weight (W_2) and divide this difference by the number of days ($t_2 - t_1$) between these two measures:

$$\text{average rate of gain} = \frac{W_2 - W_1}{t_2 - t_1}.$$

The percentage rate of increase can be expressed as

$$\frac{W_2 - W_1}{W_1} = \text{percentage of growth rate}.$$

Since values represented by this expression may be exaggerated or minimized—depending on the time periods selected for the initial and final measurement—it is seldom used. Before it can be utilized, it is essential to define the time interval during the life of the individual to which the expression applies, in order that the interval of early, rapid growth can be compared with the mature, slow growth phase.

The cumulative growth curves (Fig. 24-1) show by their characteristic S shape that growth is rapid during the early phase of life but, with advancing age, size increase becomes slower and slower until finally growth appears to cease entirely. For purposes of comparison, one usually divides the curve into three parts; a self-accelerating phase, a point of inflection or reversal, and a self-inhibiting phase.

During the self-accelerating phase, size increases by some power of the size at the time of measurement. The reason for this exponential increase can be illustrated rather simply. By assuming that an organism begins as a single cell capable of dividing itself into two cells and that each of these, in turn, divides into two more, and so on, one can write a mathematical equation expressing this relationship: $S = 2^n$, where S = size and n = number of times division has occurred. But all cells do not multiply at the same rate, and rate of weight gain or linear increase is not strictly a function of the total number of cells at any given time. So this formula is a great oversimplification of the growth phenomena.

Mathematical expressions to describe the cumulative growth curve have been formulated. From these equations growth constants can be derived and are useful to predict, under a given set of conditions, growth rate as well as mature size for an individual animal as determined by its genetic make-up.

A more appropriate expression for the self-accelerating phase can be given by the equation $dw/td = kW$, which means that the instantaneous rate of increase is proportional to the number of reproducing units—in this case represented by weight.

The point where growth acceleration stops and growth deceleration begins is known as the point of inflection; in higher animals this point coincides with the time of puberty. The reason for this break is not clearly established but its association with a time of changes of major endocrine events strongly suggests that the production of the hormones active in reproductive processes exerts an important influence.

The self-inhibiting phase, like the self-accelerating phase of the growth curve, can also be mathematically defined. Since the growth rate at this time is proportional to the growth yet to be made, it can be expressed as a function of the difference between the mature size (A) and the size at the time of estimation (W). The general equation denoting this relationship is as follows:

$$\frac{dW}{dt} = -k(A - W).$$

These expressions can be solved by the calculus. By integrating the expression $dW/dt = kW$, one obtains

$$\int_A^W \frac{dW}{W} = k \int_0^t dt; \qquad \ln W = \ln A + kt; \qquad W = Ae^{kt},$$

Where ln W = natural log of weight at time t, ln A = natural log of weight at time 0, t = time, and k = instantaneous growth rate. Similarly,

$$\frac{dW}{dt} = -k(A - W)$$

$$\int \frac{dW}{A - W} = -k \int dt$$

$$\ln (A - W) = -kt + \ln B$$

$$A - W = Be^{-kt}$$

$$W = A - Be^{-kt}.$$

Because of the complexities and vagaries of biological processes, attempts to express changes in terms of relatively fixed, often complicated mathematical relationships may be difficult to interpret. For this reason, the use of simple mathematical approximations to express growth rates or age equivalents can be as useful as complex equations. An example of this type of treatment is in the calculation of physiological age. Since animals of different breeds or species do not mature at the same rate, it is sometimes advantageous to make comparisons on the basis of physiological rather than chronological age.

Although physiological age can be compared by complicated mathematical devices, these methods do not greatly improve upon the use of a simple ratio of the mature ages of different types of animals. For example, if a Holstein steer reaches mature size at 24 months and a Hereford steer at 18 months, then the ratio 18/24 or .75 can be used as a constant to equate approximately the ages of the two animals. Thus, a 12-month-old Holstein steer has the same physiological age as a 9-month-old Hereford steer.

Linear Increase: Changes in Form. Another concept in the methods by which organismic growth may be measured is that of linear increase. This measure, in the case of the domestic mammal, is represented principally by changes in skeletal size; it is useful as a means of quantitating animal conformation in terms of correct body proportions.

In judging animals an individual makes use of visual estimates of size and structure of different body parts and forms an opinion of its value. Many attempts have been made to find measures which would express excellence of body conformation quantitatively but thus far subjective visual estimates have not been improved upon. In meat animals our greatest limitation lies in our inability to estimate carcass excellence in the living animal. Some new approaches which hold considerable promise are mentioned in Chapter 2. Size and shape of the loin eye and the nature of fat deposition, extremely important factors in determining carcass value, are especially difficult to estimate in the living animal.

A marked advance in our concepts of growth was made by Hammond (1932), who formulated a theory of differential or heterogenic growth based on measurements of different organs and tissues of sheep sacrificed and dissected at different times of development. His observations confirmed earlier studies that different parts of the body grow at different rates and provided fundamental information on the nature of the developmental changes of these different parts. For example, maximum growth rate of nervous tissue occurs at an early age, with bone, muscle, and fat following in that order. From this type of study a quantitative basis to account for changes in conformation can now be established.

Measurements of these differences have further practical considerations. They have been suggested as being useful to predict the age of maturity, the growth potential, and the functional capacity as related to structural changes in the animal.

Measures of Composition of Gain. Although the animal producer is vitally interested in rate of gain as determined by daily weight increase, he is also concerned with the composition of this gain. For a meat animal to be acceptable to the consumer it must meet certain requirements—in the case of beef, sufficient fat deposition together with a high ratio of lean meat to bone.

Current practices utilize subjective methods to evaluate these properties. Recently, however, some methods depending upon objective measures, have been investigated. Most of these techniques utilize the fact that the per cent of water in the fat-free body is constant. Since the amount of water in fat tissue is very small when compared to the amount of water in the total body, any variation in the per cent of total body water must be largely due to the amount of fat present.

Methods for measuring body water in the live animal involve dilution techniques. For example, an animal is injected with a known amount of a chemical tracer substance such as antipyrine or deuterium, and after a short interval the blood is sampled to determine the distribution of this tracer. From the ratio of the original concentration to the final concentration of this tracer material, it is a simple matter to calculate the total water. Unfortunately, dilution techniques have not been consistently successful in large ruminant animals, because of the difficulty of eliminating rumen water content.

Another method which utilizes carcass specific gravity to predict carcass and body composition has proved valuable in many instances, but since it is useful only after slaughter one cannot follow these changes at intervals throughout the growing or fattening phases in the individual animal. Nevertheless, its importance with regard to a simple method for estimating carcass fat is important and deserves some discussion.

The specific gravity of fat (S_f) and the specific gravity of the fat-free body (S_{ff}) are relatively constant for a particular species. The specific gravity of the carcass (S_c) can be determined easily by calculating the ratio of the difference between its weight in air and weight in water to the weight in air. From these three factors one can calculate the per cent of fat by the following formula: per cent fat $= (S_{ff} - S_c)/(S_{ff} - S_f)$.

Lofgreen and Garrett (1954) have determined the specific gravity of steer fat (0.894) and fat-free body (1.155). Using these values, the per cent fat can be determined. For example, if the specific gravity of the carcass is found to be 1.059; then per cent fat $= (1.155 - 1.059)/0.261 = 36.8\%$.

Although the specific gravity method is convenient when estimating total fat, measurements of carcass composition are time consuming. The techniques involve the separation of representative parts of the carcass or the whole carcass, either by physical or chemical means, into its constituents of fat, lean, and bone.

In future studies, refinements and variations of these techniques may provide useful tools for evaluating changes in chemical growth in meat animals. For example, the effects of altering the nutritional state, the influence of various hormone treatments, and a knowledge of genetic effects on differential changes in the major body components would provide important information to the animal producer. One review (Reid *et al.*, 1955) and a recent article (Meyer *et al.*, 1960) represent excellent and detailed discussions of the application of these techniques. The interested student will find them to be valuable references.

To treat in any detail these various concepts to which we have no more than briefly referred in the foregoing pages requires space far more than that allotted. It is the author's wish, however, that the student become aware of these occasionally abstract ideas of growth and seek a fuller explanation from other detailed sources such as Brody (1945), Pomeroy (1955), and Pálsson (1955).

24-3. FACTORS INFLUENCING ORGANISMIC GROWTH

With this background it is now pertinent to consider how growth rate and body composition may be influenced by nutritional and hormonal factors. It is common knowledge that the effects of disease result in a reduced growth rate; but since this result is due in the final analysis to a physiological upset which usually is associated with a reduction of appetite, pathological factors on growth need not be discussed specifically.

The Influence of Nutrition. Of the factors influencing growth, plane of nutrition plays the most important and obvious part. Since, however, a consideration of the nutrition of livestock is included in Section V (Chapters 27, 28, 29, 30), no attempt will be made to discuss specifically the influence of the various nutrients in this chapter. Rather, only the general aspects of nutrition on growth and body composition will be covered.

Effect on Fetal Growth. The effect of undernutrition of the dam on fetal growth usually results in a stunting of the fetus. This effect has been studied most extensively in sheep. Wallace (1946, 1948) demonstrated in a series of experiments that undernourishment, particularly during the last one-third of pregnancy, resulted not only in a reduction of the weight of the mother but also of the lamb. On the other hand, an extreme nutritional excess of the mother during pregnancy does not result in fetal growth above normal.

Influence of Plane of Nutrition on Body Composition. As pointed out earlier, different parts and tissues of the animal body develop at different rates, leading to changes in the proportions and composition of the body as the animal grows. By altering the nutritional state of the animal it is possible to control, to some degree, the rate at which these changes occur. For example, McMeekan (1940) showed that when pigs were maintained on a high plane of nutrition during the first 16 weeks, a time when bone and muscle were rapidly developing, rate of growth of these tissues was stimulated; if maintained on a low plane, growth rate was depressed. At a later age high nutritional plane stimulated and low nutritional plane depressed fat formation. By starting on a high plane and changing to a low plane, pigs produced carcasses with much lean and little fat; whereas if the nutritional planes were reversed, fat carcasses resulted. When lambs are treated in a similar fashion comparable results are obtained, and the development of body proportions in cattle, although not as well

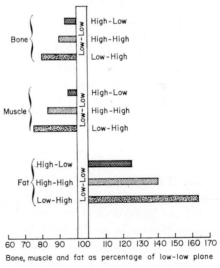

Fig. 24-2. Effect of plane of nutrition on relative composition of pig carcasses. [Reprinted by permission of the Cambridge University Press. From McMeekan, *J. Ag. Sci.*, **30**: part IV, p. 519 (1940).]

studied as in pigs and sheep, can be altered by changing the nutritional plane.

Clearly, therefore, by controlling the amount of incoming nutrients it is possible to affect the differential development of parts and tissues of the body, as determined by the particular metabolic activity of the part or tissue during the time of treatment (Fig. 24-2).

Maternal Influence on Fetal Size. As the early formative stages of growth occur in the uterus of the mammal it is of importance to consider the effects of the uterine environment upon fetal size.

In the rabbit and in other species bearing multiple young, the size of young at birth is determined by the number in the litter; the larger the litter, the smaller the individual fetus. This effect on fetal size appears to be a result of a limited blood supply due to the greater number of placentae.

In animals bearing single young, the problem becomes more complicated. There is good evidence in the case of the horse, however, that the size of the dam exerts an important effect upon the size of the fetus. Walton and Hammond have clearly demonstrated that reciprocal crosses between the large Shire horse and small Shetland pony produced cross-foals from the Shire mare which were three times the size of cross-foals from the Shetland mares. The question whether this maternal regulation can be accounted for by the availability of the supply of nutrient material to the fetus or whether it is dependent upon cytoplasmic inheritance has not been adequately answered (Fig. 24-3).

Although permanent differences between the size of these two crosses persisted, the crossbred foals from the Shire mares grew less rapidly than purebred Shire foals and the crossbred foals from the Shetland mares grew more rapidly than purebred Shetland foals. Stated differently, ultimate body size depends upon the genetic composition of the fetus as well as its maternal environment *in utero*.

24-4. THE ENDOCRINE CONTROL OF GROWTH

Of the physiological processes influencing body growth, the endocrine system plays one of the most important parts. All the endocrine glands secrete hormones which influence metabolic activity, and most exert, with the possible exception of the posterior pituitary, either direct or indirect effects upon growth processes. It is difficult to discuss the physiological action of a single hormone upon growth as an independent effect, since many if not most endocrine secretions influence a response by modifying the action of, or interacting with, other endocrine glands. Thus, it is for convenience only that each endocrine gland is considered separately in the discussion to follow; for lack of space, only those hormones exerting the most obvious

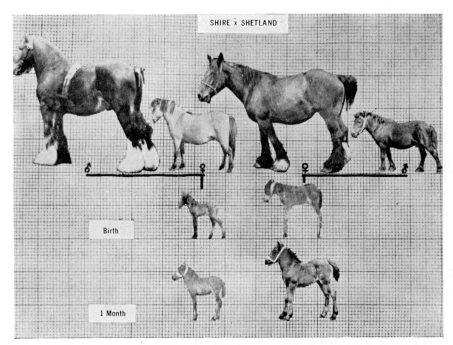

Fig. 24-3. The maternal effects on growth in Shire horse-Shetland pony crosses. [Reprinted by permission of the Royal Society of London from Walton and Hammond, *Proc. Roy. Soc. London,* Ser. B, No. 840, **125**: facing p. 322 (1938).]

effects on general body growth will be included. For this reason the student should extend his knowledge by referring to recent physiological or endocrinological textbooks.

Growth Regulation by the Anterior Pituitary. All hormones of the anterior pituitary gland are growth-promoting, but the action of several are directed more or less specifically toward particular organs or tissues. For example, adrenocorticotropin (ACTH) causes an increase in weight and functional activity of the adrenal cortex; thyrotropin (TSH) exerts a similar effect upon the thyroid; and the gonadotropins—follicle-stimulating hormone (FSH), luteinizing hormone (LH), and luteotrophin (LTH)—stimulate the gonads. Growth hormone (STH), on the other hand, has a more general action on total body growth. In addition to many diverse metabolic effects, it stimulates both muscle and bone development. From the standpoint of a contribution to a general increase in body mass, growth hormone may appear to have the most important application for animal production. This view, however, is not necessarily correct, for the other tropic substances stimulate secretion of target-gland hormones which in themselves may be equally important in influencing rates of bone, fat, or protein formation.

Nevertheless, because of the well-recognized somatotropic effect of growth hormone a somewhat detailed consideration will be given to its effect.

Hypophysectomy or surgical removal of the pituitary gland results in a cessation of growth, reflected in cessation of further increase in bone or muscle mass. If, on the other hand, either hypophysectomized or normal animals are given pituitary extracts containing growth hormone, weight gain is accelerated as a result of increased protein synthesis and bone growth. Recent studies have clearly demonstrated a partial species specificity for growth-hormone action. For example, primates will not respond to growth hormone of bovine or ovine origin but will show changes in nitrogen retention when extracts of human glands are given.

Excessive secretion or additional administration of growth hormone produces multiple effects. It causes a stimulation of skeletal growth, either during early life, by an abnormal increase in length of long bones, or after adulthood, by a disproportionate overgrowth of the skeleton. It has a protein anabolic action which is reflected in an increased nitrogen retention. It may also result in a slight increase of appetite. Chronic administration of large doses will produce in some species such as the dog, rat, and cat a diabetogenic effect manifested by hyperglycemia (elevated blood sugar), glycosuria (sugar in the urine), and ketonuria (ketone bodies in the urine). In addition to these well-known effects, it potentiates the action of the other pituitary tropic hormones on their specific end organs.

Although instances of inherited pathological changes in stature such as dwarfism in mice and humans as a result of a deficiency of growth hormone have been demonstrated, clear-cut evidence has yet to be produced that genetic dwarfism in cattle is associated with a similar deficiency.

Other studies on the content of pituitary growth hormone in domestic species have suggested an important relationship between this substance and growth processes. For example, the pituitary glands of swine selected for rapid growth contained larger amounts of growth hormone per unit of body weight than did those selected for slow rates of gain (Baird *et al.,* 1952). Similarly, differences in rates of growth of Holstein heifers were correlated with differences in pituitary content of both growth and thyrotropic hormones (Armstrong and Hansel, 1956).

These studies suggest that one may predict the growth rate of animals by determining the level of growth hormone; however, these studies were on pituitary levels. To be useful in predicting growth rate it would be necessary to determine levels of growth hormone in the blood. According to recent studies (Read and Bryan, 1960), it may soon be possible to quantitate blood levels of growth hormone. Conceivably, such a procedure might greatly accelerate progeny testing of our meat animals.

The Thyroid. Two biologically active compounds are secreted by the thyroid gland: (1) thyroxine, which is the principal circulating hormone, and (2) tri-iodothyronine, which is present in the blood in relatively small amounts. The principal action of these two substances is to increase energy production and oxygen consumption of most body tissues. Because of the general nature of these effects it is obvious that any over- or underproduction of hormones by the thyroid gland will result in a multiplicity of symptoms, not the least among which is an effect upon growth. A deficient thyroid secretion will prevent the attainment of normal adult size. Excessive fattening associated with reduced metabolic activity frequently occurs.

Following the development of an inexpensive source of a thyroid-active substance, iodinated casein, considerable interest concerning its use as a growth stimulant in domestic animals was generated. On the basis of the best available evidence, however, the use of this compound appears not to be justified as an addition to the rations of beef cattle, sheep, or swine.

Antithyroid drugs or goitrogens are substances capable of suppressing thyroid activity. Because of this action, a possible effect of these compounds on fattening processes is suggested. Although a few studies have indicated some increase in the economy of gain following the feeding of thiouracil to swine, most authorities report unfavorable results such as a reduction in appetite and growth rate. In ruminants antithyroid compounds have been of little benefit.

As growth stimulants or as a means of altering body composition, neither thyroid-active nor thyroid-suppressing compounds would appear to offer much opportunity for consistently useful applications to livestock production.

The Adrenal Cortex. The cortex forms the outer layers of the adrenal gland and plays an essential role in the metabolic activities of the body. In its absence, life cannot continue unless supportive therapy is maintained. More than forty steroids have been isolated from this gland. These include glucocorticoids, mineralocorticoids, androgens, estrogens, progestogens, and others with as yet no known biological activity.

The biological activity of these steroids excluding the androgens, estrogens, and progestogens can be generally classified into two categories: (1) those regulating electrolyte and water metabolism (mineralocorticoids), and (2) those influencing carbohydrate, protein, and fat metabolism (glucocorticoids).

In cases of adrenal insufficiency a number of characteristic symptoms occur: extreme muscular weakness, hypoglycemia, hemoconcentration, gastrointestinal disturbances, reduced blood pressure and body temperature, and kidney failure. Adult animals lose body weight and young animals cease to grow. The administration of cortical extracts will correct these conditions. Since glucocorticoids promote glucose formation from tissue also increase fat deposition. Obesity is a frequent occurrence in humans protein they may be considered protein catabolic, but in addition they may who suffer from excessive adrenal activity. These effects are two examples of how the adrenal cortex can influence growth and body composition, but because of its important role in the metabolic activities of the whole body it is apparent that almost any alteration will result in multiple responses.

The Testes. The chief hormones produced by the testes are androgens, so called because of their masculinizing effects. Testicular hormones exert a stimulatory action upon the growth of male accessory sexual tissue such as the prostrate and seminal vesicles. They bring about, in addition, pronounced changes of general body metabolism by their influence upon protein synthesis. The administration of androgens such as testosterone or methyl testosterone decreases urinary nitrogen loss, which suggests nitrogen storage in the form of tissue protein. This effect of androgens is of obvious importance and may explain the difference of size between the male and female sex.

A number of experiments have indicated that the administration of various androgenic steroids can stimulate gains in ruminants but not in swine. In treated swine, the carcasses contain less fat and more protein. The use of androgens as growth stimulants in ruminants has not been popular because the same effect can be accomplished more economically with diethylstilbestrol.

Effects of Castration. The student may wonder why the practice of castration of animals for meat purposes is almost universal, since with the removal of the testes an important source of endogenous androgens is lost. It is well established that rams, bulls, and boars grow at a faster rate than wethers, steers, and barrows, respectively. This difference in rate of size increase can be accounted for principally by greater muscle development. Because fat deposition may be considerably reduced, however, the quality and palatability of the meat are seriously affected. In addition, the undesirable odor of boar meat and the difficulty of handling mature males are further reasons for continuation of the practice. Nonetheless, further studies are essential before the possibility of increasing meat production by leaving bulls and rams intact is abandoned.

Ovarian Hormones. The principal steroid hormones produced by the ovaries are the estrogens and progestogens. Both of these substances not only exert pronounced effects upon the growth of female reproductive tissue but, in addition, may also produce a variety of effects which are manifested as changes in body weight or skeletal growth.

For example, the effects of estrogens in the bird are striking. Following the subcutaneous administration of either natural (estradiol, estriol, estrone, and other) or synthetic (diethylstilbestrol, dienestrol, hexestrol, and other) estrogens, a rapid elevation in blood lipid level occurs. This response is accompanied by an increased fat deposition, although the parallelism between the two effects is not necessarily complete. In addition, estrogen causes hyperossification of endosteal bone, but, strangely enough, large doses increase bone fragility. Although not definitely established, the latter response may be due to increased bone resorption preceding hyperossification.

The extra amount of subcutaneous fat, more tender skin, and improved finish as a result of estrogen treatment in chickens results in higher-grading carcasses, an effect of commercial importance. At the time of this writing, however, the use of these substances in birds is no longer allowed by the Food and Drug Administration because of alleged possible detriment to human health due to the questionable carcinogenic activity from estrogenic residues in the edible meat.

On the other hand, of considerable commercial importance is the response obtained when estrogens are administered to beef cattle or lambs, another example of the effect of estrogens upon body growth. In contrast to chickens, fat deposition is clearly not increased by estrogen treatment of ruminants. Instead, a marked increase in protein formation and a reduction in carcass fat content are the general responses. The effects of estrogen in the ruminant are in many respects similar to those of growth hormone and androgens in other species. The subcutaneous implantation of from 24 to 30 mg of diethylstilbestrol or the feeding of 10 mg per head per day to beef steers brings about an increase of 10 to 20% in rate of gain, causes a greater nitrogen retention, increases appetite, and improves apparent gross feed efficiency.

These responses, particularly rate of weight gain, may be influenced to some extent by the nature of the ration and the age and sex of the animal. When cattle are fed a high-concentrate diet, a greater rate of increase in daily gain is obtained than when a low-energy diet is fed. Further, growth responses following treatment of young suckling calves have been variable—few cases of accelerated gains have been reported. These two effects, however, are not apparent in sheep, which show significant responses in spite of age at treatment or dietary regime. As a general rule estrogen is more effec-

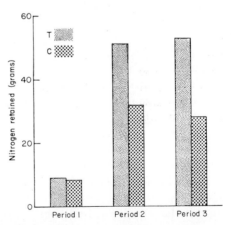

Fig. 24-4. The effect of 60 mg implants of stilbestrol on nitrogen retention in beef steers. The values for treated animals (T) are compared with untreated controls (C) and represent three different collection periods. Period 1, before treatment; period 2, 14 days after treatment; period 3, 31 days after treatment. [Data from Clegg and Cole, *J. Animal Sci.,* **13**:108 (1954).]

tive, as concerns body weight gain in the male castrate, than in the intact female.

The variety of effects of estrogen upon growth is difficult to explain. In some species such as swine and the rat, high doses result in a reduction of body weight gain, but in the chicken the response is principally one of stimulating fat deposition; in the ruminant, nitrogen retention and protein synthesis is clearly the result (Fig. 24-4).

This latter effect explains the stimulation of rate of gain with no appreciable increase in feed consumption and represents one of the most dramatic advances in the efficiency of meat production of the twentieth century.

The Effect of Pregnancy or Ovariectomy on Growth. In the rat, pregnancy has a stimulating effect upon both skeletal and tissue growth in spite of the extra burden of the fetuses. Thus, growth enhancement over nonbred littermate controls continues at a fairly constant rate for the first six pregnancies and is due chiefly to an increased appetite, which occurs as early as 48 hours after copulation (Cole and Hart, 1938).

On the other hand, pregnancy in cattle (Hart *et al.*, 1940) or in swine (Heitman, unpublished) does not cause an increased appetite or food consumption, and the slight increase in weight during pregnancy over unbred animals can be accounted for entirely by the increase in weight of the gravid uterus. The practice of breeding heifers and gilts to be slaughtered should therefore be discouraged.

Another important difference between the rat and cow is the effect of ovariectomy or spaying upon body weight gains. Following the removal of the ovaries, female rats grow more rapidly than intact controls. Although the stimulation of weight increase is largely associated with an increased fat deposition, some stimulation of skeletal growth also occurs. When heifers are spayed, an influence upon growth rate cannot be demonstrated and no benefit occurs as a result of this operation in feed-lot animals.

With the development of basic information on the role of the endocrine system on growth, important applications of the use of hormones in domestic animals have and will be found. A recent review (Casida *et al.*, 1959) summarizes much of the current knowledge and should serve the student as a useful reference.

24-5. CONCLUSION

Growth is difficult to define in a specific fashion since it includes many diverse metabolic and physiological processes. Since "true" growth usually involves an increase in cell numbers, changes in mass may not describe properly the characteristic change taking place. For example, increase in weight may include protein synthesis, fat storage, or food and water in the digestive tract.

An obvious requirement for the optimal development of an organism is an adequate and proper nutritional intake. When this requirement is met, the endocrine system plays a major role in the physiological regulation of growth by its influence upon mineral, carbohydrate, fat, and protein metabolism.

REFERENCES AND SELECTED READINGS

References marked with an asterisk are of general interest.

Armstrong, D. T. and W. Hansel, 1956. The effect of age and plane of nutrition on growth hormone and thyrotropic hormone content of pituitary glands of Holstein heifers. *J. Animal Sci.*, 15:640.

Baird, D. M., A. V. Nalbandov, and H. W. Norton, 1952. Some physiological causes of genetically different rates of growth in swine. *J. Animal Sci.*, 11:292.

*Brody, S., 1945. *Bioenergetics and Growth*. Reinhold, New York.

*Casida, L. E., F. N. Andrews, R. Bogart, M. T. Clegg and A. V. Nalbandov, 1959. Hormonal relationships and applications in the production of meats, milk and eggs. Publ. No. 714, Nat. Acad. Sci., Wash., D.C., pp. 1–53.

Clegg, M. T. and H. H. Cole, 1954. The action of stilbestrol on the growth response in ruminants. *J. Animal Sci.*, 13:108.

Cole, H. H. and G. H. Hart, 1938. The effect of pregnancy and lactation on growth in the rat. *Am. J. Physiol.*, 123:589.

*Hammond, J., 1932. *Growth and Development of Mutton Qualities in the Sheep.* Oliver and Boyd, Edinburgh.

Hart, G. H., H. R. Guilbert, and H. H. Cole, 1940. The relative efficiency of spayed, open and bred heifers in the feedlot. Calif. Agr. Expt. Sta. Bull. 645.

Lofgreen, G. P. and W. N. Garrett, 1954. Creatinine excretion and specific gravity as related to the composition of the 9, 10, 11th rib cut of Hereford steers. *J. Animal Sci.*, 13:496.

McMeekan, C. P., 1940. Growth and development in the pig, with special reference to carcass quality characters. *J. Agr. Sci.*, 30:276.

Meyer, J. H., G. P. Lofgreen, and W. N. Garrett, 1960. A proposed method for removing sources of error in steer experiments. *J. Animal Sci.*, 19:1123.

*Pálsson, H., 1955. Conformation and body composition. In *Progress in the Physiology of Farm Animals*. Vol. 2. Edited by J. Hammond. Butterworth's Scientific Publications, London.

*Pomeroy, R. W., 1955. Live Weight Growth, in *Progress in the Physiology of Farm Animals*. Vol. 2. Edited by J. Hammond. Butterworth's Scientific Publications, London.

Read, C. H. and G. T. Bryan, 1960. The immunological assay of human growth hormone. *Recent progress in hormone research*, 15:187–218. Edited by G. Pincus. Academic, New York.

Reid, J. T., G. H. Wellington, and H. O. Dunn, 1955. Some relationships among the major chemical components of the bovine body and their applications to nutritional investigations. *J. Dairy Sci.*, 38:1344.

Wallace, L. R., 1946. The effect of diet on fetal development. *J. Physiol.*, 100:34.

Wallace, L. R., 1948. The growth of lambs before and after birth in relation to level of nutrition. *J. Agr. Sci.*, 38:93, 243, 267.

Walton, A. and J. Hammond, 1938. The maternal effects on growth and confirmation in Shire horse–Shetland pony crosses. *Proc. Roy. Soc. of London,* Series B, No. 840, 125:311.

Chapter 25

Physiology of the Digestive System

In health the muscular activity of the bowel seems often to be soothing to the brain.

ALVAREZ, W. C., *An Introduction to Gastroenterology,* 3rd Ed., Hoeber, New York

25-1. INTRODUCTION

The process of digestion takes place in the digestive tract or alimentary canal. It requires little imagination or knowledge of anatomy to see that the animal body is built around this canal or hollow tube. The alimentary canal of mammals includes the mouth, esophagus, stomach, small intestine, caecum, large intestine, and rectum in all domestic animals. Ruminants and birds have additional modifications which will be discussed later. The over-all functions of the tract are (a) to store food for a short time, (b) prepare the food for absorption, (c) assimilate the useful products, and (d) reject the undigestible portion. The statement of these functions appears to be simple enough, but knowledge of the physiology of digestion had to await the development of modern chemistry, the discovery of enzymes and study of their properties, the discovery of hormones and their biological activities, development of knowledge concerning nervous control of the digestive tract, and, finally, the development of the study of cellular physiology.

Some of the early attempts to study digestion make very interesting reading (Fulton, 1930). Reaumur, a distinguished French scientist, experimented in the year 1750 with a pet kite, a bird of prey which he had trained to swallow small sponges. After a short time the bird would eject the sponges. When Reaumur squeezed out the fluid from the sponges, he was rewarded to find that the juice recovered had the power to liquefy meat. Here was preliminary evidence that there were substances—later discovered and named enzymes—present in the digestive tract which would break down foodstuffs to simpler materials.

A few years later an Italian investigator, Spallanzani, studied digestion on himself. He sewed up food in small linen bags which he swallowed. These bags were recovered after they had passed through the body and it was found that food such as meat disappeared from the bags without mastication and therefore must have been liquefied in passing through the tract. Next followed the discovery of free hydrochloric acid in the stomach by Prout in 1824 and the isolation in concentrated form of pepsin by Schwann in 1835.

One of the most fascinating experimental studies of digestion of all time was that of an American Army doctor, William Beaumont, in 1824. He had under his care a young man who, as a result of an accidental discharge of a shotgun, was left with a permanent opening (fistula) into his stomach. Beaumont carried out many physiological and chemical studies of digestion on this subject under one of the most fantastic legal contracts ever written.

He bound himself in Dr. Beaumont's employ for a period of one year to "serve, abide and continue with the said William Beaumont, wherever he shall go, . . . and to submit to such philosophical or medical experiments as the said William shall direct or cause to be made on or in the stomach of him, the said Alexis . . ." For this, he was to receive one hundred and fifty dollars a year and board and lodging.

With the subsequent discovery of additional enzymes, the chemical basis of digestion was accepted and attributed to the action of a number of digestive enzymes secreted in various parts of the tract.

Many chemical reactions need a minute amount of a starter or a key to activate them. Such a substance is called a catalyst. As an example, the hardening of vegetable oils to make a solid substance (hydrogenated oil) by the addition of hydrogen requires a catalyst such as finely divided palladium to initiate the reaction.

25-2. ENZYMES

Enzymes are defined as organic catalysts, produced by living cells but independent of living cells in their action. So far, all the enzymes which have been isolated in crystalline or chemically pure form are found to be proteins. They act as keys in opening specific chemical bonds or in activating certain reactions without being used up in the process. Thus, a given weight of a digestive enzyme will split many times its own weight of food but, being somewhat unstable organic compounds, they eventually lose activity. Their action is completely destroyed by heat and by many chemical substances, such as salts of lead, copper, or mercury.

Digestive enzymes were among some of the first enzymes studied and isolated. They were given common names—ptyalin, pepsin, and trypsin—long before their true chemical nature was established. Later, enzymes were named according to the action they promoted or were named from the compound on which they act, with the ending "ase"; for example sucrase acts upon sucrose only, maltase is specific for maltose. Pepsin and trypsin are two of the digestive enzymes which act on proteins and are classed as proteinases.

25-3. SECRETION OF DIGESTIVE FLUIDS

The classical experiments of Pavlov in the early part of this century revealed the process of physiological control of gastric secretion. Cannon developed his well-known method of showing movement of the stomach by fluoroscopic studies, a method widely used today in hospitals and clinics to diagnose gastric ulcers. Bayliss and Starling discovered the hormone secretin, which stimulates the pancreas to secrete its digestive fluid into the intestine. These three major contributions did much to extend our knowledge of digestion. There remained the problem, among others, of where and how the products of digestion were absorbed into the body from the digestive tract. While great progerss has been made in answering these questions, using modern methods of research in enzyme chemistry and isotopic-labeled compounds, there still remain many unanswered questions.

25-4. CHEMISTRY OF DIGESTION

Before the discovery of enzymes, digestion was considered to be the result of combined mechanical action and some unknown chemical action, often referred to as "fermentation," a word borrowed from the ancient art of wine making. Now it is known that the enzymes which are found in gastric juice—in pancreatic fluid and in the secretions of the small intestine—cause the splitting of certain chemical bonds in foodstuffs, a reaction in which water is used up and compounds of smaller molecular size are produced. This process is called hydrolysis. An example of hydrolysis is the digestion of the sugar maltose with the aid of the enzyme maltase to form two molecules of glucose:

$$C_{12}H_{22}O_{11} + H_2O \xrightarrow{\text{(maltase)}} 2C_6H_{12}O_6$$

$$\text{maltose} + \text{water} \longrightarrow \text{glucose}$$

Maltose is not absorbed as such but the glucose formed is readily absorbed.

In a similar manner, starches are hydrolyzed to maltose by enzymes called amylases; fats are hydrolyzed to glycerol and fatty acids by lipases. Large protein molecules are broken down by steps to polypeptides, peptides, and finally to the amino acids, the so-called building stones of all proteins.

As mentioned above, a number of enzymes have been isolated in pure crystalline form and in this pure state they have all so far been found to be proteins. This explains some of the properties of enzymes and the characteristics of enzyme action. Their activity is slowed down as the temperature is lowered and finally ceases at temperatures below freezing. At body temperature, enzyme action is rapid, but at boiling temperature action is stopped permanently. Heavy metals such as copper, lead, and mercury precipitate proteins and therefore stop enzyme action. Acid and alkali have a pronounced effect on rate of digestion with enzymes. Thus, pepsin, which acts on proteins while they remain in the stomach, is very effective in the presence of hydrochloric acid produced in gastric juice, but this action is stopped when the stomach contents are neutralized in the small intestine. Here other enzymes begin their work in the more neutral medium.

Enzymes are powerful catalysts. It has been shown, for example, that one part of crystalline enzyme such as pancreatic amylase will split up to 4,000,-000 times its weight of starch.

Digestion in Various Species. While the chemical principles involved in digestion in different species are primarily the same—that is, the hydrolysis of food substances to smaller units which can be absorbed into the system —the anatomical features which bring about these chemical reactions in various species vary considerably. It will be necessary first to describe the digestive processes of a single-stomached animal, such as the pig, dog, or man, and then consider the anatomical differences in the digestive tract of ruminants and birds.

Digestion in the Mouth. The digestion of insoluble particles is known to take place on their surfaces. Hence the advantage of mastication is to reduce the solid particles in size and thus increase the surfaces exposed to enzymes. Chemical action in the mouth is not very important since only a very few species produce ptyalin, a starch-splitting enzyme, in their saliva. Ptyalin is not present in the saliva of ruminants. Even in animals where ptyalin is present, the food is in the mouth such a short time that the action is small and is stopped by the hydrochloric acid of the stomach.

Gastric Digestion. Gastric digestion in this discussion refers to digestion (a) in the stomach of those animals with a simple stomach—man, the pig, horse, dog, and others (see Fig. 20-1) (b) in the fourth or true stomach of ruminants and (c) in the glandular stomach or proventriculus (Fig. 25-1) of birds. The peculiarities of digestion in ruminants and poultry will be taken up further on.

Gastric juice is secreted by cells of the gastric glands embedded in the

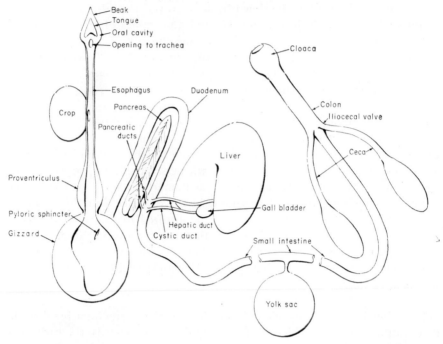

Fig. 25-1. Digestive tract of a chick. The yolk sac is in process of being resorbed.

inner wall of the stomach, the gastric mucosa. The constituents of gastric juice are:

(1) Hydrochloric acid, which lowers the *p*H of the stomach contents for optimal action of the enzyme, pepsin.

(2) Pepsin, a proteolytic enzyme, which breaks down proteins to smaller molecules, polypeptides.

(3) Rennin, another proteolytic enzyme, responsible for the clotting of milk proteins and no doubt of special significance in the newborn.

(4) Mucus, a protective secretion coating the internal lining of the stomach and presumably preventing the destruction of the stomach wall by HCl. If this lubricant is not secreted in sufficient quantities or if HCl is secreted in abnormal amounts, erosions of the stomach lining, gastric ulcers, may result.

While some fat splitting in the stomach has been attributed to the presence of a gastric lipase, this action is minor. Gastric juice does not appear to have any action on carbohydrates.

Digestion in the Small Intestine. The major part of digestion takes place in the long tube, the small intestine. Here digestion is the result of secretions containing enzymes (a) produced in the pancreas and reaching the small intestine by way of the pancreatic duct; (b) formed in the liver and secreted as bile into the intestine, sometimes by a common duct with the pancreas and in other species by a separate duct; and (c) produced by intestinal glands lining the small intestine. The excess of acid ín the partially digested material leaving the stomach is neutralized by pancreatic juice, bile, and the secretions of the small intestine. In this nearly neutral medium, enzymes now present in the small intestine carry on the remainder of the digestion processes. Starches are split to maltose and this is further split to glucose. Sucrose, if present, is split to invert sugar and any lactose to glucose and galactose. Fats are digested to glycerine and various fatty acids, and proteins are finally broken down to simple units, the amino acids. There are no enzymes secreted in the digestive tracts of animals which have been found to digest cellulose, the principal constituent of the fibrous part of foodstuffs. However, a small amount of cellulose may be broken down by bacterial action in the digestive tract of simple-stomached animals, especially in the caecum and colon, but in ruminants a considerable amount of cellulose is digested. The action is attributed to enormous numbers of microorganisms which inhabit the rumen and not to any cellulose-splitting enzyme produced in the digestive juices.

25-5. ABSORPTION OF DIGESTED PRODUCTS

Although the chemistry and physiology of absorption from the digestive tract has been intensively studied, there are many questions yet unanswered. Absorption takes place principally from the small intestine. Very little absorption of digestion products is known to occur in the mouth, gullet, or stomach; an exception is the absorption of fatty acids across the rumen wall. Some drugs are directly absorbed from these areas but the principal mechanism for absorption of the end products of digestion is found in the microscopic fingerlike projections lining the small intestine, called villi (Fig. 25-2). These projections into the interior of the canal are lined with columnar epithelial cells through which the food substances must pass. Inside the villi are small capillary blood vessels and lymph ducts, which collect the absorbed material. The study of the physiology of the epithelial cells of the villi is an extremely fascinating subject. Absorption through these cells is found to be a highly specific process. Digestion is not simply a process producing water-soluble materials. Sucrose and lactose, for example, are water-soluble but are not absorbed until they are split to hexose sugars. Glucose and galactose are molecules of identical size but the rates of absorption are quite different. Most of the fatty acids produced by fat digestion are water-insoluble but are readily absorbed from the intestine. We see then that absorption is a selective process dependent upon properties of living cells and undoubtedly due in some manner to enzymes produced in the process. Absorption, therefore, is not a matter of simple diffusion

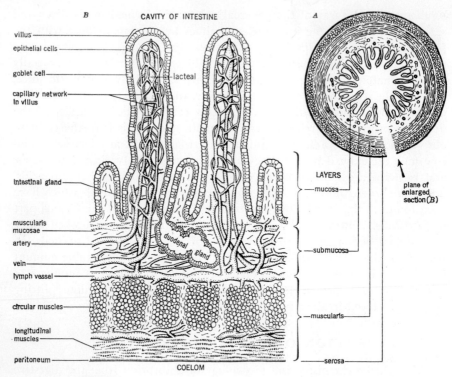

Fig. 25-2. A villus in the small intestine, lined by a single layer of epithelial cells. [From Storer and Usinger, *General Zoology*, McGraw-Hill, New York, 1957.]

through a membrane. The mechanism involved represents one of the unanswered problems to which newer methods of study—using compounds containing isotopic labels—are giving valuable clues.

25-6. PECULIARITIES OF RUMINANT DIGESTION

In herbivorous animals such as cattle and sheep, the compound stomach appears to be an evolutionary modification of the simple stomach for providing a compartment in the alimentary canal where fibrous foods may be held to undergo a soaking and "fermentation" before passing on through the canal. The ruminant stomach is actually divided into four compartments. The rumen or first compartment, is very large in the adult animal and may hold up to 50–60 gallons of soft food material (Fig. 25-3). The reticulum is the second compartment, much smaller in size. The third compartment is known as the omasum, somewhat larger than the reticulum. The fourth compartment, called the abomasum, or true stomach, is similar in function to the stomach of monogastric animals. The total capacity of the four compartments is: rumen, 80%; reticulum, 5%; omasum, 7%; and abomasum, 8%. The rumen, reticulum, and omasum are nonglandular and thus do not produce acid or digestive juices. Because proteolytic enzymes and hydrochloric acid are absent, they do, however, provide excellent compartments for the growth of many types of microorganisms taken in with the food—both bacteria and protozoa. Through the action of these microorganisms, coarse materials from roughages, containing complex polysaccharides, cellulose, and lignocelluloses, are broken down. Starches and simpler carbohydrates are also attacked by the microorganisms. Recent studies by Otagaki *et al.* (1955) have also shown that proteins may be acted upon by rumen microorganisms. Since no digestive enzymes are produced by the rumen, the action taking place resembles a fermentation involving quite a different series of chemical reactions than those resulting from the action of digestive enzymes secreted by the digestive glands. End products are many in number but principally short chain fatty acids—acetic, propionic, and butyric—are produced. It is well known that rumen microorganisms can also use simple sources of nitrogen such as ammonium salts and urea, building these up to complex proteins. Thus the ruminant is provided with a variety of proteins derived from the bodies of microorganisms. On passing into the true stomach and into the intestines, these organisms—which have multiplied in the rumen, reticulum, and omasum—are digested, and their bodies serve as a source of food protein. Several of the B vitamins are also synthesized in the rumen.

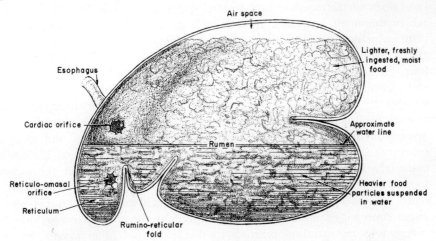

Fig. 25-3. Relationship of the rumen and reticulum. Note that the lighter roughage fills the dorsal portion of the rumen excepting for the small air space. The rumen and reticulum are only partially separated by the rumino-reticulum fold. A syringe-like action of the reticulum forces freshly swallowed food posteriorly into the dorsal rumen. [From Cole, Mead, and Kleiber, "Bloat in cattle," *Calif. Agr. Exp. Sta. Bull.* 662 (1942).]

Fermentation in the rumen results in the liberation of considerable heat. This phenomenon is of special significance in the adaptation of ruminants to the environment. If ruminants are well fed, the heat resulting allows them to withstand very cold climates. In hot climates, however, heat production increases the stress on the animal. The heat liberated following roughage feeding is much greater than that following ingestion of concentrates. Thus, in hot climates the feeding of rations low in roughage permits better adaptation to the environment.

25-7. DIGESTION IN BIRDS

Digestion in the chicken has been studied more thoroughly than in any other bird. The digestive organs of chickens are quite different in several respects from those of mammals (Fig. 25-1). However, the same types of chemical reactions take place as have been described for other types of livestock above. In the chicken, teeth are not present; hence mechanical reduction of the food must be accomplished in other ways. The esophagus has a pouchlike enlargement or crop where solid food is stored temporarily and somewhat softened. Passing on down the gullet, the food enters the stomach, which is actually made up of two separate parts, quite unlike that of mammals. The first part is the proventriculus (or glandular stomach). It has a straight narrow passageway not much larger than the esophagus, with a thick wall containing glands that secrete gastric juice and hydrochloric acid. Food does not accumulate in the glandular stomach as it does in the stomach of mammals but, after mixing with gastric juice, passes on into the ventriculus or gizzard. This is a large thick-walled muscular organ which grinds the solid food with the aid of pieces of grit which the bird has swallowed. The gizzard does not secrete any digestive fluids but simply grinds and mixes the solid food with gastric juice already supplied by the proventriculus. By contractions of the gizzard, which occur two or three times per minute, food is passed on into the first part of the small intestine, the duodenum. Here gastric digestion, started in the proventriculus and gizzard, continues in an acid medium—neutralization does not occur as it does in mammals. Pancreatic fluid and bile enter the duodenum near the second loop. The pancreatic fluid is only weakly alkaline and bird bile is acid in reaction, so very little neutralization of the acid-mixed food takes place. It has been suggested that trypsin produced by the chick pancreas may be different in its optimum reaction to that produced in mammals. In any instance, the intestinal contents remain somewhat acid throughout the whole tract, in contrast to that of mammals.

The digestive tract of birds, compared with mammals, is short and compact, a characteristic of their body, which is streamlined for flight. Digestion and absorption must therefore take place in a shorter time than in mammals, and the undigested residues which would be dead weight are ejected with very little delay. Digestion in the small intestine is further aided, as in mammals, by secretion of intestinal digestive fluids, but proceeds, as mentioned above, in an acid medium.

In the chicken there are a pair of caeca, or blind sacks, about six to eight inches long, which open from the small intestine at the junction with the colon. These thin-walled pouches are lined in their narrow portion with villi, which indicate they may be concerned with absorption. Little is known, however, concerning their function. The colon in birds is also very short, and it too, is lined with villi, so absorption must take place here.

25-8. CONTROL OF THE SECRETION OF DIGESTIVE JUICES

Both the nervous and endocrine systems are involved in controlling the secretion of digestive juices. Space will not permit a detailed discussion of these controlling mechanisms, but examples will be discussed briefly. In most instances both the nervous and endocrine systems are involved.

Control of Salivary Secretion. Let us first consider the control of salivary secretion. Though one frequently encounters the statement that the flow of saliva is regulated solely by the nervous system, this is not strictly true. As early as 1867, Eckhard reported that one of the three sets of salivary glands in sheep, the parotid glands, continues to secrete after the nerve supply has been severed. According to more recent studies, this so-called paralytic secretion depends at least to some extent upon the stimulation by the hormone, adrenaline, secreted by the adrenal medulla. If this view is correct, hormones do play some role in controlling the flow of saliva.

The increased flow of saliva associated with eating, however, is dependent upon the nervous system. This can be simply demonstrated by showing that the chewing of palatable food does not evoke the usual increase in the flow of saliva if the nervous connections to the salivary glands have been severed. The rate of flow of saliva, therefore, depends upon the stimulation of the taste buds in the mouth by chemicals of ingested food. Some foods such as fresh meat cause the secretion of saliva rich in mucin, whereas other foods cause a more profuse watery flow. The "conditioned" flow of saliva is described in Chapter 20.

Control of Gastric Juice Secretion. In gastric juice secretion, we have the best example of the complementary action of the nervous and endocrine systems. The flow of gastric juice is initiated by nervous and maintained by hormonal means.

The first phase, often referred to as the cephalic phase, is under nervous control. Proof of this was given by the great Russian physiologist, Pavlov. He used a dog with an esophageal fistula and with a small gastric pouch, known widely as the Pavlov pouch. When this dog was fed, the food was swallowed and was passed to the outside; even though food did not enter the stomach, gastric juice was secreted. Denervating the stomach abolished secretion produced in this manner. From this one may conclude that food in the mouth and pharynx stimulates nerve fibers, resulting in a reflex flow of gastric juice.

An experimental animal with a denervated stomach and a Pavlov pouch can be used to prove the existence of the second means of stimulating gastric juice secretion, the gastric phase. If certain foods are placed in the Pavlov pouch of this animal, gastric juice is secreted. The hormone gastrin, produced by the internal lining (gastric mucosa) of the stomach, is responsible for stimulating the gastric glands in this instance.

As the partially digested food reaches the small intestine, more gastrin is produced by the intestinal mucosa and transported to the gastric glands via the blood. Thus, gastrin produced by the stomach and intestinal wall maintains the secretion of gastric juice after eating has ceased.

25-9. MOVEMENTS OF THE DIGESTIVE ORGANS

Throughout the entire length of the alimentary canal, the walls of the organs have muscular layers. (The role of voluntary muscular activity associated with mastication and swallowing of food is well known.) Muscular contractions serve two main purposes: (1) mixing of the ingested food (ingesta) with the digestive juices, and (2) movement of the food along the digestive tract. In ruminants contraction of the omasum may bring about further breaking down of food particles, and the contraction of the gizzard of birds plays a similar role. Additional specialized contractions, especially significant in ruminants, facilitate regurgitation of food for further mastication and the eructation of gas accumulating in the rumen.

Mixing of the chyme (ingested food plus the digestive secretions) is performed by contractions of segments of the digestive organs. Segmental contractions are especially prominent in the small intestine. Pumping-like movements of the villi of the small intestine also help in mixing the chyme, as no doubt do the pendular (swaying) movements. All of these movements can occur without nervous activation. In other words, they are dependent upon intrinsic properties of the musculature itself; thus, we refer to them as being automatic or, more specifically, myogenic.

Peristaltic movements occur throughout the digestive tract. Two prominent English physiologists, Bayliss and Starling (1899), described peristalsis as a wave of dilation preceding a wave of contraction. Alvarez (1940), using improved techniques, questions whether the wave of inhibition is a normally occurring phenomenon, and most recent investigators conclude that the more important feature of peristalsis is a wave of contraction which sweeps the chyme caudally.

The control of peristaltic movements is independent of the central nervous system (CNS); that is, all nervous connections can be severed without abolishing them. Specialized nerve networks, Auerbach's plexuses, located in the walls of the digestive organs and with no apparent connections with the CNS, synchronize the motility so that an orderly wave of movement occurs.

One might conclude from the above discussion that muscular activity of the digestive organs is not influenced by the CNS. This is not true. Though the contractions may occur independently of the CNS, their magnitude and rate are influenced by nerve impulses over the autonomic nervous system—sympathetic fibers inhibit their activity and parasympathetic fibers carry impulses which increase muscular activity.

25-10. SPECIAL FEATURES OF RUMINAL, RETICULAR, AND OMASAL MOTILITY

The movements of the rumen, reticulum, and omasum, unlike those of the true stomach and intestines, are not governed locally but rather are dependent upon the CNS. These pouchlike organs are considered to be outcroppings of the esophagus. Thus, since the esophagus is at least partially under the control of the CNS, this type of control is not surprising.

Motility of the rumen mixes the ingesta, moves it from one compartment of the rumen to another, and moves food to the second stomach, the reticulum. Motility of the reticulum is largely concerned with the movement of food from the cardia to the posterior rumen and, conversely, from the reticulum to the omasum. Much of the early information on motility of these organs was obtained by studying cows with rumen fistulas (Fig. 25-4).

Contractions of both the rumen and reticulum are concerned in effecting the reflex acts of regurgitation and eructation. Since these acts are of special significance in the ruminant animal, a brief description will be given.

Rumination. The stomachs of the ruminant are designed to store large amounts of feed. Further, inasmuch as the food may be regurgitated and ruminated, the animal may consume the feed rapidly with a minimum of chewing before swallowing.

Regurgitation of food by the ruminant is a tranquil process when compared to the rather violent process of regurgitation or vomiting in man and other monogastric animals. By making use of animals with rumen fistulas, Schalk and Amadon (1928) showed that the stimulus for this reflex was coarse material in the rumen (Fig. 25-4). The proof consisted of inducing regurgitation and rumination by the simple procedure of inserting the arm into the rumen through a rumen fistula and rubbing a wisp of hay over the inner surface of the rumen. More recently, Cole *et al.* (1942) showed that the number of hours a cow spends ruminating depends upon the

Fig. 25-4. A cow with a permanent opening (fistula) into the rumen. To prevent loss of food and to prevent drying of the rumen mucosa, the opening is closed with a pneumatic plug. This cow delivered several calves while fistulated. [From Cole, Mead, and Kleiber, "Bloat in cattle," *Calif. Agr. Exp. Sta. Bull.* 662 (1942).]

coarseness of the roughage; animals on green alfalfa tops with soft stems and leaves ruminate very little, if at all, whereas cows on Sudan grass hay with scabrous (barblike) leaves ruminate much longer. Animals on a hay-and-grain ration ruminate for about 15 minutes at each ruminating period and spend 6–8 hours daily ruminating (Schalk and Amadon, 1928).

How is regurgitation brought about? An extra strong contraction of the reticulum floods the cardiac orifice with the soupy ingesta. Concurrently the cardia dilates, an inspiratory movement lowers the pressure in the esophagus, and finally an antiperistaltic wave sweeps the soupy ingesta to the mouth. The cow squeezes out the excess water, which she swallows, chews the cud (usually about 35 champs of the jaws per bolus), and then swallows this remasticated food. Immediately upon swallowing, the act of regurgitation is repeated and new material is brought up for rumination.

One may logically inquire as to whether the act of rumination can be controlled voluntarily. Apparently there is little if any voluntary control. A cow on very soft feed, on which there is a minimum of rumination, will frequently extend the muzzle forward and open her mouth as though attempting to regurgitate. Failure to accomplish the act, together with other information mentioned, provides strong presumptive evidence that the act is largely involuntary and dependent upon the extent to which coarse feed stimulates nerve fibers terminating in the rumen mucosa.

Eructation. As about one cubic foot of gas may be produced in the rumen hourly after a full feed, it is mandatory that a means is provided for expelling this gas. Though a small amount of rumen gas may pass across the rumen wall, enter the bloodstream, and then be exhaled with expired air, the major portion of it must be expelled by belching (eructation). Eructation is a reflex act but the normal stimulus is not known. It has been demonstrated that eructation becomes more frequent when the rumen pressure is elevated, but pressure could scarcely be the normal stimulus inasmuch as belching continues when the rumen is opened to the outside air pressure by means of a rumen fistula. Cole *et al.* (1942) suggested that ·scabrous roughage in the rumen was the normal stimulus, but convincing evidence is still lacking. The proposal was based upon the fact that bloat does not occur when sufficient coarse roughage is present in the diet. Thus it seems logical that both regurgitation and eructation would have a common stimulus.

One should not infer from this that the two acts have other characteristics in common. During regurgitation, as previously mentioned, the reticulum is contracted whereas at the moment of eructation the reticulum is dilated and the rumen is contracted. Dilation of the reticulum lowers the level of ingesta around the cardia while contraction of the rumen forces the gas to the cardia from the air pocket in the dorsal rumen.

Bloat. Inflation of the rumen with accumulated rumen gas is known as bloat (Fig. 25-5). Any anatomical or physiological defect which interferes with normal eructation results in a condition of chronic bloat. On the other hand, acute bloat occurs only under specific dietary regimes as, for example, on green legumes. Some animals bloat readily whereas others rarely bloat. Thus acute bloat depends both upon "animal" and "plant"

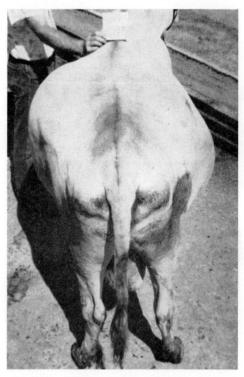

Fig. 25-5. This cow bloated following consumption of green alfalfa tops. Note the marked distension of the left body wall. Foaming of ruminal ingesta following consumption of green legumes makes eructation of gas difficult.

factors. Weiss (1953) was the first to propose that lack of sufficient salivary flow was a pre-disposing factor in bloat and Mendel (1961) has submitted data to confirm this. Presumably saliva tends to inhibit foaming of ingesta. Ingesta from legumes is particularly prone to foam. All agree that foaming of the ingesta with consequent blocking of the cardiac orifice is a major cause of bloat. Some bloat-prevention procedures such as the use of antibiotics may be effective by virtue of their inhibition of microorganism activity and a consequent reduction in gas production; other procedures, such as use of vegetable and animal oils, act by preventing foaming; the effectiveness of grass hays may be due to the increased reflex flow of saliva, as suggested by Weiss, the saliva in turn reducing foam formation.

REFERENCES AND SELECTED READINGS

References marked with an asterisk are of general interest.

*Alvarez, W. C., 1940. *An Introduction to Gastroenterology, being the Third Edition of the Mechanics of the Digestive Tract.* Hoeber, New York.

Cole, H. H., S. W. Mead, and W. M. Regan, 1942. Production and prevention of bloat in ruminants. *J. Animal Sci.,* 2:285–294.

Eckhard, C., 1944. Cited by B. P. Babkin, in *Secretory Mechanism of the Digestive Glands.* Hoeber, New York, p. 178.

*Fulton, J. F., 1930. *Selected Readings in the History of Physiology.* Charles C. Thomas, Springfield, Chap. 5.

Mendel, V. E. and J. M. Boda, 1961. Physiological studies of the rumen with emphasis on the animal factors associated with bloat. *J. Dairy Sci.,* 44:1881–1898.

Otagaki, K. K., A. L. Black, H. Goss and M.

Kleiber, 1955. In vitro studies with rumen microorganisms using carbon-14-labeled casein, glutamic acid, leucine and carbonate. *Agr. and Food Chem.,* 3:948–951.

*Pavlov, I. P., 1910. *The Work of the Digestive Glands.* Second English translation, by W. H. Thompson, C. Griffin and Co., London.

*Schalk, A. F. and R. S. Amadon, 1928. Physiology of the ruminant stomach (bovine). Study of the dynamic factors. N. Dakota Agr. Expt. Sta. Bull. 216, 1–64.

Weiss, K. E., 1953. The significance of reflex salivation in relation to froth formation and acute bloat in ruminants. *Onderstepoort J. Vet. Research,* 26:241–250.

Chapter 26

Adaptation to the Environment

Physioclimatology, bioclimatology, or environmental physiology, a rather neglected subject, is worthy of cultivation in its own right to furnish an intellectual basis for understanding and controlling the world.

SAMUEL BRODY

Of all the known forces which have directed the evolution of man and his ever-changing civilization, none have had more effect over a long period of time than the factors which constitute the climatic environment. Day-to-day changes in the environment—in temperature, light, moisture, air movement, available nutrients, a variety of radiations from the sun and outer space, and the long-range weather patterns which characterize a climate—have a profound effect on plants, animals, and man. The entire known evolution of the earth and its inhabitants is the history of soil and plant development, animal origins, evolution, and distribution, based largely on changes brought about by interactions with the environment.

The climatic environment influences nearly every economic aspect of plant and animal agriculture, crop yields and composition, animal growth, reproduction, milk production, egg production, and the efficiency of conversion of foodstuffs to economic units.

Primitive man learned to modify his environment by the use of fire as a source of heat and light, but it is only in the last century that man has utilized central heating, the electric light, mechanical refrigeration, and

431

more recently large-scale cooling and dehumidification. During the nine-teenth and early twentieth centuries man subscribed to the philosophy that the control of his own private climate was possible, but that animals should be selected for specific climatic conditions. As a result there are literally hundreds of breeds of cattle, sheep, swine, and poultry scattered over the globe. Most of them have been selected for survival under very local en-vironmental conditions. Unfortunately, the great majority of these livestock breeds are of extremely low productivity and are unknown outside their local areas.

Our present domesticated animals are the result of thousands of years of natural selection. Those which were best suited to a particular environment survived, and those which were poorly adapted either moved to a more favorable environment or perished. During the past two centuries man has made considerable progress in the selection and propagation of animals for a particular environment, and during the past several decades has learned to modify the environment for the mutual benefit of himself and animals. The role of livestock breeding in adaptation to the environment has been discussed in the chapters dealing with animal selection. Methods of modi-fying the environment will be presented in the chapters involving livestock management.

This chapter will emphasize the physiological mechanisms of adaptation such as heat production, the maintenance of a uniform body temperature, and the effects of the environment on growth, reproduction, and perform-ance. First, however, we will discuss the various components of the environ-ment.

26-1. THE NATURE OF THE ENVIRONMENT

It is becoming increasingly difficult to define the physical environment, because scientists continue to discover important new environmental fac-tors. Primitive man obviously recognized that the sun and fire provided both heat and light, that body heat could be conserved by draping the body in animal skins, and that trees and caves provided protection from the sun, wind, rain, or snow.

Hippocrates, the Greek physician who is regarded as the father of medi-cal science (460–377 B.C), was one of the first to describe the nature and effects of the climatic environment in his essay *Airs, Waters, and Places.* He recognized most of the environmental factors or influences which affect plants, animals, and man.

Thermal Environment. All of the higher animals are homoiotherms— they attempt to maintain a constant body temperature. This requires a delicate balance between the heat produced within the animal, the heat gained from the environment, and the heat lost by the animal to the environment.

In certain areas of the earth, high environmental temperatures create problems in adaptation. The digestion and assimilation of food is accompanied by a marked increase in heat production, called the heat increment of feeding. In ruminants the process of fermentation is accompanied by considerable heat production, and in all animals cellular activity of the various body systems, especially muscular activity and work, are accompanied by heat production. All productive functions, whether milk or egg production or rapid growth or fattening, are also characterized by heat production. In addition, especially during the summer months or in southern or tropical environments, solar radiation is a major factor in affecting livestock productivity because it complicates the problem of heat loss.

The first million years of man and beast, at least in the productive temperate zones, were devoted to the conservation of heat and to staying warm. In other words, the problem was one of adaptation to cold. A cow which calved in the spring and dried up a few months later, or a hen which laid a nest of a dozen eggs and then hatched the chicks, was under little climatic stress during the summer. It is correct to generalize that the animals native to North America, the British Isles, or Northern Europe are cold-weather animals. They are admirably adapted for the production of heat and surviving, when without shelter, in very cold climates.

Solar Environment. The sun performs some essential and some harmful functions for animals. It is a source of heat, the available amount depending on the distance of the animal from the sun; as reviewed by Wright (1954), the mean annual temperature decreases approximately 1°F for each degree of latitude north or south of the equator. The nature and color of the animal covering affects solar heat absorption and thus affects body temperature. Dark pigments are most absorptive of solar energy, and light-colored skin, hair, or hair tips are most reflective. A black animal would thus be at a disadvantage in the tropics. However, solar radiation may produce severe burning of the skin and may be a major causal factor of cancer of the skin (Blum, 1954). Thickened, pigmented skin is more resistant to the sun's rays than white or nonpigmented skin.

The sun may perform a useful function in animal nutrition. The exposure of animals to the ultraviolet rays of the sun activates the precursors of vitamin D in the skin to form vitamin D, necessary for the prevention of rickets. Until livestock producers learned to supply vitamin D in the ration, rickets was common in areas where sunlight is reduced during the winter.

Seasonal changes in length of day have a profound effect on some domestic animals. This is especially true with respect to the reproductive processes of chickens, turkeys, and other avian species, and in sheep. Birds usu-

Fig. 26-1. Average age of first egg (sexual maturity) for groups of pullets hatched at weekly intervals throughout 21 months and reared with either natural daylight (O) or with supplementary artificial light from the age of 16 weeks onward (L). Sexual maturity was advanced by providing extra light beginning at the 16th week, except for birds hatched at a season when daylight is increasing—for example, for birds hatched in January. [Morris and Fox, "Light and sexual maturity in the domestic fowl," *Nature,* **181**:1453 (1958).]

ally lay and hatch their eggs as day length increases. Prior to 1920 the entire poultry industry was essentially a seasonal business. Eggs were abundant and low-priced in the spring and scarce and high-priced in the winter; poultry meat was a holiday luxury. One of the first applications of environmental control was the use of electric lights in poultry houses for the purposes of stimulating fall and winter egg production (Fig. 26-1).

Sheep, unlike poultry, are stimulated to reproduce as day length decreases (Fig. 26-2). Most breeds of North American sheep have a fall breeding season and the lambs are born in the spring. In the case of cattle and swine, changes in day length have little known effect on reproduction.

Precipitation and Humidity. Under natural conditions animals were entirely dependent on natural feed supplies, and flourished when foodstuffs were abundant. In the United States the corn belt became an important producing and fattening area for livestock because of a favorable climate for both plants and animals. The great range areas of the West and Southwest were limited by seasonal fluctuations in forage and a lack of feed grains.

Altitude. It is difficult to assess the effects of the several climatic factors associated with changes in altitude. With increasing altitude there is a decrease in barometric pressure, a decrease in temperature, and a change in vegetation. Because of the reduction in barometric pressure, animals have difficulty in meeting oxygen requirements. This problem can be solved by increasing the oxygen content of the air or by increasing the atmospheric pressure. Depending upon location with respect to the equator, there may be a marked increase in solar and cosmic radiation at increasing altitudes, and the danger of severe sunburn and even skin cancer may increase.

The effects of altitude upon man have been widely studied. As reviewed by Monge (1954), people who live in the Andes Mountains of South America

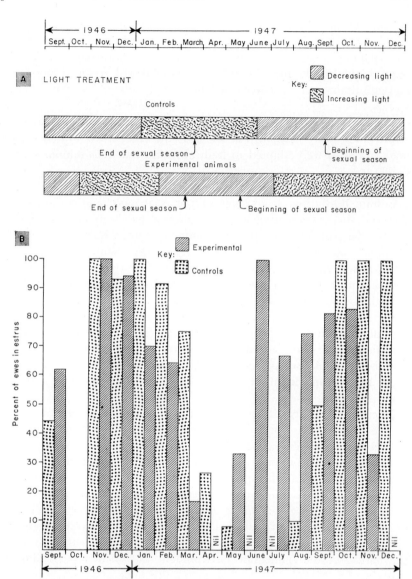

Fig. 26-2. The influence of length of daylight on the sexual season of the ewe. A, Control ewes were subjected to normal light conditions; the number of daylight hours in the experimental group was modified by placing animals in a darkened room during part of the day or by placing them in a lighted room to extend the daylight hours. Note that restricting light of the experimental ewes resulted in the sexual season beginning in May as contrasted to September for the control ewes. B, Numbr of heat periods expressed as a percentage of number theoretically possible for each month. [Adapted from Yeates, *J. Agric. Sci.* **39**:1 (1949).]

at altitudes up to 17,000 ft have developed special adaptation mechanisms. Andean man is characterized by a large chest and lung capacity, greatly increased blood hemoglobin, and a highly efficient vascular system. Men going to high altitudes must become acclimated or risk serious illness or death, and mountain-men must likewise be gradually adapted to conditions at sea level.

As described by Phillips (1949), the yak, llama, alpaca, and vicuña flourish at altitudes above 6000 ft. The llama is the chief work animal of Andean man and is so well adapted to high altitudes that it is seldom seen below 12,000 ft.

Cosmic Radiation. Knowledge of the occurrence and nature of cosmic rays and their effects upon living organisms has been gained by scientists during the past 50 years. It is clear that the entire surface of the earth is constantly bombarded by extremely high-energy cosmic rays and secondary radiations from cosmic rays. It is equally clear that such radiations may have harmful effects on living material and that at altitudes above 60,000 ft might be dangerous to space travelers.

In 1927 Muller showed that the exposure of organisms to X-ray irradiation affected the rate of gene mutations. He was later awarded a Nobel prize for this discovery, and it led to a series of other researches which indicates that cosmic radiation has and does play a part in gene mutations and is one of the mechanisms involved in natural selection of plants and animals.

Macro- and Microclimates. With the exception of climatologists, most people think of the world as being made up of a few large climatic areas. We recognize the general boundaries of the tropical zones north and south of the equator, and most of us would classify the southernmost parts of the United States in the subtropical zone. In general, however, we regard most of the continental United States as being in the temperate zone and do not think of Massachusetts as being greatly different from New York, Illinois, or parts of the Pacific Coast area. If we are to understand the role of the climatic environment in livestock production, we must learn to understand the nature of the immediate environment in which a particular animal exists.

The State of California might illustrate the point. In this state the temperature may vary from $-36°F$ to $134°F$; altitudes range from 276 ft below sea level in Death Valley to 14,495 ft at the top of Mount Whitney. The average yearly precipitation varies from less than 2 inches to 109 inches. In some mountain areas as much as 449 inches of snow have been recorded. It could be said that livestock in California might be unable to exist under the natural conditions of certain areas and might be ideally adapted to other regions.

A microclimate is the particular area in which a plant or animal lives.

It may be small or large, and many microclimates may exist on a single farm.

Most grazing animals seek shade during the summer daylight hours. Trees or wooded areas provide effective shade and cooling because they reduce the warming effects of solar radiation; they are microclimates. Swine spend much of the time in a recumbent position. A warm or cool floor, a wallow, or a mist-type spray are examples of special microclimates for swine. A southern slope is warmer than a northern slope in winter; any type of shade, building, heat lamp, chick brooder, or hole in the ground are all examples of microclimates. Fattening cattle in the Imperial Valley of California gain more rapidly when effective shades are used. In such a case the shade (a microclimate) modifies the macroclimate, thus improving the performance of cattle exposed to the high daytime temperatures of the desert.

26-2. PHYSIOLOGICAL AND PHYSICAL MECHANISMS OF ADAPTATION

Homoiothermic Animals. Most higher animals, including all the farm animals, maintain a reasonably constant body temperature. The temperature is usually lower in the early morning hours (4–6 A.M.) than in the evening (6–8 P.M.). This is called diurnal variation. There are differences between mammals; in man the normal temperature is 37°C ± 1°C, and in swine approximately 39°C ± 1°C. In birds body temperature is somewhat higher than in mammals; it is about 41°C ± 1°C in the domestic fowl.

Physiological Means of Regulating Heat Production. Any living organism might be considered as a system of continuous irreversible reactions, each of which is accompanied by the production of heat. When the animal is at complete muscular rest and in a state when absorption of food from the gut is not going on, we consider the heat being produced as *basal* heat and use the term *basal metabolic rate* to describe the condition or state. Muscular activity is accompanied by varying degrees of heat production. This heat is called *activity heat*. The body temperature may rise because of increased tissue oxidation, which is in reality increased heat production, or because of a decrease in heat loss from the body. Males usually have a higher metabolic rate than females or castrate males. The newborn and the senescent animal frequently produce less heat than the growing, highly productive animal. The high-producing dairy cow may produce twice as much heat as a dry cow of the same size. The endocrine and the neuroendocrine systems are vitally concerned in total heat production. An increase in the secretion of the thyroid, anterior pituitary, or adrenal glands or the male or female gonads may increase metabolic rate. Food is, first of all, a source of animal energy. Following the ingestion of food, especially protein, there is an almost immediate increase in heat production. This is called *specific* *dynamic effect*. It is well known that all nutrients do not have the same heat-producing properties. A gram of digestible fat produces about $2\frac{1}{4}$ times more heat than a gram of carbohydrate.

The complex process of fermentation within the rumen likewise produces considerable heat. In man the term *basal metabolism* is quite appropriate, since the postabsorptive state is reached in the early morning hours. In the ruminant it is a practical impossibility to wait until fermentation stops in the rumen, and the term *resting metabolism* is more appropriate. When body temperature increases beyond the normal range we say that a fever has been produced. Extreme muscular activity, exposure to high environmental temperatures, or interference with heat loss from the body may cause a temporary increase in body temperature. Shivering is characterized by rapid muscular contractions and is a means of increasing heat production.

One of the most classical procedures of diagnosis in clinical medicine is the measurement of body temperature. Many pathogenic organisms produce an increase in the temperature of the infected host; this symptom is called a fever. In some diseases there may be a pronounced and constant temperature elevation, and in others, such as brucellosis, the temperature may rise and fall (undulant fever).

Physical Means of Regulating Heat Loss. We have discussed the problem of maintaining a reasonably constant rate of heat production in the homoiothermic animal. In the maintenance of a constant body temperature it is extremely important that heat loss be in balance with heat production. Since the farm animals most common in North America evolved in a temperate or cool climate it is not surprising that they are more efficient in heat production than in heat loss. The practical problem of keeping these animals comfortable and highly productive during the summer is one which is receiving considerable attention by research workers.

Heat is lost or removed from living or nonliving objects according to certain physical laws. The exchange of heat from a steam radiator to the surrounding environment is not greatly different than the process of heat transfer from an animal to its environment. In animals heat is lost by radiation, convection, conduction, and evaporation. The most obvious difference between a machine and an animal is the presence in the animal of the vascular and respiratory systems and their regulation by the nervous system.

RADIATION. Heat radiates from the animal surface to the surrounding environment (Fig. 26-3). In man the radiations are in the infrared range between 5 and 20 microns. The amount of heat lost depends upon the surface area of the animal, the temperature of the skin, the nature of the coat (hair, wool, feathers), and the temperature of the environment. The larger the animal the smaller the surface area with respect to the mass of the animal. A fat, compact beef animal has less body surface per unit of weight than

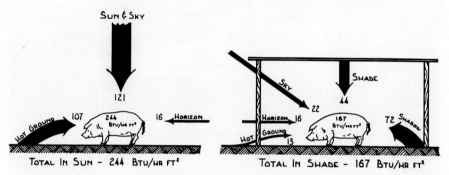

Fig. 26-3. Radiation received by an animal in the sun and in the shade on a typical August day in Imperial Valley in California. [From Bond, Kelly, and Ittner, "Radiation studies of printed shade materials," *Agric. Eng.*, 35:389 (1954).]

a thin, rangy bovine, and therefore has more of a problem of heat loss by radiation in warm weather. A single animal pulls himself into a "humped" posture in cold weather in order to reduce radiant heat loss. A group of animals may huddle together as a means of conserving heat by reducing radiant and convective heat loss.

CONVECTION. The air immediately adjacent to the skin or coat of the animal is generally warmer than the air in the surrounding environment. The replacement of the layer of warm air by cooler air removes heat from the animal body by *convection* (Fig. 26-4). As in the case in radiant heat loss, the surface area of the animal and the surface and air temperatures are very important. In addition, the velocity of the air moving over the animal surface will affect the warm air layer close to the animal and will thus regulate convective heat loss.

CONDUCTION. Heat flows from a warm to a cool medium. An animal loses heat by physical contact with the environment. Still air is a very poor conductor of heat. If the body is protected by a thick coat of hair, wool, feathers, or fat, the loss of heat by conduction to the air is small. Cold water is a highly efficient cooling medium. An animal, unless protected by fat as in the case of the whale, will become severely chilled if placed in ice water. A cold, wet concrete floor may be an effective cooling device for swine during the summer because it speeds up conductive and evaporative heat loss. During cool weather a cold floor may result in chilling in young animals such as pigs and chickens.

EVAPORATION. The loss of heat from the animal body by the evaporation of moisture from the body surface or from the respiratory system is ex-

Fig. 26-4. A fan is used to increase air movement for cooling dairy cattle by convection. The warm air next to the skin is replaced by cooler air in this manner. [Photo courtesy T. E. Bond.]

tremely important (Fig. 26-5). The evaporation of water from the body surface at 91–92°F removes 580 gram calories of heat for each gram of moisture evaporated. Evaporative heat loss is a complicated phenomenon. In man, a species with highly developed sweat glands, large quantities of water are lost by visible perspiration. The farm animals, with the exception of the horse, are classified as nonsweating. However, moisture is lost from the body surface of nonsweating species and is called *insensible perspiration*. Considerable quantities of water are evaporated from the lungs in the expired air. Under most environmental conditions inspired air is cooler and less saturated with moisture than the air in the lungs. Some moisture and heat is always lost from the respiratory system and assists in body heat loss.

The amount of heat lost by evaporation will depend on the moisture in or on the skin, the nature of the animal cover, the temperature, saturation and velocity of the surrounding air, the respiratory rate and volume, and the temperature and humidity of the inspired and expired air.

Physiological Means of Regulating Heat Loss. The temperature of a well-designed and well-constructed mechanical device is usually regulated by a sensing element called a thermostat. In a modern air-conditioning system the thermostat activates the appropriate equipment for supplying cool or warm air on demand. The correct operative temperature of an automobile motor is controlled by thermostats in the cooling system. In an animal the temperature-sensing mechanism is located in the hypothalamic area of the brain.

The blood is the medium by which heat is distributed rather uniformly throughout the body. As the temperature of the blood flowing through the hypothalamus increases above the normal range a series of nerve impulses are dispatched to the body systems concerned with heat loss. If the blood temperature drops below the normal range, the hypothalamus activates those body systems concerned with heat conservation. In addition, there are sensory receptors at the surface of the body which are also concerned with the flow of blood in the skin, activity of the sweat glands, and the erection of the hair or feathers.

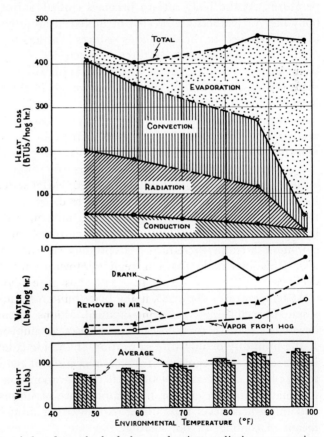

Fig. 26-5. Heat is lost from the body by conduction, radiation, convection and evaporation. Note that as the environmental temperature increases, evaporation accounts for the major portion of heat loss. [From Bond, Kelly, and Heitman, "Heat and moisture loss from swine," *Agr. Eng.*, **33**:148 (1952).]

Let us consider the adaptations which an animal would make under several different environmental conditions. At ambient temperatures of 60–65°F there is little problem of heat loss. The blood vessels in the skin are constricted, the great mass of blood is confined to the muscular and visceral organs, the sweat glands, if present, are inactive, respiration is normal, and heat production and heat loss are in approximate balance. This temperature range would be in the *comfort zone* for mature farm animals in North America. At lower temperatures, especially between 0 and 50°F, food intake and activity increase in order to increase heat production. The blood vessels in the skin become increasingly constricted and circulation in the extremities may be greatly reduced. It is well known that the fingers, toes, nose, and ears of man are particularly subject to freezing at subzero temperatures. As the body surface becomes chilled, shivering is initiated and body hair or feathers are erected or fluffed in an attempt to trap the layer of warm air next to the skin. This reduces heat loss by convection.

At environmental temperatures between 65° and 85°F, farm animals bring various cooling systems into play. With rising ambient temperature there is increasing dilation of the blood vessels in the skin. Since the blood is an effective medium of heat transfer, bringing the blood to the body surface increases heat loss by radiation, convection, and conduction. In the nonsweating farm animals there is an increase in insensible perspiration or moisture loss from the body surface. Since the principal loss of moisture comes through evaporation from the lungs, the respiration rate increases in order to speed up evaporation and, consequently, heat loss. A high-producing dairy cow requires large amounts of feed for the maintenance of lactation. Feed is a source of energy and high milk production is accompanied by high heat production. Unless effective means of cooling are available, the cow must attempt to reduce heat production as well as to increase heat loss. It is inevitable that, at high temperatures, milk production must decline.

At temperatures above 85°F the body must make drastic adjustments if a state of well-being is to be maintained. Man is fortunate in having well-developed sweat glands. Sweating increases as ambient temperature rises. If the humidity or moisture saturation of the air is low, or if evaporation is increased by air movement, the evaporation of moisture from the body surface has a considerable cooling effect. If evaporation does not occur, heat loss may be insufficient for the maintenance of normal body temperature and an artificial fever is produced. Nonsweating animals must rely on other means of cooling. In hot weather the rate of respiration of cattle, sheep, swine, and poultry is increased beyond the normal range and panting eventually occurs. Well before the panting stage, animals make whatever other adjustments are possible. They seek shade and avoid solar radiation, they reduce feed intake and lie quietly for long periods of time, and if water is available they will wade or lie in it. This increases heat loss both by evaporation and conduction.

The covering of the body surface and the tissues beneath the skin may undergo a variety of modifications. The skin may be pigmented to reduce the damage following solar radiation; this is important at the higher altitudes near the equator. Animals which evolved near the equator may have a sparse hair coat, in contrast to northern mammals. Tropical breeds of sheep have a hairlike wool rather than the dense fleece of temperate-zone sheep. Arctic birds, especially those which are aquatic, have an especially water-repellent and dense feather cover. Animals may deposit fat in thick layers beneath the skin. The fat depots may be a source of energy during periods of food shortage, but they also have a role as insulation for the prevention of heat loss. Aquatic polar animals, especially the whale, are protected from the cold by subcutaneous fat.

Critical Temperature. It has been emphasized that the homoiothermic animal attempts to maintain a constant body temperature. It has also been emphasized that the maintenance of body temperature is an extremely complicated process. The concept of critical temperature cannot be defined or described in a few words. The nutritionist usually defines the critical temperature as that environmental temperature at which the body must increase the rate of cellular oxidation by chemical means for the maintenance of normal rectal temperature. We are aware that there are wide species differences in rectal temperature and in the adaptability of the various species to fluctuating environmental temperatures. Within a species temperature may fluctuate with time of day, age, sex, and individuality. The temperature of the deep viscera is significantly greater than that of the skin, limbs, tail, comb, scrotum, and other specialized areas. Species differences in surface covering, sweat glands, surface area, genetic make-up, and adaptability, and differences in environmental conditions such as solar radiation, humidity, air movement, and air temperature have a marked effect on how and when the physical and physiological mechanisms of temperature regulation become activated. The concept that there is a specific and constant critical temperature at which the rate of chemical heat production is increased is unrealistic.

However, there is a temperature range within which a man or animal is most productive or most comfortable (Fig. 26-6). In man this is often called the *comfort zone*. A naked man at rest would probably select a temperature of 85°F as being the most satisfactory; a worker in a steel mill might prefer a temperature of 50°F or less. The animal physiologist uses the term *thermoneutrality zone* or physiologically effective temperature. This is the environmental temperature range at which a specific animal is in thermal balance and is capable of maintaining a normal body temperature without

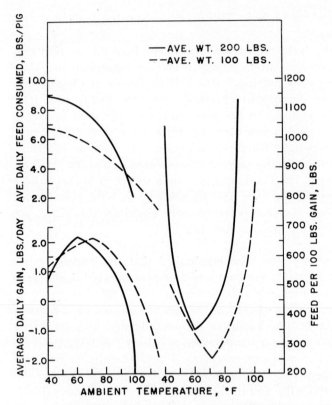

Fig. 26-6. Ambient temperature and its effect on feed consumption, average daily gain and efficiency of food utilization. [From Heitman, Bond, and Kelly, "Effect of temperature on swine," *Calif. Agric.*, **8:8** (1954).]

utilizing chemical means of thermoregulation. A highly productive dairy cow would have a much lower optimum temperature than a young calf.

Mechanisms for Adaptation to High Altitudes. Relatively little is known about the specific physiological mechanisms by which animals such as the yak and llama have become adapted to high altitudes. Studies on Andean man by Monge (1954) and current investigations in aviation physiology and space biology have given us a good basic understanding of the problem. With increasing altitude, barometric pressure and oxygen pressure drop. Man, in flight, may compensate for the reduced oxygen pressure by breathing pure oxygen, by increasing the alveolar pressure of oxygen in the lungs, or by pressurizing the surrounding environment. Andean man is forced to compensate for the reduced oxygen pressure in the atmosphere in other ways.

It is now well known that men living above 10,000 ft undergo an increase in the anteroposterior diameter of the thorax, the length of the sternum, and in the thoracic volume. This makes possible a larger exchange of air in the lungs. The capillaries in the lungs increase and expose the air to a greater capillary bed. The numbers of red blood cells per unit volume of blood are also increased, and there is an accompanying increase in total blood volume as well. As blood cell numbers increase, total blood hemoglobin increases and the tissue needs for oxygen are thus provided for. We cannot discuss the role of the blood as a source of tissue nutrients, or its role in the body buffer and excretory systems. It is of interest to note, however, that the adaptation of a man to altitudes above 10,000 ft requires an additional 2 l of blood, 676 g of hemoglobin, a 100% increase in blood bilirubin, and an 80% increase in blood pyruvic acid (Monge, 1954).

The nonadapted man, flying from sea level to high altitudes, may experience only mild discomfort, or may become severely ill. There is an immediate increase in respiration rate in an attempt to overcome the reduced oxygen pressure. Even moderate activity may be accompanied by muscular weakness because of oxygen shortage. Rapid, deep respiration may produce hyperventilation and disturb the normal acid-base balance, and chronic mountain sickness may follow.

26-3. SPECIAL ADAPTATIONS OF ANIMALS TO THEIR ENVIRONMENTS

Size and Shape. The larger animal, having a relatively small surface area with respect to body mass, is best adapted to cold climates. The European breeds of cattle and those native to the colder regions of Asia are, in general, compact and smooth skinned. Zebu cattle and other types which have become adapted to the tropics are more rangy in type and have a larger surface area (Fig. 26-7). Zebu cattle, in addition to a hump, have an extremely loose, pendulous skin with large folds along the ventral surface. The types of sheep which have developed in the cold or temperate zone are not necessarily large, but they are compact and have short necks, ears, and tails.

Type of External Coat. Sheep and goats exhibit marked variation in body covering. Tropical and desert breeds of sheep are covered by short hair rather than wool and some breeds have very little cover on the belly wall. In addition, sheep and goats in warm areas tend to have long legs, necks, ears, and tails. These modifications increase heat loss by radiation and convection. The breeds of sheep which developed in the temperate zone have dense coats of fine wool, and goats from this zone have heavy coats of long hair.

Skin Thickness and Pigmentation. Cattle breeders in temperate areas have tended to stress the desirability of a thin, pliable skin, whereas in parts

Fig. 26-7. Brahman cattle (a) are better adapted to hot climates than are the more compact breeds such as Herefords (b). Crosses of Brahmans with Herefords (c) result in animals with better conformation than the Brahmans and better heat resistance than Herefords. Animals of this cross are referred to as "Brafords."

of South America and Africa a thick hide has been favored. In tropical and subtropical regions losses due to insects, brush injuries, and solar radiation are sometimes serious. Although conclusive evidence is not available, it does appear that skin type is an important factor in adaptation. A white coat or skin has superior properties with respect to reflection of solar energy, but nonpigmented skin is particularly sensitive to both burning and skin cancer. Skin pigmentation is desirable in tropical and desert areas.

Adaptation to Feed Shortage. In only a few areas of the world is feed produced at a uniform rate throughout the year. Animals have always adapted themselves to feed surpluses and feed shortages. The farm animals common to North America tend to become fat during the summer, and draw upon the fat depots, when necessary, if food is scarce. The fat-tailed and fat-rumped sheep of Asia and Africa, Zebu cattle, and the camel have unusual modifications for fat storage. The fat-tailed sheep develops a massive fat depot when feed is abundant, but after a prolonged feed shortage the tail becomes thin and devoid of fat. The Arabian camel has long been

well known for its adaptability to the desert. Its long neck, rangy conformation, and short coat adapt it for heat loss; its broad feet fit it for desert
travel, and its fatty hump and efficient moisture conservation fit it for survival with a minimum of feed and water.

26-4. MODIFICATION OF THE ENVIRONMENT

In the chapters describing the breeds of livestock and those which dealt
with the selection of livestock for superior performance, it was emphasized
that animals can be selected for highly special functions such as the production of meat, milk, eggs, wool, or work. It was pointed out that some animals are productive only under special environmental conditions, and that
some animals have been especially selected for certain environments. In the
following chapters on livestock
management, environmental control as a factor in efficient livestock production will be discussed.

a

Environmental modification,
to be effective, must have a sound
physiological basis. One of the
first applications was the use of
heat for newborn pigs and chicks.
Heat can be transferred from the
environment to the animal by
radiation. Early systems of heating usually involved heating the
entire house, but this was costly
and inefficient and has been replaced by various types of radiant heating. Heating of the
floor and the use of efficient
brooders have reduced both animal losses and cost.

b

Poultry are particularly sensitive to changes in day length.
The proper use of lights in
poultry houses has largely eliminated seasonal patterns in egg
production and may have a profound effect on growth rate, sexual maturity, and perhaps other
functions.

Most breeds of sheep are sea-

Fig. 26-8. Shade is an important means of
reducing solar radiation of heat. Wire corrals
(a) allow for better movement of air than
do wooden corrals (b). [From Ittner, Bond,
and Kelly, "Methods of increasing beef production in hot climates," *Calif. Agr. Exp. Sta.
Bull.* 761 (1958).]

Fig. 26-9. Cooling the drinking water by refrigeration is a means of increasing gains in cattle in hot climates. The water in this tank is thus cooled and heating of the water from the sun is reduced by a shade over the tank.

sonal breeders, but some breeds are less affected by season than others. Following Marshall's (1937) observation that the transportation of sheep from the northern to southern hemisphere reversed the normal seasonal pattern, it was hypothesized that changes in day length affect reproduction. It was later shown that the experimental reduction in day length can initiate heat during the nonbreeding season. British investigators hold the view that the relations of light and darkness are more important than temperature. American workers have, however, shown that high environmental temperatures do reduce fertility in rams, and experiments in Kentucky have shown that the artificial cooling of ews did hasten the breeding season. These studies have been reviewed by Means *et al.* (1959).

As pointed out by Ittner *et al.* (1958), 51% of the cattle in the United States are produced in areas where the average July temperature exceeds 75°F and where the maximum daily temperature frequently is above 95°F. California studies have shown that a well-designed cattle shade may reduce solar radiant heat load more than 50% (Fig. 26-8). The use of wire corrals rather than dark wooden pens, increased air movement, and the use of cooled drinking water (Fig. 26-9) have all been shown to increase rate of gain under California desert conditions.

Swine producers have long recognized the value of a modified summer environment. Growing, fattening pigs will utilize any shade available and when the temperature is above 85°F will seldom leave a shade to eat. The mud wallow, which gave swine a reputation as unclean animals, was an important cooling device. Animals with access to a wallow may be expected to gain more rapidly and have lower body temperature and respiration rate during warm weather. The use of wallows, however, often introduces problems in sanitation. In the case of swine being produced on concrete feeding platforms, the use of a mist-type spray may increase rate of gain about 0.20 lb. per pig per day when temperatures are above 80°F. The application of water to the body surface increases heat loss by evaporation.

26-5. THE CHANGING GEOGRAPHY OF LIVESTOCK PRODUCTION

Under conditions of natural selection, species of plants and animals tend to concentrate where they are best suited. Until the end of the nineteenth century the pattern of crop and livestock distribution was reasonably stable. Dairy cattle and poultry were produced near the centers of population, even though they were not grain-producing areas. The commercial corn belt was reasonably well defined in the central states, and because the supply of corn was localized, the production of swine and the fattening of cattle became centered in the Corn Belt. Beef cattle and sheep were propagated in the range states because there was no alternative use for the land. The South was not regarded as suitable for livestock because of disease and parasite problems, but a more primary reason for the absence of livestock was a cotton and tobacco economy and a lack of feed grains for livestock.

The situation has changed remarkably in the last quarter century. The development of hybrid corn has extended the Corn Belt to southern, western, and tropical countries. The more recent development of grain sorghums, the establishment of the soybean, and improved methods of storing and utilizing forage have completely revolutionized our pattern of livestock production.

The broiler industry has established itself in the Deep South; Florida has become a leading cattle state; cattle feeding has spread to the range and Pacific Coast states; and swine production appears to be moving west and south.

Some of the new environments are more favorable and some less favorable than the old. The heating requirements of broiler houses in Georgia are less rigid than in New Hampshire. However, summer farrowing problems in Georgia are entirely different from those in northern Indiana or Illinois. Several points stand out. Our present strains of farm animals, including poultry, are better adapted to cold than to hot climates. Increased temperatures reduce feed intake, accompanied by reduced growth rate, milk or egg production, and to some extent fertility. However, the increasing supplies of feed in the warmer areas, year-round grazing, lower building costs, and the development of new markets are advantages which must be considered.

None of the environmental problems are insurmountable. Many have been overcome and others will be as soon as we understand them. We have developed new crops for these new areas by selection. We can expect to make some progress along the same lines by animal selection. The problems we cannot solve by selection we should solve by improved feeding and management. We should determine the optimum environment for every stage of the life cycle for each species. We should investigate the nutritional requirements under a variety of environmental conditions, and we should develop practical means of environmental control wherever and whenever they are economically justified.

REFERENCES AND SELECTED READINGS

References marked with an asterisk are of general interest.

Blum, H. F., 1954. Effects of sunlight on man. *Meteorological Monographs*, 2:43–49. Amer. Meteorological Soc.

Brody, S., 1956. Climatic physiology of cattle. *J. Dairy Sci.*, 39:715–725.

*Findlay, J. D. and W. B. Beakley, 1954. *Progress in the Physiology of Farm Animals*. Edited by John Hammond. Butterworths Scientific Pub., London, Chap. 6.

*Hutchinson, J. C. D., 1954. *Progress in the Physiology of Farm Animals*. Edited by John Hammond. Butterworths Scientific Pub., London, Chap. 7.

Ittner, N. R., T. E. Bond, and C. F. Kelly, 1958. Methods of increasing beef production in hot climates. Calif. Agr. Expt. Sta. Bull. 761.

Johnston, J. E., 1958. The effects of high temperatures on milk production. *J. Heredity*, 49:65–68.

Marshall, F. H. A., 1937. On the change over in the oestrous cycle in animals after transference across the equator, with further observations on the incidence of the breeding seasons and the factors controlling sexual periodicity. *Proc. Roy. Soc. London*, 122:413–418.

McDowell, R. E., 1958. Physiological approaches to animal climatology. *J. Heredity*, 49:52–61.

Means, T. M., F. N. Andrews, and W. E. Fontaine, 1959. Environmental factors in the induction of estrus in sheep. *J. Animal Sci.*, 18:1388–1396.

Monge, M. C., 1954. Man, climate and changes of altitude. *Meteorological Monographs*, 2:50–60. Amer. Meteorological Soc.

*Phillips, R. W., 1949. Breeding livestock adapted to unfavorable environments. FAO Agr. Agricultural Studies No. 1, Food and Agriculture Organization of the United Nations.

*Rhoad, A. O., 1955. *Breeding Beef Cattle for Unfavorable Environments*. Univ. of Texas Press, Austin.

*Wright, N. C., 1954. *Progress in the Physiology of Farm Animals*. Edited by John Hammond. Butterworth's Scientific Publications, London.

*Yeates, N. T. M., 1954. *Progress in the Physiology of Farm Animals*. Edited by John Hammond. Butterworth's Scientific Publications, London.

Nutrition and Livestock Production

Chapter 27

General Nutritional Consideration

The life of animals, then, may be divided into two acts—procreation and feeding; for on these two acts all their interests and life concentrate. Their food depends chiefly on the substance of which they are severally constituted; for the source of their growth in all cases will be this substance.

ARISTOTLE, *History of Animals,* Book VII

27-1. INTRODUCTION

Good nutrition is one of the fundamentals of livestock production; it involves the wise use of available feeds in formulating a palatable, economical, and nutritionally balanced ration for livestock and poultry. A balanced ration contains the nutrients required to maintain an optimum growth rate in the immature animal; to provide for the maintenance of essential body functions; to support reproductive processes, including egg production in poultry; to fatten animals for slaughter; and to maintain lactation in the female, either for rearing the young or for the production of milk for human consumption. Established quantitative and qualitative nutrient requirements are based on nutrition research in laboratories scattered throughout the world and, to a lesser extent, on the experience of livestock men over the centuries.

27-2. FUNDAMENTAL CONCEPTS
OF ANIMAL NUTRITION

Essential Nutrients Defined. Animal feeds contain proteins, carbohydrates, minerals, fats, and vitamins. These broad categories of nutrients can be further subdivided according to their specific chemical components; for example, minerals can be broken down into their constituent elements, and proteins can be further divided into the amino acids of which they are composed. An essential nutrient is a compound that has been demonstrated experimentally to be required by livestock to support growth, reproduction, lactation, egg production, and the maintenance of other body functions.

DETERMINATION OF NUTRIENT REQUIREMENTS. Progress in nutrition research is linked to the refinement of old methods or to the development of new methods for obtaining accurate and reproducible data on nutrient requirements, nutrient interrelationships, and factors influencing the rate and efficiency of digestion. Traditionally, the controlled feeding experiment has been used extensively. The investigator relies on such criteria as rate and chemical composition of the gain, milk production, egg production and hatchability, reproductive efficiency, longevity, and the thriftiness of the animal as means of evaluating a single feedstuff or ration. These criteria can be related to the chemical composition of the feed and to the digestibility of the total feed and of its major component. From this type of information it is possible to develop feeding guides, or standards, and to develop standard reference tables giving the average composition, digestibility, and nutrient content of a feed.

The chemical composition of a feed is usually determined by a system of Proximate Analysis (Assoc. of Official Agric. Chemists, 1955). The components analyzed by this method are defined as follows: crude fiber consists largely of cellulose and related constituents, which are insoluble after successive treatments with boiling 1.25% sodium hydroxide and 1.25% sulfuric acid; crude protein is defined on the basis of the Kjeldahl nitrogen determination; ash is the burned residue, including the minerals; fat is the ether-extractable material; and the nitrogen-free extract, or NFE, is the remainder of the dry matter, which is composed primarily of water soluble carbohydrates.

Chemical analyses give little indication of the digestibility or availability of feed nutrients in the feed or ration. Digestion trials—a combination of special feeding experiments and chemical analyses—provide such information. During such trials, animals are placed in special stalls or crates where the feed intake can be measured carefully and the excreta (urine and feces) can be collected. The portion of a feed utilized by the animal, usually over a 7- to 10-day period, can be determined by analysis. Care must be taken to adjust the animal to the ration before the test period begins, and the experiments must be properly replicated and controlled. From such data one can determine the percent of each nutrient which is digested and calculate the Total Digestible Nutrients of the feed, commonly called "TDN." TDN is the sum of digestible protein, fiber, nitrogen-free extract, and digestible ether extract. The ether extract represents fat, and is thus multiplied by 2.25, since fat has an energy value of 2.25 times that of protein or carbohydrate.

A more detailed procedure involves placing the animals in an insulated box-like unit called a "calorimeter," where the heat loss and excreta (and the carbon dioxide and water exhaled via the breath) can be measured. By this means, one may determine the net energy value of a feed. Energy values are expressed as: calories (a calorie is the amount of heat required to raise the temperature of 1 gram of water 1°C); kilocalories (kcal)—1000 calories also sometimes referred to as a large calorie; and megacalories (mcal)—1 million calories and frequently referred to as a therm.

Morrison (1956) and NRC Publications 585 (1958) and 659 (1959) are excellent sources of tabular data on feed composition, digestibility of various nutrients, and TDN contents of feeds. An example of these data is given in Table 27-1 (from Morrison).

From similar data for other feeds, one can readily estimate the digestible protein, NFE, crude fiber, and TDN for any feeds and mixtures that have been studied.

In the United States, estimates of the energy value of feeds are commonly based on calculation of TDN or digestible energy. As knowledge is made available through research, feeding recommendations can be explicitly expressed in terms of daily nutrient requirements for animals of different weights and ages or in terms of different expected rates of gain and different levels of production, for example, maintenance for wintering on the range *vs.* lactation. A series of nine National Research Council publications on

TABLE 27-1. *An example of calculating total digestible nutrients in corn (grade 2). Based on information obtained from chemical analysis and a digestion trial.*

Chemical fractions (nutrients)	Average composition*	Percent digestible	Pounds digestible*
Dry matter	85.0		
Crude fiber	2.0	57	1.14
Crude protein	8.7	77	6.70
Fat (ether extract)	3.9	90	7.90†
Nitrogen free extract (NFE)	69.2	93	64.36
Ash	1.2		
Total digestible nutrients			80.1

* Pounds per 100 lb. of corn.
† Pounds digestible times 2.25.

"Nutrient Requirements of Domestic Animals," provides excellent summaries on the nutrient requirements of each species of livestock, as well as for foxes, minks, dogs, and rabbits.

TDN figures express less accurately the energy values for roughages than for concentrates. This is because there is an exceptionally large loss of energy in the form of heat during the digestion and metabolism of roughages. However, in a cold environment, in which animals are being fed maintenance rations, this energy loss need not be considered as a net loss, since extra heat is needed to maintain the body temperature. For most productive purposes, such as fattening, net energy values would more accurately reflect the feeding value of roughages in a mild environment. Let us use an example: The TDN value of very leafy alfalfa is 52.7 as compared to 42.2 for barley straw. The net energy values (in therms per 100 lb.) for the two feeds are 43.5 and 22.4. That is, in terms of TDN, barley straw contains 80% of the nutrient value of alfalfa; in terms of net energy, barley straw contains 51.5% of the energy value of alfalfa.

Energy and protein requirements vary with the physiological condition, the size, and the level of activity of the animal. Basal metabolism—the heat production of the body at rest, following a limited fasting period—represents the energy needed to support vital functions, such as tissue repair, breathing, heart action, and maintenance of body temperature. It has been shown that energy needs for basal metabolism vary with body size. If weight (W) is measured in kilograms, the relationship $70(W_{kg}^{0.75})$ kcal per 24 hours expresses the caloric needs for animals ranging in size from a shrew to an elephant. That is, the caloric needs do not increase in direct proportion to increases in body weight, because larger bodies contain a higher per cent of bone and thus contain less active metabolizing tissue. Heat loss via the body surface is also related to body size and represents a substantial amount of the daily energy expenditure. Basal metabolism caloric needs represent 75% of the maintenance energy requirements of the "idle adult, monogastric, nonherbivorous species" and 50% for cattle and sheep. (Crampton and Lloyd, 1959, Chap. 28.)

Feeding standards reflect these basic considerations (Guilbert and Loosli, 1951; Crampton, 1956). Table 27-2 gives the TDN and DE requirements for some of the specific physiological needs such as lactation and growth.

From these data, one is led to an important concept regarding animal nutrition. A definite amount of feed (TDN) is required daily to maintain the essential life processes of an animal, and only the protein, energy, minerals, fats and vitamins ingested in excess of these requirements are available to the body for productive functions, such as growth or lactation. The maintenance requirement is comparable to the fixed operating cost of a business; profits are earned after these costs are met. For this reason, factors tending to stimulate feed intake can improve feed efficiency because the extra food goes toward productive processes.

TABLE 27-2. | *Total digestible nutrients (TDN) and digestible energy (DE) requirements for animals under different physiological states.*

	TDN (lb.)	DE (mcal)
Maintenance (cattle)	0.008 per lb. body wt	0.016 per lb. body wt.
Lactation (cow)	0.28 per lb. 4% FCM*	0.56 per lb. 4% FCM
Growth (pigs) †		
50 lb.	0.048 per lb. body wt	0.096 per lb. body wt
100 lb. meat type	0.04 per lb. body wt	0.08 per lb. body wt
100 lb. bacon type	0.036 per lb. body wt	0.072 per lb. body wt

* FCM, Fat Corrected Milk. Energy requirements directly related to energy content of milk.
† Expected gain. 1.2, 1.6, and 1.5 lb. per day respectively. NRC. Publication No. 2, Nutrient Requirements of Swine (1959).

A valuable method for determining which nutrients are required, and for discovering unknown nutrients, is the use of highly purified or completely synthetic rations. By using purified or synthetic-type rations composed of carefully prepared proteins, such as casein from milk, amino acids, sugars, mineral salts, refined fats, and vitamins, the scientist can exercise greater control over the composition of the ration than is possible when natural sources of proteins, carbohydrates, minerals, and fats are used.

ESSENTIAL NUTRIENTS: COMPOSITION, FUNCTIONS, METABOLISM, REQUIREMENTS

Protein Composition. Proteins are made up of amino acids linked together by chemical bonding (peptide linkage) in chains or polymers. Schematically, one can represent an amino acid as

$$R-\overset{\overset{\displaystyle H}{|}}{\underset{\underset{\displaystyle NH_2}{|}}{C}}-\overset{\overset{\displaystyle O}{\diagup\diagup}}{C}-OH$$

where R represents one or more carbon atoms or combinations of carbon atoms, additional amino groups, hydroxyl groups, or sulfur. There are at least 20 known amino acids that can be linked together in all possible sequences and chain lengths to form the many kinds of proteins found in the plant and animal kingdoms.

Not all amino acids occur in every protein in equal relative proportions. Corn protein (zein) is low in lysine, tryptophan, and methionine, but meat meals and soybean oil meal are relatively rich in lysine and tryptophan. Thus, by combining feeds, a ration can be formulated that will supply the proper amount and assortment of amino acids (protein) needed for each species of animal. Purified amino acid supplements could be used, but availability and cost are deciding factors in their use.

Protein Quality. Protein quality is determined largely by (1) a proper assortment of amino acids; (2) the digestibility of the protein, either in protein-rich concentrates or in the forages or grains; (3) the method of handling during processing, as with the oil-seed meals; and (4) palatability. Protein quality is especially important in the formulation of rations for young animals and when a high level of feed intake is desired, as during the growing-finishing phase of livestock production.

Soybeans contain a substance that inhibits digestion in monogastric animals. The development of a practical method of heat inactivation of this trypsin inhibitor during processing of the beans was a major contribution of research performed during the period 1925 to 1950. This research made possible the extensive use of soybean oil meal as a protein-rich concentrate in rations for all classes of livestock. Cottonseed-oil meal is an old standby as a cattle and sheep protein supplement, but the amount fed to pigs and chickens is usually limited to 5–10% because gossypol—a substance contained in the cottonseed germ—is toxic to these animals. Larger quantities can be fed if the meal is processed in such a way as to remove most of the free gossypol or if it is inactivated by chemical treatment. These two illustrations indicate the type of problem that can be encountered in developing the use of a new protein supplement.

Protein Functions. Amino acids are the building blocks of all body tissue, enzymes, blood proteins and antibodies used by the body in fighting infections, so they are absolute daily essentials to growth and life. A dietary source of some of the amino acids appears to be more essential to higher animals and birds than to others. On the basis of careful experiments on purified or synthetic diets, research has shown that amino acids can be classed as "essential" or "nonessential" for monogastric animals. Table 27-3 gives a nutritive classification of amino acids, based on the research of many in-

TABLE 27-3.	*Nutritive classification of the Amino Acids.*	
Essential (indispensable)	Semi-indispensable	Nonessential (dispensable)
Histidine	Arginine*	Glutamic acid
Lysine	Tyrosine†	Aspartic acid
Tryptophan†	Cystine†	Alanine
Phenylalanine	Glycine*	Proline
Methionine	Serine*	Hydroxyproline
Threonine		
Leucine		
Isoleucine		
Valine		

* Arginine and glycine are essential for chicks and turkeys. Serine will spare or replace glycine.
† Tyrosine will spare but not completely replace phenylalanine. Cystine will spare but not completely replace methionine. Nicotinic acid will spare but not completely replace tryptophan.

vestigators; this information appears in standard references on amino acids in nutrition (Block *et al.*, 1956; Frear, 1950).

The practical application of knowledge concerning amino-acid requirements is put to practical use in the formulation of a balanced ration. Estimates of requirements for specific amino acids and/or crude proteins as sources of these acids are available for most classes of livestock. A balanced, or complete, ration provides an ample amount of digestible protein to supply these amino acids. This means that all rations must provide an adequate amount of digestible protein and the proper assortment of essential amino acids. The amino-acid makeup of the protein in ruminant rations is not critical, because amino acids are synthesized in the rumen and a built-in supplement is thus provided.

Other nutritional factors can influence the efficiency of amino-acid (protein) utilization. Proteins will not be used efficiently if the energy level of the ration is low or if there are vitamin and mineral deficiencies. During periods of rapid growth, during pregnancy, and during heavy lactation, the amino acid requirements, and thus the protein requirements, of animals are increased, owing to the added demand for tissue synthesis and milk protein formation.

In mammals, the use of nonprotein nitrogen is restricted primarily to ruminants because of their greater capacity for microbial synthesis. Nonprotein nitrogen can replace up to one-third of the nitrogen needs of cattle and sheep if the energy level of the ration is adequate. The use of these NPN compounds, especially urea, will be discussed in greater detail in the chapter on Feeding Ruminants.

MEETING ENERGY REQUIREMENTS: CARBOHYDRATES

Carbohydrate Composition. Carbohydrates are the major source of energy in livestock feeds. Carbohydrates occur in feeds in many different chemical forms. Grains primarily contain starches and simple sugars; milk contains the sugar, lactose; and cane molasses contains sucrose; but forages contain the celluloses (water insoluble carbohydrates) and the hemicelluloses.

Metabolism and Digestion. The various carbohydrates are metabolized in the body to yield energy needed for essential body functions (see Table 27-2). The end products of carbohydrate metabolism are carbon dioxide and water, formed through a series of processes catalyzed by tissue enzymes. A significant point in connection with carbohydrate metabolism is that these enzyme systems require vitamins and minerals as cofactors or activators, whereas amino acids are components of the enzymes. Fatty acids and the deaminated amino acids can ultimately be metabolized to yield energy through the same or related systems. Thus, it is at this point that a partial explanation of the interchangeability of energy-yielding nutrients is found. Physiologically, a high-fat ration supplies the same kind of calories (energy) as do starches or sugars from corn or protein in a low-energy, high-protein ration.

Cellulose Digestion. Enzymes that will digest cellulose (in the crude-fiber component of roughages) are not present in secretions of the digestion tract. Cellulase, the enzyme that breaks down cellulose, is produced by the microflora and is present in the rumen of cattle, sheep, and goats and in the caecum of the horse. Cellulose digestion follows a different pathway than other carbohydrates. It is broken down in the rumen into volatile fatty acids—acetic, propionic, butyric, and lesser amounts of related 4- and 5-carbon acids. These acids are absorbed and can be metabolized to yield energy or serve as carbon sources for diverse synthetic processes. Acetate is a precursor for the synthesis of many important compounds, such as cholesterol, nucleic acids, and milk fat.

Improved utilization of nutrients from forages is an important area of research and a key to more efficient animal agriculture. This complex problem involves a study of the effect of lignin—a substance found in maturing plants—on ruminal digestion of celluloses and hemicelluloses. Cutting time of forage crops has a marked effect on the lignin content of many forages; digestibility drops and the quality of the forage decreases as forage becomes more mature. New York experiments have shown that the digestibility of timothy-brome hay cellulose can decrease at the rate of 0.5% per day during the maturing stages.

LIPIDS (FATS)

Composition of Fats. The lipid portion of a feed is extractable with fat solvents; lipids constitute 2–10% of the cereals and forages. Fats are made up of glycerides—esters of glycerol and fatty acids. Few fatty acids occur in free form; one of the first steps in fat digestion is hydrolysis of the ester by fat-splitting enzymes (lipases) in the small intestine, producing free fatty acids and glycerol.

Functions of Fats and Fatty Acids. Fats serve two major functions in the body; they provide energy, as discussed above, and they supply fatty acids needed for growth. A deficiency of fatty acids is unlikely with most cereal-grain–protein-supplement-mineral rations for hogs and poultry. Fatty acid deficiency has not been observed in the adult ruminant; the fat present in the dam's milk is both high in quality and ample to meet the needs of the suckling calf or lamb.

The outstanding characteristic of fatty acids is their high energy content. Fats contain approximately 9.0 kcal per gram or, 2.25 times more energy per unit of weight than carbohydrates (1g of carbohydrate contains 4 kcal; 1g of protein contains 3.9 kcal). Added energy is available to the newborn animal via high-fat colostrum milk. Modern-day, high-energy poultry rations contain up to 10% added fat as a means of giving the rations a greater caloric density.

Rancidity. Fats are subject to oxidative deterioration called rancidity. Fat deterioration occurs during storage and is speeded up by heat and the presence of alkaline minerals in feeds, especially in rations containing added fat. Antioxidants can be added to more or less completely protect fats against rancidity.

VITAMINS OR "ACCESSORY GROWTH FACTORS"

General. A vitamin may be roughly defined as an organic compound required in minute amounts for normal growth and maintenance of animal and plant life. Vitamins are effective in small amounts, functioning in the transformation of energy, in the regulation of metabolic processes, and in the biosynthesis of diverse compounds in the tissues of the body. However, vitamins are not used as structural units in the body.

The development of the vitamin concept is a fascinating story. McCollum (1957), in his history of the development of nutrition research, in which he discusses early work on the vitamins, impresses the reader with the ingenuity and dedication of early workers in this field. Early investigators found that rations composed of purified nutrients prepared from milk (protein, carbohydrates, mineral salts, fat, and water) failed to support growth. These investigators correctly concluded that milk and other feedstuffs contained, in addition to the known constituents, minute amounts of unidentified substances that are essential to life. By 1913, there was evidence that two factors existed; one, a "water soluble B," and the other, a "fat soluble A." Water soluble "B" was found to contain groups of compounds now identified and referred to as the B-complex group. More fat-soluble vitamins were isolated and identified and are now grouped with vitamin A, the name of the original "fat soluble A." Thiamine (vitamin B_1) was the first vitamin to be synthesized in crystalline form (1935), but today all the vitamins listed in Table 27-4 are available in crystalline form, and their structures have been determined.

Occurrence. Vitamins are widely distributed in nature, especially in animal products. However, all-plant rations may not contain enough vitamins for swine and poultry and usually must be supplemented with the B-complex group and especially with vitamins A and D of the fat soluble group. Vita-

TABLE 27-4. | *The vitamins.*

Water soluble vitamins	Fat soluble vitamins	Other vitamins
Thiamine (Vitamin B_1)	Vitamin A	Ascorbic acid
Riboflavin (Vitamin B_2)	Vitamin D	Inositol
Niacin	Vitamin E	Choline
Vitamin B_6	Vitamin K	
Pantothenic acid		
Biotin		
Folic acid		
Cobalamine (Vitamin B_{12})		

min supplementation will be discussed in detail in the appropriate chapters on feeding swine and poultry.

Function of Vitamins. Space will not permit an elaboration of specific deficiency symptoms for each of the vitamins or a discussion of the variations among the common classes of farm animals. Reduced growth rates and feed efficiency are the common general symptoms of vitamin deficiency in livestock and poultry. Death can occur if the deficiency is acute.

The B-complex vitamins function as enzyme cofactors and catalysts in energy metabolism. In humans, the lack of vitamins causes specific deficiency syndromes. Vitamin B_1 in the diet prevents beri-beri; niacin (nicotinamide) prevents pellagra, and riboflavin prevents cheilosis. Vitamin B_{12} is the "antipernicious-anemia factor." Human patients once had to eat pounds of liver to get a few milligrams of vitamin B_{12}, now available in crystalline form.

Fat-soluble vitamins are concerned with specific physiological functions, as are the B-complex vitamins. Vitamin A deficiency causes keratinization of epithelial tissue in the cells and upsets the chemical processes involved in vision. Vitamin D, called the antirickets vitamin, or the "sunshine vitamin," functions in activating the processes involved in the utilization of phosphorus and calcium for bone growth and development. Vitamin E is involved in oxidation-reduction (electron transfer) systems, and its deficiency is manifested by damage to the brain in chicks and by "white-muscle" or stiff-lamb disease in young lambs. Vitamin K is needed for normal blood clotting. Vitamin C is the anti-scurvy vitamin. The above list of vitamin-deficiency symptoms is incomplete, but it serves to illustrate the diverse but important functions of the vitamin group in metabolism and nutrition. More efficient utilization of feeds by livestock is possible because of the knowledge available about vitamins and the availability of supplements.

Ruminants again differ from nonruminants in the level of intestinal synthesis of B-complex vitamins. The lower digestive tract of all animals supports the growth of bacteria that synthesize vitamins, which are absorbed from the tract and utilized by the animal. Indications of the role of intestinal synthesis have been shown in studies on animals fed a bacteriostat to reduce or eliminate microbial growth in the gut. A growth response to biotin in the rat is much easier to demonstrate if sulfa drugs or some other antibiotic is added to the ration. Coprophagy (eating of feces) must be prevented in rats and mice in order to demonstrate a response to certain B vitamins, since the feces contain a high level of B-vitamins. The capacity for B-vitamin synthesis is greater in ruminants and in horses than in other mammals. It is unnecessary to add B-vitamins to supplement most cattle, horse, or sheep rations, whereas adequate vitamins, either as a supplement or in the natural feedstuff, are essentials for good poultry and swine rations as well as for very young ruminants, in which bacterial synthesis of these vitamins is inadequate.

DETERMINATION OF VITAMIN CONTENT. Once the structure of vitamins is known, their concentration in feedstuffs can be determined chemically. However, a more feasible procedure is the microbiological assay, based on the vitamin requirement of various microorganisms or molds. From the microbiological assay, a standard dose-response curve can be obtained for graded levels of a vitamin added to a nutrient media from which all the vitamins under study had been removed. Crude extracts containing the vitamins to be assayed are added to the deficient media, and the response is then compared to known standard responses. Extremely small amounts of materials can be analyzed by this technique as compared with the milligram amounts of vitamins that must be extracted from pounds of natural materials such as liver or spinach—a difficult and often frustrating experience.

MINERALS

General. The mineral requirements of livestock is an intriguing aspect of animal nutrition. Minerals (ash) constitute approximately 5% of the animal body weight. This fraction is concentrated primarily in the bones and in the teeth, which contain 99% of the body's calcium and 80% of its phosphorus. Other mineral elements present in the body in relatively large amounts are sodium, potassium, magnesium, sulfur, and chlorine. These elements, along with calcium and phosphorus, are often called the major- or macro-mineral elements of nutrition, as contrasted to a second group called micronutrient elements, which are needed only in trace amounts and are present in extremely small amounts in animal tissues. This group is composed of copper, iron, manganese, zinc, and cobalt. Trace amounts are expressed frequently in parts per million (ppm.) or in milligrams per pound of ration, whereas calcium, phosphorus, and sodium requirements are expressed as a per cent of the ration, for example, 0.25–1.0%.

All feeds contain a wide array of mineral elements, but these levels vary with such factors as forages *vs.* cereal grains; legumes *vs.* nonlegumes; and soil-mineral interrelationships. Minerals may be lacking in a soil or rendered unavailable to the plants by factors reducing the solubility, such as the alkalinity of the soil or the presence of mineral-binding complexes. Perhaps in no area of nutrition is there a closer soil–plant–animal relationship than in that of minerals.

Generalized recommendations regarding mineral supplements in livestock rations should not be made without considering the other ration components. The nutritionist must familiarize himself with the mineral composition of the feeds used and with the requirements of the animal species before formulating a ration. The age of the animal also influences its requirements; young, rapidly growing animals or birds need more phosphorus and calcium for skeletal growth than does the mature animal. The lactating animal needs calcium and phosphorus for the milk, hence its requirement is higher.

The levels of calcium, phosphorus, sodium (from common salt), trace elements, and iodine are usually of the most concern in a ration, inasmuch as the level of these elements in feeds may vary sufficiently to reduce animal performance if not properly supplemented. A number of mineral supplements are available, including such ingredients as steamed bone meal, calcium phosphate, defluorinated rock phosphate, various complex commercial mixtures, and iodized and trace-mineralized salt.

Minerals Essential to Animal Health. Phosphorus is especially important for growth; it is required, along with calcium, for bone development and for soft-tissue formation, as well as for metabolic processes. The metabolism of sugar, fat, and protein involves the phosphorylation of metabolic intermediates and the formation of energy-rich phosphate compounds for the storage and transmission of metabolically formed energy.

Calcium is needed for bone structure formation. Sodium, potassium, calcium, and magnesium help to maintain the osmotic pressure of the blood and to maintain the proper water balance between circulating fluids and the tissues. These are but a few examples of the specific functions of mineral elements. (See Crampton and Lloyd, 1959; Maynard and Loosli, 1956.)

Trace Elements Have Unique Physiological and Metabolic Roles. The role of these elements can be likened to that of vitamins. An example may help to illustrate. Iron is a part of the hemoglobin molecule; thus, a deficiency of iron can induce an anemic condition in an animal. Furthermore, copper facilitates the absorption and utilization of iron. Thus, if the ration is low in copper and iron, adding iron alone will not correct the deficiency, but a combination of iron and copper will, if it is supplied in a copper to iron ratio of 1 to 10. The newborn pig is low in body reserves of iron and must be provided with a special supplement early in life.

Cobalt is present in the vitamin B_{12} molecule. Ruminants can synthesize enough vitamin B_{12} for growth provided the ration contains at least 0.07 ppm cobalt for cattle or about 0.1 ppm for sheep. As cobalt functions in the synthesis of vitamin B_{12} in the rumen, it is effective only if taken orally.

A number of interesting mineral interrelationships have recently been investigated. Swine require zinc, and the apparent requirement is increased as the level of calcium in the ration is increased. Excess molybdenum decreases the utilization of copper. Selenium, which at 5–10 ppm in a ration produces toxic symptoms, has recently been found to reduce the vitamin E requirement if present in rations at extremely low levels—less than 1 ppm. Chicks, lambs, and rats have been used to demonstrate the selenium–vitamin E relationship. Undoubtedly more of these inhibitor-activator mineral interrelationships will be found and will provide a better explanation to a number of problems associated with production in certain areas of the country.

Usually classed with the minerals are the halogens (iodine, chlorine, and fluorine), which are important nutritionally. Iodine is needed for the formation of the hormones thyroxine and triiodothyronine and related compounds produced by the thyroid gland. A deficiency induces hyperplasia of the thyroid, called goiter in humans and "big neck" in calves. The disease impairs growth and reproduction. Many iodine deficient areas in this country and in the world have been identified; precautions are now taken to avoid a deficiency by feeding iodine to all animals. Iodinated salt is the most frequent method of supplying iodine in the ration.

Fluorine probably should not be included in the list of required minerals, but its presence at low levels (0.75 ppm) in water appears to reduce the number of cavities in human teeth. Too much fluorine can be toxic. (For special references to literature on trace elements, see Underwood, 1956; Lamb, Bentley, and Beattie, 1958.) Though rarely deficient in normal rations, chlorine is apparently a required mineral. Presumably, it functions in the acid-base relations in the body.

REFERENCES AND SELECTED READINGS

References marked with an asterisk are of general interest.

Anonymous, 1955. *Methods of Analysis.* 8th Ed. Assoc. of Official Agricultural Chemists, Washington, D.C.

*Block, R. J., K. W. Weiss, H. J. Almquist, D. B. Carroll, W. P. Gordon and S. Saperstein, 1956. *Amino Acid Handbook,* C. C. Thomas, Springfield, Illinois.

*Brody, S., 1945. *Bioenergetics and Growth.* Reinhold, New York.

*Crampton, E. W., 1956. *Applied Animal Nutrition.* Freeman, San Francisco.

*———— and L. E. Lloyd, 1959. *Fundamentals of Nutrition.* Freeman, San Francisco.

———— and V. G. MacKay, 1957. The caloric value of TDN. *J. Animal Sci.,* 16:541.

*Frear, D. E. H., 1950. *Agricultural Chemistry.* Van Nostrand, New York.

Guilbert, H. R. and J. K. Loosli, 1951. Comparative nutrition of farm animals. *J. Animal Sci.,* 10:22.

*Lamb, C. A., O. G. Bentley, and J. M.

Beattie, 1958. *Trace Elements.* Academic, New York.

*Maynard, L. A. and J. K. Loosli, 1956. *Animal Nutrition.* McGraw-Hill, New York.

*McCollum, E. V., 1957. *A History of Nutrition.* Houghton-Mifflin, Boston.

*Morrison, F. B., 1956. *Feeds and Feeding.* 22nd Ed., Morrison Publishing Co., Ithaca.

*NRC, 1959. Joint United States–Canadian Tables of Feed Composition No. 659 and Publication No. 585, Composition of Cereal Grains and Forages, 1958. Nat. Acad. of Sci. Nat. Research Council, Washington, D.C.

*Rosenberger, H. R., 1951. *Vitamins.* Interscience, New York.

Swift, R. W., 1957. The caloric value of TDN. *J. Animal Sci.,* 16:753.

*Underwood, E. J., 1956. *Trace Elements in Human and Animal Nutrition.* Academic, New York.

Chapter 28

Meeting the Nutrient Requirements of Nonruminant Mammals

28-1. INTRODUCTION

The nonruminants generally require the same nutrients indicated in the previous chapter as being required by all animals. These animals, however, differ from ruminants in that they have relatively smaller digestive tracts and therefore must have their feed in a more concentrated form. Further, swine are not able to meet their B-vitamin requirements as a result of synthesis, as is the case with ruminants as a result of fermentative action in the rumen. Horses do obtain a part of their B-vitamin supply from synthesis resulting from microfloral activity in the caecum and large intestine. Urea, or other nonprotein nitrogen, is not generally used as a source of nitrogen (protein equivalent) for either swine or horses. Hence, more attention must be given to supplying adequate amounts of the required nutrients in the rations of such animals.

28-2. MEETING THE NUTRIENT REQUIREMENTS OF SWINE

Swine have a relatively smaller frame, grow more rapidly, and reproduce at a younger age than do other farm mammals. Meeting their nutrient requirements is primarily a matter of supplying them with a ration in which ingredients other than the cereal grain, or grains, correct the nutrient deficiencies of the main energy-supplying ingredient. A balanced ration, as used in this discussion, is considered to be "a combination of feeds which supplies the required nutrients in the proper amounts and proportions to meet the nutrient requirements of the animal for a given purpose of production." The Committee of Animal Nutrition, National Research Council, in the most recent issue of Nutrient Requirements for Swine, states "In formulating swine rations, consideration should be given to the nutrients supplied in available form by natural feedstuffs. Swine rations should be supplemented only by amounts of nutrients needed to bring the natural ration up to the required level. There is no evidence that superfortification of the ration above the requirement will bring about any additional benefit. In fact, in many instances it may be harmful."

Energy. Aside from water that should be supplied fresh and in adequate amounts at all times, the two major nutrient requirements of swine are energy and protein. As shown in Tables 28-1 and 28-2, taken from *Nutrient Requirements of Swine* (National Research Council), energy requirements are expressed as the percentage of Total Digestible Nutrients in the ration. When rations are formulated on the basis of the corn, grain sorghum, wheat, or barley used as the major component, little consideration is given to the energy content of the ration, since it is assumed that it will meet or exceed the requirements of growing-finishing swine. When rations are formulated for pregnant sows and gilts, such feeds as alfalfa meal and ground oats are included to reduce the TDN content. This is especially true when the rations are to be self-fed, in which case the rations will contain 30% or more of ground alfalfa hay along with oats in many instances; some producers will use up to 30% of ground corn cobs as a bulking ingredient so sows can consume a fairly large amount of feed without becoming overfat during the gestation period.

Protein and Amino Acids. The protein requirements of swine, as shown in Tables 28-1 and 28-2, are expressed as percentage of crude protein (N × 6.25) in the ration. Recent advances in swine nutrition have supplied us with knowledge of the amino acids essential for growing-finishing swine, as well as of the requirements for these amino acids. (See Table 28-3.) Thus, in the formulation of modern rations, consideration is given not only to the crude protein content of the ration but to the quality of the protein in order that the ration as finally compounded will meet or slightly exceed the requirement of the particular weight group of growing-finishing pigs for the particular amino acids. The cereal grains are in general low in total protein, and the quality of protein is fair to poor. High protein concentrates are therefore selected on the basis of their ability to supply additional protein and to contribute sizable amounts of the amino acids that may be most limiting in the cereal grain being used. Of the high protein supplemental feeds, solvent soybean oil meal is highly favored, particularly in rations of

TABLE 28-1. Nutrient requirements of growing and finishing pigs* (expressed in percentage or amount per pound of total ration.)

| | Growing pigs | | | Finishing pigs (self-fed) | | | | | |
| | | | | Meat type | | | Bacon type† | | |
	10	25	50	100	150	200	100	150	200
Liveweight (lb.)	10	25	50	100	150	200	100	150	200
Expected daily gain (lb.)	0.5	0.8	1.2	1.6	1.7	1.9	1.5	1.7	1.7
Protein and energy:									
Crude protein (%)	24	17	15**	13	12	12	16	14	14
Total digestible nutrients (%)	80	80	75	75	75	75	70‡	70‡	70‡
Digestible energy (kcal) §	1600	1600	1500	1500	1500	1500	1400	1400	1400
Inorganic nutrients:									
Calcium (%)	0.70	0.65	0.65	0.50	0.50	0.50	0.50	0.50	0.50
Phosphorus (%)	0.60	0.50	0.50	0.40	0.40	0.40	0.40	0.40	0.40
Salt (NaCl) (%)	0.50	0.50	0.50	0.50	0.50	0.50	0.50	0.50	0.50
Vitamins:									
Carotene (mg) ‖	1.5	1.12	0.75	0.75	0.75	0.75	0.75	0.75	0.75
Vitamin A (I.U.) ‖	800	600	400	400	400	400	400	400	400
Vitamin D (I.U.)	100	90	90	60	60	60	60	60	60
Thiamine (mg)	0.6	0.5	0.5	0.5	0.5	0.5	0.5	0.5	0.5
Riboflavin (mg)	1.5	1.4	1.2	1.0	1.0	1.0	1.0	1.0	1.0
Niacin (mg)	10.0	8.0	6.0	5.0	5.0	5.0	5.0	5.0	5.0
Pantothenic acid (mg)	6.0	5.0	5.0	4.5	4.5	4.5	4.5	4.5	4.5
Pyridoxine (mg)	0.5	0.5	0.5						
Choline (mg)	500	400							
Vitamin B₁₂ (mcg)	10.0	7.0	5.0	5.0	5.0	5.0	5.0	5.0	5.0

* Beson, W. M. et al., 1959. Nutrient Requirements of Swine. National Academy of Sciences. National Research Council Publication 648. Washington, D. C.

† It usually requires 2 weeks longer to produce a 200-lb. bacon-type hog than a 200-lb. meat-type hog.

** For bacon type hog feed 16% crude protein.

‡ Rations for barrows being finished for bacon should contain 67% TDN or 1354 kcal of digestible energy per pound.

§ Digestible energy was calculated on the assumption that one pound of TDN has 2000 kcal of digestible energy.

‖ Carotene and vitamin A values based on 1 mg. carotene equals 533 I.U. vitamin A for the pig. Vitamin A requirements can be met by either carotene or vitamin A; both are not needed.

TABLE 28-2.	Nutrient requirements of breeding stock* (expressed in percentage or amount per pound of total ration.)

	Breeding stock					
	Bred		Lactating		Boars	
	Gilts	Sows	Gilts	Sows	Young	Adult
Liveweight (lb.)	300	500	350	450	300	500
Expected daily gain (lb.)	1.0	0.7			1.0	
Protein and energy:						
Crude protein (%)	15	13	15	13	15	13
Total digestible nutrients (%)	70	70	75	75	70	70
Digestible energy (kcal) †	1400	1400	1500	1500	1400	1400
Inorganic nutrients:						
Calcium (%)	0.6	0.6	0.6	0.6	0.6	0.6
Phosphorus (%)	0.4	0.4	0.4	0.4	0.4	0.4
Salt (NaCl) (%)	0.5	0.5	0.5	0.5	0.5	0.5
Vitamins:						
Carotene (mg) †	2.5	2.5	2.5	2.5	2.5	2.5
Vitamin A (I.U.) †	1200	1200	1200	1200	1200	1200
Vitamin D (I.U.)	60	60	60	60	60	60
Thiamine (mg)	0.5	0.5	0.5	0.5	0.5	0.5
Riboflavin (mg)	1.5	1.5	1.5	1.5	1.5	1.5
Niacin (mg)	5.0	5.0	5.0	5.0	5.0	5.0
Pantothenic acid (mg)	6.0	6.0	6.0	6.0	6.0	6.0
Pyridoxine (mg)						
Choline (mg)						
Vitamin B$_{12}$ (mcg)	5.0	5.0	5.0	5.0	5.0	5.0

* Beeson, W. M. et al., 1959. Nutrient Requirements of Swine. National Academy of Sciences. National Research Council Publication 648. Washington, D. C.

† Digestible energy was calculated on the assumption that one pound of TDN has 2000 kcal of digestible energy.

** Carotene and vitamin A values based on 1 mg carotene equals 533 I.U. vitamin A for the pig. Vitamin A requirements can be met by either carotene or vitamin A; both are not needed.

growing-finishing swine, because it is unique as a protein supplemental feed of plant origin in its ability to correct the essential amino acid deficiencies of the cereal grains when used to supply enough additional protein to meet the requirement of a particular weight group of pigs. Tankage and fish meal are used because they contribute sizable quantities of lysine; fish meal is also favored in pig starters because it may serve as a source of unidentified growth factors as well as of protein. The milk by-products— dried skim milk, dried buttermilk, and dried whey—are also used in pig starters because they contribute protein of high quality, B-vitamins, and the minerals calcium and phosphorus, and, in addition, they contribute to the palatability of the ration.

Example rations are presented in Table 28-4 to demonstrate the manner in which a variety of feeds can be used to meet the protein and amino acid

	Percentage of total diet	
Amino acid	Baby pigs (5–10 lb.)	Growing pigs (25–70 lb.)
L-Arginine		0.20
L-Histidine	0.20	0.20
L-Isoleucine	0.76	0.60
L-Leucine	1.25 ‡	0.60
L-Lysine	0.94 ‡	0.65
DL-Methionine †		0.60
DL-Phenylalanine **		0.50
L-Threonine	0.90 ‡	0.40
DL-Tryptophan		0.20
L-Valine		0.40

* Beeson, W. M. *et al.*, 1959. Nutrient Requirements of Swine. National Academy of Sciences. National Research Council. Publication 648. Washington, D.C.
† Cystine can replace one-half (0.3%) of the methionine requirement.
** Tyrosine can replace 30% (0.15%) of the phenylalanine requirement.
‡ This level is adequate, but minimum requirement has not been established.

requirements of three weight classes of swine. The protein supplemental feeds used in these rations have been selected for their ability to supply essential amino acids as well as protein. When a combination of barley and soybean meal is used slight deficiencies of lysine and methionine plus cystine result. The substitution of another source of supplemental protein for part of the soybean oil meal can help to overcome all the deficiency of lysine and part of the deficiency of methionine plus cystine.

Minerals. Swine require 13 mineral elements; little or no attention is given to meeting the needs for iron, copper, cobalt, manganese, magnesium, potassium, and sulfur because in nearly all instances the basic components of the ration will supply adequate or more than adequate amounts of these nutrients to meet the needs of growing-finishing swine as well as the needs of pregnant and lactating females. Sodium chloride, required and often neglected, is perhaps the most easily supplied of the minerals as it can be included as 0.5% of the complete ration or as 2.5% of the protein supplement without difficulty. Iodine deficiency in the pregnant sow results in hairless and stillborn pigs; this can easily be avoided by using stabilized, iodized salt instead of plain sodium chloride in the ration or supplement.

Calcium deficiency is most likely to occur, since swine rations are based largely upon cereal grains that are very low in this element. Such feeds as meat and bone scraps, tankage, and fish meal provide calcium and phos-

TABLE 28-4. | *Examples of rations for swine.*

Ingredient*	10 to 30 lb.	40 to 75 lb.				Pregnant females Hand-fed	Pregnant females Self-fed
Ground yellow corn	32.8	77.7		80.5	77.0	61.0	31.0
Barley			85.0				
Ground oats						15.0	30.5
Rolled oats	32.7						
Soybean meal, solvent	7.0	20.0	13.0	13.0	11.0	5.0	4.0
Linseed oil meal, expeller						3.0	
Tankage, digester	3.0				5.0	5.0	
Meat and bone scraps				6.0			4.0
Fish meal, menhaden	3.0						
Dehydrated alfalfa meal (17%)					8.0	10.0	
Alfalfa meal, suncured							30.0
Dried skimmilk	10.0						
Sugar, sucrose	10.0						
Dicalcium phosphate	1.0	1.0	0.5			0.5	
Ground feeding limestone		0.8	1.0		0.5		
Salt†	0.5	0.5	0.5	0.5	0.5	0.5	0.5
Total	100.0	100.0	100.0	100.0	100.0	100.0	100.0
Approximate nutrient content							
TDN (%)	84	78	72	78	78	74	67
Crude protein (%)	14.4	16.0	16.1	16.1	16.2	15.3	15.0
Calcium (%)	0.78	0.65	0.63	0.64	0.69	0.67	0.92
Phosphorus (%)	0.75	0.57	0.54	0.62	0.48	0.48	0.51
Vitamin A (I.U./lb.)	492	1165		1207	9155	10915	12465
Vitamin D (I.U./lb.)							271
Riboflavin (mg/lb.)	1.50	0.8	1.00	0.8	1.2	1.3	2.1
Niacin (mg/lb.)**	2.6	2.4	1.6	2.7	2.9	2.9	6.2
Pantothenic acid (mg/lb.)	5.2	3.4	3.7	3.1	3.8	4.5	7.0
Tryptophan (%)	0.22	0.19	0.26	0.18	0.19	0.19	0.19
Lysine (%)	1.02	0.74	0.63	0.71	0.74	0.65	0.65
Methionine + cystine (%)	0.58	0.53	0.42	0.52	0.51	0.50	0.48
Approximate deficiencies to be corrected, amount required							
Vitamin A (I.U./lb.)	308		400				
Vitamin D (I.U./lb.)	100	60	60	60	60	60	
Riboflavin (mg/lb.)		0.4	0.2	0.4			0.2
Niacin (mg/lb.)	3.4	2.6	3.4	2.3	2.1	2.1	
Pantothenic acid (mg/lb.)	0.8	1.6	1.3	1.9	1.2	1.5	
Tryptophan (%)							
Lysine (%)‡			0.02				
Methionine + cystine (%)			0.08				

* All ingredients expressed as pounds of feed, air dry basis.

† Provision must be made to supply 40 to 50 ppm of supplemental zinc in all rations; stabilized iodized salt should be used in sow rations.

** Calculations based on assumption that none of the niacin in cereals is available to swine.

‡ Becker, D. E., 1959. Balancing Swine Rations. Circular 811 of the Univ. of Illinois Expt. Sta. indicates the lysine requirements of pigs requiring a 16% protein ration to be 0.74% of the ration, in which case a deficiency of lysine will exist in some rations and will be magnified in the barley ration.

phorus in addition to supplying supplemental protein. Mineral supplements such as steamed bone meal and dicalcium phosphate provide both calcium and phosphorus, whereas ground feeding limestone provides only calcium. The example rations in Table 28-4 demonstrate that a wise choice of feeds makes it possible to meet the calcium and phosphorus requirements without using excessive amounts of the mineral supplements. It is also evident that the use of tankage, meat and bone scraps, and fish meal permits the use of relatively smaller amounts of calcium and phosphorus supplements than are required if all the supplemental protein in the ration is provided by soybean oil meal.

Recently it has been shown that attention must be given to supplying supplemental zinc in swine rations. A malady called parakeratosis often results in pigs if their rations contain excessive calcium or if an imbalance of calcium and zinc exists. This demonstrates the fallacy of adding excessive amounts of any one nutrient (calcium in this instance) as well as the importance of balance in the ration. Supplemental zinc is most easily provided by using zinc salts, such as zinc sulfate monohydrate, zinc sulfate heptahydrate, or zinc oxide to supply an equivalent of 40 to 50 ppm of elemental zinc.

Iron, although not required in supplemental amounts for growing-finishing pigs and for older hogs under most circumstances, is necessary for suckling pigs being reared on concrete or board floors. A lack of iron in this instance results in iron deficiency anemia—a reduction in the oxygen-carrying capacity of the blood, due to a lack of hemoglobin. This condition is characterized by thumps, roughened hair coat, and general lack of vigor and thrift. Supplemental iron can be effectively administered to the young by swabbing the sow's udder daily with a saturated ferrous sulfate solution (1 lb. of "copperas" in 3 quarts of water), starting at 3 to 4 days and continuing until the pigs are 35 days old. Uncontaminated sod placed in the nursing pen daily for a similar period also provides the pigs with a good source of iron. Recently, injectable iron compounds have been developed that, when injected to provide the 3- to 7-day-old pig with 150 mg of supplemental iron, provide good protection against nutritional anemia until the pigs are at least 35 days old and are eating sizable quantities of feed.

Vitamins. The vitamins, although not of great quantitative consequence in the ration, individually exert profound influences upon the well being of the pig, as evidenced by some of the deficiency symptoms resulting from a deficiency of one or more of the vitamins. Of the fat soluble vitamins, only vitamins A and D are carefully considered in swine ration formulation, since the pig obtains enough vitamin K from microbial synthesis in the intestinal tract as well as in the feed. The natural ingredients in well-balanced rations are usually considered to provide adequate amounts of vitamin E. Swine fed on lush pasture obtain more than enough carotene, a precursor of vitamin A, to meet their requirements. Generally, the use of 8 to 10% of dehydrated alfalfa meal or high quality alfalfa meal in the ration will result in a gross excess of vitamin A potency. If high quality yellow corn makes up 50% or more of the ration of growing-finishing swine, they will obtain more than enough vitamin A activity from the carotenoid in the yellow corn.

On the other hand, as shown in Table 28-4, rations containing less than 50% of yellow corn, and those based on barley, grain sorghum, oats, or wheat, will require some vitamin A supplementation if the pigs are fed under dry-lot conditions. Recent advances in the field of vitamin synthesis have provided us with relatively stable forms of synthetic vitamin A, which are easily added to rations to provide the desired levels of this vitamin.

Swine that are exposed to sunshine do not need supplemental vitamin D, inasmuch as the action of the ultraviolet rays upon the 7-dehydrocholesterol in the skin results in synthesis of this vitamin by the pig. If the pigs are confined during most or all of the life cycle, vitamin D can easily be supplied by adding irradiated yeast, or other compounds of known vitamin D potency. Fish liver oils will provide both vitamins A and D. Sun-cured alfalfa meal, often used in gestation rations, contains sizable amounts of vitamin D activity and, when used at 10% of the ration, will provide enough of this vitamin to meet or exceed the needs of growing-finishing swine as well as of pregnant or lactating females. It is apparent from the examples shown in Table 28-4 that rations not containing sun-cured alfalfa meal will always require supplementation with vitamin D if the animals are not exposed to sunshine.

The cereal grains contain more than enough thiamine to meet the needs of swine. Pyridoxine and biotin deficiencies have not been demonstrated in swine being fed well-balanced rations based on commonly used ingredients. Requirements for inositol, para-aminobenzoic acid, and folic acid have not been well established for swine being fed practical rations. Choline is generally assumed to be required by all age groups of swine, but the need has not been clearly established for growing-finishing pigs and for older swine. It is generally assumed that rations that are well balanced with respect to energy, protein, and other nutrients will provide enough of this constituent.

Riboflavin, niacin, pantothenic acid, and vitamin B_{12}, the most recently discovered of the B-vitamins, are given special consideration when formulating swine rations. The cereal grains are poor sources of riboflavin, pantothenic acid, and vitamin B_{12}, and although they contain fairly large amounts of niacin, it is not readily available to the pig. If animal by-products are used in rations as a major source of supplemental protein, particular attention must be given to riboflavin and pantothenic acid, since these products generally do not provide large amounts of these vitamins. Of the commonly used protein supplements of plant origin, soybean oil meal does provide fairly large amounts of riboflavin, niacin, and pantothenic acid, but some additional supplementation is necessary unless some major feed ingredient high in these vitamins is included in the ration.

Dehydrated alfalfa meal has long been looked upon with favor as a source of the B-vitamins as well as of vitamin A precursors. If 8 to 10% of high quality dehydrated alfalfa meal is included in swine rations, there is little likelihood that the ration will be deficient in vitamin A or in any of the B-vitamins, except vitamin B_{12}. Dehydrated alfalfa meal apparently reduces the palatability of pig starters and is therefore not favored for use in such feeds. It also contributes some additional fiber to the ration and is sometimes omitted from the rations of growing-finishing swine for that reason.

Many modern rations are compounded such that advantage is taken of the supply of crystalline vitamins or other vitamin concentrates that are available and which in many instances are added at the rate of 1 lb. or less per ton of complete feed, depending upon the potency of the concentrate. Vitamin B_{12} is now added to most swine rations by making use of vitamin B_{12} feed supplements, which are added in amounts that supply approximately 5 micrograms of the vitamin per pound of complete feed. The addition of tankage, marine by-products, or dairy by-products contributes some vitamin B_{12} to rations, but the content of the vitamin in such feeds is quite variable and unreliable. Thus vitamin B_{12} supplements are usually recommended in swine rations.

Lush pasture is an excellent feed in that it supplies good amounts of high quality protein. Legume pastures provide, in addition to protein, some supplemental calcium, but one of the main attributes of such pastures is that they provide swine with abundant quantities of all B-vitamins except vitamin B_{12}, with more than enough of the precursors of vitamin A, and, indirectly, with an excess of vitamin D as a result of the action of the sun's rays on the sterols in the skin of the pig.

The example rations shown in Table 28-4 were set up on the basis that no pasture would be available and that animals would be fed under dry-lot conditions. It is readily apparent that small amounts of supplemental riboflavin, niacin, and pantothenic acid are usually required to make nutritionally adequate rations. All requirements are based on those shown in Table 28-2, and the content of the various nutrients in the different rations is based on available tables of proximate analysis of feedstuffs. In calculating the content of rations, and in expressing the extent of deficiencies, the niacin in cereals was assumed to be unavailable to the pig.

28-3. MEETING THE NUTRIENT REQUIREMENTS OF THE HORSE

Horses require the same nutrients as pigs, but it is not as critical that some of the nutrients, for example, the B-vitamins, be provided orally, as it is with the pig. The caecum and large intestine of the horse occupy a relatively greater portion of the digestive tract than they do in either the pig or the cow. Some synthesis of the B-vitamins takes place in the caecum, or blind-gut, enabling the horse to meet a part of its requirements for these nutrients from this source. Owing to the large capacity of its caecum, and large intestine, the horse is able to utilize a higher roughage ration than the pig. However, the breakdown of roughages, particularly low quality roughages, resulting from bacterial action in the caecum and large intestine of the horse is less efficient than is the digestion of roughages in the rumen of cattle or sheep. Horses therefore require a high quality, easily digestible roughage if they are to rely on roughage as a major source of energy in the ration.

Water. Horses require fairly large amounts of water, and this requirement increases as a result of profuse sweating during work. Fresh water should either be available at all times or the horse should be given the opportunity to consume water between feedings. However, when horses are overheated as a result of heavy work or strenuous exercise, it is well to cool the horse to some extent prior to offering water and to prevent rapid consumption of a large amount of water when the horse is first given access to the supply.

Energy. The energy requirements of the horse are influenced by several factors: activity, amount of work done, pregnancy, lactation, and rate of development, or growth in the foal. Horses that are idle require a minimum of energy for maintenance and normal activity. Under most circumstances this energy requirement will be met from the carbohydrates and fats (energy-producing components) of a normal feed, such as good quality timothy or prairie hay. Some horsemen will also feed a small amount of leafy legume hay to serve as a source of protein, minerals, and vitamins, as well as a source of energy. When horses are at medium work, they require approximately 50% more TDN than when they are idle. Oats is a favored cereal grain for horses and is used in addition to the hay to provide the necessary added energy. Corn, grain sorghum, and other cereal grains have also been used successfully, but they are considered less desirable because of their more concentrated nature and the likelihood of digestive disturbances. Mares in the last quarter of pregnancy and not working require approximately the same amount of TDN as horses of equivalent weight at medium work. Mares in lactation require approximately 75% more TDN than mares in the last quarter of pregnancy. The energy requirements of lactating mares are met by feeding approximately the same amount of hay fed to pregnant mares, but of higher quality and containing some legume. Since these mares also require more protein, they are often fed supplemental linseed oil meal, a protein supplement of choice for horses (approximately 1 lb. daily for a 1200-lb. mare), from which they also obtain added energy. Wheat bran, because it improves the laxative nature of the ration, is often used for lactating mares, thus taking advantage of the energy, protein, and phosphorus that it contributes to the ration. Foals have a higher TDN requirement per unit of bodyweight than do older horses, and, owing to the lack of total development of the large intestine, they cannot utilize roughage as efficiently as a source of energy. However, growing colts have the benefit of the mother's milk, which is easily digested and which supplies a sizable portion of the energy requirement.

Protein. Quality of protein is not as important a consideration in the horse as in the pig, but an adequate amount of digestible protein must be supplied. Good quality grass hays will supply over half of the protein requirement of horses at rest; excellent pasture, however, particularly grass–legume, will supply all of their protein requirement. Legume hays of good quality contain from two and one-half to three times as much digestible protein as do good grass hays and are used as a replacement for part of the grass hay to provide added protein. The protein requirements of horses are not increased greatly by work; thus, the addition of grain to supply the energy required for work also provides enough supplemental protein. Mares in the last quarter of pregnancy require approximately 20% more digestible protein than do horses of equivalent weight at medium work. Linseed oil meal and wheat bran can be added to the daily ration in an amount required to supply the additional protein for mares of a given weight; or, a higher proportion of the hay ration can be made up of leafy legume hay.

The protein requirements of lactating mares are nearly double their requirements during the last quarter of pregnancy. This requirement is met by using some high quality legume hay in the ration along with the protein in the cereal needed to meet the total energy requirements. Some supplemental protein is also provided through the use of high protein supplemental feeds, usually of plant origin, and wheat bran. Foals, during early life, will obtain the needed protein from the mare's milk. As the colts grow, they continue to demand additional amounts of protein to support good growth, but these needs are easily met by the use of high quality hays, usually grass–legume mixtures, some grain, and whatever amount of protein supplement may be required to fulfill the total need at a particular stage of development.

Minerals. Minerals serve structural and regulatory functions in the horse as they do in other animals. Unfortunately, extensive research has not been conducted on the horse's requirements for certain minerals required by other animals, nor is good information available on some of the possible deficiency symptoms. Calcium, phosphorus, and salt are known to be required, and, although they can be easily supplied, they are too often lacking in the rations of some horses.

The calcium and phosphorus needs of horses at rest do not differ appreciably from those of horses at work. These needs can usually be met by the amounts of these elements contained in good quality hays produced on good soils and from the cereals used to meet the energy needs of horses in a particular category. Horses at work often sweat profusely and lose a large quantity of salt in this manner. However, this salt can easily be replaced by offering salt (either in block or granular form) free-choice at all times. If granular salt is used it should be offered in a salt box protected from the weather. The salt requirements of brood mares and of foals are also easily met by offering salt free-choice.

Brood mares require more calcium and phosphorus (particularly during lactation) than do other horses. Although part of the mare's requirement is met by the ingredients of the total ration, particularly phosphorus, if such feeds as linseed oil meal and wheat bran are used to meet a part of the protein need, it is wise to offer the mares access to a mineral mixture. A mixture of two parts of steamed bone meal or dicalcium phosphate and one part of stabilized iodized salt (0.01% potassium iodide) will be consumed as needed by the mares if it is offered in a compartment of the salt-mineral box. Foals and growing colts have relatively higher needs for calcium and phosphorus than do mature horses. As with brood mares, the amounts of calcium and phosphorus not supplied in the basic components of the ration can easily be met by providing a simple mineral mixture in the salt-mineral box.

In the brood mare, a lack of iodine does not manifest itself as an obvious deficiency. However, offspring from mares fed iodine deficient rations may be born dead or, if alive, may be so weak that they are unable to stand and nurse. Crops produced in many areas of the United States are deficient in iodine, making it of paramount importance that this mineral be supplied. The easiest and simplest way to provide it is through the use of stabilized salt, which provides several times the amount of iodine needed by pregnant mares, if the salt contains potassium iodide at the level indicated above.

Vitamins. Horses no doubt require the B-vitamins, just as do other animals, inasmuch as these vitamins are required for a wide variety of reactions involved in intermediary metabolism within the animal body. Deficiency symptoms have not been described for horses fed "normal" rations that provide adequate energy, protein, and minerals. It appears that the needs for these nutrients are met by the B-vitamins supplied in the basic feedstuffs and in part by the vitamins being synthesized in the caecum. Likewise, the horse's requirements for the fat soluble vitamins E and K appear to be met by the basic feeds and by the vitamin K synthesized in the intestine.

A deficiency of vitamin A results in deficiency conditions such as night blindness, other abnormalities of the eye, and reproductive failure. Vitamin A is derived from its precursor, carotene, by horses fed good quality roughages. There is little likelihood of a deficiency of vitamin A if horses are fed either good quality green hay produced within the year or green silages, or if they are pastured on succulent pasture. Crystalline vitamin A concentrates can be used to correct obvious deficiencies in the ration. Cod liver oil, which is also a potent source of vitamin A as well as of vitamin D, can be used for this purpose.

Vitamin D deficiency is not likely to be a problem in horses, since most horses are exposed to sunshine during a part of the day. The deficiency is most likely to occur in foals that are confined, in which case it will appear as rickets. Rickets—a disease of young, rapidly growing animals—is due to a lack of vitamin D, and possibly to a lack of calcium and phosphorus as well. This deficiency prevents the bones from ossifying properly; the cartilaginous areas of the bones are enlarged and weakened, resulting in crooked limbs. Horses that are fed sun-cured forage will obtain adequate vitamin D, as will horses exposed to sunshine while working or on pasture. If animals are to be confined in order that they can be developed rapidly, supplemental vitamin D can easily be supplied by adding irradiated yeast or cod liver oil (or some other vitamin D supplement) to the ration to supply 300 International Units (I.U.) of the vitamin daily per 100 lb. of body weight.

REFERENCES AND SELECTED READINGS

References marked with an asterisk are of general interest.

*Becker, D. E., 1959. Balancing swine rations. College of Agriculture Cir. 811. University of Illinois.

*Hanson, L. E., 1958. Fifty years of progress in swine nutrition. *J. Animal Sci.,* 17:1029.

National Research Council (NRC). Natl. Acad. of Sci., 1949. Recommended nutrient allowances for domestic animals, No. VI. Recommended nutrient allowances for horses.

*————, 1959. Nutrient requirements of domestic animals. Nutrient requirements of swine. Publication 648.

*————, 1959. Joint United States–Canadian Tables of feed composition. Publication 659.

*Squibb, R. L., 1958. Fifty years of research in America on the nutrition of the horse. *J. Animal Sci.,* 17:1007.

Chapter 29

Meeting Nutrient Requirements for Ruminants

The specific food of animals again should be observed, as well as that which cannot be used.

FRANCIS BACON, *"Advancement in Learning"*

29-1. THE RUMINANT ANIMAL

The ruminant animal is represented by cud-chewing, four-footed mammals, such as cattle, sheep, goats, deer, elk, antelope, giraffes, and camels. Ruminants have a four-compartment stomach consisting of (1) the rumen, (2) the reticulum, (3) omasum and (4) abomasum or true stomach (Fig. 25-3). The rumen is the largest of the four stomachs and functions as a fermentation vat to break down roughage feeds into a form that can be digested by the animal. Billions of bacteria and protozoa live in the rumen (about 250 billion per teaspoon of rumen contents) that are capable of (1) converting tough, fibrous material (cellulose, hemicellulose) into digestible products, (2) synthesizing all the B-complex vitamins and vitamin K, (3) converting nonprotein nitrogen such as urea into bacterial protein, and (4) manufacturing certain unidentified factors essential for growth, fattening, and reproduction. The large capacity of the ruminant digestive tract, coupled with the presence of a large microbial population, makes beef cattle, dairy cattle, and sheep well adapted to utilizing roughages such as hay, pasture, and silage,

479

TABLE 29-1. *Capacity in per cent relative to total of digestive systems of different types of animals. [From Crampton, E. W. and L. E. Lloyd, 1959. Fundamentals of Nutrition. Freeman, San Francisco.]*

System	Ox	Sheep	Horse	Pig	Man
Gastric					
Rumen	53	53			
Reticulum	2	5			
Omasum	5	2			
Abomasum (stomach)	6	7	9	30	17
Total gastric	66	68	9	30	17
Small intestine	20	20	30	33	66
Caecum	2	2	16	4	
Large intestine	11	10	45	33	17
Total	100	100	100	100	100

as well as grains and grain by-products. Some roughage or fiber is essential for normal rumination and biosynthesis. In contrast, single-stomached animals, such as swine, rats, and mink, are not well adapted to digesting fibrous feedstuffs. In the horse, as well as in other nonruminant herbivora, such as the rabbit and the guinea pig, the caecum and/or colon, which is greatly enlarged, serves as the principal site for the bacterial breakdown of roughage. The relative capacity of the various segments of the alimentary tract of some farm animals and of man is given in Table 29-1 (Crampton, 1959). The data in Table 29-2 clearly illustrate the difference in ability of certain animals to digest crude fiber.

TABLE 29-2. *Crude fiber digestion of alfalfa hay. [From Ruminant Nutrition and Physiology. AGRA Data, Vol. 3, No. 4. Chas. Pfizer & Co., Terre Haute, Indiana.]*

Animal	Percent digestion
Cattle	44
Sheep	45
Horse	39
Elephant	34
Swine	22

29-2. WATER

Water is the most important single nutrient required by animal life. Because water is relatively plentiful and inexpensive, it is seldom considered with the nutrients.

Chemically, pure water is H_2O; but drinking water for livestock contains

TABLE 29-3. | *Water content of cattle at various ages.*

Stage of development	% water
Embryo	95
At birth	75–80
At 5 months	66–72
Maturity	50–60
Very fat	50 or less

varying amounts of mineral elements. In some areas, water also carries toxic elements such as fluorine; in other areas, it contains too much salt (alkaline water). Minerals supplied by water should be recognized in formulating rations for livestock.

Basic research has shown that a mammal can survive after having lost most of its glycogen and fat and 40% of its protein, whereas the loss of 10% of its water causes serious disorders, and the loss of 20% causes death. Water makes up about 50–75% of the body weight and decreases in amount with age (Table 29-3). Aging has often been referred to as a dehydrating process. During the early postnatal growing phase the tissues contain 75% water. The percentage decreases as the animal matures and lays down fat.

All metabolic functions of the body are dependent on water. Some important characteristics and functions of water are: (1) ideal solvent to facilitate chemical reactions, (2) high specific heat (ability to dissipate heat), (3) good transporting medium for nutrients, secretions, and excretions, (4) lubricant for joints, and (5) cushion for nerves.

Preferably, water should be supplied continuously to ruminants on an *ad libitum* basis, but sometimes this is impractical on the range. During the winter, water should be heated to prevent freezing. Frozen, slushy ice-water will decrease intake and depress growth, fattening, and milk production. Heating water above the freezing point is of no advantage.

In general, ruminants require about 4 lb. of water for each pound of dry feed consumed. Milk secretion increases an animal's water requirement and this requirement is directly related to the amount of milk produced. An excellent review of the water requirements of livestock has been prepared by Leitch and Thomson (1944).

The approximate daily water consumption by farm animals is as follows:

Type of livestock	Gallons per day
Dairy Cow	20
Beef Cow	10
Hog (100 lb.)	2
100 Chickens	4
100 Turkeys	7
Sheep	2

29-3. CARBOHYDRATES

Carbohydrates as a livestock feed are divided into two categories: (1) starches and sugars, which are highly digestible and which furnish the major source of the more readily available energy for fattening cattle and sheep and for milk production; and (2) crude fiber (cellulose, hemicellulose, and lignin), the less digestible portion of feeds. In feed analysis, the soluble fractions (starches and sugars) are referred to as nitrogen-free extract (NFE); crude fiber is that part which is insoluble in dilute acids and alkali. Technically, lignin is not a carbohydrate, but it usually occurs in the crude-fiber fraction. It is nondigestible and is unaffected by bacterial action in the rumen. Feeds high in lignin have a low feed value partly because lignin depresses digestibility of the cellulose present. Wood and the more woody parts of plants are rich in lignin.

Corn, barley, wheat, sorghum grains, molasses, and oats and their by-products are important sources of digestible starches or sugars. However, it should be pointed out that in range areas, beef cattle and sheep are raised essentially on native pastures and on hay high in cellulose. Recommendations on the specific energy requirements and other nutrients for all classes of beef cattle, dairy cattle and sheep have been formulated (National Research Council, 1956, 1958, 1958).

29-4. CRUDE FIBER—ROUGHAGE

Ruminants are adapted to living essentially on roughages combined with a few minerals, water, and other nutrients to balance the diet. A large majority of range cattle and sheep follow this nutritional pattern; wild animals such as elk, deer, and moose live entirely on native forage and browse. Roughages are essential for proper functioning of the rumen and for biosynthesis of nutrients by microorganisms. However, Mead and Regan (1931) and, more recently, Matrone *et al.* (1959) discovered that bulk or roughage is not absolutely essential in the diet of ruminants. Although this finding is scientifically correct, it is of little practical value at the present time. Simultaneously, Geurin *et al.* (1960) discovered that steers or heifers can be fattened on a ration consisting of 9 parts barley and 1 part protein supplement, without any roughage other than the fiber furnished by the barley. The "key" to low-fiber diets is a well balanced supplement. Also, it has been observed that the roughage requirement of steers can be satisfied by oats but not by corn or sorghum grain. According to the NRC report on beef (1958), the minimum requirement for roughage under the usual feeding conditions is 0.5–0.8 lb. for each 100 lb. liveweight of fattening cattle. Cattle receiving inadequate roughages are frequently subject to bloat, going off feed, scours, and various digestive disturbances.

Roughages, especially high-quality legumes, are extremely important in dairy cattle rations for the most efficient milk production. Usually dairy cattle receive 66–75% of their daily dry-feed intake from hay, silage, or pasture. Good milk yields are often produced on roughages alone, without grain feeding. Several experiments (Martin *et al.*, 1954; Stoddard *et al.*, 1949; Tyznik and Allen, 1951; Van Soest *et al.*, 1954) have proved that cows fed on a limited roughage intake that is high in concentrates tend to decline in milk and fat secretion. Bulky and high-fiber feeds, such as oats, brewers dried grains, beet pulp, and citrus pulp, are not satisfactory replacements for roughage in the diet (Becker *et al.*, 1955). Roughages for dairy cattle should not be finely ground. Powell (1939) found that feeding cows finely ground hay as the only roughage caused a significant decrease in the fat content of milk.

Sheep require higher quality roughage in their diet for maximum gains and reproductive efficiency than either beef cattle or dairy cattle. Pregnant ewes will not develop strong, healthy lambs on poor quality roughages unless they are properly supplemented. Fattening lambs are very sensitive to the ratio of concentrates to roughage in the ration. Several experiments (Bell *et al.*, 1956; Dayton *et al.*, 1957) have indicated that the ideal ratios of concentrates to roughage for fattening lambs range from forty-sixty to fifty-fifty. Lowering the roughage or fiber in the ration to a low level results in digestive disorders, enterotoxemia (overeating disease), poor gains and poor feed conversion. Roughages should either be fed whole, chopped, or pelleted to sheep; finely ground roughages cause digestive disturbances.

Pelleting Feeds. Research reports from several experiment stations have shown that the pelleting of poor grade hays and other roughages will increase consumption by ruminants, improve daily gain, and increase feed efficiency. Tests at the Illinois Agricultural Experiment Station (Webb *et al.*, 1957) have shown that beef calves gain 1.73 lb. daily on a pelleted hay, whereas they gain only 0.63 lb. on the same hay baled or chopped. Two hundred and twenty pounds of beef were made from a ton of pelleted hay and 115 pounds of beef from a ton of the same hay baled. Pelleting high-energy diets has not improved the daily gain of cattle, but, in some instances, it has increased the feed efficiency about 14%. A test performed at Purdue University (Perry *et al.*, 1958) has shown that pelleting a diet containing 70% corn cobs and 30% concentrate increased the daily gain from 1.57 to 1.98 pounds, and the steers on the pelleted rations required 14% less feed per unit of gain. Similar diets containing only 20–45% corn cobs showed no improvement in daily gain or feed efficiency.

There is a great interest in pelleting all types of roughages used in the U.S.A., such as sorghum or corn silages. Cattle will usually eat pelleted feed much faster than meal. Also, it permits the simultaneous feeding of nutrients in a condensed form.

According to a review made by Loosli (1959) on pelleted feeds for ruminants, "the use of wafered or pelleted forage for lactating cows has not increased feed intake or milk yields. When the hay has been finely ground before pelleting, the fat content of the milk is lowered and digestibility is depressed. The use of pelleted concentrates for dairy cows is increasing, and this trend will probably continue."

Although the fundamental reason is not known, it appears that diets high in fiber are more adapted to pelleting than those high in energy. Condensing a bulky feed like hay allows the animal to consume more, permitting a larger intake of nutrients above maintenance requirements.

29-5. FAT

Fat, an essential nutrient for life, is based on the presence of certain essential unsaturated fatty acids, namely, linoleic, linolenic, and arachidonic. Even though the essential nature of these unsaturated fatty acids has been shown in monogastric animals, fat-deficiency disease rarely occurs in farm animals. Thus, fats serve essentially as a source of energy for ruminants. Feed grains contain 3–5% fat (ether extract) and forages about 2.5%.

Fats are not extensively used as an addition to ruminant rations because energy from cereal grains is usually cheaper than from fat. They are frequently used in small quantities to reduce dustiness in milled rations for fattening beef cattle. No minimum requirements for fat have been established for beef cattle or for sheep.

Cornell workers (Lucas *et al.,* 1943) reduced the fat content of a dairy cattle grain ration to 0.66% by extraction, compensating for the energy lost by adding starch, and observed a significant drop in milk production. After extensive research, these workers concluded that a grain mixture for dairy cattle should contain a minimum of 4% fat (ether extract). Most dairy cattle rations will contain this amount of fat. Supplementing lactation diets with different types of fats does not increase either milk flow or milk fat content.

29-6. PROTEIN

If conditions are such that energy intake is adequate, protein ranks first as the most limiting factor in practical ruminant rations. Adequate protein is supplied only by green pasture, by abundant legume forages, by grass hays cut at an early stage of maturity. All of the grains and nonlegume roughages, when mature, are deficient in protein and must be supplemented in order to meet the daily requirement of cattle and sheep.

Crude protein (nitrogen × 6.25) is usually a good measure of the nutritional value of protein for ruminants, if the nitrogen content of the feed is composed of not more than one-third of the protein equivalent from nonprotein nitrogen and the remainder consists of true protein. The microorganisms in the rumen are capable of synthesizing part of their protein requirement from such nonprotein nitrogen compounds as asparagine, urea, and ammonium salts. Loosli *et al.* (1949) have shown that lambs on near-protein-free, purified diets can synthesize from urea all 10 of the amino acids that are essential for swine. Analysis of the rumen samples revealed that the concentration of the various amino acids was 9–20 times greater than in the feed. Therefore, protein quality, or the balance of essential amino acids, has not been an important consideration in selecting protein supplements for ruminants. However, research done at Purdue (Perry *et al.*, 1960; Beeson *et al.*, 1960) has indicated that for fattening beef cattle, a daily feeding of 10 g of lysine per steer will improve a ration supplemented with a high level of urea. Apparently the amino acid lysine is one of the limiting nutritional factors in the utilization of large amounts of urea by cattle.

Many experiments have clearly shown that protein quality is of no practical value in balancing rations for beef cattle, dairy cattle, and sheep after the rumen develops. Prior to rumen development, the young calf and lamb are nonruminants and thus require high-quality proteins containing essential amino acids, which are usually supplied by the mother's milk or some equivalent substitute. Cottonseed, linseed, and soybean oil meals or meat and fish by-products can be used as part of the supplementary protein for ruminants with good results; but ordinarily the cost per unit of protein contained in the latter is too high as compared to the plant protein supplements.

According to NRC (1958) recommendations, the total protein requirements for beef cattle range from about 7.5% for mature, nonlactating cows to 10% for weaning calves. Obviously, the protein requirement is relatively low compared with other species of animals. For specific requirements, refer to the N.R.C. bulletin "Nutrient Requirements for Beef Cattle."

The protein requirements for dairy cattle are dependent on three major factors: (1) weight of cow, (2) amount of milk produced and, (3) stage of pregnancy. On a practical basis, protein for dairy cattle is supplied in the grain mixture that is fed along with the farm grown roughages. The percent protein in the grain mixture is adjusted according to the amount of protein contained in the roughages, ranging from 13% protein for legume roughages to 18% protein for nonlegume roughages.

Sheep are not sensitive to protein quality; therefore, either cottonseed, linseed or soybean meal can be used as a protein supplement. Young lambs prior to the development of the rumen need high quality milk proteins. The percent protein required is essentially the same as for beef cattle.

29-7. UREA AS A SOURCE OF PROTEIN

The use of urea to meet part of the protein requirements of ruminants—beef cattle, dairy cattle, and sheep—is increasing and will continue to expand as we learn more about the nutrients required for microbial synthesis of protein from urea. In 1959, over 75,000 tons of urea were used in ruminant rations, whereas, in 1957, only 64,000 tons were used—a 15% increase in a short span of two years.

The limiting factors in the use of urea are not the supply or the cost but the lack of basic knowledge on the nature of protein synthesis by microbial life in the rumen and on the nutrients required—both qualitative and quantitative—for maximum production. We must find the answers to the simple question "Does a ruminant have the potential to synthesize more than one-third of the protein needs from urea?" When we unlock the secrets of protein synthesis in the rumen, a majority of the supplementary protein (50–75%) can be furnished by urea (Beeson *et al.*, 1960).

What Is Urea? How Does It Function? Urea is a simple, nonprotein organic compound that contains, as a commercial preparation, 42% nitrogen and is potentially equivalent to a 262% protein feed. However, urea alone has no protein value for livestock. Bacterial protein of good quality is formed in the rumen by bacterial synthesis and is subsequently digested by enzymes in the stomachs and intestines of the host ruminant. Urea has no practical function in monogastric animals.

Safe Levels of Urea to Use. When fed at the proper daily level to cattle, urea is an excellent substitute for crude protein; but when fed at excessive levels, it is toxic. For maximum performance, the daily intake of urea for beef cattle should not exceed 0.2 lb. per head or not more than one-third of the protein requirement. The daily intake—not the percentage—is the "key" to the formulation of urea feeds. For example, you can feed up to 4 lb. daily of a supplement containing 5% urea but not more than 2.0 pounds of a supplement containing 10% urea. Therefore, it is difficult to set down "iron clad" rules for urea formulation on a percent basis.

According to Reid (1953), research with dairy cows has shown that, from the standpoint of milk yield and maintenance of body weight, there is no significant difference between the value of urea nitrogen (fed at levels up to 27% of the required nitrogen) and the nitrogen from natural protein supplements. Urea may safely compose up to 3% of the concentrate ration or up to 1% of the total diet for milking cows.

Urea and other forms of nonprotein nitrogen can be used to replace one-fourth to one-third of the protein in a sheep ration. Fattening lambs are rather sensitive to the taste and quality of feeds and tend to go off feed more often when urea is fed. Growing lambs and mature sheep seem to be better adapted to the utilization of urea.

29-8. VITAMINS

Ruminants are especially designed to synthesize most of their vitamin requirements by the microflora in the rumen. After the rumen develops, the only dietary vitamins required are the fat soluble vitamins A, D and E; the B-complex vitamins and vitamin K are produced in adequate amounts by biosynthesis.

Vitamin A. Carotene, or provitamin A, furnishes the major source of vitamin A for ruminant animals. Vitamin A, as such, does not occur in plant life—only carotene. Carotene is abundant in green feeds such as de-hydrated alfalfa meal, high quality legume hays, and green pasture. Caro-tene is unstable and easily destroyed by the oxidation and heat encoun-tered during the usual storing and curing of feeds.

Carotene must be converted into vitamin A before it can be utilized by the animal. Neumann *et al.* (1960) recently observed that beef cattle may develop symptoms of vitamin A deficiency in the feed lot, even when a supposedly adequate amount of carotene is supplied by the natural feeds (Fig. 29-1). The theory has been suggested that an excess amount of nitrates and nitrites in grains and forages (due to heavy nitrogen fertilization) in-terferes with the conversion of carotene to vitamin A in the body of farm animals. If this is true, then we must reassess the carotene–vitamin A con-version in ruminants and rely more on synthetic vitamin A to meet the requirements where crops containing high amounts of nitrates and nitrites are produced. This same phenomena may not apply to livestock in range areas that are not heavily fertilized with nitrogen.

There is some disagreement in the literature on the relatively biological activity of carotene and vitamin A. The majority of data indicates that the carotene requirement (on an International Unit basis) is four times that of vitamin A. If carotene is expressed on a weight basis, 1 mg of carotene is roughly equivalent to 400 I.U. of vitamin A. For further information on each species, refer to the N.R.C. publications on Beef Cattle (1958), Dairy Cattle (1958), and Sheep (1957).

The daily vitamin A needs of ruminants are dependent on: (1) the age of the animal, (2) the life-cycle phase, that is, growth, fattening, or repro-duction, (3) the stability of carotene or vitamin A in feeds, and (4) the factors that influence metabolic conversion of carotene to vitamin A, such as raw soybeans, nitrates, nitrites, and others.

In general, the carotene requirements of beef cattle, as recommended by the NRC (1958), range from about 1.5 mg per 100 lb. body weight for growth and fattening to about 10 mg per 100 lb. body weight for lactating cattle.

Research done at Purdue (Beeson *et al.*, 1960) has indicated that yearling steers on a self-fed fattening ration of 8 parts ground ear corn and 1 part of soybean meal require 16,000 to 32,000 I.U. of synthetic, stabilized vita-min A per steer daily, in addition to the 25 mg of carotene furnished by the yellow corn (Fig. 29-1). Eventually, synthetic vitamin A may assume a new role in ruminant nutrition.

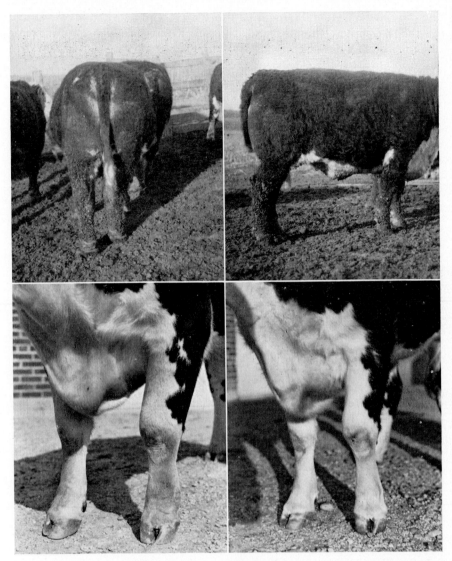

Fig. 29-1. Swelling (generalized edema or anasarca) often develops in cattle suffering from vitamin A deficiency. Deficiency under feedlot conditions has caused considerable loss to cattle feeders and slaughterers. In the top picture of feedlot cattle note swollen legs, dry hair coat, and edema in the abdominal region. The lower left picture shows anasarca in an experimental case; the lower right shows the disappearance of swelling following vitamin A therapy. [Photos by L. L. Madsen, Bureau of Animal Industry.]

Dairy cattle vary somewhat in their ability to convert carotene to vitamin A, depending on the breed. Guernseys are poor converters of carotene as compared to Holsteins and Brown Swiss. Logically, this would accent the need for supplementing vitamin A in the rations fed to Guernsey cows and their newborn calves. On an average, the carotene and vitamin A requirements of dairy cattle are 4 mg of carotene or 1600 I.U. vitamin A daily per 100 lb. of body weight for growth of dairy heifers, maintenance of mature cows, and maintenance of breeding bulls (NRC, 1958). However, during the last 3 months of pregnancy it is necessary to add to the maintenance requirement of cows 30 mg. of carotene or 12,000 I.U. of vitamin A per head daily, regardless of weight.

Vitamin D. In most areas of the world, sun-cured roughages or direct exposure to the ultraviolet rays of the sun will supply sufficient vitamin D for ruminants. Certain atmospheric conditions filter out the ultraviolet rays from the sunlight, namely, (1) clouds, (2) dust, (3) smoke, and (4) fog and haze. Window glass (unless made permeable to ultraviolet rays) and dark-pigmented skin and hair also have this effect. Under the above conditions, or when animals are confined indoors away from direct sunlight, a dietary source of vitamin D is essential.

Beef cattle and dairy cattle require about 300 I.U. of vitamin D per 100 lb. of body weight daily, according to research on calves. Little is known about the actual vitamin D requirement for beef cattle beyond the weaning stage of life. This is a fertile field for research. In most areas where beef cattle are raised and fattened for market, sufficient vitamin D is supplied by the sun's rays or by sun-cured forages. There is no vitamin D activity in growing plants, such as pasture. A majority of the vitamin D is produced after the plant is harvested and exposed to the sunlight.

Wallis (1938, 1944) has indicated that vitamin D is essential for maintenance, reproduction, and lactation of the mature dairy cow. Susceptibility to milk fever can be reduced by feeding massive doses of vitamin D (30,-000,000 I.U. daily) to the cow 3 to 7 days prior to calving and 1 day after parturition (Hibbs and Pounden, 1955). (See Chapter 32 for further details.) The same result may be obtained by feeding a ration low in calcium and high in phosphorus for about 3 weeks prepartum, in which instance the parathyroid gland is stimulated to maintain normal blood calcium levels (Boda and Cole, 1954). When young calves are confined to barns without direct sunlight, the ration should be fortified with 200 I.U. of vitamin D per pound of diet (Fig. 29-2).

Suckling lambs receive enough vitamin D from their mother to prevent rickets (vitamin D deficiency) for four to six weeks. Also, lambs are usually in the sunlight. In New Zealand, Andrews and Cunningham (1945) found that 180 I.U. of vitamin D per 100 lb. of body weight daily was not adequate for sheep. The N.R.C. Subcommittee on Sheep Nutrition (1957) has

Fig. 29-2. This calf developed severe rickets while receiving a ration deficient in vitamin D, and without sunlight. [Huffman et al., Michigan Agricultural Experimental Station.]

set the vitamin D requirement of sheep at 250 I.U. per 100 lb. of body weight daily. Under most conditions, sun-cured hays and/or sunlight will supply adequate vitamin D for sheep. However, it should be re-emphasized that artificially dehydrated hays, green pasture, grains, grain by-products, and soybean meal are poor sources of vitamin D. The most potent natural source of vitamin D_2 is irradiated yeast.

Vitamin E. Vitamin E (alpha tocopherol) has been known as the antisterility vitamin and is required for normal reproduction in both the male and female in some species. Except for dairy cattle, the vitamin E quantitative requirement for ruminants has not been clearly determined.

It has been tentatively estimated that both beef and dairy calves require about 40 mg of alpha tocopherol (vitamin E) per 100 lb. body weight per day. Vitamin E deficiency occurs most frequently in young calves and is characterized by muscular dystrophy or white muscle disease. However, under most conditions, natural feedstuffs contain adequate amounts of vitamin E to prevent a deficiency without supplementation. A summary of the literature (Harris, 1949) on vitamin E indicates that adult dairy cows and bulls receive sufficient amounts from natural feedstuffs.

Young nursing lambs are very susceptible to vitamin E deficiency if the ewe does not receive adequate amounts during pregnancy and lactation.

Deficiency of vitamin E in young lambs is manifested by stiffness, which is usually followed by death. This has been referred to as stiff lamb disease, white muscle disease, or muscular dystrophy. Willman *et al.* (1945) showed that stiff lamb disease can be cured by treating the lamb with 500 mg of alpha tocopherol acetate orally or by injecting 300 mg of alpha tocopherol. After the initial treatment, the dosage should be reduced to 100 mg orally or to a 60-mg injection of alpha tocopherol every other day until the lambs recover. The minimum vitamin E requirement for sheep is not known. According to Willman *et al.* (1945), a vitamin E deficiency in lambs can be prevented by feeding either wheat bran or wheat germ meal to the ewes.

Vitamin B Complex; Vitamins C and K. Members of the water soluble vitamin-B complex—namely, thiamine, riboflavin, niacin, pantothenic acid, pyridoxine (B_6), folic acid, biotin and vitamin B_{12}, and also vitamins C (ascorbic acid) and K—are synthesized by microorganisms in the paunch or intestinal tract in adequate amounts for normal growth, fattening, and reproduction of ruminants. Prior to rumen development (during the first 8 weeks of life), the young calf has a dietary requirement for the B-vitamins and vitamin K; however, these vitamins are usually adequately supplied by the colostrum, cow's milk, or milk substitutes, which are fortified with all the vitamins. A deficiency of B-vitamins may occur if the synthesizing power of the rumen is upset by some disease or acute nutritional deficiency. Vitamin K may become critical if cattle are fed on spoiled sweet clover hay. Sweet clover is high in dicumarol, which counteracts the function of vitamin K and results in a "hemorrhage disease." However, feeding vitamin K will overcome the effect of dicumarol. Dietary vitamin C is required only by man, monkey, and guinea pig.

29-9. MINERAL ELEMENTS

Thirteen mineral elements are recognized as being essential for maintenance, growth, fattening, and reproduction in ruminant animals. Inorganic elements are not only essential for metabolic functions of animal tissues but also for biosynthesis of nutrients by the billions of microorganisms living in the rumen.

The essential mineral elements are classified as follows:

Major or macro elements	*Trace or micro elements*
Calcium	Iron
Phosphorus	Copper
Sodium	Manganese
Chlorine	Iodine
Magnesium	Cobalt
Potassium	Zinc
Sulfur	

According to Underwood (1957), an Australian authority on mineral metabolism, the trace elements listed below should be classified as "probably essential trace elements."

Barium	Molybdenum
Bromine	Selenium
Fluorine	Strontium

At present, there is not sufficient evidence to put these elements in the essential category, but more refined research may classify these as well as many of the other elements as essential.

In specific areas of the world, certain toxic elements are concentrated in the soil, rock deposits, feed, and/or water, resulting in chronic or acute toxicity in ruminants. The most common toxic minerals are fluorine, molybdenum, and selenium. Note that some elements are toxic in excessive amounts, although they may be essential in limited amounts. Lead and arsenic are also toxic, but are not ordinarily a natural hazard. However, livestock have suffered or died from lead poisoning by eating fences or fence posts painted with lead-base paints.

Other nonessential elements that occur in the ruminant body in measurable amounts are aluminum, arsenic, boron, lead, nickel, rubidium, and silicon.

Calcium and Phosphorus. Calcium and phosphorus have a close interrelationship in animal metabolism and need to be present in the ration at a ratio varying from 1:1 to 2:1. Wider ratios can be tolerated; but under this regime, each element is utilized less efficiently and may result in a deficiency. A narrow calcium-phosphorus ratio is essential for normal calcification of bone, for reproduction, and for lactation.

In general, grains, grain by-products, and plant protein concentrates are low in calcium and are relatively good sources of phosphorus, whereas roughages are fair to good sources of calcium and are low or deficient in phosphorus. Many rations for ruminants are deficient in either calcium or

TABLE 29-4. *Calcium and Phosphorus Supplements.*

	Calcium		Phosphorus	
Mineral Supplement	(%)	(g/lb.)	(%)	(g/lb.)
Bonemeal, steamed	30.0	136	13.9	63
Defluorinated phosphate	21.0	95	9.0	41
Dicalcium phosphate	26.5	120	20.5	93
Monosodium phosphate			22.4	102
Limestone	38.3	174		

phosphorus or both. A few mineral supplements that can be used to fortify rations with calcium and/or phosphorus are given in Table 29-4.

The greatest demand for calcium and phosphorus is during early growth and lactation. This is exemplified in the calcium and phosphorus requirements for dairy cattle, as recommended by N.R.C. (1956), expressed as a percent of the total air-dry ration.

Stage of life cycle	Calcium (%)	Phosphorus (%)
Maintenance of mature cows	0.12	0.12
Lactating cows	0.30	0.25
Maintenance of breeding bulls		
1600 lb. weight	0.13	0.13
Normal growth of dairy heifers		
100 lb. weight	0.77	0.66
600 lb. weight	0.19	0.22

Beef cattle and sheep requirements for calcium and phosphorus vary with age, weight, growth rate, and stage of pregnancy and lactation. Most of the phosphorus deficiency in beef cattle and sheep occurs either under natural range conditions, when these animals are wintered on poor quality roughages, or when they are fed on high amounts of molasses and beet pulp (Fig. 29-3).

Even though there is some variation in requirements, if all beef and sheep rations were balanced to contain 0.25% calcium and 0.20% phosphorus, the requirements would be met.

It is a widespread practice to give all ruminants free access to a mineral mixture composed of 2 parts bonemeal or dicalcium phosphate and 1 part salt to take care of individual variations in the day-to-day calcium, phosphorus, and salt needs.

Sodium and Chlorine (Salt). Salt is universally deficient in all common foodstuffs used for animal feeding. Since the creation of animal life, it has been known that both domestic and wild animals have an intense craving for salt and will even walk miles or risk grave danger to satisfy this need. Salt is used to move cattle, sheep, antelope, deer, and elk on open ranges from one grazing area to another. Wild animals are often concentrated around natural salt licks. In many areas it is illegal for hunters to attract wild game by the use of salt. All ruminant rations must be fortified with salt either as a part of the diet or on a free-choice basis. There is no danger of salt poisoning in ruminants. It has been said that "without salt, food loses its savor."

Grain mixtures for dairy cattle should be fortified with 1.0% salt. Salt requirements for fattening cattle can be satisfied by adding 0.5% salt to the total ration. Even though salt is included in the grain mixture or protein supplement, cattle should always have free acecss to salt.

Fig. 29-3. Phosphorus deficiency in feedlot cattle. The steer in the upper picture was fed a ration consisting of wet beet pulp, alfalfa hay, and beet molasses containing 0.12% phosphorus. The steer shown in the lower picture received the same ration plus one-tenth pound daily of steamed bone meal, which brought the phosphorus content up to 0.18% and provided an average total intake of 17.0 g of phosphorus daily. [Idaho Agricultural Experimental Station. Photo by W. M. Beeson.]

Sheep consume more salt in relation to body weight than cattle. In dry lot tests, fattening lambs consumed about 0.3 oz per head daily, and on wheat pasture, 1 oz daily. Under western range conditions, sheep will consume from 0.5–0.75 lb. of salt per head per month.

Magnesium. Very little is known about the magnesium requirement of ruminant animals. Huffman *et al.* (1941) showed that 13.6–18.2 mg of magnesium per pound of body weight was required daily for calves on a whole milk diet. Breirem *et al.* (1949) found that cows receiving 20 to 25 g of magnesium per day had normal serum magnesium levels (2.2–2.4%), whereas cows ingesting only 10 g daily showed symptoms of magnesium deficiency. Magnesium requirements have not been determined for sheep. Since farm-grown feedstuffs and range forages contain 0.1–0.5% magnesium, there is very little danger of a deficiency unless some element or substance interferes with its utilization.

Although "grass tetany" has been associated with low magnesium blood values, it is not due to a magnesium deficiency in the diet, because the magnesium intake is normal (Bartlett *et al.*, 1954). Probably some inorganic or organic compound in the pasture grasses renders the magnesium unavailable.

Potassium. A minimum potassium requirement for ruminants has not been determined, nor has a deficiency been reported in animals that have been fed the usual rations. Since corn contains 0.27% potassium and roughages contain 1–2% of this element, it is not necessary to consider adding potassium to practical ruminant diets. In semipurified rations for sheep, it has been found that 1% potassium in the total diet will meet their requirement.

Sulfur. Inorganic sulfur is utilized by microorganisms in the rumen to synthesize the amino acids cystine and methionine. Block and Stekol (1950) discovered that radioactive sulfur fed orally as sodium sulfate to a lactating cow appeared in the cystine and methionine fraction of the milk proteins. The protein in most animal tissues contains approximately one part of sulfur for each 15 parts of nitrogen.

Several experiments have indicated that the sulfur requirement of ewes for wool and reproduction is about 0.08–0.1% of the total ration or 1.0–1.4 g of sulfur daily. Wool or hair requires large quantities of sulfur; its sulfur content ranges from 3.5–5.0%. There is no advantage in feeding sulfur to sheep unless the ration contains less than 0.1% sulfur. Roughages contain from 0.10–0.60% sulfur and the commonly fed grains about 0.12–0.20% sulfur.

Cobalt. Cobalt deficiency occurs frequently among ruminants in various regions of the world, owing to the low cobalt content of soils and plant life

Fig. 29-4. Cobalt deficiency. The upper picture shows a heifer suffering from anemia and lack of appetite and exhibiting the characteristic roughness of hair coat. Administration of cobalt brought about remarkable recovery of appetite and disappearance of symptoms, as shown in the lower picture. [Michigan Agricultural Experimental Station, East Lansing, Mich. Photo by C. F. Huffman.]

(Fig. 29-4). Cobalt is essential for the biosynthesis of vitamin B_{12} by rumen microorganisms and is an integral part of the vitamin B_{12} molecule.

Beef cattle require about 0.03–0.05 mg/lb. of air-dry feed. The cobalt requirement for dairy cattle has not been determined, but a cobalt deficiency for growing and milking cattle can be cured by feeding 0.3–1.0 mg of cobalt per head daily (Filmer and Underwood, 1936).

A cobalt intake of 0.1 mg daily will meet the requirement of a 120-lb. sheep.

A simple way to meet the cobalt requirement of ruminants is to give them free access to a mixture of 1 oz of cobalt sulfate or carbonate per 100 lb. of salt. As a recent development, cobalt bullets placed in the reticulum or rumen of sheep have been effective in meeting the daily rquirement under range conditions.

Iodine. Iodine deficiency in ruminants occurs in the areas of the United States adjacent to the Great Lakes and in the inland part of the Pacific Northwest region. This element is most critical during the reproductive phase of animal life and manifests itself by weakness and goiter in the newborn (Fig. 29-5). Iodine requirements of cattle have been estimated at 400–800 micrograms per head daily. A deficiency of iodine can be eliminated by using stabilized, iodized salt containing 0.01% potassium iodide (0.0076% iodine).

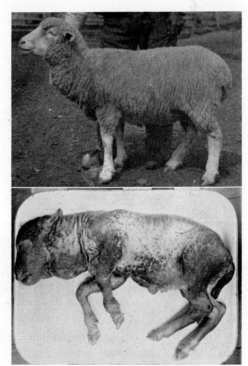

Iron. To date, no quantitative studies have been made to determine the iron requirement of ruminants. Research done at Purdue, using semi-purified diets with sheep, has indicated that the iron requirement for growing-fattening lambs can be met by 32 mg (70 ppm) of iron per pound of total ration. When ruminants are born, they have good stores of iron in the liver, which carry them over the period during which they are living on milk alone. Natural feeds con-

Fig. 29-5. Top: Ewe showing typical goiter due to iodine deficiency. Bottom: Woolless newborn lamb as a result of iodine deficiency of the ewe. [Courtesy of Montana Veterinary Research Laboratory, Bozeman, Mont.]

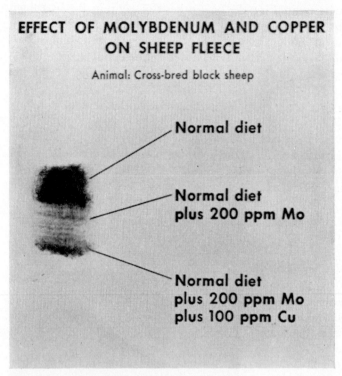

EFFECT OF MOLYBDENUM AND COPPER ON SHEEP FLEECE

Animal: Cross-bred black sheep

Normal diet

Normal diet plus 200 ppm Mo

Normal diet plus 200 ppm Mo plus 100 ppm Cu

Fig. 29-6. Effect of molybdenum and copper on wool color. [Courtesy Dr. Harold Goss, University of California at Davis.]

tain 40–400 mg of iron per pound; therefore, this should supply adequate amounts.

Copper. Under natural range conditions in Florida and Australia, copper deficiency has been identified in both cattle and sheep (Fig. 29-6). Copper deficiency occurs on range forage that contains less than 5 ppm of copper; it also occurs if an excess amount of molybdenum (20–100 ppm) is present in dry forage (Becker *et al.*, 1953). It is estimated that cattle require 1.8–2.5 milligrams of copper per pound of total air-dry feed. Pregnant ewes need about 5 mg of copper daily. In deficient areas, copper deficiency can be prevented by fortifying the salt with 0.5–1.0% copper sulfate (Marston, 1952). Excess amounts of copper are toxic.

Manganese. Bentley and Phillips (1951) reported that rations containing less than 10 ppm (4.5 mg/lb.) of manganese were inadequate for the growth of young Holstein heifers. Twenty ppm (9.0 mg/lb.) of manganese in the total air-dry feed was satisfactory for normal body functions. Although manganese is required by both beef cattle and sheep, no quantitative measurements have been made. Under feed lot and range conditions, natural feedstuffs (except corn) contain 7–50 mg of manganese per pound. Roughages are richer in manganese than are grains.

Zinc. The zinc requirements for ruminants have not been established. According to research on swine, zinc is made partially unavailable to the animal by feeding excessive levels of calcium (Luecke *et al.*, 1957; Conrad and Beeson, 1957) or by the phytic acid contained in soybean oil meal (Plumlee *et al.*, 1960). Swine require a minimum of 50 ppm (23 mg/lb.) of zinc in a ration containing soybean protein. In light of these findings, the zinc requirement and interrelationship in ruminants need to be studied. At present, we assume that ruminant feeds contain adequate amounts of zinc.

REFERENCES AND SELECTED READINGS

References marked with an asterisk are of general interest.

Andrews, E. D. and I. J. Cunningham, 1945. The vitamin D requirements of sheep. *New Zealand J. Sci. Tech.*, 27A:223–230.

Bartlett, S. B., B. Brown, A. S. Foot, S. J. Rowland, R. Allcroft and W. H. Parr, 1954. The influence of fertilizer treatment of grassland on the incidence of hypomagnesaemia in milking cows. *British Vet. J.*, 110:3.

Becker, R. B., P. T. D. Arnold, W. G. Kirk, G. K. Davis and R. W. Kidder, 1953. Minerals for dairy and beef cattle. Fla. Agr. Expt. Sta. Bull. 513.

——, P. T. D. Arnold, J. M. Wing, Jack McCall and G. K. Davis, 1955. "Subnormal milk"—its production and correction. *J. Dairy Sci.*, 38:618–619 (Abstract).

Beeson, W. M., W. H. Gossett, and T. W. Perry, 1960. Lysine, methionine and zinc bacitracin as additions to Supplement A to a 64% protein-urea supplement for fattening beef steers. Purdue Agr. Expt. Sta. Mimeo AS-278.

Bell, T. D., D. Richardson, R. F. Cox and J. W. Needham, 1956. The relationship of physical balance in the utilization of pelleted and non-pelleted rations for lambs. Forty-third Annual Livestock Feeders Day, Kansas Agr. Expt. Sta. Cir. 335.

Bentley, O. G. and P. H. Phillips, 1951. The effects of low manganese rations on dairy cattle. *J. Dairy Sci.*, 34:396.

Block, R. J., and J. A. Stekol, 1950. Synthesis of sulfur amino acids from inorganic sulfate by ruminants. *Proc. Soc. Expt. Biol. Med.*, 73:390.

Boda, J. M. and H. H. Cole, 1954. The influence of dietary calcium and phosphorus on the incidence of milk fever in dairy cattle. *J. Dairy Sci.*, 37:360–372.

Breirem, D. K., F. Ender, K. Halse and L. Slagvold, 1948. Experiments on hypomagnesemia and ketosis in dairy cows. *Acta. Agr. Suecana.*, 3:89–120.

Conrad, J. H. and W. M. Beeson, 1957. Effect of calcium level and trace minerals on the response of young pigs to unidentified growth factors. *J. Animal Sci.*, 16:589–599.

*Crampton, E. W., 1956. Applied Animal Nutrition. Freeman, San Francisco.

*—— and L. E. Lloyd, 1959. Fundamentals of Nutrition. Freeman, San Francisco.

Dayton, E. W., B. C. Breidenstein, E. E. Hatfield, H. W. Norton and U. S. Garrigus, 1957. Effect of ratio of concentrates to roughage on rate of gain and carcass quality. Illinois Sheep Day Report, University of Illinois, Urbana, Illinois.

*Dukes, H. H., 1955. *The Physiology of Domestic Animals*. Comstock Publishing Associates, Ithaca.

*Ensminger, M. E., 1960. *Beef Cattle Science*. Interstate, Danville, Illinois.

Filmer, J. F. and E. J. Underwood, 1936. Wasting disease—diagnosis, prevention and treatment. *West Australia Dept. Agr. J.*, 13:199.

Geurin, H. B., J. L. Williamson, J. C. Thompson, H. L. Wilcke and R. M. Bethke, 1960. Rolled common barley serves as both grain and roughage for fattening steers. *Feedstuffs*, 32:28.

Harris, P. L., 1949. Practical nutritional aspects of vitamin E. *Ann. N.Y. Acad. Sci.*, 52:240.

Hibbs, J. W. and W. D. Pounden, 1955. Studies on milk fever in dairy cows. IV. Prevention by short-time prepartum feeding of massive doses of vitamin D. *J. Dairy Sci.*, 38:65.

Huffman, C. F., C. L. Conley, C. C. Lightfoot and C. W. Duncan, 1941. Magnesium studies with calves. II. The effect of magnesium salts and various feeds upon the magnesium content of the blood plasma. *J. Nutrition*, 22:609.

*Kammlade, W. G., Sr., and W. G. Kammlade, Jr., 1955. *Sheep Science*. Lippincott, Chicago.

Leitch, I., and J. S. Thomson, 1944. The water economy of farm animals. *Nutr. Abstracts and Reviews*, 14:197–223.

Loosli, J. K., H. H. Williams, W. E. Thomas, F. H. Fennis and L. A. Maynard, 1949. Synthesis of amino acids in the rumen. *Science*, 110:144–145.

———, 1959. Pelleted feeds for ruminants. Proc. Distillers Feed Conf., Distillers Feed Research Council, Cincinnati, Ohio.

Lucas, H. L., J. K. Loosli, and L. A. Maynard, 1943. A study of the effect of dietary fat and fat-soluble vitamins upon milk and fat secretion. Cornell Univ. Agr. Expt. Sta. Mem. 251.

Luecke, R. W., J. A. Hoefer, W. S. Brammell and D. A. Schmidt, 1957. Calcium and zinc parakeratosis of swine. *J. Animal Sci.*, 16:3–11.

Marston, H. R., 1952. Cobalt, copper and molybdenum in the nutrition of animals and plants. *Physiol. Rev.*, 32:66.

Martin, T. G., G. E. Stoddard, and R. S. Allen, 1954. The effects of varied rates of hay feeding on body weight and production of lactating dairy cows. *J. Dairy Sci.*, 37:1233–1240.

Matrone, G., H. A. Ramsey, and G. H. Wise, 1959. Role of sodium and potassium cations in volatile fatty acid metabolism of ruminants. Proc. Cornell Nutr. Conf. for Feed Mfg., 1959. Cornell University, p. 36.

*Maynard, L. A. and J. K. Loosli, 1956. *Animal Nutrition*. McGraw-Hill, New York.

*Morrison, F. B., 1956. *Feeds and Feeding*. The Morrison Publishing Company, Ithaca.

Mead, S. W. and W. M. Regan, 1931. Deficiencies in rations devoid of roughage for calves. I. The effect of the addition of cod-liver oil and alfalfa ash. *J. Dairy Sci.*, 14:283–293.

National Research Council, 1956. *Nutrient Requirements of Dairy Cattle*. Natl. Acad. of Sci. Natl. Research Council Pub. 464.

———, 1957. *Nutrient Requirements of Sheep*. Natl. Acad. of Sci. Natl. Research Council Pub. 504.

———, 1958. *Nutrient Requirements of Beef Cattle*. Natl. Acad. of Sci. Natl. Research Council Pub. 579.

Neumann, A. L., 1960. Another Look at Vitamin A in Cattle Feeding. Proc. Illinois Nutrition Conf., University of Illinois, Urbana, Illinois.

Perry, T. W., W. D. Whitfield, and W. M. Beeson, 1958. The value of pelleted rations containing varying levels of corncobs for fattening beef steers. Purdue Agr. Expt. Sta. Mimeo. A.S. 245.

———, W. M. Beeson, and M. T. Mohler, 1960. High protein-urea supplements with and without lysine for fattening steer calves. Purdue Agr. Expt. Sta. Mimeo. A.S. 277.

Plumlee, M. P., D. R. Whitaker, J. H. Conrad, W. H. Smith, H. E. Parker, and W. M. Beeson, 1960. The effect of phytic acid and other organic factors on zinc utilization by the growing pig. *Feedstuffs,* 32:10.

Powell, E. B., 1939. Some relations of the roughage intake to the composition of milk. *J. Dairy Sci.,* 22:453–454.

Reed, J. T., 1953. Urea as a protein replacement for ruminants. A Review. *J. Dairy Sci.,* 36:955–996.

Sisson, Septimus and J. M. Grossman, 1938. The Anatomy of Domestic Animals, W. B. Saunders Company, Philadelphia.

*Snapp, R. R. and A. L. Neumann, 1960. *Beef Cattle.* Wiley, New York.

Stoddard, G. E., N. N. Allen, and W. H. Peterson, 1949. Some effects of a low roughage, high concentrate ration on the fat of cow's milk. *J. Animal Sci.,* 8:630–631 (Abstract).

Tyznick, W. and N. N. Allen, 1951. The relation of roughage intake to the fat content of the milk and the level of fatty acids in the rumen. *J. Dairy Sci.,* 34:493 (Abstract).

Underwood, E. J., 1956. *Trace Elements in Human and Animal Nutrition.* Academic, New York.

——, 1957. Trace element interrelations in animals. Proc. Cornell Nutr. Conf., Cornell University, 1957.

*United States Department of Agriculture, 1939. Food and Life. Yearbook of Agriculture. Washington, D.C.

*——, 1956. Animal Diseases. Yearbook of Agriculture. Washington, D.C.

*—— 1959. Food Yearbook of Agriculture. Washington, D.C.

Van Soest, P. J., N. N. Allen, and L. R. Maki, 1954. The effect of restricted roughage, high-concentrate diet upon milk fat, blood glucose and blood ketones. *J. Dairy Sci.,* 37:660–661 (Abstract).

*Wagnon, K. A., R. Albaugh, and G. H. Hart, 1960. *Beef Cattle Production.* MacMillan, New York.

Wallis, G. C., 1938. Some effects of vitamin D deficiency on mature dairy cows. *J. Dairy Sci.,* 21:315.

——, 1944. Vitamin D deficiency in dairy cows. S. Dakota Agr. Expt. Sta. Bull. 372.

Webb, R. J., G. F. Cmarik, and H. A. Cate, 1957. Comparison of feeding three forages as baled hay, chopped hay, hay pellets and silage to steer calves. *J. Animal Sci.,* 16:1057 (Abstract).

Willman, J. P., J. K. Loosli, S. A. Asdell, F. B. Morrison and Peter Olafson, 1945. Prevention and cure of muscular stiffness ("stiff-lamb" disease) in lambs. *J. Animal Sci.,* 4:128–132.

Chapter 30

Meeting Nutrient Requirements for Poultry

30-1. INTRODUCTION

The quantitative nutritive requirements of poultry species have been more thoroughly studied and are better established than those for any other economically important animal species. This is due primarily to the convenience with which chickens and other domestic birds can be used for laboratory research on problems of fundamental interest in nutrition and to the intense interest in solving practical problems regarding their nutrition as a basis for improving production practices. Experimental poultry nutrition has been an extremely active field for the past 30 years, and a large share of the improvements in productive efficiency is due to recently acquired knowledge of nutrition.

The value of a diet in meeting the nutritional needs of an animal—and in serving as raw material for food production in animal agriculture—is the resultant of two important properties: the concentration of indispensable nutrients the diet contains, and the amount of the diet the animal consumes. Voluntary food intake is a primary determinant of the nutritional status and productivity of an animal. This is particularly true in the feeding of poultry, because the systems of management normally used in practice involve large groups of individuals and permit free access to food and water, allowing the animal to determine the rate and pattern of food intake.

The basic information needed for formulating rations satisfactory for animal production are: (1) the quantitative nutrient requirements of the animal, (2) the distribution of these nutrients in the available feedstuffs and specialized supplements, and (3) feeding experience showing that the feedstuffs and combinations are acceptable to the animal.

30-2. TOTAL FOOD REQUIREMENTS; INPUT–OUTPUT RELATIONSHIPS

Poultry are almost always managed and fed in large flocks, without any effort to limit food intake. Among the important factors governing the rate of feed consumption are: environmental conditions, age and rate of growth in young animals, size and rate of egg production in mature layers, and the nutritive characteristics of the diet. Table 30-1 gives representative data showing the growth rates and feed requirements of various domestic poultry. The data are typical of performance under commercial conditions. There are, of course, large differences in rate of growth among the different types of poultry, but all of the data illustrate two important points. First, the male grows more rapidly and more efficiently than the female. The efficiency of growth is roughly indicated by the amount of feed required to produce a unit weight of animal at a given age. Second, the efficiency of growth progressively declines as the size and age of the animal increases. This, of course, is because the larger animal requires a larger amount of food for body maintenance and uses a progressively smaller proportion of its food intake for the synthesis of new tissue.

The commercial broiler industry is based on the use of very rapidly growing strains of meat-type chickens fed highly efficient rations. Feed input, representing about 70% of the cost of production, is typically 2.2–2.4 lb. of feed per pound of broiler produced at a market age of 8–9 weeks and at a live weight of about 3.5 lb. These production targets contrast sharply with typical performance data of less than ten years ago, when it required 10–12 weeks to produce a 3 lb. broiler on a feed requirement of 3–3.5 lb. of feed per pound of chicken.

Illustrated in Table 30-2 are typical data showing the feed requirement for egg production. This is influenced both by the rate of egg production and by the size of the bird. The maintenance requirement is a high proportion of the total food intake—about 16 lb. per 100 hens per day for 4-lb. hens, and approximately 20 lb. for 6-lb. hens. After the maintenance need is met, there is an essentially linear increase in the feed requirement as the rate of production increases, approximating 3 lb. of feed for each 20 eggs produced. Because the increased requirement for egg production is small in relation to the maintenance need, the efficiency of egg production in terms of feed consumed per dozen eggs laid improves rapidly as production

TABLE 30-1. | *Representative data illustrating growth rates and feed requirements of various domestic poultry.*

Class	Age (weeks)	Average weight (lb.)	Cumulative feed consumed (lb.)	Feed per lb. (lb.)
Broilers*				
Males	2	0.4	0.6	1.5
	4	1.2	2.0	1.7
	6	2.3	4.5	2.0
	8	3.5	7.6	2.2
	10	4.9	11.8	2.4
Females	2	0.4	0.6	1.5
	4	1.1	1.9	1.7
	6	2.0	4.0	2.0
	8	2.9	6.5	2.2
	10	4.0	10.0	2.5
Egg-strain pullets†	4	0.6	1.5	
	8	1.4	4.2	
	12	2.1	7.6	
	16	2.7	11.7	
	20	3.1	16.0	
	24	3.5	21.0	
Turkeys (Broad Breasted Bronze)				
Males	4	1.7	2.1	1.2
	8	5.1	8.8	1.7
	12	10.1	23.7	2.3
	16	15.4	41.4	2.7
	20	20.3	61.2	3.0
	24	25.1	85.0	3.4
	28	29.6	118.0	4.0
Females	4	1.4	1.8	1.3
	8	4.4	7.9	1.8
	12	7.6	18.2	2.4
	16	10.9	32.2	3.0
	20	13.6	49.0	3.6
	24	15.7	67.7	4.3
	28	17.1	88.0	5.1
Ducks (White Pekin)	2	1.1	1.7	1.6
	4	3.6	8.5	2.4
	6	5.5	15.9	2.4
	8	7.1	24.3	3.4

* Data typical of meat-strain chickens reared on a ration containing approximately 1450 kcal of metabolizable energy per pound

† These data relate to egg-strain pullets reared in confinement on a ration containing 1300–1400 kcal of metabolizable energy per pound.

TABLE 30-2. | *Daily feed requirement for egg production as related to production rate and body size.**

Production rate (%)	4-lb. hens		6-lb. hens	
	lb. feed per 100 hens	lb. feed per dozen eggs	lb. feed per 100 hens	lb. feed per dozen eggs
0	16		20	
20	18	10.8	23	13.8
40	21	6.4	26	7.8
60	24	4.8	29	5.7
80	27	4.0	32	4.7

* Average consumption based on a ration containing approximately 1350 kcal of metabolizable energy per lb.

rate increases. Because the larger hen has a larger maintenance requirement, its efficiency is poorer at any given rate of production than that of the smaller hen. Thus, any factors that improve the rate of egg production will increase the efficiency of performance; conversely, factors that limit or reduce egg production will have an adverse effect on efficiency.

30-3. ENERGY IN POULTRY NUTRITION

The nutrient most directly related to food intake and efficiency is energy. This is because energy is the primary factor controlling food intake in the animal; to state it another way, the animal eats primarily to satisfy its energy requirement and regulates food intake accordingly.

The energy values of feeding materials and diets are determined and expressed in calories, kilocalories (kcal), or megacalories (mcal), which are heat units. (See Chapter 27 for definitions.) Figure 30-1 shows a schematic representation of the path of food energy in the animal and illustrates the terms used to define the energy content of foods. The energy usable by the animal can be determined either as digestible energy, metabolizable energy, or net energy, depending on the extent of the measured energy losses (indigestible residues, urine, and the so-called cost of utilization). In birds, metabolizable energy is the simplest to determine because the fecal and urinary wastes are excreted together. Table 30-3 shows metabolizable energy values for a variety of common feedstuffs and illustrates the wide range of values that characterize available feeding materials.

Owing to the diverse nature of feedstuffs it is possible, by appropriate choice, to formulate rations of varying energy concentration (measured in kilocalories/pound or some other similar measure of concentration). Changing the energy concentration (density) of the ration markedly changes its

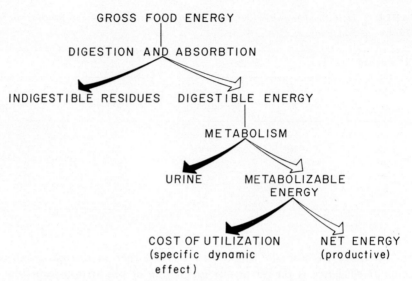

Fig. 30-1. Utilization of food energy. Nonproductive portions of gross food energy are indicated by solid arrows.

feeding characteristics, as illustrated in Table 30-4. These data, taken from several long-term experiments, show the effect of changing dietary energy level on the performance of laying hens. Note that the rate of egg production increases, though not markedly, as the energy concentration of the diet is increased. There is also a marked reduction in feed intake, both in quantity consumed and in the amount required per dozen eggs produced. However, the energy intake per hen per day, expressed in metabolizable energy kilocalories, is nearly constant over the wide range of diets used. These data show that hens regulate feed intake primarily to achieve a certain energy input, which under the conditions of these experiments (Central New York State) approximated 350 kcal per day. Under other climatic conditions, it would be expected that the level of energy intake would be different. The data in Table 30-4 show the average performance over a long period of time. Hens also adjust seasonally, to regulate energy intake according to need. The data in Table 30-5 illustrate the seasonal fluctuation in the relative food intake of laying hens showing a higher level of consumption during cold weather and a lower level of consumption during warm weather.

Similar relationships between energy concentration and food intake occur in broilers, turkeys, and other poultry reared for meat production. In these birds, there is a general tendency for growth rate to increase as the energy concentration of the ration is increased, and there is also improvement in feed efficiency (amount of feed per unit gain).

TABLE 30-3. | *Average composition of poultry feedstuffs.*

Energy, protein and minerals	Metabo-lizable energy (kcal/lb.)	Crude protein (%)	Fat (%)	Crude fiber (%)	Calcium (%)	Phos-phorus (%)
Grains						
Corn	1560	9	4	2	0	0.3
Milo	1480	10	3	2	0	0.3
Wheat	1500	10	2	2	0	0.3
Barley	1280	9	2	5	0.1	0.4
Oats	1190	9	5	11	0.1	0.3
Rye	1300	12	2	2	0.1	0.3
Grain products						
Wheat bran	500	15	4	10	0.1	1.3
Wheat standard middlings	800	16	5	8	0.2	0.9
Wheat flour middlings	1200	17	4	5	0.1	0.8
Wheat red dog flour	1300	17	2	1		0.4
Hominy feed	1300	11	6	5	0	0.5
Protein supplements						
Soybean oil meal (44%)	1020	46	1	6	0.3	0.7
Soybean oil meal (50%)	1150	51	1	3	0.3	0.6
Cottonseed meal	1000	43	2	10	0.2	1.1
Corn gluten meal	1500	43	2	4	0.2	0.4
Meat scraps (50%)	900	51	10	2	5.1	10.6
Meat scraps (55%)	900	56	10	2	4.0	8.0
Fish meal (60%)	1350	62	8	1	2.8	5.5
Vitamin supplements						
Dried whey	830	13	1	0	0.9	0.8
Dried brewers yeast	1000	45	1	3	0.1	1.4
Distillers dried solubles (corn)	1320	27	9	4	0.4	1.4
Alfalfa meal (17%)	620	18	3	24	0.3	1.6
Alfalfa meal (20%)	720	21	3	20	0.3	1.7
Fats						
Beef tallow	2860		100			
Pork fat	3980		100			
Fish oils	3660		100			
Soybean oil	4200		100			
Minerals						
Dicalcium phosphate					27	19
Steamed bonemeal					29	13
Defluorinated phosphate					29	13
Limestone					38	0

TABLE 30-4. *Relation of dietary energy level to egg production and food intake in layers.*

	Average performance (11 months)			
Diet energy level (ME) (kcal/lb.)	Egg production (%)	Feed intake per 100 hen days (lb.)	Feed per dozen (lb.)	Kilocalories per hen per day
1070	65	31	5.7	322
1230	67	29	5.2	355
1370	68	26	4.6	353
1410	70	25	4.4	355
1450	71	24	4.2	356

Metabolizable energy is a conveniently measured and highly precise means of determining energy content or "physiological fuel values" of diet materials. Although there are some minor differences, due to differing protein metabolism, the metabolizable energy values for poultry are very similar to the energy values commonly used in computing the energy of human diets. For the most part, metabolizable energy values are additive and are an adequate measure of the energy supplied by a diet to the biological machinery of the animal. However, the use of certain diet mixtures quite high in protein or fat will produce changes in metabolism that alter the efficiency with which energy is utilized. In theory, net (or productive) energy, which attempts to account for these discrepancies, would be a more

TABLE 30-5. *Seasonal fluctuations in relative food intake of layers.*

Month	Relative food consumption [*]
October	95
November	98
December	101
January	103
February	107
March	107
April	107
May	100
June	94
July	94
August	95

[*] Monthly intake expressed as percentage of annual average; corrected for rate of production and weight gain or loss.

accurate measure of energy value. However, these values are highly variable and extremely difficult to determine; thus, their theoretical advantage is lost. At the present time, therefore, metabolizable energy values are considered the most useful in formulating poultry rations.

Inasmuch as energy values can be determined directly only from the results of tedious feeding experiments, it is desirable to have some means of estimating by chemical analysis the energy value or digestibility of a feedstuff. The determination of crude fiber estimates the indigestible portion of a feedstuff or ration, and it is frequently used as a rough measure of digestibility or energy value. Table 30-3 summarizes the crude fiber content of common feedstuffs. Although there is a general relationship between energy value and fiber content, the relationship is not sufficiently close to permit estimation of feeding value from fiber content. The state of the fiber in the feedstuff (whether it is separate from the digestible portion or intimately distributed throughout the material), as well as the chemical nature of the indigestible material, greatly influences the utilization of the feedstuff. In essence, crude fiber content can be a rough guide, but it can also be highly misleading.

The major sources of energy in poultry rations are the grains. Whether a ration is high, moderate, or low in energy value will be determined primarily by the choice of the grain base. Corn and milo are the grains highest in energy value; barley and oats are intermediate; milling by-products can be quite low. Of particular current interest is the recent finding that enzyme concentrates produced by microbial fermentation, when added to diets based on western barley as the grain, markedly improve growth, feed efficiency, and energy value of the diet. So far, the mechanism of this action and the nature of the enzyme materials that may be responsible has not been determined. This is one of the few instances in which supplementation of an animal diet with an enzyme active material has been effective in improving nutrient utilization.

30-4. PROTEIN AND AMINO ACIDS

The protein requirement is second only to the energy need in size. Protein is required to supply the amino acids necessary for the synthesis of body tissues and for the formation of eggs. Both the total protein requirement and the requirement of young and adult birds for individual amino acids have been studied extensively. For a given state of growth or egg production (viewing protein as the amino acid mixture necessary) a relatively fixed total amount of protein is required per day. Since the total food intake of the animal is primarily determined by the energy requirement, it follows that the protein need can be expressed in relation to the energy concentration of the diet. The estimated protein requirements of chickens and turkeys are shown in Table 30-6, both as a percentage of a typical diet and in grams of protein per megacalorie (therm). Neither of these measures is completely accurate. Expressing protein requirement as a percentage of the diet is a convenient measure but does not reflect the variation in food intake that would result from a variation in the energy concentration of the diet. However, expressing the protein requirement in relation to energy concentration is also not entirely accurate, because the amount of protein needed depends on its amino acid pattern, which in turn governs the efficiency with which the protein meets the amino acid requirements. However, for practical purposes, using the protein supplements which are most commonly employed, the estimated requirements shown in Table 30-6 are a satisfactory basis for formulation purposes.

The chick requires twelve essential amino acids—that is, provision must be made in the diet for these amino acids because either they are not synthesized by the chick or the rate of synthesis is not sufficient to meet the full requirement. This is a larger number of essential amino acids than is required by other species. In addition to those required by the rat, the chick has a dietary requirement for glutamic acid and glycine.

TABLE 30-6. | *Approximate minimum quantitative requirements of poultry for critical nutrients.*

Nutrient	Chicks 0–6 weeks	Chicks 6–20 weeks	Hens Layer	Hens Breeder	Turkey poults 0–8 weeks	Turkey poults 8–24 weeks	Turkey hens
Protein (%)	20	17	15	15	28	22–16	18
Protein (g per therm)	75	58	55	55	110	73–55	65
Amino acids, as % of protein							
Lysine	5.0	5.0	3.3	3.3	5.0	5.0	*
Methionine + cystine	3.5	3.5	3.5	3.5	3.2	3.2	*
Tryptophan	1	1	1	1	1	1	*
Arginine	6	6			6	6	*
Calcium (%)	0.8	0.8	3.0	3.0	1.5	1.5	3.0
Available phosphorus (%)	0.5	0.5	0.4	0.4	0.5	0.5	0.5
Manganese (mg/lb.)	25	25	15	15	25	25	15
Zinc (mg/lb.)	20	30	*	*	30	30	*
Vitamin A (I.U./lb.)	600	600	2000	2000	2400	2400	2400
Vitamin D_3 (I.C.U./lb.)	90	90	225	225	400	400	400
Riboflavin (mg/lb.)	1.3	1.0	1.0	1.7	1.7	1.7	1.5
Pantothenic acid (mg/lb.)	4.2	3.0	2.1	4.2	5.0	5.0	7.3
Niacin (mg/lb.)	12	12	*	*	35	35	*
Choline (mg/lb.)	600	*	*	*	900	900	*
Vitamin B_{12} (mg/lb.)	4	1	1	2	*	*	*

* Quantitative need not established.

TABLE 30-7. | *Amino acid content of some feedstuffs.*

Feedstuffs	Arginine (%)	Lysine (%)	Methionine + cystine (%)	Tryptophan (%)
Grains				
Corn	0.5	0.2	0.36	0.10
Milo	0.4	0.3	0.31	0.12
Barley	0.6	0.5	0.37	0.15
Wheat	0.4	0.3	0.30	0.12
Protein supplement				
Soybean oil meal (50%)	3.6	3.2	1.57	0.64
Cottonseed meal	3.3	1.6	1.50	0.50
Corn gluten meal	1.4	0.8	1.70	0.21
Meat scraps (55%)	3.8	3.8	1.50	0.40
Fishmeal	4.7	6.0	2.74	0.83

The most critical amino acids in practical diets are those shown in Tables 30-6 and 30-7. These are the most limiting amino acids in the protein mixtures that are commonly used in poultry feeding. Under all but the most unusual circumstances, diets that are adequately provided with the amino acids indicated (lysine, methionine and cystine, tryptophan, and arginine) will also be adequately supplied with the other essential amino acids. The study of amino acid requirements of poultry is a highly active field at the present time, and further knowledge of quantitative requirements and the effects of amino acid balance and interrelationships upon them will undoubtedly modify our concepts of protein nutrition.

Proteins, in essence, supply the amino acids necessary for body maintenance and the synthesis of tissues and products. The efficiency of a protein in meeting amino acid needs depends on how well its amino acid pattern matches the requirements of the animal. Tables 30-7 and 30-8 illustrate the amino acid content of some feedstuffs, particularly the primary protein resources and the amino acid pattern in eggs and poultry meats. Each of the major feedstuffs has a characteristic amino acid pattern. The grains, as a class, are deficient in lysine and marginal in tryptophan. Soybean oil meal, which is the primary protein resource for most of the United States, is deficient in the sulphur amino acids (methionine and cystine) but is a good source of lysine. Cottonseed meal, a major resource on the Pacific Coast and in the Southwest, is most limiting in lysine. Meat scraps—a by-product of the packing industry and rendering plants—is low in sulphur amino acids and in tryptophan. The best balanced of the major protein sources is fishmeal.

Protein nutrition is critical, and amino acid balance is of particular

TABLE 30-8. | *Amino acids in eggs and poultry meats.*

Amino acid	% in protein of:		
	Eggs	Chicken meat	Turkey meat
Lysine	6.4	8.8	9.0
Methionine + cystine	5.5	3.9	4.1
Tryptophan	1.7	1.2	1.3
Isoleucine	6.6	5.3	5.3
Leucine	8.8	7.2	7.6
Phenylalanine	5.8	3.9	4.0
Tyrosine	4.4	3.5	3.7
Threonine	5.0	4.2	4.2
Valine	7.5	4.9	5.0

significance, because amino acids cannot be stored as such. The efficiency of a protein in promoting growth or the manufacture of eggs depends on the simultaneous supply of all the amino acids essential to the process; an imbalance at one time cannot be compensated for by supplementation at a later time.

In addition to amino acid pattern, some other characteristics of certain protein feedstuffs affect their feeding value. Soybean oil meal, which is produced from soybeans by extraction of the fat, must be subjected to moist-heat treatment in order to make it satisfactory for feeding chickens and other simple-stomached animals. This is because the soybean contains heat-labile inhibitory factors that markedly interfere with the utilization of the diet and which greatly inhibit growth. These inhibitors interfere with digestive enzymes and also exert other deleterious effects. Cottonseed meal, which is prepared by removal of the oil from cottonseed, contains a toxic substance known as gossypol. When present in sufficient amounts, it retards the growth of chicks and turkey poults and also causes a marked reduction in hatchability when fed to breeder hens. Gossypol, in combination with certain substances in cottonseed oil, produces a characteristic discoloration and blemishing of the egg yolk when fed to laying chickens. For these reasons, cottonseed is used in moderate amounts in the diet, and the amount of gossypol is carefully determined in order to avoid difficulties. Careful processing of cottonseed low in gossypol results in a cottonseed meal that can be used in a substantial amount in the ration (10%) without producing a deleterious effect on egg quality or growth. The cottonseed produced in California, for instance, is taken from low gossypol varieties, whereas, in other areas, the cottonseed used has a much higher gossypol content.

30-5. VITAMINS

Vitamin A. A severe deficiency of vitamin A in chicks produces a marked retardation of growth, general weakness, a staggering gait, and poor feathering. Resistance to infection is reduced. Various epithelial (covering) tissues are affected, including the intestinal lining, the tear glands, the eyelid, the mucous membranes of the mouth, the esophagus, and the respiratory and urinary systems. Salts of uric acid accumulate in the kidneys and ureters. In the mature fowl, the symptoms are similar to those for chicks but develop more slowly, and the eye disorder becomes more acute. Egg production may be markedly affected.

Vitamin A may be provided in two ways. It can be supplied either in the form of fish liver oils or as the synthetic substance (usually palmitate). Carotenoid pigments, which occur in plant materials, can also contribute vitamin A activity. These pigments, of which the most important is β-carotene, are converted to vitamin A in the animal's body, primarily by the intestinal mucosa.

Vitamin D. Lack of vitamin D in the absence of direct sunlight produces the nutritional deficiency known as rickets. Growth is retarded and lameness develops. The absorption and utilization of calcium and phosphorus is upset by a lack of vitamin D. As a result, these minerals are not deposited in normal amounts in the bone structure of the body. Abnormal bone development can be seen most readily in the legs and at the junction of the ribs with the breast bone and spine—the hock joint becomes enlarged, and the rib-ends become enlarged (beaded).

In mature layers, vitamin D deficiency causes the laying of thin-shelled eggs, followed by a decrease in egg production. Demineralization occurs, accompanied by an increase in the fragility of the leg and wing bones. Hatchability is greatly reduced.

Poultry differ from other species in that they have a specific requirement for one form of vitamin D. The most effective form of vitamin D for poultry is vitamin D_3, which is derived from the animal sterol cholesterol. Other species can use this form of vitamin D and also vitamin D_2, which is a derivative of the plant sterol ergosterol. Because of this specific requirement, vitamin D_3 is measured in International Chick Units, and the requirement is stated in these units.

Vitamin E. A lack of vitamin E in the growing chick results in the condition known as nutritional encephalomalacia. This produces a paralysis with head retraction, which is due to lesions in the brain (cerebellum).

In mature birds, prolonged vitamin E deficiency results in sterility of the male and failure of the female to produce hatchable eggs. Vitamin E is unstable in natural feedstuffs and is particularly labile in the presence of rancidifying fat. The best sources of vitamin E are the cereal grains, alfalfa meal, and crude vegetable oils. The use of antioxidants in the ration helps to preserve vitamin E activity. Also, it appears that certain antioxidants can replace vitamin E in certain functions within the animal body, thereby reducing the dietary requirement to a very low level.

Vitamin K. A deficiency of vitamin K greatly delays the clotting of blood. Chicks deficient in this vitamin may bleed to death from a minor injury or bruise. In fact, hemorrhage in chicks fed certain diets led to the discovery of this vitamin. Vitamin K may be provided in the diet by adding alfalfa meal, sources of vegetable oils, or the synthetic chemical compound. The requirement for vitamin K is greatly increased when sulfa drugs are present in the diet, and may be an important consideration in medicated rations.

Riboflavin. A riboflavin deficiency in young chicks produces retarded growth and paralysis of the legs, commonly called curled-toe paralysis. In severe cases, marked changes occur in the nerves serving the limbs, which can be seen easily on autopsy. In breeding hens, this deficiency produces reduced hatchability of eggs. A much more severe deficiency can reduce the rate of egg production. Among the sources of riboflavin are: milk products, yeast, fermentation products, alfalfa, and the synthetic vitamin.

Niacin. In chicks, a deficiency of this vitamin results in inflammation of the tongue and mouth, growth retardation, poor feather development, and a leg disorder similar to perosis, described later under manganese deficiency.

The turkey poult's requirement is much higher than the chick's, and a deficiency produces a typical leg disorder similar to perosis.

Pantothenic Acid. Pantothenic acid deficiency in chicks produces retarded growth, poor feathering, and marked changes in the skin around the mouth, vent, and feet. The dermatitis appears as crusty scabs on the skin or as an actual thickening and cracking of the skin of the feet. Deficiency in the adult fowl results in a reduction in hatchability.

Vitamin B$_{12}$. Deficiency of this vitamin results in markedly retarded growth. It is also necessary for hatchability. The primary sources of vitamin B$_{12}$ are animal products (meat and fish). It is also produced commercially by fermentation.

Choline. Retarded growth and perosis (see manganese) are produced by a lack of choline in the diet of young chickens and turkeys.

The chicken requires other vitamins as well, including thiamine, pyridoxine (vitamin B$_6$), biotin, folacin, and possibly ascorbic acid under some

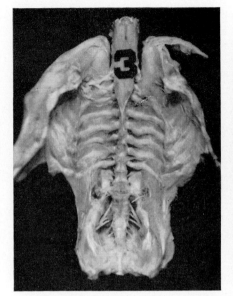
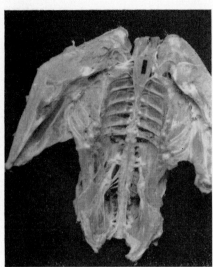

Figs. 30-2 and 30-3. Appearance of ribs in vitiman D-deficient (3) and normal (1) chicks. Note enlarged cartilaginous ribs and the beaded rib ends in the rachitic chick. [Courtesy Department of Poultry Husbandry, Cornell University.]

conditions. However, the requirements for these nutrients are normally met satisfactorily by practical rations, and they are not normally considered to be of critical significance. Quantitative requirements for the most important factors are summarized in Table 30-6 and illustrations of typical deficiency symptoms are shown in Figs. 30-2 to 30-7.

Shown in Table 30-9 are representative data on the vitamin content of some feeds. It is of interest to point out the higher requirement for several vitamins shown by the breeding hen as compared with the layer. The difference in requirement is due entirely to the need for a higher level of vitamin deposition in eggs to be used for hatching, as compared to the dietary level needed to support satisfactory egg production as such. The amount of the vitamin deposited in the egg is related to the

Fig. 30-4. Leg paralysis in the young ribo-flavin-deficient chick, sometimes called "curly-toed paralysis." [Courtesy Department of Poultry Husbandry, Cornell University.]

TABLE | *Vitamin content of some feedstuffs.*
30-9. |

Feedstuff	Vitamin A (I.U./lb.)	Riboflavin (mg/lb)	Niacin (mg/lb)	Pantothenic acid (mg/lb)	Choline (mg/lb)
Grains					
Corn	2000	0.5	10	2.6	200
Milo		0.4	13	5.0	200
Barley		0.8	24	3.7	530
Oats		0.4	8	6.8	430
Wheat		0.5	27	6.4	450
Grain products					
Wheat bran		1.4	95	13	490
Wheat middlings		0.9	45	9.0	490
Hominy feed	5000	1.1	20	3.9	440
Proteins					
Soybean oil meal		1.5	12	6.6	1250
Corn gluten meal	10,000	0.7	23	4.7	150
Cottonseed meal		2.2	15	4.7	1280
Meat scraps		2.4	26	2.2	900
Fish meal		2.2	25	4.0	1600
Vitamin supplements					
Dried whey		14	5	22	900
Dried brewers yeast		16	200	50	1800
Distillers dried solubles		7.7	52	10	2200
Alfalfa meal	100,000	7.4	17	19	450

amount in the diet, within limits. The reason for reduced hatchability in vitamin deficiency in breeding hens is, of course, the insufficient level of the factor in the egg to support embryological development.

Basic research with simplified and purified diet mixtures has shown that at least one and possibly several additional vitamins have yet to be discovered. Feeding materials which are evidently rich sources of these unidentified factors are fish products, milk products, organ tissues such as liver, and fermentation materials. Such sources are frequently used in critical rations (for young chicks and breeding hens) to insure adequate nutrition.

30-6. MINERALS

The mineral factors of major significance in practical nutrition are calcium, phosphorus, manganese, zinc, and sodium. The chicken is known to require iron, copper, potassium, magnesium, iodine, sulphur, selenium, and cobalt, but the requirements for these minerals are normally met in practical rations; thus, specific supplementation is not required.

Calcium. In the chick, calcium is required primarily for bone formation; the minimum requirement approximates 0.8–1.0% of the diet. Higher levels can be tolerated, provided that phosphorus nutrition is adequate, but excess calcium tends to interfere with the availability of other minerals, particularly manganese and zinc, with the result thtat excesses are avoided.

The laying hen has a critical requirement for calcium, which is utilized in the formation of egg shells. In calcium deficiency, the hen can mobilize reserves from the bones to make 3–4 eggs, but will then produce thin shelled eggs. Calcium deficiency in the hen also results in depletion of bone minerals and development of fragile bones; if the deficiency is imposed on a hen in high production, a paralysis known as "layer fatigue" may occur. An average, normal egg shell contains approximately 2 g of calcium. High-producing flocks will average 240 eggs per hen; the amount of calcium in this number of eggs is 20–30 times greater than that present in the entire body of the hen. The turnover of calcium in the hen is rapid and great. Dietary calcium is used with about 50% efficiency for egg shell formation, thus the dietary level must be quite high (3% or more) to meet the need at high levels of egg production.

Phosphorus. The phosphorus requirement is highly critical. A severe deficiency in the young chick quickly leads to the cessation of growth, followed by death. A moderate deficiency results in decreased bone calcification. Not all forms of phosphorus are equally well utilized by poultry. The inorganic phosphates, such as dicalcium phosphate, defluorinated phosphate, and bone meal, are well utilized. The phosphorus in plant materials, such as grains and vegetable proteins, is largely unavailable to poultry. Approximately 30% of the plant phosphorus is in a form that can be utilized by poultry, whereas 70% is in the form of phytin, which is unavailable. Estimated quantitative requirements, as illustrated in Table 30-6, are based on available rather than total phosphorus.

Fig. 30-5. Classical perosis due to manganese deficiency. The extreme case in which the Achilles tendon has slipped out of place is incurable. [Courtesy Department of Poultry Husbandry, Cornell University.]

Fig. 30-6. Manganese deficiency. Hock joint enlargement and twisting of leg (center chick), compared to normal chick (right). The Achilles tendon has slipped out of place in the chick on the left, producing extreme perosis or "slipped tendon." [Courtesy Department of Poultry Husbandry, Cornell University.]

Manganese. The trace mineral manganese is required by poultry for proper mineral metabolism. The deficiency results in a syndrome known as perosis, which is a bone malformation. It also causes enlargement and flattening of the hock joint and the slipping of the Achilles tendon from its normal position, which twists and distorts the leg. In addition, the long bones of the body show a marked shortening and thickening.

In laying and breeding hens, manganese deficiency results in lowered egg production, reduced shell thickness, and reduced hatchability. Embryonic development is abnormal and is characterized by the formation of a parrot-like beak and a shortening of the long bones in the embryo.

Zinc. A deficiency of zinc produces retarded growth and feather development and a shortening and thickening of the long bones. There is an enlargement of the hock joint, but slipping of the tendon does not usually occur.

Sodium. Salt supplementation of practical rations is necessary to meet the sodium requirement. Levels of salt supplementation normally constitute 0.25–0.5% of the ration.

30-7. ANTIBIOTICS

One of the most interesting research findings in recent years has been the effect of antibiotics in stimulating the growth of young animals. This was first discovered in research with chicks, and has been investigated

Fig. 30-7. Thiamine (vitamin B_1) deficiency produces a paralysis in chicks which can be dramatically reversed by administering the vitamin. This deficiency rarely occurs in practice because common feedstuffs, especially grains, are good sources of thiamine. [Courtesy Department of Poultry Husbandry, Cornell University.]

extensively. Small amounts of antibiotics (penicillin, Aureomycin, Terramycin, bacitracin) added to the diet of the chick produce a marked increase in growth rate and improve the efficiency of growth. It is now known that the extent of improvement depends upon environment; in a completely germ-free environment, no stimulatory effect is obtained. Also, in a new or thoroughly clean environment, antibiotics are ineffective in improving growth. However, in a "contaminated" environment, for example, quarters in which chickens have been reared previously, antibiotics are effective in improving growth; unless they are used, the bacteria of the environment will retard the growth of chicks. The mechanism of antibiotic action, therefore, is to overcome the growth-retarding effect of the bacterial environment of the animal. Other growth-stimulating substances, such as arsenic derivatives and certain drugs, apparently produce effects quite similar to the antibiotic. It is of particular interest that very low levels are effective (2–10 parts per million) and that such levels have no consistent effect on the total numbers or types of bacteria in the intestinal tract of the bird.

30-8. EXAMPLE RATIONS

Shown in Table 30-10 are typical practical rations used for feeding various kinds of poultry. They represent combinations of feedstuffs and specialized supplements that adequately supply the estimated requirements of the birds. The nutrient levels contained in these rations are usually substantially higher than those indicated as the minimum needs in Table 30-6. This is because it is desirable to exceed the minimum levels in formulation in order to avoid deficiencies as a consequence of ingredient variability or environmental circumstances that may alter the requirement. As an exercise, it may be of interest for you to compute the nutrient content of the various rations shown, using the data on ingredient composition presented in the various tables in this chapter.

30-9. FEEDING METHODS

The discussion in this chapter, and the examples given, have dealt with feeding mixtures as complete rations. In practice, poultry rations may be fed as complete (so-called all-mash) rations, or as two-component rations, often termed grain-plus-mash feeding programs. The latter are used especially when home-produced or locally-produced grains are available at low cost.

All-mash rations are normally used for young chicks and poults (starter period, to 8 weeks of age). Either complete rations or grain-plus-mash rations may be used for the rest of the rearing period, and for the feeding of adult stock. In a grain-plus-mash system, the mash portion is formulated such that, when a predetermined proportion of grain is fed with it, the resultant

TABLE 30-10. | *Typical feeding mixtures for poultry.*

Ingredient	Chick starter (per ton)	Chick grower (per ton)	Chicken layer (per ton)	Chicken breeder (per ton)	Poult starter (per ton)	Poult grower (per ton)	Turkey breeder (per ton)
Milo	955	815	1135	1100	675	865	1000
Corn	300	300	200	200	300	200	200
Barley	—	300	—	—	—	300	200
Soybean oil meal	250	180	200	200	500	200	150
Cottonseed meal	150	150	100	—	100	100	—
Meat scraps	100	50	50	50	100	50	100
Fish meal	50	50	50	100	100	100	100
Dried whey	50	25	25	50	50	25	40
Distillers dried solubles	50	25	—	50	50	25	40
Dried brewers yeast	—	—	—	—	20	20	20
Alfalfa meal	50	50	80	100	50	50	60
Dicalcium phosphate	10	20	30	20	10	20	10
Limestone	30	30	120	120	40	40	70
Salt, iodized	5	5	10	10	5	5	10
Manganese sulfate	0.4	0.4	0.4	0.4	0.5	0.5	0.5
Zinc carbonate	0.1	0.1	0.1	0.1	0.2	0.2	0.2
Vitamin A (million I.U.)	1	1	5	5	4	4	4
Vitamin D_3 (million I.C.U.)	0.5	0.5	0.8	0.8	1.0	1.0	1.0
Riboflavin (g)	1.0	0.5	1.0	3.0	1.0	1.0	3.0
Niacin (g)	10	5	—	—	40	40	—
Calcium pantothenate (g)	1	1	—	3	3	2	7
Vitamin B_{12} (mg)	4	2	—	4	—	—	—
Choline chloride (g)	—	—	—	—	400	200	—
Vitamin E (thousand I.U.)	2	—	—	4	5	3	30
Antioxidant (such as BHT or ethoxyquin)	.2	—	—	.2	.2	.2	.2

mixture meets the requirements of the birds, and is essentially the equivalent of a complete ration. The usual practice is to formulate the mash mixture so that it can be fed with an equal amount of grain. For instance, a mash containing 22% protein would be fed with an equal amount of grain containing 10% protein to form a layer ration containing 16% protein. The mash part would be fed *ad libitum,* and the grain portion would be fed either in measured amount or *ad libitum*. Often, the *ad libitum* feeding of both components to layers (so-called free choice feeding) will result in over-consumption of grain, but this is a variable that depends on strain of birds and other conditions. Experimental observations indicate wide individual variations in eating habits under such conditions.

Free choice feeding of a grain-plus-mash system is often used in rearing chickens and turkeys, and is quite successful. It is probable that a properly formulated all-mash ration will be more efficient owing to its better nutrient balance.

In the primary grain-producing areas a system termed grain-plus-"concentrate" feeding is used, in which the concentrate is a mixture of the non-grain components of the ration. Such a concentrate is typically high in protein (32–40%), mineral, and vitamin content and is designed to be fed with a high proportion of grain.

When whole grains are fed, a grit must also be provided for proper grinding by the gizzard. An insoluble (granite or stone) grit is commonly used. In feeding layers in a grain-plus-mash system, not all of the high level of calcium required is incorporated in the mash part of the ration. Instead, supplementary calcium is supplied *ad libitum* as crushed oyster shells or calcite crystals (grit). Calcite grit serves also as a grinding agent for hens; however, it should not be used for chicks or poults because it will result in excessive calcium intake.

The science of nutrition is a living and growing field of study. A great deal of research effort is being directed toward improved understanding of nutritional requirements and characteristics of various species of poultry. Changes in feeding practices as a consequence of new findings are very likely to come about, thus continuing the steady trend of change that has been characteristic of this field.

REFERENCES AND SELECTED READINGS

Almquist, H. J., 1952. Amino acid requirements of chickens and turkeys—A Review. *Poultry Sci.* 31:966.

Byerly, T. C., 1941. Feed and other costs of producing market eggs. Maryland Agr. Expt. Sta. Bull. Al.

Ewing, W. R., 1951. *Poultry Nutrition.* W. R. Ewing, Publisher, Pasadena.

National Research Council, 1956. Composition of concentrate by-product feeding stuffs Committee on Feed Composition. Natl. Acad. of Sci., Natl. Research Council. Publ. 449.

National Research Council, 1958. Composition of cereal grains and forages. Committee on Feed Composition. Natl. Acad. of Sci., Natl. Research Council. Publ. 585.

National Research Council, 1960. Nutrient requirements of poultry. Committee on Animal Nutrition. Natl. Acad. of Sci., Natl. Research Council. Publ. 827.

Norris, L. C., 1958. The significant advances of the past fifty years in poultry nutrition. *Poultry Sci.* 37:256.

Livestock Management

Chapter 31

Beef Cattle Management

Be thou diligent to know the state of thy flocks, and look well to thy herds.

Prov. 28

31-1. INTRODUCTION

Sound, modern-day beef cattle management involves the application of the sciences of genetics, physiology, nutrition, and microbiology to the production of beef cattle. The beef animal readily adapts itself to a wide variety of environmental conditions. Management practices will vary, therefore, according to environment. The successful beef cattle producer will use those management practices found to be most desirable and profitable for his area.

31-2. AREAS AND PHASES OF PRODUCTION

Approximately 68 million head of beef cattle (cows, heifers, calves, steers, and bulls) are on farms in the United States, although certain types of production are more common in certain areas. The seventeen Western states are predominately range states. Many areas in this section are not suitable for the production of harvested crops, but the native forage available does provide suitable grazing for livestock. Beef cattle production constitutes a major part of the agricultural economy of this section. Many commercial range herds contain 500–1000 cows.

The Western area produces the necessary young females for herd replacements and herd bulls are secured from registered herds located in this and other parts of the nation. For many years this area has been the principal source of stocker and feeder cattle for the Corn-Belt feeder. Recent years have seen the development of highly specialized feeding areas in the West and Southwest, some of which can accommodate 50,000–100,000 cattle at one time.

In Western states are many famous grazing areas, noted for their abundance of high-quality grasses. These include the Sandhills of western Nebraska, the Jackson Hole area of Wyoming, the Flint Hills of south central Kansas, and the Osage in northern Oklahoma. The forage available in these areas is highly prized. In recent years there has been an increase in commercial cow herds in these specialized grazing areas. Feeder calves are often identified according to the area in which they originate, such as Sandhill calves or Flint Hill calves.

The Midwest, or corn belt, has long been famous as a region for fattening beef cattle. Here the most common type of beef production is the farmer-feeder operation. While the fattening of beef cattle predominates, some commercial cow herds are found. These are usually small herds numbering from 20 to 100 head, depending on the size of the farm operation.

The southern section of the United States has experienced a great change in agricultural production in recent years. With reduced cotton acreage and an increase in grasses and soil-improving crops, beef cattle have played a much larger role in utilizing the forage. As a result, beef cattle have increased very rapidly in the South in the past twenty years, and Southern calves compete with feeders and stockers produced in the West. Fattening cattle for slaughter has also increased. One major difference found in the southern section is the widespread use of Zebu or Brahman cattle. Brahman bulls crossed on native stock produce offspring that are better adapted to hot and humid climates. Many calves are now sold for slaughter directly off the cow.

While beef cattle are not as important in farming operations in the East and Northeast, certain sections such as Lancaster County, Pennsylvania, are noted for fattening cattle for market.

The raising of registered beef cattle is a specialized phase of beef production. Registered herds are found in all sections of the nation. The objective of the breeders of registered cattle should be to provide high-quality herd bulls for commercial operators. Many purebred herds of beef cattle are maintained by owners who have other business interests but who consider it an interesting side line.

Many management practices are common to all areas. The great diversity of climate, soils, and rainfall will, however, necessitate a variety of management practices.

31-3. MANAGEMENT OF THE BREEDING HERD

In commercial range herds a single individual may care for a hundred or more brood cows. Additional labor is required only when the entire herd is being sorted or animals are being handled for routine operations such as vaccination, branding, or castration. In some registered herds a single individual may be responsible for only a few animals, especially when a portion of the herd is being prepared for show and sale. Registered animals must be identified as individuals, while animals produced in most commercial herds are handled in groups.

Growing and Development of Beef Females. The growth and development of the beef heifer is very important. Management practices during the period from birth to first lactation may influence lifetime productivity. The development of the beef heifer is determined by her inherent capacity for growth and by the nutrients provided. Studies by Chambers (1954) indicate that a heifer should weigh approximately 600 lb. before she is exposed to the bull, since heifers of this weight have less trouble at calving time than do smaller heifers. Some breed registry association will not record calves from dams under 2 years of age. Many ranchers feel that a range cow should calve first at 3 years of age. In many parts of the West this is the most common age for heifers to produce their first calf. Studies by Pinney *et al.* (1960) have shown that there is some advantage in having heifers calve first at 2 years of age. Results of one such long time study is shown in Table 31-1.

Care of the Cow Herd. The ratio of the number of calves weaned each season to the number of cows maintained in a herd is one of the most important measures of the economical production of beef. This ratio is usually designated as per cent calf crop. For example, if 100 cows exposed to bulls in a given season wean only 90 calves, this would be expressed as a 90% calf crop.

Normally a beef cow will produce a calf each 12-month period. Running

TABLE 31-1.	*Production records of 11½ year-old cows that calved first as two- or as three-year-olds.**

	Age at First Calving	
	Two-Year-Old	Three-Year-Old
Number of cows at start of experiment (10/48)	60	60
Number of cows remaining (10/59)	41	42
Number of possible calvings	532	480
Number of calves weaned	484	422
Per cent calf crop weaned	91.0	87.9
Number of calves weaned per cow	9.10	7.91
Average wean weight (corrected for age and sex)	476	487
Average calving date	3/11	3/9

Oklahoma Agricultural Experiment Station Publication MP-57, 1960.

Fig. 31-1. Commercial cow and calf operations in the western United States are best adapted to range conditions. The forage in this California foothill range is still lush but approaching maturity in the latter part of May. The cows were supplemented with cottonseed meal during the scarce forage season the previous fall and early winter. [Courtesy K. W. Wagnon.]

the bull with the cow herd the year long may result in a slightly higher per cent calf crop, but most better commercial herd owners prefer to run their bulls with the cow herd during a specified season, resulting in calves that are more uniform in age and weight. Such calves will usually sell to a better advantage.

The beef cow may be managed to produce a calf at any season of the year, but spring or fall are more favorable for growth and development of the calf. In most Western range areas, herds are managed so that calves are dropped in the spring months. In these range areas, spring calves are more desirable because of the availability of forage during spring and early summer months. To fit in with an abundant feed supply, fall and winter calves are common throughout the Southern and Southwestern areas of the country. Many factors—winter and summer forage, labor, market conditions—must be taken into consideration before determining whether fall or spring calving is most desirable.

The beef cow will normally give birth to a live calf without assistance. The cow herd should be observed daily during the calving season and the herdsman should make sure that all cows are accounted for during this herd check. Calving cows not with the herd should be located in order to check the newborn calf or render assistance in case of difficult calving. Heifers calving for the first time should be separated from the older cows and observed at more frequent intervals. This allows the herdsman to assist with abnormal births or other calving difficulties and will result in a higher per cent calf crop.

To be a profitable member of the herd a cow must wean a calf each year. Calf weight at weaning time is usually a reliable measure of a cow's productivity. Botkin and Whatley (1953) have shown that the cow tends to repeat her performance from year to year, as measured by the adjusted weaning weight of her calves. Gifford (1953) has stated that the more milk a cow produces in a given lactation, the heavier will be her calf at weaning. It appears that a moderate flow of milk over the entire lactation period is more desirable than a heavy milk flow in the early stages, followed by a rapid decline in milk production.

During the spring and summer months, most cow herds are maintained on pasture, which, if well managed, will normally provide sufficient feed for the lactating cow (Fig. 31-1). During periods when the forage is dormant, or during droughts, it may be necessary to provide supplemental feed in order to maintain a desirable milk flow for the calf. Cows nursing calves during the winter will normally require some supplemental feed.

A common practice under range conditions is for the dry cow to graze cured native grass throughout the winter. Such range forage is usually supplemented with sufficient protein and energy feeds to meet the needs of the cow (Fig. 31-2). Other systems of winter management involve the use of

Fig. 31-2. When forage is scarce, supplementation of the range with cottonseed meal is frequently advantageous. Note the thin condition of the animals as compared to animals in Fig. 31-1 near the end of the green forage season. [Courtesy K. W. Wagnon.]

winter pastures, with a reserve feed supply in case of drought or pasture failure.

The beef cow normally needs little special attention during pregnancy other than routine care and management. It is unwise to handle cows through a squeeze chute or in close quarters during the latter part of pregnancy. Injuries or added stress during this period may result in abortion. The average length of gestation in the beef cow is about 280 days (see Chapter 6). First-calf heifers will sometimes calve earlier than this, while older cows may have a somewhat longer gestation. Beef calves are ordinarily weaned from the cows at 6 to 10 months of age. Calves of about the same age are removed at the same time. A 3- to 5-day "bawling out" period, by both cows and calves, usually follows weaning.

Herd owners follow the practice of culling a cow when she ceases to be a profitable member of the herd. Culling is usually based on age, unsoundness or disease, and productivity. Production records, when available, can serve as an effective tool to aid in culling the cow herd. A cow should be left in the herd as long as she weans a calf heavier than a first calf heifer.

Care of Herd Bulls. One of the most important decisions to be made in the management of the cow herd is the selection of the herd bull. The ideal bull would be one that is physically sound, structurally correct, and capable of siring uniform high-quality calves over extended periods of time. He should be active, vigorous, and yet mild tempered. Consideration should be given to soundness in feet and legs. Fertility and the adaptability of the individual bull to his environment are also important.

Bull calves are normally weaned at 7 to 8 months of age. Individual calves which show promise of developing into high grading bulls are often given special attention. In some registered herds promising calves are "gain tested" in order to select the bulls more effectively. Well-balanced rations which will permit the calf to express his growth potential should be used in such gain tests. Following the completion of a feeding test, bulls should be fed and managed to permit their normal growth. To be useful for as many years as possible the herd bull should be maintained in good flesh.

Young bulls can be used for light service as early as 1 year of age, but most ranchers prefer them to be at least 2 years old. When hand mating is practiced, a bull may be used on 50 to 75 cows in a given season. Under pasture mating conditions one bull will be required for each 15 to 30 cows. The number of cows per bull will depend on the age and vigor of the bull, the terrain, and size of the pasture. By the use of artificial insemination it is possible to use a bull on several hundred cows in a given season. In herds where spring-dropped calves are desired, the bull should be mated during late spring and early summer. For fall-dropped calves the breeding season occurs during the winter months.

Herd bulls not in use should be maintained in a good thrifty condition.

When forage is inadequate, supplemental feeding should be practiced. Adequate exercise is important and feet should be checked frequently, and trimmed if necessary, to maintain a sound animal. Good herd bulls are normally used until they become unserviceable.

31-4. MANAGEMENT OF STOCKER AND FEEDER CATTLE

Stockers and feeders are market terms used primarily to describe steers and heifers from weaning age to maturity. Stockers are usually lighter in weight and in thinner condition; such animals are usually maintained on roughage or grazed on pasture prior to fattening. Feeder cattle are usually heavier and in higher condition, and are usually placed in the feed lot and fattened for market. When selecting stocker and feeder cattle consideration should be given to age, sex, condition, and general health.

Stocker cattle wintered in good thrifty condition and making weight gains of $\frac{1}{2}$–$\frac{3}{4}$ lb. daily will usually be more profitable than cattle wintered to make greater weight gains. During the summer months stocker cattle are usually maintained on pasture, and will make gains of 1–$2\frac{1}{2}$ lb. per head daily. Gains will depend on the forage available, age, sex, and condition of animals at the beginning of the grazing season.

31-5. CARE AND MANAGEMENT OF FEED-LOT CATTLE

In recent years cattle-feeding operations have becomes highly specialized. While much of the full feeding of cattle is still done in the Corn Belt by farmer feeders, the South, Southwest, and Western areas have developed highly specialized cattle-feeding operations, much of it mechanized. A modern cattle feed lot is truly a beef factory (Fig. 31-3).

When selecting cattle for the feed lot, consideration should be given to grade, sex, age, condition, and freedom from disease and parasites. Disposition of animals placed in the feed lot is very important. Animals that are wild or of a nervous temperament will seldom do well.

Successful feed-lot operation requires advanced planning and careful supervision. Lots should be cleaned, water tanks cleaned and filled, and adequate feeding facilities made available. When animals are received—usually following a long haul by truck or rail—they should be given access to water and a limited quantity of grass hay, and then be permitted to rest for a time before being handled or sorted. Cattle that are to be full-fed on grain should be started on feed gradually. A daily grain allowance of 1 lb. for calves and 2 lb. for older animals is considered safe amounts with which to start. These amounts should be increased gradually over a period of 10–14 days.

Fig. 31-3. Mr. Harvey McDougal, owner of the McDougal Livestock Company, Collinsville, Calif., overlooking a portion of the feedlot accomodating 15,000 head. The yard is designed for feeding from an automatic delivery truck. Note the slope of the yards for drainage and the mounds in each pen for loafing areas in wet weather. Concrete or redwood log aprons about 10 feet wide along the feed troughs prevent miring. [Photo by Don Holt.]

Cattle are assumed to be on full feed when they are consuming approximately 2 lb. of concentrates (or 3 lb. of a mixed ration) for each 100 lb. of body weight. Mixed rations containing 35–50% chopped roughage can safely be offered feed-lot animals in greater initial quantities. Rations of this kind can also be increased at a faster rate than high-concentrate rations. A common practice is to allow cattle a self-feeder in the lot.

Initial weight and condition, kind of ration used, desired market weight, and grade are factors that determine the length of the feeding period. When feed-lot cattle have reached the desired market weight and grade they should be sold. Weight gains made in the later stages of the feeding period are much more costly than gains made earlier; therefore it is important to "top out" cattle as they reach desired weight and grade.

All cattle, when handled or worked—as in dehorning or branding—will lose weight. During shipment, too, whether by truck or by rail, animals will lose weight. This weight loss is referred to as shrink, and it is affected by length of haul, weather conditions, condition of animals prior to shipment, type of ration fed, and fill at the market. When animals are to be shipped from feed lot to market they should be handled in the normal or accustomed manner prior to shipping. Any abnormal change in ration or other nonroutine changes will usually result in greater shrink to market.

Feed-lot cattle are subject to several familiar ailments. Perhaps most common is going "off feed," usually resulting from some digestive disturbance or other organic cause. Many feeders look first to the feed supply to make certain that no abrupt changes have been made in the ration or that spoiled feed has not been used. Another common feed-lot problem is the occurrence of "bloat" among individual animals, although this seldom occurs in a large number of animals at the same time. "Urinary calculi" results from blocking of the urinary tract by calcium deposits from the bladder. This ailment occurs infrequently but when it does prompt action must be taken to save the animal. "Foul foot," characterized by severe lameness in advanced stages, is sometimes a serious problem in all classes of cattle. Many experienced feed-lot operators have ways of treating minor cases of these ailments. In acute or persistent cases it is wise to seek the service and help of a qualified veterinarian.

31-6. COMMON MANAGEMENT PRACTICES

Marking and Identification. For many years stockmen have made a practice of marking their animals primarily to establish and maintain ownership. The development of our purebred breeds of livestock has made it necessary that individual animals be identified. In fact, purebred registry associations require that each individual animal recorded in the herd books be permanently marked and identified.

The most common means of marking beef cattle for permanent identification is hide branding. Much of the history and tradition of the Western ranges centers around this practice, and it is still widely used in the West and Southwest. Hot iron brands are applied with either a fixed-style brand or a so-called "running iron." Chemical brands are used in a limited way. Other means of marking range cattle include ear notching, ear slitting, and slitting a portion of the dewlap to form wattles.

In purebred herds the most common method of identification is ear tattooing. When properly applied, this provides a lifetime identification and in no way disfigures the appearance of the animal. Other means used to mark and identify individual animals are: horn brands in the case of horned cattle, numbered neck chains or neck straps, and numbered metal or plastic tags. In many experimental herds a hot-iron number brand is used as a permanent mark of identification. While this method may be objectional in herds of registered cattle because it disfigures the hide, it does offer a permanent, easy way of identifying individual animals.

Vaccination. Beef calves are born with—or develop it shortly after birth —immunity to certain diseases. For some diseases this immunity is only temporary or of limited duration. Vaccines have also been developed which will supplement this natural immunity and, for a few diseases, provide lifetime protection against their occurrence. Some of the more common diseases for which vaccines are available are blackleg (*Clostridium feseri*), malignant edema (*Clostridium septicus*), and contagious abortion (*Bacillus abortus*). The advice and service of a well-qualified veterinarian is of utmost importance in maintaining herd health and sanitation.

Parasite Control. Beef cattle are subject to the usual cattle parasites. Two of the most common external parasites are flies and cattle lice. In some sections of the country screwworms are a serious problem during the late summer and early fall months. Certain internal parasites are also common in cattle, perhaps the most usual being the cattle grub, in the late winter and early spring months. This parasite may be very costly to the cattle feeder at certain seasons since buyers will usually discount an animal that is heavily infested with cattle grub. In some areas of the country certain kinds of stomach worms are a serious menace.

The control measures recommended by livestock specialists in the various areas are usually effective in controlling most of the common cattle parasites. When using chemicals to control parasites it is very important to observe all the precautions and recommendations of the manufacturer, especially when applying the product to feed-lot animals. Regulations of the Pure Food and Drug Administration of the Federal Government require that animals slaughtered for beef contain no chemical residues which may result from treating them for parasite control.

Castration. Bull calves are castrated primarily for economic reasons. Steers produce a more desirable beef carcass and they are more docile than bulls. Castration may be done at any age, from day-old calves to mature animals, but it is somewhat more hazardous to castrate a calf after 3 months of age. The most common method of castration involves the surgical removal of the testicles from the scrotum. While this is a rather simple operation, an inexperienced person should consult a veterinarian or other qualified person before attempting to castrate a bull calf. During the operation the general rules of animal health and sanitation must, of course, be observed.

Recently Pope *et al.* (1959) have shown that it is possible to accomplish many of the results of castration through stilbesterol implants. Weight gains and carcass characteristics of intact bull calves implanted with 24 mg stilbesterol at $3\frac{1}{2}$ months of age were intermediate between intact bull and steer calves of the same age.

Dehorning. Some breeds of beef cattle are horned. While well-trained horns may be considered a desirable asset in a registered herd, they are not desirable in commercial herds. Commercial cattlemen follow a practice of dehorning all but the herd bulls, since dehorning commercial beef animals ordinarily increases their market value. Horned animals may be dehorned at any age; it is much more desirable, however, to dehorn them as calves. Many herd owners follow a practice of dehorning, castrating, and vaccinating at the same time, usually prior to 3 months of age.

There are several common dehorning tools. They include a dehorning tube, dehorning spoon, specially designed dehorning pincers or clippers, and a dehorning saw. A bell-shaped hot iron and an electric heated hot iron are also available as dehorning tools. Still other herd owners use a caustic chemical as a means of dehorning very young calves.

Before attempting to dehorn an animal the inexperienced person should be instructed by an individual familiar with the use of a particular dehorning tool. Some general precautions should be exercised in dehorning. Avoid extremes in weather conditions, and avoid dehorning during fly season. Early spring or late fall are generally considered the most desirable seasons for dehorning animals. The animal's health and customary sanitary precautions must be observed.

Record Keeping. Complete and accurate herd records are a valuable asset to the management of any beef cattle herd. Herd records are essential in the operation of a purebred herd when the management expects to register the animals. Breed registry associations have established certain basic requirements which must be met before animals can be recorded in the herd books. In addition to making sure that animals meet the basic eligibility requirements for registry, the breeder must provide information on date of birth, sex, color and markings, whether horned or polled, tattoo or other individual identification, name of animal, breeder, first owner, and perhaps a statement relative to whether the calf is the result of artificial insemination. In short, the owners of a registered herd must have a complete set of records.

The more progressive owners—of both registered and commercial herds —maintain records of the productivity of their cow herds. From an economic standpoint such records are very valuable. Records may include information on number of calves born, number weaned, weaning weight and grade, and whatever other information is desired by the owner. Such records provide valuable information when selecting herd replacements and aid in culling the cow herd.

Fig. 31-4. A good set of records will help in deciding which of these cows is the more profitable. (See text.)

In recent years beef cattle producers have shown much interest in records of performance and production of beef cattle, for such records serve to identify the most efficient animals. Data on regular calving, mothering ability of the cow, rate and efficiency of gain, and quality of carcass are all very important in determining net income from a beef cattle enterprise.

In 1955 a national organization was established to encourage the keeping of records on the performance of beef cattle, for purpose of selecting and producing more productive breeding cattle. Many states have similar organizations administered by the State Agricultural Extension Service or by a state association. Many well-known herds, both registered and commercial, are now keeping and using performance records to aid in the improvement of their cattle.

The importance of keeping accurate records in a selection program is illustrated by the two cows shown in Fig. 31-4; both have raised eleven calves under identical environmental and feed conditions. Calves from the cow shown at left (No. 44) have averaged 521.3 lb. at 210 days of age. Calves from the cow at right (No. 125) have averaged 383.1 lb. at 221 days of age. The difference in lifetime production of these two cows is 1520 lb.; in other words, cow 44 has produced the equivalent of three additional calves, weighing 506 lb. each, with little additional feed or maintenance costs.

Equipment for Beef Cattle. Equipment for handling beef cattle should be practical, safe, and reasonable in cost. Major items of equipment required include adequate shelter, good fencing, paved feed lots where animals are confined to a small area, adequate water and feeding facilities, corrals, holding pens, some form of restraint equipment, and preferably a scale.

Shelter requirements for beef cattle vary, depending on climatic conditions. In midwestern and northern range sections animals must be provided protection from wind and rain. Beef cattle can withstand severe cold if they are adequately fed and kept dry. Continued exposure to cold winter rains and wind will result in severe weight loss as well as a much higher body maintenance requirement. Open sheds facing the south generally provide sufficient shelter except in case of severe winter storms.

In much of the West and Southwest, especially the more arid regions, many cow herds are maintained the year long on pasture, the only shelter being that of timber and other natural windbreaks. In areas where shelter must be provided, consideration should be given to the location of sheds and barns. Shelter areas should be well drained and readily accessible from both pasture and service areas. Where winter feeding is done inside barns or sheds the feeding areas should be convenient to both the feeder and the cattle.

Good fences, properly constructed, are one of the most valuable assets on livestock farms and ranches. Fencing need not be expensive, but the useful life of a fence will be largely determined by the manner of its construction.

Corrals or holding pens are essential when groups of animals are to be handled, and should be designed for convenience and ease of handling. They should be strong and made from material requiring a minimum of maintenance. Gates in pasture fences and corrals should be sturdy and located to provide easy access to all areas where animals are to be moved and handled. On many large ranches an auto gate or "cattle guard" is located alongside the gate used to move animals from pasture to pasture. Cattle guards save considerable time and labor when driving about the ranch.

One of the most essential items on cattle farms and ranches, even though not generally included as equipment, is an adequate water supply. In many areas natural streams or lakes provide excellent water sources. Since great numbers of beef cattle are raised in the more arid sections of the country, the problem of an adequate supply becomes a major concern on many large ranches. Farm ponds or earthen tanks are widely used in the range area as a source of stock water. Windmill-operated wells are also commonly used to supply water. On many large ranches one man or a crew of men is detailed to the job of keeping the windmills in good repair.

Cattle-feeding equipment should be convenient, have a low maintenance cost, and remain serviceable over an extended period of time. The amount and kind of feeding equipment required depends on the size and type of cattle operation on a given farm or ranch. Many cow herds are maintained on the range with little or no feeding equipment. During periods when supplemental feeding is necessary, herds may be fed pelleted protein supplement on the ground. In areas where more frequent feeding is required feed bunks are desirable.

One desirable item of equipment, regardless of the size of operation, is a "squeeze chute," used to restrain animals when they are being handled. A well-designed, sturdy, well-located loading chute is an essential item on farms and ranches where numbers of animals are moved by truck.

Saddle horses are also very necessary on large cattle ranches. This is one phase of agriculture where the horse is still as valuable as he was fifty years ago. Many of the large cattle ranches in the West still keep a band of mares and a good stallion to grow the saddle stock needed on the ranch.

Other items of needed equipment include balling guns, branding irons, calf puller, castrating knife, dehorning equipment, fencing equipment, flashlights, lariat rope, saddles, syringes, tattoo machine, and a supply of common biologics and medications.

Special Problems in Management of Herds of Registered Beef Cattle. The management of herds of registered beef cattle presents some problems not found in the operation of commercial herds. The detailed records needed to register animals, the merchandising of animals, fitting for showing at livestock expositions, and special herd health consideration are concerns not ordinarily connected with management of commercial cow herds.

One of the major problems in the conduct of a registered herd is the merchandising of cattle. Registered animals can be and sometimes are sold through the normal market channels. In order to provide the operator with a reasonable return on his investment registered animals must sell for substantially higher prices than commercial animals. Successful selling of registered animals requires salesmanship, advertising, fair dealing, and a reasonable guarantee as to the soundness of animals sold. Animals are normally bought and sold by private contract or at public auction.

Fitting and showing of registered animals at livestock shows provide an opportunity to display part of the herd to the public. Many herd owners feel that this is one of the most effective forms of herd advertising. Records of performance may have greater advertising value than show-ring winnings.

Federal and state animal-health agencies regulate the interstate movement of breeding animals. The official state animal-health agency issues health certificates which permit interstate movement of breeding stock. The prudent cattleman will make sure that breeding animals purchased in another state have been tested for contagious diseases and that an official health certificate—showing them to be free from diseases—accompanies the interstate shipment of such animals. Animals exhibited at livestock shows must be accompanied by an official health certificate.

Sound beef cattle management will always pay good dividends.

REFERENCES AND SELECTED READINGS

References marked with an asterisk are of general interest.

Botkin, M. P. and J. A. Whatley, Jr., 1953. Repeatability of production in range beef cows. *J. Animal Sci.,* 12:552.

Chambers, D., J. A. Whatley, Jr., and W. D. Campbell, 1954. A study of the calving performance of two-year-old Hereford heifers. Okla. Agr. Expt. Sta. Misc. Publ. MP-34.

Gifford, W., 1953. Record of performance tests for beef cattle in breeding herds. Ark. Agr. Expt. Sta. Bull. 531.

Pinney, D., L. S. Pope, A. B. Nelson, D. F. Stephens, and G. Waller, Jr., 1960. Effect of different amounts of winter supplement on the performance of spring calving beef cows. Okla. Agr. Expt. Sta. Misc. Publ. MP-57(60).

Pope, L. S., E. J. Turman, L. E. Walters, K. Urban, and J. Halbert, 1960. Implanting steer, bull, and heifer calves in a fat slaughter calf program. Okla. Agr. Expt. Sta. Misc. Publ. MP-57(26).

*Snapp, R. R. and A. L. Neumann, 1960. *Beef Cattle.* 5th Ed. Wiley, New York.

*Wagnon, K. A., R. Albaugh, and G. H. Hart, 1960. *Beef Cattle Production.* Macmillan, New York.

Chapter 32

Dairy Cattle Management

There is in all of us a psychological tendency to resist new ideas.
BEVERIDGE, W. I. B., *The Art of Scientific Investigation,*
Random House, New York, 1959

32-1. INTRODUCTION

Since the beginning of history the cow has been useful to man in many ways. Not only has she been a source of food and a beast of burden, but she has even played an important role in his religion, mythology, and political economy. Dairying undoubtedly had its beginning long before the advent of historical writings; the oldest graphic records are pictures discovered in the Libyan caves, believed to have been made no later than 9000 B.C.

The oldest written records, the cuneiform writings of the Sumerians, indicate that dairying existed 6000 years before Christ. Remains of Swiss lake dwellers that date back about 4000 B.C. include not only the skeletons of cattle but also equipment for cheese making. Records of an era a thousand years later, discovered in Egypt in excavations of tombs, reveal that milk and milk products were probably widely used by the Egyptians. The Old Testament contains many references to milk and butter.

Yet in spite of man's dependence on the dairy cow during these early historical times, accomplishments in dairying during the thousands of centuries indicated are insignificant in contrast with developments of the last century.

One hundred years ago, dairying was largely a family affair. Even in towns and villages most families kept a cow for their own use; the milk was consumed largely in the raw state, and the surplus was made into butter and cheese in the home. Dairying gradually became more specialized, and people bought milk, butter, and cheese from farmers farther out in the country.

Today, obtaining milk from the cow is only a first step in the very complex process of producing dairy foods. With the gradual development of large centers of concentrated populations, the dairy industry has become divided into three separate and distinct phases—production, processing, and distribution. The producer of milk plays an important role in this extremely complex industry.

Since dairy products constitute a quarter of the human diet, the steady increase in population has required a tremendous increase in annual milk production. Farm income from milk amounted to 4.7 billion dollars in 1960, during which period dairy cows in the United States produced 122.9 billion pounds of milk, an increase of 5.2 billion over that produced in 1946, even though the numbers of cows have decreased since 1946 in every year except 1953. In contrast, the average production of milk per cow has increased 43% in the past 14 years (USDA, 1961).

Increasing costs of production—a result of the rising costs of labor, feed, and modern equipment—have necessitated greater efficiency in production. Dairymen have been forced to improve the methods of feeding, breeding, and caring for the dairy cow—phases that may be combined under the general term "management."

Progress in methods of management has been considerable, but many problems still await solution. Testing associations have published results that suggest what more can be done. During 1960, cows enrolled in the Standard Plan of the Dairy Herd Improvement Association testing program produced at an average yearly rate of 11,045 lb. of milk and 428 lb. of milk fat (USDA 1961), whereas all cows in the United States averaged only 7004 lb. of milk and 263 lb. of fat (USDA 1961). This difference reflects improved management and the use of bulls capable of siring daughters that respond to such management. If even 50% of the cows in the United States produced as much as those in the Standard D.H.I.A., the 122.9 billion lb. of milk produced by about 18 million cows in 1960 could be produced by less than 14 million.

Consider also that many cows under excellent managerial conditions have produced over 25,000 lb. of milk and 1000 lb. of milk fat. There are at least two reasons why one could not expect today to obtain a herd average comparable to the recent world record of the Holstein cow Princess Breezewood R. A. Patsy—36,821 lb. of milk and 1866 lb. of milk fat on twice-daily milking in 365 days. First, we do not have enough information on the mode of inheritance of maximum capacity for milk and fat production, and, second, the care and feeding of this animal was doubtless more elaborate than would be consistent with present commercial practice. Even so, information on such inheritance is increasing, and improved managerial practices will continue to improve average production per cow.

Modern dairy management encompasses a wide field of activities involving a constantly increasing application of many sciences. Only the briefest reference can be made here to its numerous phases. Training in chemistry, genetics, and nutrition, and specialized courses in feeds and feeding methods and dairy cattle management are required for comprehensive understanding of the problems involved and the advances of the last 25 years.

Initial outlay is large in establishing a dairy herd, with its requirements for land, buildings, corrals, and equipment. As a rule dairymen start with milking cows so as to provide an immediate cash income. For the purpose at hand, however, we will start with the calf and continue briefly through the various phases of dairy management.

32-2. CALF RAISING

It is becoming increasingly difficult to maintain and improve a dairy herd by purchasing replacements for the milking herd. With purchased stock the dairyman is unable to follow a breeding program that will improve the productive capacity of his herd. He is also in constant danger of introducing infectious diseases. For the average dairyman, herd improvement involves raising female calves sired by bulls of superior transmitting ability.

The dairy calf is born following a gestation period averaging 278 to 288 days, depending on the breed—shortest for the Jersey, longest for the Brown Swiss. At birth the normal calf has a strong inherent capacity to grow. The dairyman, however, must provide the proper environment (feed and care) for development to be normal. Successful methods of raising calves are based on fundamental principles of nutrition, physiology, and disease control.

The growth of the calf from birth until it enters the milking herd falls naturally into five stages.

The first stage is the two days following birth, when, starting within an hour of birth, the calf should receive colostrum, the mammary secretion produced by the cow immediately following parturition. Colostrum is not only nutritionally most nearly perfect for the newborn calf but it contains antibodies that help the calf resist certain infectious diseases encountered during the first few days of life (Smith and Little, 1922).

The second stage extends through the second week of life. At this time the calf should receive whole milk fed at a rate of 7–8% of its body weight. If an unlimited milk-feeding method is to be used after two weeks, the daily rate may be increased to 10%.

The third stage is from 2 weeks to 6 months, during which a change is usually made to one of the minimum milk methods, wherein a limited amount of milk is supplemented with a partial milk replacer. Research at many colleges and universities continues to seek more exact information on the specific nutrients required by the young calf. This third stage carries the calf past the period of greatest mortality, averaging about 10–12%, largely from infectious diseases. Unsanitary conditions and improper nutrition are important factors in reducing the young calf's resistance to disease. Where climate is favorable, many dairymen use individual pens that can be moved to clean ground each time they start a new calf; see Fig. 32-1.

The fourth stage, from 6 months to 1 year, presents a relatively simple problem. During this period calves usually receive pasture and concentrates, and hay also if pasture is poor or unavailable.

During the fifth stage, from 1 year to 2 years of age or more, the feeding program is similar, requiring only sufficient feed for normal growth. It is during this period of development that the heifer is bred for first preg-

Fig. 32-1. Calf mortality due to disease may be reduced through use of movable calf pens where climatic conditions permit.

TABLE
32-1. | *Age and weight schedule for breeding dairy heifers.*

Breed	Age to breed (months)	Normal weight (pounds)
Holstein	18–20	850–900
Ayrshire	17–19	700–750
Guernsey	16–18	600–660
Jersey	15–17	525–570

nancy. Age alone does not necessarily determine the proper time for breeding, since rate of growth can be materially influenced by feed intake. Table 32-1 shows the ages at which heifers may be bred if they have made the indicated normal growth.

The advantage of early calving is evident in that the period between birth and first lactation is unproductive. Nevertheless, premature breeding is a serious mistake since body size and milk-producing capacity are related. After freshening the undersized heifer is unable to consume enough food for both maximum production and growth. Heifers raised in different herds but sired by the same bull show marked differences in producing ability, due to size and finish at time of first calving; see Table 32-2.

TABLE
32-2. | *Heifers raised in different herds, but sired by the same bull, show marked differences in producing ability due to size and finish at time of first calving.*

	Herd number								
Sire number	1	2	3	4	5	6	7	8	9
	Heifers' producing ability* (lb. milk fat)								
62A	316		369	376	386				
333C	277					374		375	
370A	365					456	435	448	
372A	284	312		380				374	
372B		297		347					
372C	302	320		361		384			
374B		280		316					369
375B	297					380			362
375E		296	336					389	
498B		286	308	348					
572B		387	379					441	472

* All records are for junior two-year-olds; 305-day lactations; twice daily milking.

32-3. THE MILKING COW

The average heifer freshens at the age of 26–28 months. During the first lactation she needs feed to continue growth, besides producing milk. In succeeding lactations the amounts of feed needed will increase for the normally expected increase in milk production as well as for body maintenance. During the last stages of pregnancy the cow requires additional nutrients for growth of the fetus and for building up reserve body tissues for use during the next lactation. These nutrient requirements, established in numerous feeding trials, are presented in the form of feeding standards—for example the Morrison Feeding Standard (Morrison, 1956) or that adopted by a committee of the National Research Council (National Academy of Sciences, 1956).

Roughages and Concentrates. Feeds used by the dairy cow may be divided into two general classes—roughages and concentrates. Roughages contain a relatively high percentage of fiber and have a comparatively low feeding value; examples are hays, pastures, and silages. These feeds usually supply nutrients at lower cost than do concentrates, although that might be changed by land prices and/or transport costs in some areas. Classed as concentrates are grains and their by-products, and by-products of oil-bearing seeds. They contain less fiber than roughages and a higher percentage of total digestible nutrients. Both roughages and concentrates may be divided into those containing high and low percentages of protein.

Vitamins and Minerals. The experienced operator of a dairy herd seldom has difficulty in supplying needed vitamins in sufficient amounts. Green plant tissue supplies carotene, the precursor of vitamin A. The relationship was discovered only as recently as 1919 (Steenbock, 1919), but it was thousands of years earlier that lack of green feed was associated with the most typical symptoms of vitamin A deficiency. The evidence is in the Bible (Jeremiah 14:6): "And the wild asses did stand in the high places, they snuffed up the wind like dragons; their eyes did fail, because there was no grass."

The entire vitamin B complex is synthesized in the rumen of the cow. A calf whose rumen has not reached sufficient development obtains B vitamins from its food. There is evidence, however, that under certain artificial feeding conditions the calf may require a supplementation of some members of the B complex (Ronning and Benevenga, 1960).

Vitamin D is supplied through sunlight and sun-cured roughages. The cow usually experiences no difficulty in supplying its needs of this vitamin from natural sources; the calf, in contrast, may require supplementation if allowed too little milk or roughage or if raised in a part of the country with insufficient sunlight.

Vitamin E has been shown to be necessary for normal reproduction in the rat; this has not been demonstrated in the cow (Gullickson *et al.,* 1949). Even so, a deficiency of this vitamin has been associated with cardiac damage. However, since all common feeds contain some vitamin E, it would be difficult to formulate a ration, for cow or calf, that is deficient in this vitamin.

The dairy cow requires many minerals for proper body functioning and milk production. Those needed in largest amounts are calcium and phosphorus. Normal feeding of legumes supplies sufficient calcium, and concentrates fed in proportion to milk production supply adequate phosphorus. Minerals needed in lesser amounts (often referred to as trace minerals) are also supplied by the natural feeds. In certain sections of the country, however, the soils, and thus the feeds grown thereon, have been found to be deficient in phosphorus and the trace minerals—iron, cobalt, iodine, copper, magnesium, and manganese (Becker *et al.,* 1953). In such areas mineral supplementation is common.

A disease known as milk fever (parturient paresis), usually limited to high-producing cows, is caused by a lowered blood calcium (hypocalcemia). The condition rarely occurs before the third lactation, making its appearance during the first week following, or even during, parturition. The disease progresses with increasing paralysis, prostration, and coma, ending in death unless calcium gluconate is administered intravenously or unless the udder is inflated to reduce milk secretion. Presumably the parathyroid glands, which have as their sole function the control of blood calcium, are unable in the case of high-producing cows to quickly increase their secretory activity in order to mobilize the large amounts of calcium required for milk secretion which occurs during or immediately following parturition. Boda and Cole (1954) suggested that the activity of the parathyroid glands could be increased through the use of a low calcium–high phosphorus diet during the month previous to parturition, followed by a normal legume hay and concentrate ration. This management program was highly effective in reducing the incidence of milk fever. Hibbs and Pounden (1955) have shown that milk fever can be prevented by feeding massive doses of vitamin D for 3 to 7 days before calving.

The chief value of the dairy cow is in her ability to consume large quantities of roughages and convert them into milk, an important human food. The modern cow, however, through breeding and selection has been developed to such a high degree of productivity that she cannot consume enough roughage to meet all of her needs. In addition, therefore, she must receive some concentrates. The composition of the concentrate will depend to a large extent on the quality of the roughage. Legumes, being high in protein, may be supplemented with cereal grains; grain hays, being low in protein, must be supplemented with a percentage of high-protein feeds —the oil meals, for example.

A brief discussion such as this cannot enumerate the various conditions that determine concentrate allowances; courses in animal nutrition are designed for this purpose. Generally speaking, the amounts fed depend on the productive capacity of the cow, the relative costs of nutrients in roughages and concentrates, and the price of milk.

32-4. ECONOMY OF HIGH PRODUCTION

Neither herd size nor total milk production determines profit in the dairy business. Profit is determined by income in excess of cost of production. Feed represents 50–60% of the total operating expense. The second-largest cost is labor. Other costs include veterinary fees, depreciation, supplies, repairs, utilities, taxes, and interest on investment. A low-producing cow costs about as much to maintain as a high-producing cow. True, feed needs increase with increases in milk production, but the cash return on milk increases faster than increases in feed expense. This fact has been demonstrated many times in studies of cows of various levels of production in the Dairy Herd Improvement Associations (Fig. 32-2).

The reason why the high producer is profitable is that she uses a smaller proportion of her feed in maintaining her body, even though her inherited stimulation to produce more milk results in a greater food consumption (Fig. 32-3). This has been demonstrated effectively by Eckles (1956).

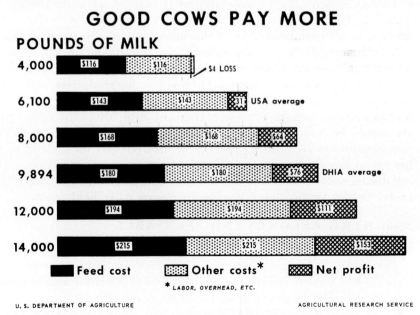

Fig. 32-2. In low-producing cows all income goes into costs.

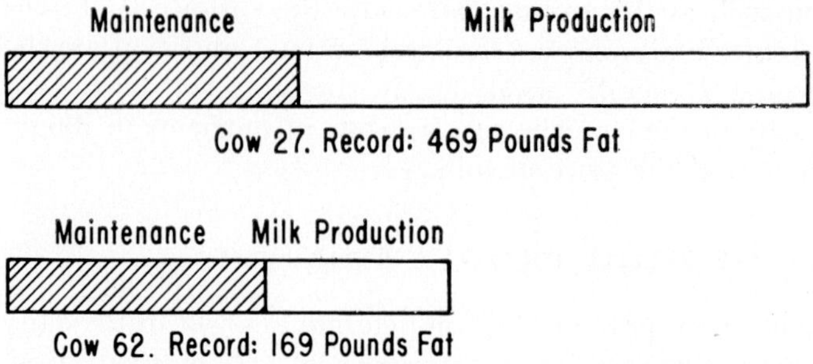

Maintenance   Milk Production

Cow 27. Record: 469 Pounds Fat

Maintenance   Milk Production

Cow 62. Record: 169 Pounds Fat

Fig. 32-3. The use of feed by No. 27 and No. 62. The amount used for maintenance was about the same for both. In addition, No. 27, on account of her greater internal stimulation to produce milk, used 2.6 times as much feed for milk production as No. 62. The higher producer uses more feed, but is the more economical because of the smaller overhead in the form of maintenance. [From Eckles, Dairy Cattle and Milk Production (5th ed.), Macmillan, New York, 1956.]

Profit in the dairy business depends both on having cows with inheritance for high production and on providing them an environment that permits full expression of their inherited potential.

32-5. PRODUCTIVE LIFE OF THE DAIRY COW

Though individual cows have lived to 17 years or more, the average cow leaves the herd at between 5 and 6 years of age. Since cows calve, on the average, at approximately 2 years this allows only 3–4 years of productive life. Each year, 20–25% of the animals over 2 years old are culled or lost from the milking herd because of low production, infertility, mastitis, miscellaneous diseases, or accidents. Thus, since the productive ability of a cow tends to increase with each succeeding lactation up to maturity (around 6 years old), the average cow leaves the herd at or before the age at which she should be returning the greatest profit. The net return from the first two lactations of an average producer will scarcely pay for the cost of raising her to first freshening. Improvements in management practices, including disease control and breeding for high production, will reduce this excessive cost of replacements, thereby increasing dairy herd profit.

32-6. HERD RECORDS INDISPENSABLE FOR MAXIMUM PROFIT

The modern dairyman cannot operate successfully without complete herd records—but unused records are wasted records. A record system must be easy to maintain; otherwise it will soon be neglected.

There are a number of satisfactory methods. Figure 32-4 shows a system adequate for all records but those on herd health and production; those

COW No.	DATE OF BIRTH	DATE OF LAST CALV-ING	DATE TO BREED	BREEDING DATES AND BULL USED	DATE DUE	DATE CALVED	No. SEX AND WEIGHT	DATE TO BREED	BREEDING DATES AND BULL USED	DATE DUE	DATE CALVED	No. SEX AND WEIGHT

BREEDING & CALVING SCHEDULE   DATE FROM_____ TO_____

Fig. 32-4.   A convenient form for recording breeding and calving data. It serves also as an inventory of the heard.

may be kept in a herd book, examples of which are shown in Figs. 32-5 and 32-6. Another successful method, even for large herds, has been a card file in which each card contains the lifetime breeding and calving records of a single cow. The following records are essential.

Dropped *May 1st 1950*   Name *Anna May*   Herd No. *98*   Reg. No. *3347467*

Purchased from_____   Bred by *Joe Green*   Sold to *Culled 3/25/55 - Sterility*

Sir Calantha

Segis Sid Herd No. 1A

Sylvia

Anna May

Vacinated for Brucellosis 9/15/50

Retained Placenta 8/17/53

Treated for Mastitis 2/20/55

Black Beauty

Lady Fayne Herd No. 59

Lady Pontiac

BREEDING RECORD

Date of Service	Number of Bull	Date of Calving	Sex of Calf	Name of Calf	Herd No.	Remarks
11/2/51	3 A	8/14/52	F	Betty May	153	
11/5/52	5 B	8/17/53	M	Bobby Anna May	98A	Sold John Smith 1/6/54
12/30/53	5 B	10/7/54	F	Cathy May	175	Died 10/20/54 - Scours
12/8/54	3 A					
12/29/	3 A					
1/19/55	5 B					
2/11/	5 B					
3/3/	16 C					

Fig. 32-5.   Herd book form—front side. A permanent record of ancestry, breedings, calvings, health, and date and reason for disposal.

PRODUCTION RECORD

MONTH	YEAR 1952 Milk Lbs.	Fat %	Fat Lbs.	1953 Milk Lbs.	Fat %	Fat Lbs.	1954 Milk Lbs.	Fat %	Fat Lbs.	Milk Lbs.	Fat %	Fat Lbs.	Milk Lbs.	Fat %	Fat Lbs.	Milk Lbs.	Fat %	Fat Lbs.	Milk Lbs.	Fat %	Fat Lbs.	Milk Lbs.	Fat %	Fat Lbs.
January																								
February																								
March																								
April																								
May																								
June																								
July	13			18																				
August	928	4.3	39.9	775	4.4	34.1																		
September	1736	4.2	72.9	1816	4.1	74.4	20																	
October	1678	4.1	68.8	1700	4.1	69.7	1440	4.3	61.9															
November	1452	4.1	59.5	1502	4.0	60.1	1860	4.1	76.2															
December	1487	3.7	55.0	1500	3.9	58.5	1790	4.0	71.6															
January	1348	3.7	49.9	1400	3.8	53.2	1610	4.0	64.4															
February	1215	3.7	49.9	1360	3.8	51.6	1300	3.7	48.1															
March	1116	3.5	39.1	1225	3.6	44.1	1200	3.7	44.4															
April	1114	3.6	40.1	1213	3.7	44.9																		
May	980	4.0	39.2	1224	4.0	44.9	Culled 3/25																	
June	440	4.2	18.5	1002	4.0	40.1																		
July	dry 6/22			950	4.1	38.9																		
August				336	4.2	14.1																		
September				dry 8/12																				
October				305 d																				
November				14343		565																		
December	908 d			356 d			165 d																	
Total	13494	3.91	528	15901	3.95	629	9200	3.97	367															

Fig. 32-6. Herd book form—back of Fig. 32.5. Production records are essential for effective management.

(1) Herd inventory	(4) Calving dates, and sex and herd number of calf
(2) Breeding dates and bull used	(5) Milk and fat production
(3) Due dates	(6) Herd health

Herd Inventory. Identification of all animals in the herd, whether pure-bred or grade, is highly important for intelligent breeding and feeding programs. A simple numbering system is desirable; the animal is identified by number soon after birth by ear tag, neck chain, ear tattoo, or brand.

Breeding Dates and the Dry Period. Breeding dates are necessary for prediction of expected calving date so that a sufficient dry period will be provided. Generally speaking, efficiency is greatest when the calving interval is 12 months and the period of lactation is 10 months. A cow will produce less milk if milked continuously than if she has a dry period of 6 to 8 weeks. The proper interval between lactations will depend on the cow's condition of flesh. Milk production is a heavy drain on the cow; she needs a rest period for restoring body reserves, particularly of calcium and phosphorus, since milk contains a high concentration of these minerals.

The Service Sire. The bull used for service should also be recorded, in both grade and purebred herds, so that the resulting calf, especially a female, can be identified with its sire. The progeny test measures genetic progress through the sire. The milk and fat production of each daughter of the sire is compared with her dam's production, or the daughters may be compared with their stable mates or contemporaries. This latter method has the advantage of eliminating yearly variations from changes in feed and care.

Records of the production of both daughter and dam or of stable mates are not necessarily made at the same ages. Results of progeny tests are commonly expressed in terms of twice-daily milking, a lactation of 305 days, and mature age. Factors have been developed for converting immature records to mature age and for adjusting records made by cows milked more than twice daily (USDA, 1955). Take as an example a Holstein cow that freshens at 2 years of age, is milked thrice daily, and in 305 days produces 8000 lb. of milk and 320 lb. of milk fat. To estimate the production of this cow when mature, and if milked twice daily, multiply the above production figures by the factor 0.83 for number of times milked daily and by 1.31 for age. That gives 8698 lb. of milk and 348 lb. of milk fat.

Calving Dates. Calving dates, sex, and herd numbers of all calves should be recorded at time of birth, and the calf identified with its dam. These records, together with identification of the sire, are essential for an accurate progeny test.

The date of calving is important for another reason. It has been established that the normal healthy cow should not be bred for at least 60 days following parturition. The reproductive tract requires that much time in which to regain its normal physiological state. Cows that have had an abnormal gestation period, either too short or too long, or have experienced dystocia or retained placenta, will usually require a longer rest period. Such cases should be referred to the veterinarian.

The Estrous Cycle, Pregnancy Diagnosis, and Due Dates. Next to low production, infertility is the reason for culling the largest percentage of cows from many dairy herds. This is a subject on which volumes have been published (Cole and Cupps, 1959) and on which research is still being conducted at many institutions. Accurate records of breeding dates followed by a pregnancy diagnosis not only will indicate the extent of trouble but in some cases will reveal the cause.

When the cow is pronounced pregnant the due date should be calculated on the basis of the normal gestation period for her breed, and recorded on the calving schedule. Many cases of low breeding efficiency have been traced to carelessness in recognizing and recording the estrous periods. The herd should be observed at least twice daily. Cows may not always show the most obvious symptom of "heat"—standing for other cows to mount. If all observed periods are recorded and the cows involved are watched closely during the period 18 to 24 days later, there is more chance of catching those that do not show pronounced symptoms of "heat." The estrous cycle of the normal cow varies between 18 and 24 days. The estrous period, or the time during which the cow will accept the bull for service, lasts about 18 hours. Ovulation occurs about 10 hours after the end of estrus (Trimberger, 1948; Moeller and VanDemark, 1951). Variations may indicate abnormal conditions not conducive to efficient reproduction.

Milk and Fat Production and the Testing Programs. The milk and fat production of the cow determines her economic value and is the basis for feeding, culling, and breeding for improvement of the herd. Efficient management requires regular and continuous production testing of the entire herd and recording the results in a systematic manner.

A number of programs are available for production testing. The National Cooperative Dairy Herd Improvement Association provides three types of programs. These are designed primarily for grades (cows ineligible for registration in the herd books of the breed associations), but they are also available to breeders of registered purebreds. The breed associations provide two programs; only registered purebreds are eligible.

The National Cooperative Dairy Herd Improvement Association is sponsored by the Agricultural Research Service, U.S. Department of Agriculture, and the Extension Services of the Land Grant Colleges. Each local association is operated under the direction of a board of directors consisting of participating dairymen assisted by the college of agriculture extension service. Dairymen may select one of three available programs—the Standard, the Owner-Sampler, or the Weigh-A-Day-A-Month plan. Under the Standard Plan, a supervisor hired by the association visits the herds on test once a month and weighs the milk produced by each cow during a 24-hour period. The percentage of fat in the milk is determined by the Babcock test on composite samples of the morning and night milkings. From the 24-hour test the supervisor estimates the monthly production of each cow, from which is calculated the herd's annual average. In most states the supervisor also records the amount and cost of feed and determines income per cow. Of the two and one-half million cows included in all three plans, 72% are tested under the Standard Plan (USDA, 1961). The next largest number, 25%, are enrolled in the Owner-Sampler program, in which owners of smaller herds may obtain the necessary information at less cost, since the owner rather than the supervisor weighs and samples the milk. The samples are tested at a central laboratory, and the monthly production is calculated and entered in the owner's herd book. The Weigh-A-Day-A-Month plan is the least costly but supplies less information. The milk of each cow is weighed by the owner; the milk is not sampled for fat determination. The local extension agent calculates the monthly production of each cow and returns the information to the owner on a form provided. All three plans include almost 15% of the milking cows of the nation.

Two programs, Advanced Registry and Herd Improvement Registry, are provided by the breed registry associations for testing registered purebreds. They are jointly referred to as Official Testing. For these two systems of testing the Purebred Dairy Cattle Association, an organization of representatives of the breed associations, has established rules and regulations that, with few exceptions, are the same for all breeds.

A Superintendent of Official Testing is appointed by the College of Agriculture. His duty is to approve the appointment of supervisors who do the testing and to direct the programs in accordance with established regulations.

The Advanced Registry testing program provides for the testing of selected cows. The owner is required to record and forward to the breed association individual daily milk weights (optional with Jerseys). Test periods must be preceded by a preliminary milking, at which the supervisor observes that the cow has been milked dry.

Herd Improvement Registry is increasing in popularity since it provides for testing the entire herd at a relatively low cost and gives a more accurate measure of the productive ability of the breeder's herd than does the testing of selected individuals. Neither daily milk weights nor dry milkings are required.

Herds engaged in either A.R. or H.I.R. testing programs are visited each month by the supervisor, who is required to identify each cow by comparing her color markings or ear tattoo with those shown on her registration certificate. During a 24- or 48-hour period the supervisor weighs the milk of each cow and tests it for fat. His report is sent to the State Superintendent, who checks and forwards it to the breed association. Production tests are published at regular intervals by the breed associations. When tests have been completed, in either 305 or 365 days, production certificates are issued for cows on Advanced Registry, and to owners of herds completing a year's record in the Herd Improvement Registry.

Another testing program recently adopted and supervised by both the State Extension Dairyman and by the Breed Superintendent of Official Testing is called Dairy Herd Improvement Registry. It provides that records made by cows registered in the breed association and tested under the Standard plan of the Dairy Herd Improvement Association may be used if such records meet certain requirements in addition to those provided for the Standard plan.

Detailed rules are in "Unified Rules for Official Testing," revised in 1960, obtainable from the secretary of the Purebred Dairy Cattle Association, Peterborough, New Hampshire.

Health Records. Since disease takes a heavy toll of dairy cattle, health records can be extremely valuable. A disease of great economic importance is mastitis, since it causes reduced milk flow and is responsible for a high percentage of cows culled from the herd. Mastitis is an inflammation of the udder, caused either by infection or by undue stress on the delicate mammary tissue, or by a combination of both. It is becoming increasingly evident that the most important factor in controlling this disease is management rather than treatment. Most cows are milked by machine and many dairies are also equipped with milk pipelines that carry the milk directly from the cow to refrigerated bulk tanks. Proper use and care of this equipment is an important factor in controlling mastitis. Modern milking machines operate on the principle of an alternating vacuum between the teat cup liner and the teat, regulated by a pulsator, while a constant vacuum is maintained between the teat cup shell and the liner. The amount of vacuum and the pulsation rate vary with machines of different makes, because of differences in design. It is important to operate milking machines in accordance with recommendations of the manufacturer and to keep all equipment in first-class operating condition. Improper operation of the milking machine can cause abnormal stress on the mammary tissue, a contributing factor in the development of mastitis.

The teat cup assembly and the milk pipeline must be thoroughly cleaned and sanitized after each milking, both to ensure a clean milk supply and to reduce transmission of mastitis organisms from infected to uninfected cows.

Modern milking practices require preparation of the cow for proper letdown of milk before teat cups are applied, and prompt removal of teat cups when udders are evacuated.

In many herds it is common practice to conduct routine examinations for mastitis. The findings can help the dairyman locate the causes, whether infection or improper operation of the milking equipment. Herd health records should include dates and herd numbers of animals vaccinated for various diseases. Reproductive difficulties, examinations, and treatments should be carefully recorded.

Additional Records. The breeder of purebreds requires additional records. He is responsible to his breed registry association for the accuracy of the ancestry of all animals offered for registration. Special care must be exercised in recording the sire and dam of each calf born in the herd. The breeder of purebreds should maintain a herd book in which the ancestry of all animals is recorded in an accurate and systematic manner. Calves offered for registration in the breed association are reported on application forms that require detailed information on date of birth, proposed name, color markings or other identification, and the registration names and numbers of sire and dam. When the application has been accepted, the breed association issues a certificate carrying the name or names of breeder and owner, registered name and number of the animal, its identification, and the registered names and numbers of its sire and dam. These registration certificates should be filed in an orderly manner for future reference.

Breeders participating in the breed association type classification program should file these records preferably by sires. Such information should be studied to determine what improvement in body conformation, if any, is being made by each successive sire.

32-7. THE HERD SIRE

No other decision is more closely related to the dairyman's success or failure than is selection of the herd sire. Many examples could be cited, but the University of California Loan Bull Project demonstrates well how production can be increased with good sires. Sons of University bulls with several generations of proved high production were loaned, over several years, to cooperating dairymen. The results are shown in Table 32-3. That the increase in production was due largely to the inheritance introduced by the sires is indicated by the small amount of culling for low production, since most of the herds increased in cow numbers through heifers sired

TABLE 32-3. | *Increase in milk production as a result of genetic improvement.*

Herd no.	Before Using University Sires (3-Year Average)		After Using University Sires (Last 3-Year Average)	
	Number of cows in herd	Average yearly production* (pounds M.F.)	Number of cows in herd	Average yearly production* (pounds M.F.)
1	19	305	303	439
2	16	354	143	454
3	19	301	208	429
4	17	360	38	448
5	46	368	94	447
6	18	337	44	501
7	13	352	60	417
Average	21	340	127	448

* Dairy Herd Improvement Association records.

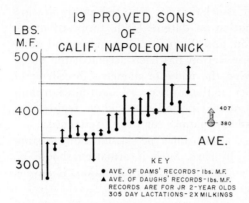

Fig. 32-7. The genetic value of a sire as reflected in the producing ability of his sons' daughters.

within the herds. Nineteen sons of California Napoleon Nick (Fig. 32-7) were used in the project, and he himself was used in four of the herds, with the results shown in Fig. 32-8. Genetic improvement must be combined with good management if milk production is to increase.

Management of the Sire. Management of the herd sire is comparatively simple, requiring only good judgment on the part of the caretaker. During early life, male and female calves are fed similarly except that the milk feeding period of the young bull should be extended to 6 or more months of age so as to promote early sexual maturity through maximum growth. Male calves should be separated from the heifers when they are 4 to 5 months old. When milk feeding is discontinued the future herd sire should have free access to best-quality legume hay, if possible, and 4 or more pounds of concentrates daily. The amounts of these feeds up to 3 to 4 years of age must be sufficient to promote rapid growth. The mature

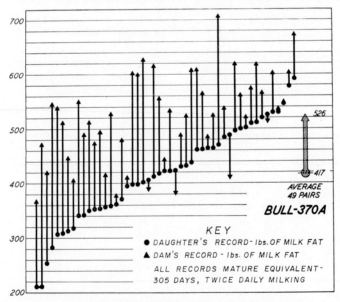

Fig. 32-8. Low production is the major reason for disposal of cows from the milking herd. Superior sires reduce cost of herd replacements.

bull, 4–5 years old and older, should be fed only enough to maintain thrifty conditions. Unlimited amounts of feed, even of good roughage alone, will make him overly fat, and therefore a sluggish and uncertain breeder. The mature bull should receive a limited amount of good-quality roughage, 10–15 lb. daily, and 4–6 lb. of concentrates, which may be those fed the milking herd. The amounts, naturally, will depend on body size and the extent of use of the bull.

The reason for the interest in early sexual maturity is that a long time is required to determine the true value of the bull. A bull well cared for can be used in natural service once weekly, beginning at 1 year of age. Many bulls, however, are not well enough developed for service under 18–24 months of age. Even when bulls are used as early as 1 year, it is seldom possible to complete the progeny test before the bull is 5 to 6 years old.

32-8. ARTIFICIAL INSEMINATION

Artificial insemination is the most revolutionary development in the history of dairying. Possibilities for its use in the improvement of dairy cattle and other livestock are almost unlimited. The first unit was organized in 1938, in Clinton, New Jersey, by Professor E. J. Perry, following his enthusiastic report on a program in Denmark. From a small start, with 1050 cows enrolled the first year, the program has expanded to every state until, in 1960, 7,144,679 cows were artificially inseminated with semen from 2544 bulls—an average of 2808 cows per bull (USDA, 1961). In natural service, bulls seldom breed as many as 50 cows a year.

Artificial insemination organizations may be cooperatives or privately owned. In either case, sires are carefully selected, usually by a bull committee. Since these bulls are used to service large numbers of cows the committee can be very selective and can afford to pay the high prices asked for outstanding proved sires or well-bred young bulls. The semen from these bulls then becomes available to all dairymen who wish to make use of the service, most of whom could not afford to own such bulls. Other advantages include elimination of the danger of handling bulls on the farm, low cost of service, and less chance of disease spread than in natural service. For further information on this subject consult Perry (1960) and Salisbury and VanDemark (1961).

32-9. CONCLUDING REMARKS

The trend in dairying has been toward larger and higher producing herds, owing largely to the narrowing spread between costs of production and return on investment. To satisfy sanitation requirements, expensive barns and equipment are needed; for this reason, the size of herds has been increased so that these facilities may be used for a higher percentage of the day, in order to justify the cost of barns and equipment. High labor costs have resulted in the installment of labor-saving equipment and have stimulated effort toward higher production. The cost of maintaining a low producer is nearly equal to that of a high producer. Artificial insemination has simplified the planning of a breeding program and has proved to be the cheapest means by which the dairyman can obtain semen from superior sires to increase production. Knowledge of the nutritive value of feeds and feeding according to production but in line with the cost of the feed and the selling price of the product is an important consideration. Feeds of similar nutritive value often vary in price. The ratio of concentrates to roughage will differ, depending on the costs of the nutrients in these feeds and on the price the dairyman receives for his milk. Proper milking practices can improve production and reduce mastitis, one of the diseases responsible for the heavy loss of cattle from the milking herd. Other diseases, some of which are responsible for low breeding efficiency, must be controlled to reduce culling and to thus lower the cost of production. Dairying has become a highly specialized enterprise requiring a strong background of knowledge in biological sciences as well as training in business management.

REFERENCES AND SELECTED READINGS

References marked with an asterisk are of general interest.

Becker, R. B., P. T. DixArnold, W. G. Kirk, George K. Davis, and R. W. Kidder, 1953. Minerals for dairy and beef cattle. Florida Agr. Expt. Sta. Bull. 513.

*Cole, H. H. and P. T. Cupps, 1959. *Reproduction in Domestic Animals.* Vols. 1 and 2. Academic, New York.

*Eckles, C. H. and E. L. Anthony, 1956. *Dairy Cattle and Milk Production.* 5th Ed. Macmillan, New York, p. 145.

Gullickson, T. W., L. S. Palmer, W. L. Boyd, J. W. Nelson, F. C. Olson, C. E. Calvery, and P. D. Bayer, 1949. Vitamin E in the nutrition of cattle. I. Effect of feeding vitamin E poor rations on reproduction, health, milk production and growth. *J. Dairy Sci.,* 32(6):495–508.

Moeller, A. N. and N. L. VanDemark, 1951. The relationship of the interval between inseminations to bovine fertility. *J. Animal Sci.,* 10:988.

*Morrison, F. B., 1956. *Feeds and Feeding.* The Morrison Pub. Co., Ithaca. pp. 1087–1088.

*National Research Council, Natl. Acad. of Sci., 1956. Nutrient Requirements of Domestic Animals. No. 111, Nutrient Requirements of Dairy Cattle, Publ. 464, revised.

Perry, E. J., 1960. *The Artificial Insemination of Farm Animals.* 3rd Rev. Ed. Rutgers University Press, New Brunswick, New Jersey.

Ronning, M. and N. J. Benevenga, 1960. B-vitamin requirements of calves fed a high carbohydrate diet. *J. Dairy Sci.,* 43(6):892 (Abstract).

*Salisbury, G. W. and N. L. VanDemark, 1961. *Physiology of Reproduction and Artificial Insemination of Cattle.* Freeman, San Francisco.

Smith, T. and R. B. Little, 1922. The significance of colostrum to the newborn calf. *J. Expt. Med.,* 36:181–198.

Steenbock, H., 1919. White corn vs. yellow corn and a probable relation between the fat-soluble vitamin and yellow plant pigments. *Science,* 50:352–353 (New series).

Trimberger, C. W., 1948. Breeding efficiency in dairy cattle from artificial insemination at various intervals before and after ovulation. Nebr. Agr. Expt. Sta. Research Bull. 153.

USDA, 1955. Agr. Research Service, Dairy Husbandry Research Branch. ARS-52-1.

———, 1961. National Cooperative Dairy Herd Improvement Program. Agr. Research Service, 37(2):44–93.

———, 1961. Agr. Marketing Service, Crop Reporting Board. Milk production and dairy products. Washington, D.C.

———, 1961. National Cooperative Dairy Herd Improvement Program. Agr. Research Service, 37(3):44–97.

———, 1961. Economic Research Service, April 1961.

———, 1961. Communication from J. F. Kendrick, Asst. to Chief Dairy Herd Improvement.

Chapter 33

Swine Management

33-1. INTRODUCTION

The evolution of a concept of swine management developed during the present century in the United States and Canada has carried the industry far from the "pigsty" and "pork barrel" era. There are still pigsties to be found today, but certainly the economic pressures of the modern world are converting the swine industry into one comprised of larger units, founded on sound business principles and operated on a scale that can justify more extensive utilization of scientific knowledge and automation. This improvement is destined to intensify as human populations continue to expand and as we move gradually out of periods of grain surpluses and into increasing competition for food between man and his livestock. For a more extensive insight into potential competition for basic food resources, see Leitch and Godden (1941).

One of the outstanding characteristics of swine is their ability to act as a marketing medium for surplus grain or grain damaged by frost, drought, rust, rain, or storage. At times this has been a mixed blessing; when large quantities of feed grain are available, swine marketing increases with resultant price depressions. Hog production has been particularly vulnerable to cyclic fluctuations in selling prices; economists believe, however, that the trend to larger production units and to greater specialization will have a moderating effect on the marketing aspects. The potential effects of expanding human population on the demand for meat has interesting possibilities, too.

Somewhat traditionally, the student of animal husbandry has been taught that the three fundamental factors governing success or failure in the livestock business were feeding, breeding, and management. What is management? Is it, as implied, something separate from the other phases of production? Perhaps management should be defined as the responsibility for securing an optimal blend of all the various aspects of production—physiological, nutritional, and genetic, as well as marketing—so as to maximize net profits.

The material in this chapter is designed to focus brief attention on some of the production problems not dealt with in detail elsewhere and which have tended, by tradition, to be regarded as management problems. Actually the keen student will find extensive discussion on many of the following points in the literature and will find also that these areas are not immune to scientific advance, change, or debate.

33-2. SWINE PRODUCTION AS A BUSINESS

Why Raise Pigs? Pigs long ago earned the title of "mortgage lifters," ample testimony that they have generally been profitable to raise. In numbers and in terms of human consumption, swine and pork products rank a close second to cattle in both Canada and the United States.

Other factors favoring swine production are the high yields of edible meat from the market hog and the multiplicity of products manufactured by packing houses from hog carcasses.

As long as consumer demand, domestic or export, is ample to sustain adequate prices in relation to alternative types of production, and particularly when abundant supplies of low-cost grains are available, there will be a thriving swine industry. The operator who stays in business and who is able to survive the recurring periods of low prices will be the man who likes pigs and who maintains enough interest in them to keep himself up-to-date on the subject. We have not yet reached the era when pigs—or any other class of animals, for that matter—can be raised by a robot!

Size of Operation and Capitalization. With the day of diversified farming on the decline, economists are suggesting that units marketing less than 200 to 300 hogs per year are likely to be submarginal in nature and not in a position to realize satisfactory returns to labor and capital. Conversely, operations resulting in the sale of 700 to 1000 hogs or more annually represent reasonable major enterprises (Figs. 33-1 and 33-2). Only when specialization is quite intensive is there likely to be sufficient economy of overhead to sustain production with narrow operating margins or enough net-income incentive to induce the maximum capitalization and general development of the enterprise.

Statistics on the costs of production of pigs vary with time and location but feed costs usually represent 50–75% of the total costs. So important are the feed costs that the difference between low and high feed efficiency (lb.

Fig. 33-1. Interior view of a 500-ft facility for fattening swine that is designed to accommodate 1000 or more animals. The round self-feeders are filled by means of an automatic unloading truck. Note the tilt-up walls adjoining the alley; they are raised 4 inches above the level of the floor so that pens can be cleaned by hosing into gutter along side of alley. [Photo by Don Holt.]

feed/lb. gain) often spells the difference between profit and loss. So far as overhead costs are concerned, the allowance for permanent facilities apparently should be in the range of 7–19% of the gross returns. Currently this would be equivalent to a new-cost overhead investment of from $250–300 per litter. Keeping below this limit constitutes a definite challenge to management.

Hog production is financed in a variety of ways. Until relatively recently swine producers were independent operators, but the advantages of larger operations have introduced *contract farming* or *vertical integration,* whereby a large share of the necessary capital is made available by feed companies, abattoirs, or other interests. Similar mutual arrangements are possible between owners of breeding stock and the caretaker; a kind of landlord-tenant relationship. Credit facilities may also be considered particularly for short-term operating loans but it is to be remembered that swine production, as it increasingly specializes, is becoming more and more of a business venture requiring careful management of all aspects of production.

Production Systems

THE PIG BREEDER. The producer of registered gilts and boars has been the mainstay of the swine industry. Upon him has rested the major responsibility for maintaining and improving the quality of commercial swine, for he has supplied many of the boars and sows used in commercial herds. Traditionally the livestock exposition has been the "testing ground" and show window for his produce but during the last quarter century increasing attention has been paid to progeny and performance testing, including carcass quality appraisal, which provide more useful and direct evaluations.

THE COMMERCIAL PRODUCER. Commercial operation involves the maintenance of sufficient brood sows and boars to produce the feeder pigs needed to fill the available facilities. Ordinarily the operator retains his own female replacements but purchases his sires from purebred breeders.

"PIG HATCHERIES," FEEDER PIG PRODUCERS. Much of the risk of mortality in swine production is associated with the period between conception and the time of weaning. Therefore special attention is required at this stage. Specializing in the production of feeder pigs offers distinct advantages to the industry and a special challenge to enterprising swine breeders—the production of disease-free pigs of outstanding genetic value is an excellent goal. Unfortunately, many such ventures have failed, mostly for reasons associated with inadequate facilities, poor disease control, or unsound financing.

Fig. 33-2. A portion of facility shown in Fig. 33-1 to show how manure is hosed into gutter along side of alley. [Photo by Don Holt.]

FEEDER OPERATIONS. This type of swine enterprise depends on the purchase of feeder pigs. The operations are usually conducted on a relatively large scale, often utilize cooked garbage, and consequently may be located near cities.

Feeder units of this type engender a greater degree of risk of diseases and parasites because the previous history of the pigs is often unknown and pigs may have become available as feeders because of their previous un-thriftiness. Consequently, special precautions for disease and parasite control must be adopted routinely and the operating margin of profit must be wide on account of the extra risk.

33-3. MAINTAINING THE BREEDING HERD

Assessment of Quality in Swine. Quality must be determined in relation to the important economic traits. These differ somewhat depending on sex and whether the animals are being kept for breeding or for market. Swine shows have played an important role in furthering the production of superior breeding stock but to expand their influence will necessitate the inclusion of carcass and performance data into the judging standards.

Performance Testing and Progeny Testing Programs. Denmark leads the world in hog-testing programs. It has long had a clear objective—to produce lean pork on the most economic basis—and has adopted central station testing and formulated policies whereby the superior strains of breeding stock would be utilized most effectively. Canada has had a testing policy in operation since 1928, patterned to a considerable degree after the Danish system (Fig. 33-3). Both countries were able to organize their schemes on national bases and were perhaps fortunate in being able to concentrate efforts on single breeds.

Somewhat by contrast, the performance testing of swine in the United States did not receive real impetus until the post-World War II era, when great surpluses of animal fat had accumulated. The National Association for Swine Records has now adopted a Production Registry (P.R.) policy and a program for Certified Meat Hogs. It is possible for a breeder, subject to the regulations of the particular breed involved, to obtain official recognition for prolificness of sows (including their nursing ability, as reflected by 56-day weights of the progeny), for breeding performance of boars that sire 15 or more P.R.–qualifying litters, and for litters (matings) that yield desirable meat-type carcasses within a 180-day age limit.

The Canadian Record of Performance program involves the preweaning inspection of litters on the farm for litter size, disease, abnormalities, breed disqualifications, and so on. Then, if accepted, two gilts and two barrows are station tested. The pigs are fed standard rations to 200 lb. liveweight, are slaughtered, and the carcasses are evaluated. The final report sum-

Fig. 33-3. Interior view of a Record of Performance swine testing station in Canada. Each pen houses 4 litter mates between 50–200 lb. Pigs are self-fed balanced rations and slaughtered at 200 lb for carcass evaluation. [From National Bacon Hog Policy Production Service, Ottowa, Canada.]

marizes the performance with respect to litter size, maturity, carcass score, and feed efficiency; it includes similar statistics for the average performance of all pigs tested in that particular station. The breeder can readily determine, if he tests a fair sample of his herd, how his stock rates in any respect with other breeders' pigs and can, from the published reports, decide what breeders have the quality features that he needs in his next sire. (More details on performance testing are given in Chapter 16.)

Choice of Breed. The motivating force behind the selection of a breed often contains emotional elements and while this bespeaks something of the potential success of a livestock man, one's emotions should not preclude sound judgment based on factual evidence of economic performance. Some breeds are decidedly superior to others in terms of prolificness, vigor, carcass quality, and feed efficiency, and these factors should be considered. Furthermore the producer should not render himself immune to the periodic advances made through animal breeding research and performance-testing programs.

Selection of Female Breeding Stock. Gilts should be from a sow with a superior record in terms of as many important economic traits as possible: soundness and health, prolificness, mothering ability, type, and quality (Fig. 33-4). When performance-testing data are available, it may be possible to select with knowledge of several generations' performance. The particular mating is important. Gilts from tested matings and from strains testing well over several generations are the best selections.

Gilts will breed, if well grown and developed, by the age of 5 to 6 months, but research has proven that larger, stronger litters will be obtained if breeding is delayed until gilts weigh 250–280 lb.

Selection of Boars. This aspect of management cannot be overemphasized. It is unwise to buy a sire that does not have the genetic material necessary to maintain or improve quality in his offspring. The operator should carefully examine the variations in net profits that might occur on his farm as a result of failure to attain reasonable goals in feed efficiency, market quality, and freedom from abnormalities.

Most breeders buy young unproven boars largely because of the physical problem of breeding young gilts to mature boars. The use of breeding crates, and perhaps ultimately of artificial insemination, may greatly extend the usefulness of mature boars of proven quality. Far too many boars are recognized as outstanding breeders only after their disposal. The advantages of crossbreeding for the commercial hog raiser are discussed in Chapter 16.

Animal Identification. Any program of selection requires that pigs be identified at least as to sire and dam. The easiest method to follow is that

Fig. 33-4. An ideal blend of type and performance. Glenafton Duchess 94M-511603-, herself a show winner and from a litter of champions, she scored on R.O.P. 13-156-87-4.25, 13 pigs weaned, 156 days maturity to 200 lb, 87 carcass score and 4.25 lb feed/lb carcass gain (3.33 lb feed/lb live gain). She has 16 functional nipples and a strong family history of both R.O.P. and show winnings. [Courtesy E. F. Richardson & Son, Semans, Sask.]

of ear notching with special pliers. There are several systems that can be used, depending on the number of swine that have to be identified (Fig. 33-5). Purebred swine must be identified by inked ear tattoos, according to regulations set forth by the appropriate registration authorities.

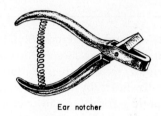

33-4. HOUSING AND EQUIPMENT

Swine Performance and Environment. Swine production on this continent embraces a very wide range of climatic conditions and involves extremely important considerations of housing, insulation, shade, cooling, heating, and so on, that vary from region to region. For the first few days of life pigs have an optimum environmental temperature of about 80°F; growing pigs (of 50 lb. upward) appear to have an optimum temperature of

Ear notcher

Fig. 33-5. Ear notching is a convenient method of identification. Several numbering systems are available. This one allows numbering about 10,000 pigs without repeating numbers. A maximum of two notches is permitted in the 1 and 3 areas, but only one notch in the central (9) areas.

60–75°F. Mature pigs can be maintained satisfactorily during winter temperatures as low as −30° to −40°F if given well-bedded sleeping shelters. Growing and mature pigs begin to exhibit signs of heat stress at about 80°F. Any extended departure from the zone of thermal neutrality involves some reduction in performance. Bearing in mind that swine production is a business, the operator must assess the hazards of unfavorable environment and weigh the risks against the costs of alternative remedial action.

Characteristics of Good Housing. It is difficult to arrive at decisions as to suitable layouts in this field of changing ideas. Great advances have been made in automation, building materials, heating, and ventilation facilities. Regardless of the design and facilities ultimately chosen, however, the costs should be kept in line with regional recommendations of farm economists. As a rule the heaviest investment per unit of floor space will be in the farrowing quarters, where special attention is needed to control temperature, humidity, ventilation, diseases, parasites, and accidental mortality. The amount of space required for swine depends upon the age and reproductive state (Table 33-1).

Class of swine	Floor space in square feet
Dry sow	20–40
Sow and litter (in farrowing stall)	35–40
Sow and litter (in pen)	50–80
Weaning to 125 lb.	4–10
125 lb. to market weight	8–15

Feeders and Waterers. Slop-feeding of pigs, except in garbage-feeding operations, is now largely history. Lactating sows are individually fed and sometimes receive their rations wet, but self-feeders (sometimes automatically filled by augers extending from feed grinders or mixers) and automatic waterers are in widespread use for market hogs. In this way the pigs can have free access to balanced diets and will gain rapidly and efficiently if the feeders are properly designed and operated to minimize waste.

Swine-handling Equipment. Much time can be lost if the facilities for moving and controlling pigs in barns or on pastures are inadequate. Care should be taken to ensure that gates, doors, and alleyways are designed with a view to efficient handling. Clubs, canes, and brute force are incompatible with sound management and good husbandry. Simple plywood "wings," electric prods, hurdles, loading facilities, and gates are much more effective.

Scales. Every swine producer needs a reliable scale to know when pigs are ready for slaughter and to assist in his selection of breeding stock. Weight guessing and indirect weight estimates based on body measurements are either too cumbersome or too inaccurate for use in an efficient enterprise. If the scale is portable it can be inserted into an alley when required and the pigs can be maneuvered through it easily.

Barn-cleaning Devices. Mechanical manure handling saves much labor. The method adopted could be one of many: gutter cleaners, which require minimum shoveling of manure; tractor and front-end loader for use in large or open lots; and flushing with water into a storage tank, followed by periodic pumping out and spraying on farm land as fertilizer.

Sanitation. Diseases and parasites being major hazards (see Chapter 43), the importance of good sanitation is obvious. This is particularly true in

Fig. 33-6. A modern design farrowing house with capacity for 45 farrowing crates. (Left) Overall view. Facility is designed for cleaning by flushing with hose; over 3000 pigs were farrowed here between March and November, 1961. (Right) Close-up showing flooring made of 9 gauge, diamond-shaped pressed metal. Each pen measures 5 feet by 7 feet with a crate 26 inches wide. [Photo courtesy Don Holt and Dr. P. C. Enge.]

the farrowing area because of the high susceptibility of newborn pigs until their resistance is built up by colostrum and by exposure to prevailing disease germs. The sanitary advantages of concrete, and perhaps asphalt, over porous, absorbent material are readily seen. No sow should be allowed to farrow in quarters that have not been thoroughly scrubbed and disinfected with a hot 1–2% lye solution or some other approved disinfectant.

The sources of feed and drinking water should be designed and located so as to minimize dangers of contamination. Pastures and dry lots may be heavily infested with parasites and disease germs; while some cleaning procedures can be taken it is probable that pasture rotation and feed medication are more realistic approaches to outdoor problems of this type.

Farrowing Facilities. It is desirable, if not essential, to conduct farrowing operations in quarters separated from other swine (Fig. 33-6). The period from birth to weaning is especially critical. Newborn pigs are easily crushed or trampled; their metabolism is very high and consequently they have relatively large milk requirements; their temperature regulatory system is slow to adjust to the extra-uterine environment and they are born with virtually no disease antibodies in their blood. Consequently such devices as radiant-heated floors, heat lamps, guard rails in farrowing pens, and farrowing crates or stalls have been widely adopted in efforts to reduce the hazards (Fig. 33-7).

33-5. CARE OF THE PREGNANT SOW

Shelter and Exercise. The preferred accommodation for the bred sow is a pasture lot provided with an inexpensive shelter to protect her from

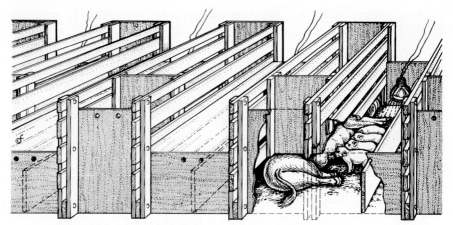

Fig. 33-7. A battery of farrowing stalls. Equipped with heat lamps and sometimes radiant-heated floors in the sleeping areas for the piglets, these stalls restrict sow movement and reduce mortality at farrowing time.

inclement weather. Locating the feed and water supply some distance from the shelter will induce more exercise.

Feeding. During the summer a nonlactating sow can derive most of her nourishment from green pasture. It is advisable, however, to ensure adequate intakes of essential nutrients by providing supplementary feeds— depending on the quality of the pasture and the condition of the sow. Sows tend to fatten excessively so energy intakes may have to be limited by reducing the grain intake or by feeding a low-energy ration.

The nutritional hazards vary with region and season but iodine, vitamin A, and calcium are commonly deficient in the major swine-producing areas. Most cereal grains also contain too little protein. While good pasture may alleviate some of these problems, great care should be exercised in making decisions on the feeding of bred sows. Reproductive failures due to faulty feeding are costly and entirely too common.

Prefarrowing Care. Several days prior to the expected farrowing date (112 days gestation period) the pregnant female should be brought to the farrowing quarters, washed off with soap and water, and placed in a clean pen. Operators using farrowing crates or stalls may prefer to delay close confinement until immediately before farrowing in order not to restrict exercise.

The onset of parturition, together with decreased activity and feed changes, may lead to constipation of the sow. This condition should be avoided by encouraging water consumption by wet feeding, or by including

10–25% wheat bran in the ration. There is a definite possibility that toxins absorbed or retained in the body as a result of constipation may adversely affect milk yield and quality and consequently prove harmful to the new-born pigs.

33-6. CARE OF THE LACTATING SOW

Accommodations. Accommodations may vary from somewhat elaborate indoor housing in pens, stalls, or crates to a small summer shelter on fresh pasture. With greater specialization in hog production, the sow and litter will probably be housed indoors, where it is easiest to provide the necessary special care.

Sow and litter pens containing sleeping platforms of concrete surfaced with asphalt have given good service. An adjoining brooder—enabling the piglets to travel directly from platform to brooder—is also advantageous. The brooder arrangement provides opportunity for the young pigs to be fed and handled separately and gives them safe sleeping quarters.

Feeding. The nutrient requirements of the sow do not differ appreciably in terms of ration composition between gestation and lactation, but a lactating sow or gilt will consume about twice as much food. The feed intake is governed largely by the milk yield and there is evidence of great variability in milk production between individuals and breeds. Studies reported in 1935 (Hughes and Hart; Bonsma and Oosthuizen) and more recently in 1960 (Allen and Lasley) indicate 56-day milk yields of about 350–400 lb. Lodge (1959) reported an average production in the sows he studied of 993 lb. Contained in these reports are indications of definite breed differences in yield and in time at which the peak of lactation is reached. Obviously there is a challenge to the breeder to select for good milking sows as well as reason to watch feeding methods.

Special care should be taken to encourage high feed consumption by sows. Heavy body-weight losses are not uncommon during lactation and may to some extent be unavoidable, but it is most economical to use food directly for milk production rather than to form body fat as an intermediate. Again, the introduction of substantial quantities of stored fat into the pool of absorbed nutrients may tend to unbalance the nutrient ratios.

Rebreeding. Sows may be observed in heat sometime during the first few days after farrowing. If bred at this time very few conceive. The sow should be bred at the first or second heat period after weaning. Early-weaning practices will enable some acceleration of breeding schedules. Treatment of lactating sows 40 or more days after farrowing with equine gonadotropin will induce estrus and ovulation with consequent conception following mating. This process, however, has not been used commercially to any extent. There is some evidence that "flushing" (breeding during a period of rapid gain) pays dividends, hence delaying breeding until the postweaning recuperative period seems to be advantageous.

Weaning. The preferred practice is to remove the sow from the pen and thus leave the piglets in familiar surroundings. In order to reduce the risks of udder inflammation the sow should be kept on reduced feed for several days after weaning and some operators who practice hand feeding reduce the allowance a day or two before weaning as well.

33-7. CARE OF THE SIRE

Accommodation. Mature boars can be handled most easily and may retain better temperaments if they are housed with bred sows, but when boars must be isolated they require somewhat stronger and higher partitions or fences than sows. The boar should have plenty of exercise area and should not be penned adjacent to other boars unless separated by a solid fence.

Feeding. The nutritional requirements of the boar vary with his age. Young boars are best maintained on a grower-type ration to ensure normal growth and development. High fit is undesirable. Older boars normally do well on a dry sow-maintenance ration that is either low in energy (maximum 70% TDN—total digestible nutrients) for self-feeding or restricted in amount to about 6–8 lb. per day.

Management of the Sire. Young boars in their first season of service are best hand mated to a maximum of about 5 females a week and 20 or 30 in the season. The intensity of service of course varies with vigor, temperament, and other factors. Boars should not be used for breeding until about 8 months of age.

Older boars may breed twice daily. Some have been known to handle 100 sows or more in a season but they were exceptional boars, under excellent management. Boars seldom remain useful after an age of about 5–6 years.

De-tusking and Castration. Mature boars should have their tusks removed at least once a year, as a safety measure for the operator and as a precaution against fighting with other swine. This is done by securely snubbing the upper jaw with a rope or cable to a post and clipping the tusks near the gum line. Similar means of restraint can be used for castration of large boars—an operation made necessary by the fact that boars must be castrated a month or two prior to slaughter for human consumption.

33-8. CARE OF YOUNG PIGS

The First Week. The first week of a pig's life is especially critical. During this time its temperature-regulating mechanisms are not fully functional, thus being endangered by chills. It is vitally dependent upon getting colostrum so as to obtain disease antibodies; in the pig, unfortunately, they are not transferred prenatally across the placenta. The small pig is also very subject to mechanical injury. Consequently an unfavorable environment—in terms of physical facilities, temperature, ventilation, or sanitation—may provide sufficient stress to precipitate pneumonia, diarrhea, rhinitis, or some other disorder.

Early versus Late or Normal Weaning. The swine industry has been built upon a program involving weaning at 6 to 8 weeks of age. As a result of phenomenal increase in nutritional knowledge during the past quarter century, however, it is now possible to wean pigs much earlier. In many operations weaning is practiced at from 1 to 3 weeks, with subsequent feeding on rather complex early-weaning formulas. Early weaning requires somewhat more elaborate facilities to care for the pigs and involves judicious use of more costly feeds, but there are compensations: the litters are more uniform because weak pigs get a chance to obtain adequate nourishment before receiving too great a setback, and the sow is ready for rebreeding at least a month earlier.

Opinions vary on the overall advantages of early weaning. Each producer should examine the relative merits of the two systems in light of his own facilities and marketing programs before deciding on his course.

A special problem in the piglet is control of anemia. This calls for the administration of a suitable iron preparation, commencing not later than the second or third day after birth. Either reduced iron, ferrous sulphate, one of a variety of proprietary oral mixtures, or, more recently, injectable iron may be selected. The injections are currently popular because one or two injections suffice, whereas oral preparations must be given at least weekly until substantial amounts of solid feed are being consumed.

Castration and Identification. For the easiest operation, male pigs intended for slaughter should be castrated during the first two months of life. Pigs could be ear notched at this time, or earlier, for purposes of identification. Castrating should not be done coincident with weaning or vaccination because excessive stress may precipitate other problems.

Feeding Formulas and Programs for Pigs up to 3 Months of Age. During this period the pig normally makes the transition from the mother's milk to dry feed. Consequently two factors are of prime importance: (a) the new diet must be palatable, and (b) the diet must be nutritionally adequate. In addition, it is commonly recommended that certain additives like anti-biotics and perhaps antihelminthics be included to provide extra protection against diseases and parasites. Because of the complexity of the ration the producer therefore frequently finds it to his advantage to rely upon com-mercially prepared rations, often pelleted or crumbled and sweetened. Such rations are rather costly compared to those used for older swine and based on home-grown feeds, but relatively small amounts are needed. It is very important that pigs do not receive a setback at this stage.

33-9. CARE OF GROWING PIGS (50–100 lb.)

Accommodation. There is an increasing tendency to raise pigs for market entirely indoors (Figs. 33-8 and 33-9). Pigs will do well on pasture and can derive much of their supplementary feed requirements from fresh green vegetation, but pastures tend to give rise to problems of parasites, sunburn (of white breeds), fencing, pasture seeding and maintenance, and others, which some operators prefer to avoid.

For indoor housing, pigs of this age require about 4 to 8 square feet of floor space. The larger the group, the less space required per pig. How-ever, from the standpoint of ease of observation for impending trouble the groups should be kept down to reasonable size—say a maximum of 50 or 60 pigs per lot. Pigs varying widely in size or weight should be divided into relatively uniform weight groups.

Cannibalism occasionally develops in market pigs. Although the causes are unknown it appears that overcrowding and faulty nutrition may be contributing factors. Once tail chewing commences, steps must be taken immediately to isolate the offending pigs and to exam-ine management procedures for possible causes.

Fig. 33-8. The feed hopper at right is sus-pended from a track; it is electronically con-trolled and is on a time clock. It automati-cally distributes feed and releases water to the hogs four times daily. [Photo by Don Holt.]

Feeding Formulas and Objec-tives. The growing stage of the pig's life involves major physio-logical emphasis on growth of muscle and skeleton and low pri-ority on fat synthesis. High-qual-ity pork products contain rela-tively little fat finish and a large proportion of lean meat. One should therefore capitalize on the pig's natural growth poten-tial by providing rations ade-

quately fortified with protein
(both as to level and quality),
minerals, and vitamins. Rapid
growth rates are to be desired at
this stage. A compensation for
adding commercial supplements
to farm grains is the high efficiency of feed conversion because
of the low fat content of the
gains. Good pigs, properly managed and fed, require less than
3 lb. feed per pound of gain at
this stage, whereas 4 or 5 lb. of
feed will be used per pound of
gain during the period just prior
to marketing.

Fig. 33-9. Same hopper as shown in Fig.
33-8. The water valve has been tripped by
the hopper and water is streaming from the
pipe onto the feed. This barn has a dunging
alley which is cleaned with a mechanical
scraper. [Photo by Don Holt.]

The feeder ordinarily uses local farm grains as the basis of his
feeding program from 50 lb. size
on up to market size, but maximum feed efficiency requires adherence to regional recommendations for supplementation. None of the grain species is
nutritionally adequate for pigs. Perhaps something less than maximum feed
conversion will be desirable during times when the cost ratios between grain
and supplements are widely divergent. Interesting publications are available
on this challenging border between nutrition and economics.

33-10. CARE OF FINISHING PIGS (100–200 lb.)

Objectives. The primary objective in the production of a market pig is
to satisfy the consumer demand as reflected through the meat-packing industry. It is difficult, however, to have a clear objective of market demand
unless payment is made on a carcass basis and unless reasonable price incentives are paid for quality. In Canada, rail grading of market-weight hogs
(140- to 195-lb. carcasses) has been in effect since 1935 and has been compulsory since 1940. The ideal carcass weighs between 135–170 lb., has a
minimum length from forerib to aitchbone of 29–30 in., a maximum
shoulder fat of $1\frac{3}{4}$–2 in., and maximum loin fat of $1\frac{1}{4}$–$1\frac{1}{2}$ in., each factor
varying with carcass weight.

With the demand for more lean and less fat, plus the desire to keep rate
of gain high and feed costs down, there are clear challenges to the nutritionist, the geneticist, the practical breeder, and also to the meat industry,
which may have to supply material encouragement to the producer in the
form of appropriate price differentials. At least part of the answers currently
available are (a) to market pigs at weights of 200 lb. or less, so as to produce

less fat and to avoid the poor feed efficiency of fattening per se; (b) to use breeds of pigs of lean, meat, or bacon type; and (c) to feed low-energy (maximum 70% TDN) rations during the 120–200 lb. stage so as to reduce rate of gain and degree of fattening. The latter, while usually effective in improving carcass quality, requires careful evaluation from the economic point of view with each set of cost-price conditions.

33-11. PRODUCTION OF BREEDING STOCK, AND HERD REPLACEMENTS

Since the primary objective in selecting herd replacements is to provide seed stock for commercial hog production, the feeding and management practices should be basically the same. The results of the special attention given to "show pigs" have too often led to serious disappointment when such animals were selected for breeding stock. The factors of prime importance are reliable evidence of superior performance in all important economic traits plus evidence of freedom from physical unsoundness, diseases, and parasites. As mentioned previously, good pastures are desirable for breeding stock, at least by the time they reach 100–200 lb. Exercise is beneficial and excessive fattening is highly undesirable.

An interesting recent development is the production of "pathogen-free" breeding stock. This technique, developed at the Hormel Institute and first applied in practice in Nebraska, involves farrowing pigs aseptically by hysterectomy. The pigs are then reared artificially in an isolated environment and constitute the nucleus of a new pathogen-free breeding herd. In this way the pigs are protected from exposure to the more troublesome diseases, such as virus pneumonia and atrophic rhinitis, for which no good preventative or curative measures exist.

It is important to realize that pathogen-free pigs have not been protected from *all* disease hazards. If this were the case they and their progeny would have little chance of survival upon exposure to commercial herds because so much of a pig's resistance to infection depends upon acquired immunity. The Nebraska results to date, however, are encouraging and may well play an increasing role in disease control in swine, at least until more direct and positive countermeasures against certain diseases are available.

33-12. DISEASES AND PARASITES OF SWINE

Space does not permit discussion of these very important issues. As testimony however to the extent of losses encountered in the U.S.A., the 1956 USDA Yearbook "Animal Diseases" indicates that of the 40 million pigs lost in 1954 some 50% of these succumbed to diseases or parasites.

Swine are subject to a variety of nutritional deficiency diseases resulting from faulty feeding (see Chap. 28); also to lice and mange, some six kinds of internal parasites, about 25 diseases of bacterial, viral or unknown origin. Many of these are regional and seasonal in occurrence. The swine breeder would be very much amiss not to be familiar with the symptoms, causes and control measures for problems likely to be encountered in his area. Full information is of course available in publications on Swine Diseases and from qualified veterinarians.

REFERENCES AND SELECTED READINGS

Reference marked with an asterisk is of general interest.

Allen, A. D. and J. F. Lasley, 1960. Milk production of sows. *J. Animal Sci.*, 19:1, 150–155.

Bonsma, F. N. and P. M. Oosthuizen, 1935. Milk production in Large Black sows. *So. African J. Sci.*, 32:360–378.

Hughes, E. H. and H. G. Hart, 1935. Production and composition of sow's milk. *J. Nutrition*, 9:3, 311–321.

*Leitch, I. and W. Godden, 1941. The efficiency of farm animals in the conversion of feedingstuffs to food for man. Imp. Bur. Animal Nutrition. Tech. Comm. Rpt. 14.

Lodge, G. A., 1959. The energy requirements of lactating sows and the influence of level of food intake upon milk production and reproductive performance. *J. Agr. Sci.*, 53:2, 177–191.

Chapter 34

Sheep Management, Including Feeding

Sir, I am a true laborer: I earn that I eat, get that I wear, owe no man hate, envy no man's happiness, glad of other men's good, content with my harm, and the greatest of my pride is to see my ewes graze and my lambs suck.

SHAKESPEARE, *As You Like It*

34-1. INTRODUCTION

Sheep are unique among domestic animals in their adaptation to adverse conditions. They can convert forage—from marginal agricultural land, mountains, hills, moorlands, plains, and deserts—into valuable products for mankind: wool, lamb, mutton, and pelts.

Latitude, altitude, and climatic conditions affect sheep farming. Methods of sheep husbandry may be different on farms or ranches within the same district. Sheep breeders of the past partly solved their problems by developing breeds to suit the divergent conditions of the various areas in which they lived. The many different breeds of sheep found today were each developed to suit a certain type of environment. Merinos and Rambouillets are favored because of their hardiness in hot desert areas with sparse vegetation. Mutton breeds such as Suffolk and Hampshire are popular in cooler climates with abundant vegetation. The increasing importance of lamb as meat has resulted in the development of Columbias and Targhees, which cross well with Suffolk and Hampshire rams to produce an excellent carcass and a heavy fleece and yet maintain the gregarious trait of the Rambouillet.

Today the importance of correct feeding, management, selection within a breed, and crossbreeding are more widely recognized. One thing is certain —breed alone cannot substitute for feed and management. Regardless of the breed used, sheep must be well fed and managed to obtain the maximum yield of lamb and wool. Economical maintenance of breeding animals, a large lamb crop, continuous and rapid growth of lambs, heavy weaning weights, and heavy clean fleece weights are all based largely on adequate nutrition and management.

Adequate nutrition and management for maintenance, reproduction, growth, fattening, and wool production are complicated because sheep are maintained under many environmental conditions. Farm and feed lot are much different from range areas. Variations in environment, however, are not limited to different geographical areas. Great differences may be found on neighboring farms or ranches.

34-2. METHODS OF SHEEP RAISING

Climate, topography, soil, vegetation, and availability of water vary greatly throughout the United States. This has resulted in a diversified agriculture. Four general systems of commercial sheep production fit into the agricultural pattern: (1) range sheep production, (2) farm flock production, (3) purebred breeding, and (4) fat lamb production.

Range Sheep Production. Range sheep are raised in all the seventeen Western states. This area comprises about 40% of the continental United States and approximately 70% of the sheep are located here. Other types of sheep raising are also practiced in the area where there are irrigated valleys or where there is an abundant feed supply. The area can be divided into nine range regions (Fig. 34-1): (1) tall grass, (2) short grass, (3) desert grass, (4) bunchgrass or palouse grass, (5) northern or intermountain shrub, (6) southern desert shrub, (7) chaparral, (8) pinion juniper, and (9) coniferous forest. There is no sharp boundary line between many of these regions, and there is justification for further separation of some of the regions. Space will not permit a detailed discussion of each of these regions.

Ranges on the Great Plains are often grazed year long to best advantage. However, most ranges of the mountain, desert, and foothill areas are best adapted to grazing at only one season of the year. These ranges can be roughly grouped into winter range, spring-fall range, and summer range. The season of year that a range should be grazed is determined by availability of stock water, elevation, depth of winter snow accumulated, season of plant growth, ability of forage to cure, danger from poisonous plants, and the time the range is needed to balance the forage supply on the ranch.

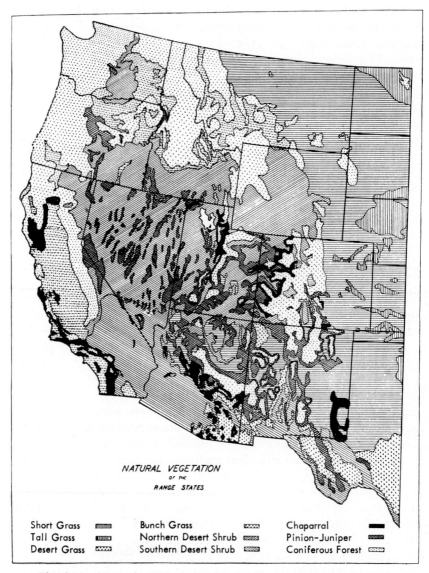

Fig. 34-1. Natural range vegetation regions of the range states. [From Stoddard and Smith, Range Management, McGraw-Hill, 1953.]

The rangelands on the lower elevations are normally grazed during the winter (Fig. 34-2). In this area the precipitation is commonly less than 10 in., soils are often saline, and irrigation water is not available. Desert shrub, sagebrush, and grass forage types are predominant.

The spring-fall range occurs in areas where elevation, growing season, rainfall (10–18 in.), topography, and soil characteristics are intermediate.

Vegetation usually consists of sagebrush, juniper, mountain brush, and related types.

Summer range areas occur in the mountains where precipitation is greatest (18 in. and over), but where low temperatures, short growing season, and steep topography preclude crop production. Ponderosa pine, spruce, fir, aspen, and alpine grasses and sages are found in these areas.

With the exception of the coastal region a continental climate exists in the Western United States; there are dry hot summers and cold winters with considerable snow.

The sheep in the range areas are largely Rambouillet, Columbia, and Targhee breeding flocks. Purebred rams of these breeds are used to produce replacement ewe lambs, which are kept in the range flocks or sold to areas in the Midwest or East as foundation ewes. The ewes are bred largely to Suffolk or Hampshire rams to produce blackface market lambs.

The Farm Flock. Farm flocks are raised all over the United States; however, they are concentrated in the humid farming areas of the Central, Southern, and Eastern states. There are also farm flocks on the irrigated farms of the Western states. The aim of the farm flock producer is to grow fat lambs which can go to market as soon as they are weaned, and consequently most of the farm flocks are of the mutton type.

Fig. 34-2. Sheep on the winter range in southern Utah. This range is typical of much of the Intermountain Region. The valleys are broad with low mountains. Note the playa in the background.

The Purebred Breeder. Most of the purebred sheep enterprises are located in the areas where farm flocks are produced; however, there are some purebred breeders who raise sheep under range conditions part of the year.

The aim of the purebred sheep breeder is to raise rams to sell to commercial sheepmen and to sell rams and replacement ewes to other purebred breeders. The raising of purebred sheep is a specialized business. Attention must be given to: selection and matings of individual animals to produce animals of high inheritance for characteristics which are wanted in the breed; accurate records of each animal; feeding and management to develop inherent characters to their maximum; a keen knowledge of how to show animals, and of how to build a favorable reputation.

Lamb Feeding

REPLACEMENT LAMBS. Most range operators and farm flock owners in the West select their outstanding ewe lambs and grow them out for replacements for ewes that are culled from the flock each fall. Farm flock owners in the Midwest, East, and South often buy Western ewe lambs for replacements.

HOT-HOUSE LAMB PRODUCTION. To produce hot-house lambs, ewes are bred early so the lambs can be put on the market from December to April. The operator must skillfully feed, house, and manage the ewes and lambs so that the lambs can be marketed at 6–12 weeks of age, when they weigh 30–60 lb.

EASTER LAMBS. There is a large demand for lambs at Easter, with a wide range as to quality and weight. Usually, however, the lighter weights are preferred.

SPRING LAMBS. If lambs are marketed after Easter and before July 1, they are referred to as spring lambs. These lambs are marketed directly off their mothers and have been on excellent pasture or they have been creep-fed grain.

FATTENING LAMBS ON PASTURE OR RANGE. Many of the lambs in the United States are born in the spring and fattened on pasture or range without any grain feeding. In the Intermountain region lambs are usually weaned in August or September. The fat lambs, weighing 85–100 lb., are sent directly to market. The thin lambs and those under 85 lb. are put in dry lot and fattened on irrigated or on improved dry-land pasture hay and cropland aftermath and marketed at a weight of 90–100 lb.

FATTENING LAMBS IN DRY LOT. Lambs from range ewes which are not fat when weaned are usually shipped to areas where there is an abundant feed supply and fattened by feeding large amounts of hay and grain in a dry lot (Fig. 34-3). The main areas for dry-lot feeding are eastern Colorado, the Corn Belt states, California, and to some extent the irrigated valleys of the Intermountain states.

a

b

Fig. 34-3. (a) View of lamb feeding facility accommodating 30,000 head at Sutter Basin Corporation, Robbins, Calif. Storage facilities for feed are in the background. (b) View of same feedlot showing arrangement of mangers for chopped hay or for silage and of self feeders for concentrates. Automatic unloading wagons deliver food without entering lots.

34-3. NUTRITION AND MANAGEMENT OF RANGE SHEEP

For adequate nutrition of range sheep the forage should contain an ample supply of protein, energy, minerals, and vitamins. The animals should also have plenty of water. Under favorable conditions and on well-managed ranges, forage consisting of browse, grass, and forbs frequently supplies all the nutrients necessary. However, it becomes necessary to supplement the sheep's diet under conditions of scarcity of forage—especially on the winter range—under unfavorable climatic conditions, or where there are nutrient deficiencies in the forage. The condition of the sheep, the amount and kind of forage on the range, climatic conditions, and the time of year will determine when and what kind of supplements to feed.

Nutrient Deficiencies of Range Forage. Usually nutrient deficiencies occur most frequently on the winter range. Aside from a lack of water and salt, the deficiencies common among sheep grazing on winter-range forage, particularly on mature, dried forage, are phosphorus, protein, and energy. Calcium deficiency is rarely encountered.

On some ranges carotene (vitamin A) may be deficient, especially on a grass-type range or when there is a late spring. However, sheep store a considerable amount of this vitamin in their liver during the summer when grazing on succulent green forage, and if the winter is open and an early spring comes, animals usually will not suffer from a vitamin A shortage. Plant analyses and supplementary feeding trials show that sheep in the Intermountain area usually do not suffer from a lack of vitamin A. For these reasons vitamin A concentrates need not be added to supplemental feeds in this area.

Data are scanty on whether range sheep lack vitamin D; however, this vitamin is synthesized in the skin by the ultraviolet rays from the sun. In areas of adequate sunlight, a vitamin D supplement is not recommended until it is shown that it increases production.

Sheep are able to synthesize in their rumen all the known B vitamins; therefore supplementary sources of these vitamins are not needed.

Many areas within the United States are deficient in trace minerals. Since the cost of supplying supplements of iodine, cobalt, and copper is so slight, it may be good insurance to use trace-mineralized salt.

Classes and Composition of Feeds to Supplement Range Sheep. The classes of feeds for supplements include (1) roughages consisting of green, leafy, early-bloom alfalfa or clover hay; (2) energy feeds—barley, corn, wheat, and molasses (to increase palatability and give adhesive qualities in a pellet); (3) protein concentrates such as cottonseed meal, linseed-oil meal, soybean meal;* (4) vitamin supplements rich in carotene or vitamin A—dehydrated alfalfa, leafy, green, early-bloom sun-cured alfalfa meal, or vitamin A concentrates, and (5) mineral supplements high in phosphorus (bone meal, dicalcium phosphate, defluorinated phosphate, or monosodium phosphate), sodium and chlorine (salt) and possibly in some areas cobalt (cobalt sulfate, cobalt chloride, or cobalt carbonate), copper (copper sulfate), and iodine (potassium iodide).

In the Western range area the following feeds will usually be the most economical to use in supplementing range sheep: alfalfa hay, barley, solvent-extracted cottonseed meal, bone meal, or dicalcium phosphate, salt, and alfalfa meal. Corn or sorghum grains may replace barley in the Plains States.

Formulation of a Supplement for Range Ewes. The basis of formulating a supplement for range ewes is to obtain the composition of the grazing sheep's diet, then add sufficient nutrients to make up any deficiencies. In preparing the supplement keep the following points in mind:

1) Add sufficient phosphorus supplement to satisfy the allowance of a 130-lb. ewe.

2) Add sufficient protein supplement to satisfy the protein requirement.

3) If a vitamin A supplement is needed, add sufficient vitamin A to take care of the requirement.

4) Add 1% salt or trace-mineralized salt.

5) Make up the balance of the pellet with one of the energy feeds.

6) The rate of feeding is important. As the amount of feed is increased, the percentage of protein, phosphorus, and vitamin A can be decreased. Also, less expensive energy feeds such as barley or corn can be increased. It will not usually be economical to feed supplements at a level to keep ewes gaining or to maintain their weight throughout the winter months because they are usually in good condition when they go to the winter range.

Suggested pattern formulas for supplementary feeding are given in Table 34-1. The feeds have been classified according to their nutritive content, and suggested maximum amounts of each feed to use under usual conditions in the West are given. Three suggested formulas are also given; many other formulas can be devised by using different combinations of feeds.

A 12% protein pellet or corn or barley should be used on sagebrush range types since the diets of sheep grazing on these areas are usually high in protein. These feeds can also be fed during emergencies, along with alfalfa hay. A 24% protein pellet is better adapted for feeding on mixed browse-grass types. A 36% pellet or cottonseed meal should be used with saltbush types where there is an abundance of grass or wherever grass predominates.

* Information concerning cottonseed meal, linseed-oil meal or soybean meal in this chapter will refer to solvent-extracted meals.

TABLE 34-1. | *Pattern for range supplements for sheep.*

Main groups	Subgroups	Feedstuff	Suggested maximum	High	Medium	Low
				Proportions of individual feeds — Recommended amount of protein		
			(%)	(%)	(%)	(%)
Energy feeds	Grains	Barley	75		32.25	57.0
		Corn	60	5.0	10.0	15.0
		Wheat	60			
		Milo	60			
		Oats	15			
		Screenings No. 1	10			
	Mill feeds	Wheat mixed feed	10			
		Shorts	10			
		Molasses	15	5.0	5.0	10.0
		Beet pulp	10			10.0
Protein supplements	30–40% protein feeds	Cottonseed meal	75	62.5	32.5	5.0
		Linseed oil meal	25			
		Soybean meal	75	10.0	10.0	
		Peanut oil meal	25			
		Urea (26.2% protein), not over 25% of protein equivalent in pellet				
	20–30% protein feeds	Corn gluten feed	15			
		Corn distillers' dried grains	10			
		Wheat distillers' grains	10			
		Brewers' dried grains	5			
		Safflower meal	25			
		Cull beans	15			
Mineral supplements		Bone meal		4.0	3.0	2.0
		Defluorinated phosphate				
		Dicalcium phosphate				
		Disodium phosphate				
		Monocalcium phosphate				
		Monosodium phosphate				
		Salt or trace mineralized salt		1.0	1.0	1.0
Vitamin supplements		Dehydrated alfalfa meal	20	12.5	6.25	
		Sun-cured alfalfa meal	20			
		Fish oils				
		Vitamin A and carotene concentrates				
Total				100.0	100.0	100.0
Suggested composition						
Total crude protein (%)				36.0	24.0	12.0
Phosphorus (%)				1.5	1.0	0.5
Carotene (mg/lb.)				15.6	7.8	
Rate of feeding (lb. per day)						
Ewes				0.25	0.33 to 0.50	0.20 to 1.0

Cottonseed Meal and Salt. Within recent years salt has been used to regulate the consumption of cottonseed meal. This method of feeding saves labor and is recommended where it is not possible to hand feed the animals—that is, where range sheep are handled under fence. It should be kept in mind, however, that salt is used to regulate the amount of meal consumed and it should not be used if the intake of supplement can be controlled by hand feeding.

It is essential that the animals be started on small amounts of cottonseed meal and salt by hand feeding for a week or more. The salt in the mixture is gradually increased from a sprinkling the first day to the full proportion to be fed in the self-feeders. A mixture of 0.5 lb. of salt and 1.0 lb. of cottonseed meal, solvent extracted, is suggested at first. However, if the animals eat too much of the mixture the salt should be increased, and if they eat too little it should be decreased.

Salt-meal mixtures greatly increase water consumption. If this method of feeding is followed, the animals should have access to water every day since the extra salt must be excreted through the urine. If water is hauled, an adequate supply should be available. If additional phosphorus or trace minerals are needed they could be added in the correct proportions to the salt-meal mixture.

Water. It is usually assumed that water is readily available to sheep, but on many range areas it is the limiting nutrient and may be unpalatable because of dirt, filth, or high mineral content. In other instances water may be potentially available, but because of ice or inadequate facilities the sheep do not obtain an ample supply.

If water or snow is not available, it should be hauled to the sheep. For best production range sheep should be watered once each day, but the cost of supplying water sometimes makes it advisable to water range sheep every other day. On some winter ranges reservoirs have been built to provide water for sheep (Fig. 34-4). When soft snow is available range sheep do not need additional water. When the snow is crusted with ice the crust should be broken so the sheep can obtain water. When dry feed such as alfalfa hay and pellets is used, sheep may not obtain sufficient water from snow. When hungry and thirsty sheep are brought into the home ranch after a blizzard, they should be given small amounts of water and feed for a few days until they recover. This will prevent losses from an overconsumption of water and feed.

Range Sheep Management. Largely because of differences in environment, management practices vary widely in different areas, or even in a given area—because of limited availability of summer ranges at higher elevations, or because of unique availability of by-product feeds.

Both the physiology of sheep and the environment play important roles

Fig. 34-4. These sheep are being watered in a reservoir on the winter range.

in determining management practices. Sheep are seasonal breeders and thus, until we are able to control the time of initiation of the sexual season, the lambing season must, of necessity, be limited according to the season in which ewes will breed. Furthermore, lactation in the ewe requires plentiful nutrients, and therefore lambing is planned to allow for abundant forage during the period between lambing and weaning. Again, lambing during midwinter in colder climates is usually avoided because the young lamb is more subject to adverse climatic conditions than is the mature animal.

The following description of range-sheep management is widely applicable in the Western United States. The student should bear in mind, however, that it is merely an example which will allow for an orderly discussion of the major factors involved in sheep management.

Lambs are weaned in late August, September, or early October, at which time the ewes are on the high summer range. The heavy lambs are sent directly to market and the smaller lambs are sent to the feed yards. About October 15 the ewes are trailed to the fall foothill range, where they remain for about two weeks, and are then trailed to the winter range. This trail may be 50 to 250 miles long. At the beginning of the trail the ewes are in good condition, since they have been on lush feed all summer. When they arrive at the winter range they have lost some weight. In recent years many operators ship their animals by truck or rail instead of trailing them.

The forage on the winter range is dormant this time of year and in most areas is low in protein and phosphorus. Because of this the sheep do not consume sufficient amounts of feed to keep them gaining. They should usually be fed about 0.25 to 0.5 lb. of one of the pellet mixtures outlined in Table 34-1. This extra feed helps to balance the diet and increases the chance for the ewe to become pregnant.

For range lambing the rams are usually put in with the ewes during November or December, depending on the facilities the operator has for lambing. For shed lambing the rams are put with the ewes after the lambs are weaned in August. The rams are left with the ewes for about six weeks.

January, February, and March are critical months on most winter ranges. During this time it is recommended that the ewes be fed 0.25 lb. or more of one of the pellet mixtures of Table 34-1. If the ewes become snowbound during January and February, they should be fed about 2 lb. of alfalfa hay and about 1 lb. of the 12% protein pellet (Table 34-1).

By adequate feeding and good management of the ewes on the winter range it is possible to increase the lamb crop 15–30% and the amount of wool produced per ewe by about 1 lb. Death losses of ewes will also be less.

Fig. 34-5. In the West many sheep are sheared with portable apparatus. This procedure protects the range from being trampled and overgrazed, since only one band of sheep is sheared in a given area.

SHEARING. In April the ewes are usually sheared with portable shearing machines (Fig. 34-5). The wool is usually not graded at shearing time, but the black wool is generally separated from the white wool and the lamb wool (first-year wool) from the rest of the wool. The tags are also usually taken off of each fleece and packed separately. The wool is put in large bags for shipment to market. Sorting of the wool into grades is almost always done in warehouses in the West or at Boston.

After the ewes are sheared they are trailed to the spring range, where they are lambed. There are essentially two types of lambing procedures— range lambing and shed lambing.

RANGE LAMBING. For range lambing a protected area is selected, with sagebrush or scrub oak on the south slopes of the foothills, where there is plenty of water and grass. The ewes are divided into groups of about 500, and each group is bedded in one area. Each morning the ewes that have not lambed are moved to a new area.

Sometimes small portable tents are used to put over the lambs and ewes at the time of lambing; these are especially useful if it is storming. The ewes that have lambed are kept in the area for two or three days, until their lambs become strong. The better operators feed the ewes a high-pro-

Fig. 34-6. When ewes are lambed on the range they are spread out over a large area. These ewes have just lambed.

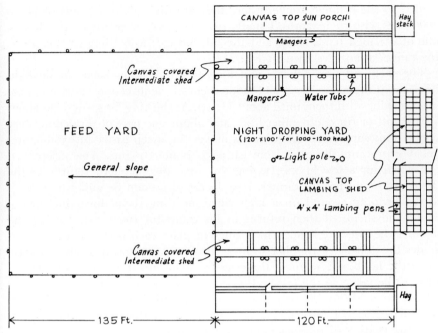

Fig. 34-7. Range lambing sheds and feed layout for caring for ewes. It is best to locate these facilities in areas where there is plenty of spring pasture. Adapted from a plan suggested by the Animal Husbandry Department, Montana State College.

tein pellet fortified with salt and bone meal or dicalcium phosphate after lambing. Many shepherds think that this procedure prevents lambs from eating soil and keeps ewes from eating poisonous plants.

As the lambing proceeds, three groups of animals are made up: those that have lambed (Fig. 34-6), those that are about to lamb, and those in which lambing is not imminent. (For details on how to treat the lambs at birth see Section 34-6.)

SHED LAMBING. For range shed lambing, feeding yards and pasture may be provided. If possible, ewes are lambed on crested wheatgrass pasture or a good mixed legume and grass pasture. If pasture is not available, yards are provided (Fig. 34-7) and racks to feed hay are put in the yards. Ewes are usually put in the yards one month before lambing. Grain is fed in a reversible bottom trough (Fig. 34-8), which gives a clean surface to feed on each day. Ewes are fed alfalfa hay and about 0.5–0.75 lb. of barley. The ewes are given free access to salt and one part of dicalcium phosphate and one part trace-mineralized salt.

SUMMER RANGE. Soon after lambing is completed the ewes and lambs are trailed to the summer range, where they are divided into bands of about 1000 ewes with their lambs. Usually two men look after one or two bands; one of the men tends camp and the other does the herding. A "home on the range" camp is shown in Fig. 34-9.

The shepherd uses a horse and dogs to handle the sheep. At daylight he goes out to see the sheep and guide them in the direction he wishes them to go, staying with them until about 11 A.M. At this time he gives them about 3 parts salt or trace-mineralized salt and about one part of dicalcium phosphate. This supplement of minerals makes the sheep easier to handle, and possibly prevents the ewes from eating poisonous plants. The sheep then bed down for a few hours. During this time the shepherd returns to the sheep camp and has his dinner. Late in the afternoon he guides the sheep to the bedding ground on a high ridge, bedding them down just before dark. The shepherd then returns to his camp for the night. During the summer the ewes are bedded in a different place each night. The shepherd guides the grazing of the sheep to use the forage to advantage. In October, when the lambs are weaned, the ewes are made up into bands of 2000 to 4000, to be taken to the fall and winter range.

The range sheep industry produces wool and feeder lambs which are marketed direct or fattened on crop aftermath and pasture or in dry lot with the feeding of roughage and concentrates.

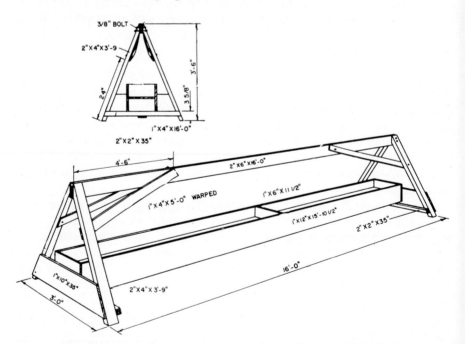

Fig. 34-8. A grain trough which can be turned over before each feeding. This keeps the grain clean and fresh.

Fig. 34-9. The camp tender and the shepherd live in a "home on the range." In some areas tents are used along with pack animals. Dogs are used along with horses on most western ranges. Note the mutton hanging on the front of the camp. It is wrapped up and put in the bed during the day to keep it from spoiling.

34-4. FARM SHEEP PRODUCTION

Range sheep are kept on the range all the time, except for short periods when they may be fed hay and concentrates. They are kept in large bands. Farm sheep, on the other hand, are usually kept on improved pastures during the summer and are fed hay and concentrates during the winter. Farm sheep can be expected to produce more wool and lambs than range sheep because they are maintained on a higher plane of nutrition and receive better management.

General Feeding Practices. Farm sheep are fed largely on pasture, crop aftermath, and harvested roughages. At times they need to be supplemented with protein concentrates, phosphorus, calcium, copper, cobalt, and vitamins A, D, and E.

Sheep do best if provided with a succulent, fertilized pasture composed of legumes and grasses. The best utilization is achieved by dividing the field with hurdles or temporary fences and grazing the pasture in rotation. A good irrigated pasture will carry 8 to 12 ewes and their lambs per acre. The pasture should be clipped at intervals to remove unconsumed forage and provide a young vigorous growth. Where the pasture is part of a crop rotation system, the control of parasites is simplified, because the sheep do not graze the same areas continuously.

Sheep do best on hay which contains a high leaf-to-stem ratio. This can be achieved by cutting legumes in the early-bloom stage and grasses just as they begin to head or before too much stem develops. The green color is kept in the hay and the leaves are conserved by harvesting in a minimum time and storing under a shed to protect the hay from the weather. Sheep prefer alfalfa, clover, or lespedeza hay. Useful mangers for feeding hay are illustrated in Figs. 34-10 and 34-11. In the West the standard grain is barley; in the Midwest and East it is corn.

FEEDING MINERALS. Sheep should have free access to crushed salt in one side of a self-feeder and one part dicalcium phosphate and one part salt in the other side. If trace minerals are needed a trace-mineralized salt mixture can be used in place of plain salt. Trace minerals usually added to salt include iodine, cobalt, manganese, and copper. One pound of salt or trace-mineralized salt is usually added to every 100 lb. of concentrate or pellet mixture and 1 lb. of dicalcium phosphate. A mineral feeder is shown in Fig. 34-12. When sheep are fed roughage composed entirely of corn silage

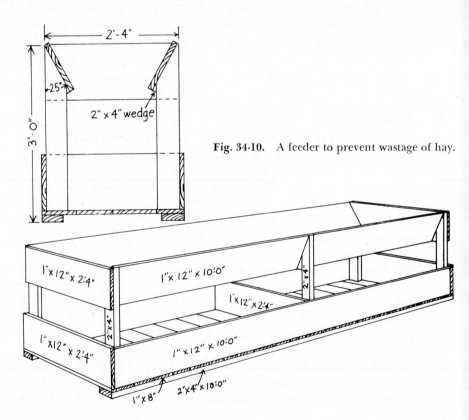

Fig. 34-10.   A feeder to prevent wastage of hay.

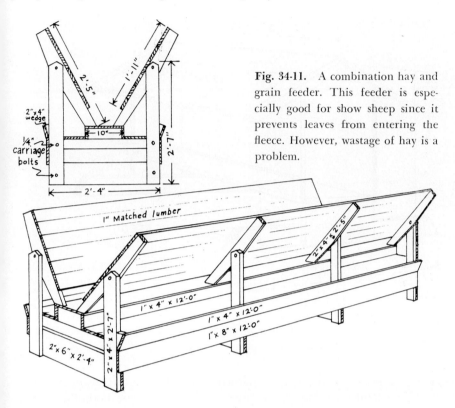

Fig. 34-11. A combination hay and grain feeder. This feeder is especially good for show sheep since it prevents leaves from entering the fleece. However, wastage of hay is a problem.

and cereal grains, 0.02 to 0.03 lb. of limestone (38% calcium) should be added to the daily ration.

34-5. MANAGEMENT DURING THE BREEDING SEASON

Anestrus and Estrus. Ewes have a period of anestrus during which estrus does not occur, and a sexual season during which estrus occurs at 17-day intervals. The period of anestrus varies among breeds, but usually occurs between January and June. Ewes strong in Dorset or Tunis blood may come into estrus in June and July. Some Merino and Rambouillet ewes also come into heat in early summer. Other breeds usually come in heat in late summer or fall.

Estrus in ewes ranges from 20 to 42 hours, with an average of 30 hours. Ovulation occurs about 24 to 30 hours after the onset of estrus. If the ewe is not bred, or if she fails to conceive, estrus recurs after an interval of 14 to 19 days with an average of 17 days.

Time of Year to Breed. The time of year to breed ewes depends on the method of sheep raising, climatic conditions, and the feed and equipment available at lambing time. If range ewes are lambed without sheds the

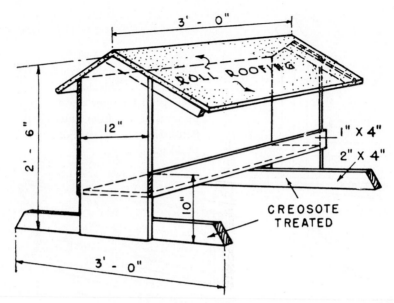

Fig. 34-12. A portable mineral box. Salt or trace mineralized salt is fed in one side of the self feeder and a phosphorus supplement composed of one part salt and one part dicalcium phosphate is fed in the other side.

lambs are usually born in April and early May. If sheds are available, range and farm lambs are born in February and March. For hothouse, Easter, and early spring lambs the ewes are bred so that the lambs are born in December, January, and February.

Puberty. Puberty is the age when sexual maturity is reached. Rams reach sexual maturity from 4 to 7 months of age, but there is considerable variability. Many ewes will breed at 8 to 10 months.

If the ewe lambs are born in January and February and are well matured, it is possible to breed them in the first fall. If born later than this, it pays to wait until the next breeding season. Ram lambs that have developed well may be used on 15 to 20 ewes the first breeding season, but usually they are not used until after they are one year old.

Flushing. Flushing consists of supplying the ewe with an abundance of feed to make her gain in weight just before and during the breeding season. It is believed that this process increases the number of eggs ovulated.

After the lambs are weaned the ewes are usually kept on pasture. In some cases they may be fed on roughage. They should be managed so they are in a thrifty condition—not too thin or too fat. About 3 to 4 weeks before the breeding season the amount of feed is reduced until the ewes are losing weight. Two weeks before the breeding season the amount of feed

TABLE 34-2. | *Grain mixtures for ewes.*

	Mixture no. *			
	1	2	3	4
Feed	(lb.)	(lb.)	(lb.)	(lb.)
Wheat bran	10			
Whole barley, corn, or wheat	60	70	75	50
Whole oats	30		20	50
Beet pulp, dried		25		
Cottonseed, soybean, linseed, or peanut oil meal		5	5	
Salt or trace mineralized salt	1	1	1	1
Dicalcium phosphate or equivalent	1	1	1	1

* Use mixtures 2 and 3 if the roughage is poor and more protein is needed.

is increased to permit the ewes to gain weight. This may be done by feeding 0.5–0.75 lb. of grain (Table 34-2) or by putting the ewes on fresh succulent pasture. Breeding is begun 2 weeks after the ewes have started to gain. The supplementary feeding is continued during the breeding season, usually 6 weeks in length.

In warmer climates the flock is sheared and a cool place is provided for the sheep. In cooler climates the ewes are crutched and most of the belly of the ram is sheared. If early lambs are desired the flock may be put in a dark building and held there to decrease the amount of light. The decreasing amount of light causes the ewes to come into heat sooner.

Number of Ewes per Ram. The average number of ewes bred per ram is as follows:

Age	Farm	Range
Ram lamb	20	15
Yearling	35	30
Mature	40	35

If the ewes are hand bred, one ram can serve up to 100 ewes. Under this system it is best to use a teaser ram, with an apron tied under his belly to prevent breeding, or a vasectomized ram. His chest is colored every two days, so that he marks the ewes in heat, and at night the painted ewes can be put with the ram for breeding. The breeding ram may be painted on the brisket or he may be fitted with a harness which carries a colored crayon. Only paints which can be scoured from the wool should be used.

It is wise to check the ram for live viable sperm, blindness, normal testicles, inflamed penis, lameness, and crooked legs before he is used for breeding. It pays to use high-quality purebred or crossbred rams.

TABLE 34-3. | *Ration for ewes.*

| | Ration no. | | | |
| | 1 (lb.) | 2 (lb.) | 3 (lb.) | 4 (lb.) |
Feed				
Legume hay, such as alfalfa, clover, or lespedeza	3.0–4.5	1.5–2.0	2.0–2.5	
Corn or sorghum silage		4.0–5.0		6.0–8.0
Native hay or straw			1.0–1.5	
Cottonseed, soybean, linseed, or peanut oil meal, 90%; limestone, 10%				0.25

The Pregnant Ewe. The length of the gestation period in ewes is approximately 5 months. The down breeds such as the Hampshire and Suffolk have the shortest gestation period—144 to 148 days. The gestation period of long wools, including the Romney and Lincoln, is 146 to 149 days. Fine-wools, including the Rambouillet, have the longest gestation period—148 to 152 days.

In warmer climates pregnant ewes can be kept on pasture throughout the winter, but in cooler climates they are kept on fall pasture or crop aftermath until snow comes. They are then fed one of the rations outlined in Table 34-3. Usually it pays to begin feeding 0.5–0.75 lb. of one of the concentrate mixtures (Table 34-2) six weeks before lambing.

34-6. MANAGEMENT DURING LAMBING

Sheds. A shed for sheep should provide a dry place for the sheep to lie, free from drafts but with adequate ventilation. The shed should be located on high, well-drained ground with the yards on the south side or away from the prevailing wind. A shed is preferred, 20 to 30 feet deep, with the slope all in one direction; see Fig. 34-13. With this type of shed all the moisture does not go into the yards and the sun will shine in to keep it dry. It can be made adaptable to the various management operations.

Except for lambing the shed can be left open. During lambing season, part or all of the shed can be closed in by using portable panels. Solid wooden panels free of cracks can be put at the bottom and canvas panels can be put above these to enclose the front of the shed. Early lambing necessitates warm quarters, which can be insured by insulating a small area of the shed, to be closed off and used for lambing pens. In New Zealand and Australia most of the sheds are equipped with a slatted floor. In certain areas in the United States, the slatted floor might be used to an advantage.

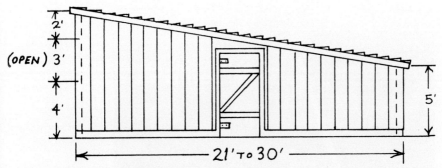

Fig. 34-13. An open shed. All the slope is in one direction. This prevents water from going in the corral.

Immediately after lambing the lambing shed should be cleaned. Lime should be put on the floor. The canvas is removed and the shed is exposed to the sun. These measures help to control disease.

Shed Lambing

PREPARATION FOR LAMBING. Lambing pens are usually set up in a portion of the sheep shed usually about ten days before the ewes are to lamb or a special lambing shed with lambing pens is provided. If the weather is cold some of the pens are equipped with brooders and heat lamps. Bed the pens daily with dry straw; if lambs are kept dry and free of drafts, they can stand considerable cold. Legume hay is placed in each pen. Water is provided in each pen by using a bucket or by placing a small V-shaped trough in the back.

Unless the ewes are already sheared, they are crutched and the wool removed from around the udder about 4 weeks before lambing. This prevents the lambs from sucking strands of wool when they nurse.

NORMAL LAMBING. When lambing time approaches the vulva swells, the udder fills, and the ewe is uneasy. A hollow appears between the ribs and the hip, and the ewe begins to strain. The water bag that has cushioned the unborn lamb bursts with a gush of fluid. Usually the ewe will lamb without help. In a normal birth, both front feet appear first, with the head lying snugly between them.

HELPING THE EWE TO LAMB. The ewe should not be helped unless the lamb is in an abnormal position or is excessively large, or unless the ewe has strained an hour or more and no part of the lamb appears. Before aiding in the birth, the attendant needs to wash his hands and arms in soap and water and be certain that his fingernails are short. He then lubricates his hands and arms with mineral oil or soap. He lays the ewe carefully on her right side by holding her under the jaw with the left hand, reaching under her with the right hand, and grasping the right hind leg well toward the hoof. He pulls gently on the ewe's leg so she will go over on her side.

Fig. 34-14. This is an excellent type of chute for separating sheep into various groups. By having cutting gates along the chute the sheep can be separated into several groups. [Courtesy Department of Animal Husbandry, Kansas State University.]

The attendant washes the vagina with soap and water, and then carefully inserts his hand.

The lamb should be born with the front feet first and the head lying between the forelegs. After its position has been determined, it is put in the correct position by pushing it forward to allow room to straighten out all parts into a normal lambing position. The attendant pulls outward and downward as the ewe strains. After the birth the ewe should be examined to make certain there are no other unborn lambs. The attendant inspects the ewe's udder and milks it a little to see that the milk canal is open. If the lamb is weak, he places the ewe's teat in its mouth and milks a little milk into it. In doing this, care must be taken that the milk does not get into the lamb's lungs.

In cold weather a lamb brooder is used to keep the lambs warm. Single lambs are left in the lambing pen for about 12 hours. Twin lambs are left for about 24 to 48 hours or until the ewe claims them.

As each ewe lambs, a number should be stamped on her side and the same number stamped on the side of her lamb or lambs. This permits immediate identification of lambs that may have become lost or are not receiving proper care from their mothers. Care should be taken to use paint that will scour out of the wool.

In purebred flocks ear tags are used, showing the name of the owner and the number of the sheep. Sometimes permanent numbers are tattooed in the ears. A good numbering system consists of putting a 0, 1, 2, 3, 4, 5, 6, 7, 8, or 9 in front of the identifying number to indicate year born. For example, all lambs born in 1960 would carry a 0, and all 1961 lambs would carry a 1. With this system age can be readily determined. With purebred flocks accurate records should be kept of dates of birth of lambs and ancestry.

Feeding Lambs and Ewes During Lactation. After the ewes lamb, their ration is gradually increased. Ewes can be fed one of the rations of Table 34-3 plus 0.5 to 1.0 lb. of one of the grain mixtures of Table 34-2. If succulent pasture is available ewes usually do not need any grain.

When it is desired to market the lambs early, they are usually fed extra hay and grain in a lamb creep. A lamb creep consists of a small pen with openings for the lambs, but not for the ewes. The lamb creep should be provided with a trough to hold a grain mixture for the lambs and a rack for leafy, green legume hay.

34-7. LAMB AILMENTS

Chilled Lambs. If a lamb is chilled, it can be rubbed dry with a coarse cloth or a sack. If the lamb continues to shake, it can be wrapped in a blanket or put under a heat lamp placed in the corner of the lambing pen. Boxes heated with jugs of hot water also make good lamb warmers. A stiff, cold lamb can usually be revived by putting it up to its neck in water, as hot as your elbow will bear, for 2 to 10 minutes. When it revives, it can be rubbed vigorously with a coarse cloth until dry, given some warm milk, and wrapped in a sheep skin or old blanket. At this time it may be well to inject the lamb with penicillin and streptomycin to prevent secondary complications such as pneumonia.

Feeding and Care of Orphan Lambs. If possible, an orphan lamb should be given to another ewe that has lost her lamb. The ewe is tied in a lamb-ing pen; the lamb is smeared with the ewe's afterbirth, or some of the ewe's milk is rubbed on her nose and rump. If this fails the hide of the ewe's dead lamb can be put on the orphan lamb. Sometimes a dog tied near the pen will help; sometimes tranquilizers are helpful.

In feeding orphan lambs they are usually given some colostrum from their mother or from other ewes that have just lambed, or some from a cow. A supply of cow's colostrum may be kept frozen for this purpose. The orphans are then transferred to cow's milk with a high-fat content or to artificial milk warmed to about 90–100°F. A medium-sized duck-bill nipple is used. The lambs should be fed often (6 to 8 feedings per day to begin with) and in small amounts (1–2 oz. per feeding). At 6 weeks the daily feedings are gradually reduced to 3 or 4, and the amount at each feeding is gradually increased to 10–16 oz.

Pinning. The first feces from the lamb is called muconium; it is often sticky and sometimes pins the tail of the lamb to its body. To control this "pinning" the tail should be pulled away from the body and the accumu-lated feces removed.

Turned Eyelids. A lamb sometimes has eyelids which will turn inward (entropium). This is corrected by tying a tuck in the lower eyelid causing the trouble, using heavy thread, or by removing a small elliptical piece of skin about one-fourth inch in length, just below the edge of the eyelid. A 10% solution of argyrol or saturated solution of boric acid is used to clear the eyes.

34-8. LAMB FEEDING

Fattening in Dry Lot. To make a profit in feeding lambs in dry lot the feeder must exercise judgment and skill. Feeder lambs are usually purchased from the range operator, from a commission firm, or from an auction. Most range feeder lambs are produced from white-faced ewes, Rambouillet, Columbia, or Targhee by mating to purebred Suffolk or Hampshire rams.

Though practices vary widely, dependent upon climatic conditions, lambs in most range areas in the United States are usually weaned in Au-gust, September, or early October. They are then topped out. Fat lambs weighing more than 85 lb. are sent directly to slaughter; the thin lambs weighing 65 lb. or more are sold as feeders.

After trucking or shipping the lambs from the range to the feed yard, they are rested in dry lot and given free access to water, hay, and salt for a few days. Preferably during this time, they are vaccinated for sore mouth and a disorder from overeating (enterotoxemia) and treated for internal parasites if the need is demonstrated.

If crop aftermath is available lambs may be turned in to eat the grain stubble, corn, or beet tops. They are then put in dry lot and fed grain and roughage to finish them for market. In commercial feed lots the lambs are put directly on hay and concentrate.

HAND FEEDING. The lambs are separated into weight groups (Fig. 34-14) and started out on about 0.1 lb. of grain per head per day and given all the alfalfa or clover hay they will consume. The concentrates are gradually increased and the hay decreased according to the schedule in Table 34-4. Oats are an excellent grain to start lambs on feed. Pattern concentrate mixtures are shown in Table 34-5. Toward the end of the feeding period bulky concentrates such as oats, beet pulp, or wheat bran are decreased and high-energy concentrates such as barley, corn, or wheat are increased. When the lambs are hand fed, excellent gains can be obtained with barley or corn as the only concentrate. Corn, alfalfa, or grass silage can replace about half the hay. It takes about 3 lb. of silage to equal one pound of hay.

TABLE 34-4. | *Feeding schedule for fattening lambs.*

	Hand feeding		Self feeding	
Days on feed	Grain mixture* (%)	Hay (%)	Grain mixture* (%)	Hay (%)
7 to 14	25	75	25	75
15 to 28	35	65	45	55
29 to 56	44	55	55	45
57 to 100	55	45	55	45

Use a grain mixture* such as this or
one made up from Table 34-5.

Grain	%
Whole or rolled barley, maize or wheat	65.0
Dried molasses beet pulp or oats	33.0
Salt or trace mineralized salt	1.0
Dicalcium phosphate	1.0
	100.0

* If hay is of poor quality, add 5–10% of linseed meal, cottonseed meal, solvent extracted, or soybean oil meal

TABLE 34-5. | *Pattern formula and recommended formulas for fattening lambs (amounts per 1000 lb.).*

Feedstuff	Maximum (lb.)	Proportions for formula No.:			
		1 (lb.)	2 (lb.)	3 (lb.)	4 (lb.)
Corn	855	755			530
Barley	855		755	483	
Wheat	500			200	
Milo	500				200
Beet pulp dried	200		200	100	
Oats	100			100	100
Wheat bran	200				
Wheat mixed feed	200	200			
Cottonseed meal*	25	25			
Soybean meal*	25				
Linseed oil meal*	25		25		
Peanut oil meal*	25				
Corn gluten feed	100				
Corn distillers' grains, dried	100				100
Brewers' grains, dried	100				
Coconut oil meal	50				50
Cull beans	150			100	
Bone meal	10	10			10
Defluorinated phosphate	10		10		
Dicalcium phosphate	7			7	
Salt	10	10	10	10	10
Trace mineralized salt	10				

* Replace these feeds with the grains when choice legume hay is fed.

If lambs scour, they should be checked for infectious diseases and coccidiosis. The concentrates should be cut down and about one-third of the hay replaced with straw.

SELF-FEEDING. Under commercial conditions one of the easiest ways to feed lambs is self-feeding. The hay is put through a hammer mill and the concentrates are usually rolled or chopped coarsely and mixed in the proportions given in Table 34-4. Barley, corn, wheat, or oats or a mixture of

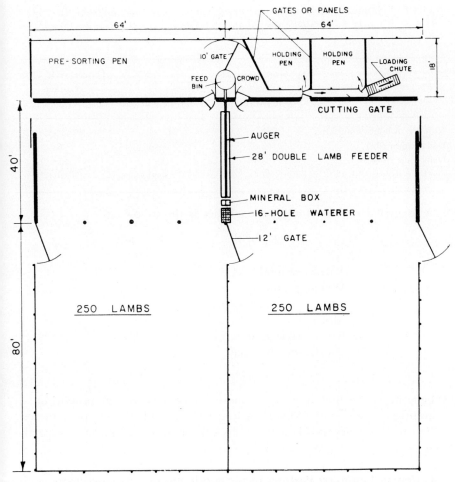

Fig. 34-15. A feedlot layout for feeding 500 lambs on pellets.

these concentrates is also satisfactory. If these concentrates are used, 0.5 lb. salt and 0.5 lb. dicalcium phosphate or equivalent are added to each 100 lb. of roughage and concentrates.

PELLET FEEDING. Until recently pellets were used largely to supplement range ewes or to feed to lambs along with hay as a creep feed. Now many large commercial feeders are pelleting the entire diet for fattening lambs. A feed-lot layout for feeding pellets to 500 lambs is shown in Fig. 34-15.

Several experiments comparing pelleted and nonpelleted diets for lambs have been summarized in Table 34-6. Lambs on a pelleted ration ate 6% more feed, gained 23% more in weight, and required 14% less feed per pound of gain than those fed nonpelleted rations. These results are phenomenal and show that lambs can make good use of an all-pelleted diet.

TABLE 34-6. | *Summary of nine feeding experiments comparing pelleted diets versus nonpelleted diets for lambs (all diets contained more than 50% roughage).*

Item	Pelleted ration	Nonpelleted ration	Difference in favor of pellets (%)
Number of lambs compared	789	947	
Daily ration (lb.)	3.62	3.42	6
Daily gain (lb.)	0.48	0.39	23
Feed per lb. gain (lb.)	7.27	9.00	−19

A suggested mixture for a pelleted diet is the following:

Ingredient	Per cent
Alfalfa hay	65
Barley, ground	9
Wheat, ground	10
Beet pulp, dried, or oats	10
Molasses	5
Salt or trace-mineralized salt	0.5
Dicalcium phosphate	0.5
	100

When the entire diet is pelleted, more hay can be fed in proportion to concentrates than under other feeding systems. Whether it pays to feed pellets to lambs depends largely on the cost of pelleting and processing the feed.

Fattening Lambs on Pasture. In the South and in California many lambs are fattened on pasture. In these areas alfalfa fields are also used, particularly early in the spring. Later in the season, when losses from bloat may become severe, sheepmen generally prefer native feed such as bur clover and alfilaria for finishing spring lambs. Sudan grass is an excellent summer pasture crop under irrigation and it is a favorite green forage crop among purebred breeders. In the early lamb districts, the lambs are always marketed by late May, before the green feed dries up.

ROTATION OF PASTURES. Good pasture, with plenty of fresh green feed, is necessary to produce an ample milk flow in ewes and to develop the lambs quickly. This necessary condition can be provided by dividing pastures into small units by cross fencing.

A 32-in., 8-bar woven wire fence, with one barbwire at the bottom and two at the top, is best for sheep pastures. In some cases it is desirable to provide dog-proof fences, especially around the yards and barn. Such a fence can be constructed by using 32-in., 8-bar woven wire, with one barb-wire offset at the bottom, 4 barbwires at the top, and one additional barb-wire offset 5 in. on the outside and raised 2 in. With correct spacing of wire, this will give a 60-in. fence. The posts should be 8 ft. apart.

Temporary fences can be made of panels. The ewes and lambs are turned into each pasture in rotation and kept there for about two days. This prac-tice insures a fresh feed supply for the ewes and lambs at all times. The lambs develop more rapidly, attain a heavier weight, and a larger number of sheep can be grazed on a given area.

34-9. CONTROL OF PARASITES

The more important parasites of sheep include stomach worms, nodular worms, bankrupt worms, lungworms, tapeworms, liver flukes, coccidia, ticks, and lice.

Phenothiazine controls stomach and nodular worms. Each year, the ewe flock and rams should receive phenothiazine at the following times: (1) two weeks before breeding season; (2) before beginning any lot feeding in cold climates or in the fall in warm climates where sheep are kept on pas-ture; (3) within the week before ewes and lambs go to spring pasture; (4) from June 15 to June 30, all ewes and lambs weighing over 40 lb. (other lambs should be treated as soon as they reach 40 lb.); and (5) when lambs are weaned both ewes and lambs should be treated.

Ticks (keds) can be controlled by dipping or spraying with benzine hexa-chloride, DDT, or lindane or by dusting with rotenone.

34-10. HANDLING SHEEP

Catching Sheep. Catch a sheep by the flank or by the hind leg (least pre-ferred method). Never catch or hold a sheep by the wool since this will cause bruises. With the left hand under the jaw and the right hand on the sheep's rump, the animal can easily be controlled. To hold a sheep, place the left hand under the jaw, kneel down and place the right hand on the right side near the top of the withers. To mouth a sheep, straddle the neck, raise the head with the left hand under the jaw, and part the lips with the right hand. To examine the conformation of the sheep keep the fingers close together.

To put the sheep on its rump reach under the belly and grasp the right hind leg with the right hand. Pull with the hand and at the same time press the side with the right knee and raise up on the jaw with the left hand. The sheep can easily be put on its side by the same procedure, without raising up on the jaw.

Use of Dogs. In early days, the blackface sheep of Scotland were termed "Colly" and the sheep dogs were called "Colly dogs." This became the

"Collie" of today. A well-trained Border Collie is a distinct asset to any sheepman, and can gather, drive, or pen sheep. A highly trained dog can also catch and hold a sheep by the wool on the forequarters, without breaking the skin with its teeth. Although it is not usually good practice to catch a sheep by the wool, it may be necessary to catch an individual sheep to treat it for an ailment such as maggots when the animals are in large pasture areas.

34-11. PREDATORS

On western ranges large losses of sheep occur from predators, thus resulting in widespread control programs: the use of government trappers and private trapping and hunting, much of it stimulated by livestock associations. The coyote, a species of wolf, is by far the most important predator. Other predators include bobcat, bear, and cougar (puma or mountain lion). Through the use of poison baits, trapping, and cyanide guns most of these predators are being controlled. This may have resulted, unfortunately, in an increase in the population of small rodents and rabbits, which take a great deal of range forage in some areas.

REFERENCES AND SELECTED READINGS

References marked with an asterisk are of general interest.

Alexander, M. A., W. W. Derrick, and K. C. Fouts, 1952. Farm sheep facts. Neb. Agr. Ext. Serv. Circ. 255.

Austral. Sci. and Indus. Res. Organ., 1951. Drought feeding of sheep. C.S.I.R.O. Series. Melbourne.

*Belschner, H. G., 1956. *Sheep Management and Diseases.* 4th Ed. Angus and Robertson, London.

Cook, C. W., L. A. Stoddart, and L. E. Harris, 1954. The nutritive value of winter range plants in the Great Basin. Utah Agr. Expt. Sta. Bull. 372, pp. 1–56.

Cox, R. F., T. D. Bell, and H. E. Reed, 1951. Sheep production in Kansas. Kansas Agr. Expt. Sta. Bull. 348.

*Harris, L. E., C. W. Cook, and L. A. Stoddart, 1956. Feeding phosphorus, protein and energy supplements to ewes on winter ranges of Utah. Utah Agr. Expt. Sta. Bull. 398, pp. 1–28.

Jordan, R. M., 1950. Sheep production in South Dakota. S. Dak. Agr. Expt. Sta. Circ. 82.

*Kammlade, W. G., Sr., and W. G. Kammlade, Jr., 1955. *Sheep Science,* Revised Ed. Lippincott, New York.

*McKinney, J., 1959. *The Sheep Book.* Wiley, New York.

*Morrison, F. B., 1956. *Feeds and Feeding.* The Morrison Pub. Co., Ithaca.

*National Research Council, Natl. Acad. Sci., Committee on Animal Nutrition, Subcommittee on Sheep Nutrition. Nutrient requirements of sheep. Pub. 504. Washington, D.C., (Revised 1957.)

Slen, S. B., F. Whiting, and K. Rasmussen, 1953. Range sheep production in western Canada. Canada Dept. of Agr. Pub. 886.

*Stoddart, L. A., and A. D. Smith, 1954. *Range Management.* 2nd Ed. McGraw-Hill, New York.

Wallace, L. R., 1948. The growth of lambs before and after birth in relation to the level of nutrition. *J. Agr. Sci.*, 38:93–153.

Watson, I., 1958. Range sheep production. New Mexico Agr. Ext. Serv. Circ. 290.

Weir, W. C., and R. Albaugh, 1954. California sheep production. Calif. Agr. Expt. Sta. Manual 16.

Willman, John P. Sheep production. Cornell Et. Serv. Bull. 828 (Revised 1955).

Chapter 35

Horse Management

Look back at our struggle for freedom,
  Trace our present day's strength to its source;
And you'll find that man's pathway to glory
  Is strewn with the bones of a horse.

ANON.

35-1. INTRODUCTION

Horses and mules in the United States have declined steadily in numbers
from a high of almost 27,000,000 in 1918 to 3,089,000 on January 1, 1960
(Agricultural Statistics, USDA). In addition to a decline in total numbers

TABLE 35-1. *Number and value of horses and mules in the United States (1918–1960).*

Year	Thousands	Value per head ($)
1918	26,723	109
1920	25,742	108
1925	22,569	69
1930	19,124	74
1935	16,683	84
1940	14,478	88
1945	11,950	84
1950	7,781	61
1955	4,309	56
1960	3,089	95

TABLE 35-2. | *Leading states in numbers of horses and mules in the United States, 1960 (Agric. Statistics, USDA).*

1960	Thousands	Value per head $	Total value $1000
Texas	218	79	17,222
North Carolina	179	60	10,740
Mississippi	163	93	15,159
Kentucky	162	85	13,770
Tennessee	159	81	12,879
Alabama	118	63	7,434
Missouri	110	67	7,370

there has been a drastic shift in the predominant type of horses. The draft horse, which made up 75% of our horse population in 1918, has been almost completely replaced by tractors and trucks so that our horse population today is nearly all light horses and ponies. Table 35-2 shows the 7 states that had more than 100,000 horses and mules in 1960.

Although breeds and types are widely dispersed throughout the country, the Quarter Horse breed is most popular in the range country of the West and Southwest. The American Saddle Horse is most popular in Kentucky, Tennessee, Missouri, and Virginia, while the Thoroughbred is most numerous in California, Kentucky, Maryland, and New York. Palominos, Pintos, Appaloosas, and Arabians are found principally in the West, the Tennessee Walking Horse in the South and southeastern states, while ponies, both Welch and Shetlands, are gaining in favor all over the country.

Most Americans, rural or urban, love horses, and a great revival of interest in them has spread across the nation since World War II. With increased time for recreation, riding clubs, sheriffs' posses, trail rides, and horse shows have sprung up in every state. Horses in the United States today (1960) provide more pleasure, sport, and recreation for more people than in any other period in the history of our country, and the trend is likely to continue. Man has not yet found a better recreation than riding a horse.

35-2. REPRODUCTION

Female

AGE AT PUBERTY. Small, early-maturing breeds of horses and ponies reach sexual maturity as early as 12–18 months, whereas larger, slower-maturing types do not as a rule reach sexual maturity until they are 24–30 months of age. Liberal feeding, producing rapid growth and body development, results in earlier sexual development than scant feeding or a low plane of nutrition. Year-round grazing on the adequate forage available in the southern or semitropic climates produces earlier maturity than in grazing in northern climates with long severe winters, especially if wintering rations are inadequate.

AGE TO BREED. Size rather than age may be a more practical indication of proper time for first breeding. Small, early-maturing types and breeds may be sufficiently mature to breed as two-year olds, whereas the larger breeds are normally not bred until they are three, and thus foal when they are four. Although the added nutritional demands of the developing fetus are not great, the demands of lactation are heavy. It is therefore unwise to breed a filly until she has reached nearly mature size. If she is undersize or too immature, her own body needs for maintenance and growth plus the necessary milk for her foal are beyond her capacity. Even with liberal feeding the young lactating mare cannot assimilate enough food to meet her requirements. Accordingly, she becomes thin and her foal fails to make normal growth. The foal may be permanently stunted and the mare fails to come into estrus (heat) or fails to conceive. Thus we have a stunted foal and a barren mare, living testimonials to poor management.

THE ESTROUS CYCLE

Estrus. Estrus (or heat) is the period during which the mare will accept the stallion. Although the mare may exhibit signs of estrus at any time during the year, the spring months of March through May are the periods of greatest sexual activity. The duration of estrus averages 5–7 days but may vary in extreme cases from 2 to 15 days. The time between the beginning of one estrous period and the next averages about 21 days and the events occurring during this period are known as the estrous cycle. According to Hammond (1952) the length of the estrous cycle varies directly with the duration of estrus. Mares which remain in estrus 5–7 days will have a 21–23-day cycle. A longer estrus results in a longer cycle. Hammond also found that very young or very old and thin mares remain in estrus longer than the average, due to the slow ripening of the egg. Mares having an abnormally long estrus are usually poor breeders. Improving the nutritional level of mares in poor condition immediately prior to and during the breeding season improves the regularity of the estrous cycle and increases the chances for conception.

Ovulation. Ovulation generally occurs about 24 hours before the end of estrus in the mare. Healthy mares in normal condition are fairly regular in their cycles and ovulation occurs at about the same time in each estrus. By daily rectal palpation during estrus an experienced person can determine within a few hours the exact time of ovulation. Knowing when a given mare will ovulate permits mating her to the stallion at the proper time so that many live sperm will be present to fertilize the egg.

Fertilization. Fertilization depends to a great extent on timing of mating during estrus as it relates to ovulation. It has been established by research with other farm animals that the egg remains capable of fertilization only a short time after ovulation, possibly less than 24 hours. Sperm remain alive and capable of fertilizing the egg only a short time inside the female genital tract, possibly 24 to 48 hours. Furthermore, it has been established that 6–12 hours may be required for the sperm to travel from the vagina or cervix of the female, where semen is deposited by the stallion during mating, to the upper or ovarian end of the Fallopian tube where the egg is deposited at time of ovulation. To insure fertile mating requires knowledge of the duration of estrus and time of ovulation in the mare so that she may be bred about 2 days before the end of estrus. Experience has proven this to be the optimum time to breed when only one service is given. Breeding on the third day of estrus and on alternate days thereafter as long as the mare remains in heat is a common practice when the stallion is not overworked.

IMPLANTATION. Following fertilization, which normally occurs in the fimbriated or upper end of the Fallopian tube, the fertilized egg descends through the tube to the uterus. It is not known exactly how much time is required for this descent in the mare, but it has been found to vary from 2 to 5 days in other farm animals. During this period and for a number of days thereafter the developing embryo is nourished by direct absorption from the fluids of the Fallopian tube and uterus ("uterine milk"). How long the embryo is nourished directly by absorption from the uterine milk is unknown, but within 5 weeks following fertilization in the mare the embryo is loosely attached to the uterine wall. This attachment is made between embryonic membranes and the sensitive endometrium of the uterus, through which the embryo receives nourishment from the mother.

GESTATION. Gestation is the time or period from fertile mating to birth of the foal, a period of 340 ± 20 days. Like the duration of estrus, the gestation period is subject to considerable variation. The plane of nutrition affects the gestation period; a low plane tends to lengthen, a high plane shortens gestation. Other factors such as age, season, and individuality may influence the gestation period.

DIAGNOSIS OF PREGNANCY. Because of the comparatively low conception rate (65–70%) in mares compared to other farm animals, their value per head, and their long gestation period, early pregnancy diagnosis is important. Failure of the mare to come into estrus on schedule (15–16 days) following date of last service is indicative of pregnancy. However, many mares will skip two or more cycles and then return to estrus. Others will show no signs of estrus but fail to produce a foal. Why many mares behave in this manner is not understood, but a disturbance of the delicate hormone balance necessary for implantation and nourishment of the embryo is suspected. Probably fertilization occurs, but the embryo dies and is resorbed.

The blood test: Cole and Hart (1930) and later Catchpole and Lyons (1934) found that between the 45th and 145th days after breeding, the blood serum of a pregnant mare contains enough gonadotropin to give a reliable test when injected into laboratory animals. A small quantity of serum injected into 21-day-old female mice or rats will, if the mare is pregnant, stimulate the ovaries and uterus to mature size and sexual activity in a 48-hour period. This is a reliable and highly useful test because it can be made early in pregnancy.

Rectal palpation: It is also possible to diagnose pregnancy by inserting the hand into the rectum of the mare and palpating the uterine horns through the rectal wall. This requires some skill but with practice and skill it is a quick and reliable technique any time after 60 days from last service.

Male

AGE AT PUBERTY. The colt (young male) normally first exhibits an interest in the female as a yearling and will try to mount a mare in estrus. However, except for small, early-maturing types, sexual maturity does not occur until the colt approaches two years of age. As in fillies, plane of nutrition influences growth and sexual development.

BREEDING CAPACITY. Colts that are large and well developed may be given light service as two-year-olds, being limited to 10 to 12 mares during a 6- to 8-week season, but here again individual variation will determine the capacity of a given colt. A three-year-old horse can service 25 to 30 mares in a season, and active stallions 4 years old and over may service 50 to 60 mares in a 90-day season if hand mated with good management.

FERTILITY AND STERILITY. It is not uncommon to find stallions that fail to settle their mares. Examination of the semen usually reveals abnormal sperm. A normal stallion ejaculate will vary from 50–100 ml, with a sperm concentration of 100–200 millions per ml. Although it is not known exactly what the minimum requirement is for high fertility, experience has demonstrated that a significant reduction below the normal average in volume or sperm count results in lowered fertility. It has also been reported by several research workers that less than 70% normal sperm is an indication of lowered fertility. Frequent microscopic evaluation of semen for sperm numbers, motility, and abnormality is routine procedure in a well-managed stud.

Management at Breeding Time

SYSTEMS OF MATING. Among wild horses stallions fight for their mares and the victor has his band of mares, which he keeps together. Stallions are still turned out on the open range with bands of mares on some ranches in the West and Southwest. Most mares are bred by stallions on halter, however, and artificial insemination is practiced to a limited degree.

THE MARE. Healthy normal mares usually come into estrus between the 5th and 7th day after foaling (foal heat) and remain in estrus until the 10th or 13th day. Accordingly the usual practice, where it is desirable to keep the mare on schedule, is to breed her on the 9th day after foaling. If for any reason the mare has not recovered completely from foaling, or has any type of infection in her reproductive tract, she should not be bred until she is completely sound and free of infection.

To protect the stallion and for ease in handling, mares should be hobbled and the tail wrapped for breeding. It is also advisable to wash the external genitalia of the mare with a mild soapy water. Following mating, mares should be isolated and kept as quiet as possible for a minimum of 12 hours.

THE STALLION. Only mature stallions (4 years and over) should be permitted to run with a band of mares and 20 mares is about the maximum number if the breeding season is restricted to 60–90 days. Where hand mated, the stallion should have an individual stall or shed with an adjoining exercise paddock. Exercise and green feed or good-quality hay plus enough grain to maintain weight are essential. Avoid overfeeding and confinement without exercise. Stallions should be trained to mount and dismount properly. Where a stallion is being stood for public service, only clean, healthy mares should be accepted. It is advisable to thoroughly wash his penis with a mild soap solution after each service to reduce danger of carrying infection from one mare to the next.

ARTIFICIAL INSEMINATION. Artificial insemination has been practiced in a limited way for many years. It was originally used as a last effort to breed mares that failed to conceive from normal service. More recently it has been used to extend the services from valuable sires. Modern techniques allow the stallion to mount a mare in estrus, and by directing the penis of the stallion into an artificial vagina, a normal semen ejaculate is collected. From this one collection, 5 to 10 mares can be inseminated, depending on the volume and sperm count. The semen may be introduced directly through the cervix into the uterus by means of a sterile syringe and plastic tube, or by means of a gelatin capsule. In either event sanitation and knowledge of semen characteristics are essential. Unlike bull semen, satisfactory techniques for dilution and storage have not been developed, hence use of stallion semen is limited to a relatively short time after collection. By reducing the temperature of the semen to 34–36°F and excluding oxygen by sealing in small containers, the life and fertilizing capacity of good semen can be extended to 24–48 hours. Some breed associations have restricting clauses concerning artificial insemination.

35-3. THE MARE AND HER FOAL

Care of Mare Before She Foals. As with all pregnant animals, the mare should be maintained in normal flesh and permitted or forced to get regular and moderate exercise. Confinement and overfeeding should never be permitted. Pasture which provides green feed, exercise, and sunshine is an excellent environment. Where it is necessary to confine the mare, she should be exercised daily until she foals. If pasture is not available or if it is sparse, the mare should be allowed all of the hay, preferably good-quality grass or mixed hay plus oats if necessary to maintain her in good strong flesh, but without fat.

At Foaling Time. The weather will determine the protection the mare needs at foaling time. Clean pasture is a good place for the mare to foal, although this may make it difficult to observe her regularly or to give assistance when needed. If confined, she should be in a clean box stall at least 12 x 12 feet, bedded with clean straw or shavings. If the temperature is low it may be advisable to close up the stall, to prevent drafts and chilling. Except for severe weather a dry windbreak is all the protection needed.

Because of the great variation in length of gestation of mares it is difficult to predict foaling date. Frequent observation is essential. The presence of milk in the udder and a waxy (colostrum) exudate from the teats usually indicates foaling within a few days. As labor approaches the mare may exhibit signs of nervousness and fail to eat, or she may lie down and get up frequently. As long as she is making progress she should not be disturbed. But if little or no progress is being made, after a period of 2 or more hours of hard labor, assistance should be given. Normal presentation of foal is front feet first with head between forelegs. If the position is normal, assistance can be rendered by steady pulling out and down as the mare labors. A soft, cotton rope may be attached to the feet to permit a stronger pull. Should the foal be in malposition—the head or either foot turned back—a veterinarian or an experienced person should be called to correct the position and deliver the foal.

Care of Newborn Foal. Tincture of iodine should be applied to the navel cord. If the foal is normal and strong, it will be on its feet within $\frac{1}{2}$ to one hour after birth. Its legs are long and unsteady and it may be necessary to help it up and assist it to nurse. This is usually all the attention a newborn foal needs. If the weather is severe, however, it is well to dry the foal by rubbing vigorously with a towel or burlap bag. The mare's udder should be checked for milk and the teats squeezed to expel any dried colostrum that might clog the canals. Preferably, the mare and foal should be turned out on pasture as soon as possible.

35-4. NUTRITIONAL REQUIREMENTS

Very little is known about the nutrition of horses, and most of the data available have been collected on draft horses. There is real need for specific nutritional requirements for horses by weight and according to the work they are called on to do. Only limited data are available on the minimum requirements for maintenance, work, growth, the pregnant or nursing mare, or for the weanling.

Some general principles concerning the feeding of horses are discussed in Chapter 28. More specific information is provided here. Table 35-3 gives the maintenance requirements as influenced by age, and Table 35-4 gives the nutrient allowances for mature horses under various physiological conditions such as resting, working, pregnancy, and lactation.

TABLE 35-3. | *Physiologically equivalent ages, body weights, and nutrient allowances.* *

	Kind of horse	Percent of mature weight						
		(10)	(20)	(30)	(40)	(50)	(60)	(100)
Average age in months	Light weight	0.5	2.0	4.0	6.0	10.0	14.0	44.0
Average weight in pounds	Light weight	100	200	300	400	500	600	1000
Total daily feed, pounds (maintenance)	Light weight		8.3	9.7	11.0	12.3	13.5	12.6
Daily feed intake, percent of body weight (maintenance)	Light weight		4.2	3.2	2.8	2.5	2.2	1.3
Daily intake of digestible nutrients, pounds (maintenance)	Light weight		5.2	6.1	6.9	7.7	8.4	7.9
Digestible nutrients, percent of total feed	All weights		62.5	62.5	62.5	62.5	62.5	62.5
Digestible protein, percent of TDN	Light weight		20.0	16.2	13.6	11.0	9.2	7.8
Calcium (percent of TDN)	Light weight		0.52	0.47	0.43	0.38	0.35	0.25
Phosphorus (percent of TDN)	Light weight		0.45	0.42	0.40	0.37	0.35	0.27

* Guilbert, H. R. and J. K. Loosli, 1951. Comparative nutrition of farm animals. National Research Council reprint series No. 132.

TABLE | *Daily allowances for mature horses.**
35-4.

Body wt (lb.)	Dry matter (90% basis)		TDN		Digestible protein		Calcium (g.)	Phosphorus (g.)
	Maintenance (lb.)	Work (light) (lb.)	Maintenance (lb.)	Work (light) (lb.)	Maintenance (lb.)	Work (light) (lb.)		
400	6.2	8.2	3.9	5.1	0.31	0.38	7.3	8.5
600	8.5	11.0	5.3	6.9	0.42	0.52	9.9	11.0
800	10.6	13.8	6.6	8.6	0.53	0.65	12.2	13.7
1000	12.6	16.2	7.9	10.1	0.62	0.76	13.7	15.4
1200	14.4	18.6	9.0	11.6	0.71	0.88	15.7	17.7
Mares (last quarter of gestation)								
400		8.6		5.4		0.46	7.8	7.8
600		11.7		7.3		0.62	10.6	10.6
800		14.4		9.0		0.77	13.1	13.1
1000		17.0		10.6		0.91	15.4	15.4
1200		19.5		12.2		1.09	17.7	17.7
Mares (lactating)								
400		12.3		8.8		1.01	12.3	11.2
600		16.7		11.9		1.37	16.7	15.2
800		20.6		14.7		1.70	20.6	18.7
1000		24.4		17.4		2.01	24.4	22.2
1200		28.0		20.0		2.30	28.0	25.4

* National Research Council, 1949. Nutrient Allowances for Horses.

35-5. MAINTAINING HEALTH AND SOUNDNESS

Importance. Because his usefulness is so dependent on his ability to perform the tasks called for, soundness and health are of first importance. Normal eyesight, sound feet and legs, and good lungs are a must in a top horse. Likewise freedom from parasites and disease are essential to a healthy, good-working horse. Space does not permit more than a general statement on preventive measures that are consistent with good management practices.

Parasites. According to Dr. A. O. Foster (1942), "Some 150 kinds of internal parasites infest horses and mules, and probably no individual animal is ever entirely free of some of them. Fortunately, comparatively few do real damage—but those few can be extremely harmful and sometimes deadly." Conditions favorable for parasitic worms occur when numbers of horses are maintained on the same restricted pasture acreage for prolonged periods of time. Most actual damage to the horse is done by the immature or larval forms, after they have entered the host and before they reach the adult stage. Almost every tissue in the body of the horse is subject to attack by immature parasitic worms. The alimentary tract, lungs, body cavity, and blood are most frequently parasitized.

WORMS. Adult female worms in the digestive tract produce thousands of eggs which pass out with the feces. With proper moisture and temperature the eggs develop into infective embryos. When ingested with forage by the grazing animal, the embryos are liberated in the small intestine and start the life cycle over again.

Every effort should be made to avoid heavy stocking on small areas. Horses having access to large pastures in dry climates are less likely to become heavily parasitized. Manure from stalls should not be scattered on horse pastures until after it has thoroughly heated from composting. Light stocking and rotation grazing help reduce parasitism.

Intestinal worms are especially harmful to young horses, causing stunting, unthriftiness, and susceptibility to other disorders. It is good management to treat them periodically, but therapeutic doses are necessary to be effective and, because the drugs are toxic, skill is required. Therefore it is wise to have a veterinarian treat the horse or prescribe treatment. Fecal examination by a veterinarian will reveal the degree of infestation (egg count) and determine the need for treatment. Treatments may be necessary at any season, but ridding the young horse of parasites in the fall before going into the winter is a necessity for a healthy, vigorous horse the following spring.

BOTS. Bot flies are serious pests to horses throughout the United States. They appear in the spring and deposit their eggs on hairs under the throat or on the neck, legs, or belly. Horses are annoyed and frightened by bot fly strike and frequently become uncontrollable. Eggs hatch from the heat and moisture of licking and are taken into the animal's mouth. The larvae eventually attach themselves to the animal's stomach where they mature, 10 to 11 months after being ingested. Mature larvae pass out in the feces. Hundreds of the larvae the size of the end of a man's finger may be attached to the wall of the stomach. In such heavy infestation serious damage is done.

Control measures consist of rubbing the eggs off the hairs before they hatch by means of a hot, wet rag or by clipping the hairs. Internal treatment, 4–6 weeks after the external treatment and after a killing frost in the fall, will rid the horse of bot larvae in the stomach. Carbon disulfide is the most effective chemical and should be administered by a veterinarian.

OTHER INSECTS. There are numerous common insect pests of horses such as mosquitoes, house flies, horse flies, deer flies, gnats, fleas, lice, and ticks. In large numbers any of these pests can become a real problem. Prevention of breeding by sanitary measures, elimination of stagnant water, screens, and use of sprays are effective measures of control.

Diseases. Only the more common diseases will be included in this brief discussion.

ENCEPHALOMYELITIS. (Sleeping sickness.) This occurs throughout the United States. There is an Eastern and a Western type; although the symptoms are identical there are two types of viruses. The disease is believed to be transmitted by blood-sucking insects and is most prevalent in late summer and early fall, disappearing after killing frost. Vaccination is the only safe preventive and all horses in areas where the disease occurs regularly should be routinely vaccinated each year, in the spring or early summer.

PERIODIC OPHTHALMIA. (Moon blindness.) "Experts estimate that 1 out of every 10 horses in the U.S. is affected with this recurrent inflammation of the eyes that may end in loss of sight" (Mott and Seibold, 1942). Horses of all ages are susceptible, but it is more common in mature animals. The acute inflammation of the inner portions of the eyes may subside after a few days, but repeated attacks damage the eyes and frequently lead to blindness. There are no known preventive measures nor any effective treatment for advanced cases. Keeping the affected animal in a dark stall, the use of cold packs or compresses to the eye, and mild laxatives may help relieve the condition (Roby and Mott, 1956).

Unsoundnesses. Any unsoundness which interferes with action, speed, strength, or endurance is serious in the horse. The feet and legs are the most commonly affected parts. This is because they support the weight of the horse and rider and provide the means of locomotion. Conformational defects, strain, or injury may be responsible for unsoundness of feet and legs. The old axiom—"No feet, no horse" or "No legs, no horse"—are worth keeping in mind when buying or evaluating a horse.

Many unsoundnesses of the feet and legs can be traced to conformational defects. Straight rather than sloping shoulders, with short, straight pasterns, gives the horse a poor natural shock-absorbing mechanism. This condition is hard on horse and rider, and it is widely believed that such horses are susceptible to stiffness, lameness, ring bones, and sidebones.

The hock joint is one most frequently unsound, due in part to conformation defects such as sickle hock, cow hock, or too straight a leg. Such defects weaken the joint, and, since all of the driving force of the horse is transmitted through the hock, it is subjected to constant and sometimes great strain in the running horse or by the quick stops, starts, and turns of the cutting horse.

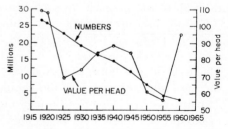

Fig. 35-1. Horse and mule numbers and value per head in the United States, 1918–1960. [From USDA.]

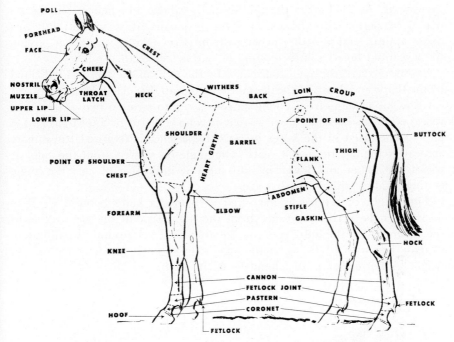

Fig. 35-2. The parts of a horse. [From Oregon 4-H Horse Bulletin H24.]

Clean, flat joints and bones are much preferred to round, meaty bones and joints. Figures 35-1 and 35-2 show the parts of the horse and the location of some of the more common unsoundnesses.

35-6. DETERMINING THE AGE AND HEIGHT OF HORSES

It is extremely important to be able to determine age accurately. Ordinarily horses are not ready for much work until the age of 3. Provided they are sound, they will appreciate in value until 7–8 years of age, then depreciate with each additional year. As a matter of policy all horse breed associations add another year to the age of a horse on January 1. Thus a foal becomes a yearling on January 1, regardless of the month in which it was born.

The young animal has 24 temporary teeth, commonly called milk teeth, consisting of 12 incisors and 12 molars. The milk teeth are shed and replaced by permanent teeth at fairly definite periods, which serve as a guide in determining the age of young horses (Fig. 35-4). At 6–10 months the foal will have all 12 incisors or front teeth—3 pairs above and 3 pairs below. The crown on the middle pairs will show wear at 1 year of age, the intermediate pairs will show wear at $1\frac{1}{2}$ years, and by 2 years all teeth will show wear. At 2½–3 years the middle pairs (above and below) will be replaced by permanent incisors, at 4 the two pairs of permanent intermediates appear, and at 5 the corner pairs of permanent teeth appear, giving the 5-year-old horse a "full mouth" of permanent teeth.

Beyond 5 years, the age is estimated by the wear of the teeth as indicated by the shape and depth of the dental cavity or cup (Fig. 35-4). With wear and age, the cup changes from a long narrow cavity to a round dental star. The wear occurs in the same order as that in which the teeth appeared, and is most pronounced in the lower incisors. Experience is required to estimate accurately the age beyond 8 years. The angle (as viewed from the side) at which the upper and lower incisors meet is indicative of age, the angle getting smaller with increasing age.

The height of a horse is measured in hands, a hand being 4 in. The measure is the vertical distance from the highest point on the withers to the ground, with the horse standing squarely on level ground. A calibrated, straight bar with a sliding right angle arm is used for determining the height. A horse that is 15-2 hands is 62 in. high.

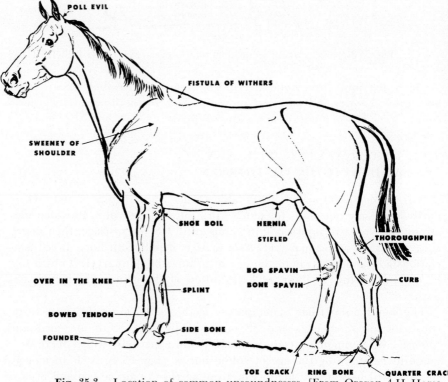

Fig. 35-3. Location of common unsoundnesses. [From Oregon 4-H Horse Bulletin H24.]

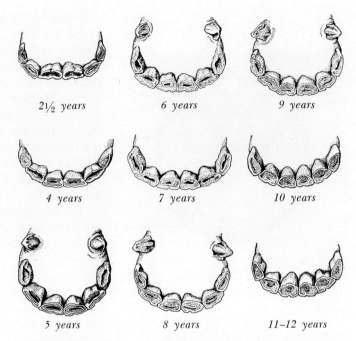

2½ years   6 years   9 years

4 years   7 years   10 years

5 years   8 years   11–12 years

Fig. 35-4. The appearance of the incisors from age 2 to 12 years. [From USDA Farmers Bulletin 2127.]

35-7. CARE AND TRAINING

Housing. Except for newborn foals or extremely old or sick horses, shade and a dry windbreak are all the protection needed from the elements. Too much protection in the form of warm, poorly ventilated or drafty stalls is worse than not enough. If a horse is adequately fed he can tolerate most any kind of weather.

Clean stalls and paddocks free from loose wire, nails, glass, or other sharp objects are much more important than the kind of stall or barn. Most injuries to horses can be prevented. Box stalls should be not less than 12 x 12 ft., with solid walls at least 4 ft. high and ceiling 10 ft. high or more. Avoid cracks where a foot can get hung. Board fences around paddocks and small lots are much safer than wire. Farm machinery should never be left where horses exercise.

Exercise. All horses need exercise and will get enough when left out on pasture. If confined to a stall, they should be turned out for exercise or ridden daily. Horses left in stalls without exercise frequently get stiff, their lower legs swell, and they go stale. Next to feed and water, exercise is the most important requirement of a horse.

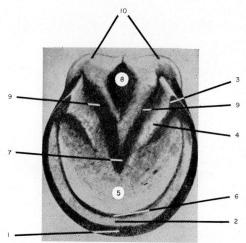

Fig. 35-6. Ground surface of a normal front foot. [From Sisson, *Anatomy of the Domestic Animals,* (4th ed.), Saunders, Philadelphia, 1953.]

Grooming. A good horseman keeps his horse well groomed. Regular and thorough brushing not only keeps the horse clean, but keeps his coat glossy and his skin healthy, and strengthens his loyalty and devotion to his master. To spare the brush is to spoil the horse. It is especially important to "rub him down" and "cool him out" after a hard and hot workout. He should be wiped dry, rubbed vigorously, blanketed (in cool weather), and walked for 20–30 minutes while he cools.

Feet. The hard, horny outer covering of the foot, known as the wall is like the nails of the fingers (Fig. 35-6). It continues to grow throughout life and requires regular and correct trimming. The frequency of trimming varies with individuals, the kind of terrain, and weather the horse is kept confined or is on pasture. If on sandy or gravelly pasture, feet wear enough that little trimming is necessary. On wet, soft ground or in confinement feet should be checked every 6 weeks and trimmed to shape as needed. Regular cleaning of the feet to remove manure or dead tissue is essential to maintaining sound feet of a horse kept in the stall or in a muddy paddock.

Horses used regularly need shoes, and this is a job for a farrier. Good farriers trim and shape the foot and correct ill-shaped feet before fitting the shoe. Shoes need to be reset about every 6 weeks, due to wall growth. Keeping a horse properly shod is expensive but is a necessity if he is to travel over rough or gravel roads.

Training and Handling of Foals. A foal should be haltered at a week to 10 days of age and handled regularly to gentle him early. At 2 months his feet should be trimmed and at regular intervals of 4–6 weeks thereafter. Keep the foot level with heels down to encourage pressure on the frog.

Foals should be weaned at 4–6 months of age and this requires good management. Take the mare from the foal quietly and far enough that the foal cannot hear its mother. The foal should be left in a clean, tight, and safe stall, fed lightly, kept quiet, and watered by hand. Turn the weanling out to exercise in a tightly fenced paddock as soon as it can be done with safety. As soon as the weanling is eating well, treat him for internal parasites.

Start handling him in the stall as soon as he settles down, by brushing, foot inspection, tying up, and response to halter. Accustom him to discipline and to all routine handling until he no longer shows signs of fear. Allow the weanling all the good mixed legume hay he will eat and gradually increase the oats to 5–6 quarts daily, depending on size, appetite, and condition. This routine should be followed until spring, when the weanling is ready to turn to pasture or continue his training.

Colts. Unless they are to be used for breeding, colts should be gelded in the spring when yearlings. Normally colts can safely be run in groups of 3 to 5 as yearlings, although occasionally it is necessary to separate them.

Yearlings. Breed and future use will determine the schedule of training for the yearling. Racing horses and those being prepared for yearling sales are kept on a regular schedule of schooling, grooming, and feeding for maximum growth and good manners by sale time. They are introduced to the bridle, the saddle, and the exercise boy—in that order—and by fall of their yearling year they are large for yearlings and well advanced in training.

Many yearlings raised for ranch work or for pleasure are allowed the run of the pasture during the summer and get no further training until they are 2-year-olds and big enough to be saddled and broken to ride. This requires good horsemanship. It is much better to make the training from foal to 2-year-old a continuous unbroken process, through saddle and rider. The rider should be light in weight (not exceeding 120 lb.) and ride just enough to acquaint the yearling with the saddle and rider. As the yearling approaches 2 years of age, he can carry a heavier load, stand more work, and graduate into a "man-sized" horse with limited work. From that point on his training continues; reining, cutting, changing leads, learning the gaits, and good manners. The finished product will depend on the breed and what is expected of him, but the basic early training is the same for all horses.

Few persons have the patience and "horse sense" to train a horse properly. Horses are like humans: they require time, kindness, firmness, and understanding. No finer example of affection, loyalty, and understanding can be found between man and beast than that which exists between man and his well-trained horse.

REFERENCES AND SELECTED READINGS

References marked with an asterisk are of general interest.

Catchpole, H. R., and W. R. Lyons, 1934. Gonad Stimulating Hormone of Pregnant Mares. *Am. J. Anat.*, 55:167.

Cole, H. H. and G. H. Hart, 1930. Sex Hormones in the Blood Serum of Mares. *Am. J. Physiol.*, 94:597.

*Foster, A. O., 1942. Internal Parasites of Horses and Mules. Keeping Livestock Healthy. USDA Yearbook of Agriculture, p. 459.

*Hammond, J., 1952. *Farm Animals, Their Breeding Growth and Inheritance*, Second Edition, Edward Arnold & Co.

Mott, L. O. and H. R. Seibold, 1942. Periodic Ophthalmia of Horses. Keeping Livestock Healthy. USDA Yearbook of Agriculture, p. 402.

*Roby, T. O. and L. O. Mott, 1956. Equine Periodic Ophthalmia. Animal Diseases. USDA Yearbook of Agriculture, p. 531.

Chapter 36

Poultry Management

36-1. INTRODUCTION

In approaching the problems of poultry management one is impressed by the similarity of good management practices for all livestock. Common sense indicates the importance of good nutrition, adequate housing or environmental control, disease prevention, and cost-accounting or business methods. These factors transcend such classifications of management of poultry, swine, horses, or cattle. The distinctive features are to be found when one asks the question, How is the poultry business different from the others?

A few examples of distinctiveness may be cited. Poultry females lay eggs and have a short productive life. Since they are not ruminants, a concentrated ration is required. Body temperature is high, 106°F or more, and since they are small with more surface area per unit of weight, nonsweating, and covered with feathers, poultry do not withstand heat as well as larger farm animals. Poultry, being omnivorous, are more cannibalistic than herbivorous animals. Poultry production has a very short economic cycle. Less than a period of two years elapses between peak egg prices. In recent years the seasonality of egg prices received by the producer has been considerably reduced.

Because the poultry industry has a short economic cycle, it reveals changes that have been and are taking place in animal agriculture throughout the United States. Exhibition shows and judging have joined cockfighting in the historical past of poultry. The farm flock, formerly the backbone of the poultry industry, also will soon be nonexistent. Poultry production is a highly specialized business, and large-sized flocks are the rule rather than the exception. Whereas a man could formerly make a comfortable living with 1000 laying hens, he now needs 5000 or more. Twenty years ago, 1000–

2000 turkeys raised for meat would produce a living; it now takes 10,000 or more turkeys to provide the same standard of living. These increases in efficiency have resulted from advances in mechanization and efficiency of production. Oddly enough, the prices the consumer pays have not increased. Only when one considers that the value of the dollar is only half of its value a decade ago does the significance of the accomplishment become clearly apparent.

High cash costs, small margins of profit, and larger volume have been associated with the agricultural revolution. Poultry farming today is a modern business requiring accurate records and sound management of both money and poultry. The businessmen have entered the poultry farmer's field. The size of flocks is continually increasing. One economist has calculated that 50,000 flocks of 5000 layers producing at 70% could supply the entire nation's egg requirement. Some flocks in California now have over 100,000 hens. One might reverse the numbers above so that 5000 flocks of 50,000 hens could do the job. Furthermore, fewer hens are now producing more eggs. In the United States during a 5-year period, 1950–1954, the total number of laying flocks declined nearly one-fifth, from 4.2 to 3.4 million. In terms of percentages there was a tremendous increase in flocks with 3200 or more hens.

The hatchery business changed drastically in the years 1953 to 1957. The number of hatcheries declined from 7000 to 5000—a 27% decrease. It is noteworthy that failure of a franchised hatchery—one under contract with a breeder to merchandise their chicks—rarely occurred. Small breeder-hatcheries were hard hit, and many became franchise hatcheries in order to survive.

The fryer or broiler business has become localized in most states where it is an important business. Georgia is one of the leading states in the production of fryers.

Turkey production for many years has been localized in areas which had a climatic advantage in the control of the diseases "blackhead." With the discovery of suitable drugs to control the disease, production has increased tremendously in other areas, particularly Minnesota, now the leading state in turkey production.

California ranks first in farm income from eggs, followed by New York, Iowa, and Minnesota. In the future we may expect large mechanized commercial egg plants. Egg production will approach a 300-egg average. In 1960 in California egg production for the average hen led the nation with 229 eggs; the United States average was 206 eggs. There are fewer egg handlers in the egg business. Those that are still in the business have increased in size and have become more mechanized. Egg handlers are insisting that their producer follow rather rigid management and handling practices. The candling of eggs by hand will soon disappear as a common practice.

Ownership of poultry operations was one of the first agricultural businesses to become integrated. This integration combines many operations formerly handled by independent business agents. The business of grower, hatcheryman, feed manufacturer, feed salesman, and poultry processor may be owned and operated by the same management. Many partial types of integration are also possible. The man raising the poultry may be paid wages by the integrated organization or own his own farm and be paid so much per pound, per bird, or per dozen. Often there is a bonus to stimulate efficiency. Production units are large, and by careful planning, spreading the risks, and increasing the volume, this type of operation has frequently been successful in fryer and turkey production. There is growing evidence that in the future egg production will also be integrated. Company-owned flocks may in the future be restricted in growth by the size of investment required.

Sources of credit have played a major part in the expansion and integration of the poultry business. In addition to private sources, cooperatives have played a part in financing their producers. Credit in vast amounts is extended by feed companies and hatcheries. The poultry processor also extends credit to assure full use of his equipment. It is now clear that one does not start in the poultry business unless he has a market for his products. One does not make money on poultry every year, or indeed every other year.

36-2. OPTIMUM ENVIRONMENT

The optimum environment for poultry is a goal which is neither easy to describe nor to attain. On one hand, there are the environmental factors: temperature, light, humidity, air movement, and altitude. On the other hand, we have the various species, breeds, and ages of poultry, all of which have a bearing on the optimum for a particular environmental factor. To make the situation more complex we have interactions between air temperature, humidity, and air movement, which are fairly well known for man. These factors also have a similar effect on the comfort of poultry. The construction of multidimensional graphs are difficult to grasp and are even more difficult to construct. However, simple graphs have been made to give the optimum environment of five of the recognized environmental factors on chickens. The graphs are drawn freehand using points of maximums, minimums, and optimums published in the literature. The graphs indicate a few of the gaps in our knowledge of optimum environment. Age of the bird is given on the abscissa. (Figs. 36-1 to 36-5).

The environmental conditions best suited for poultry production dictate to some degree the type of housing required. Poultry may be kept (1) on the range, (2) in litter floor housing, (3) on wire floors or slats, or (4) in individual cages. The agricultural engineer may design houses without windows for control of light and air movement, reducing to a minimum the hazard of the human factor.

Ventilation. Strangely enough the main function of ventilation is not to supply oxygen and remove carbon dioxide. It is to remove ammonia and water and to aid in temperature control. Therefore it is not surprising to see in Fig. 36-1 that air temperature greatly influences the need for air exchange. When the air temperature is 90–99°F, a ventilation rate of 2000 cubic feet of air per minute per 100 birds may be desirable. Tests on efficiency of windbreaks have shown that the velocity of the wind coming through does not vary greatly whether the fence is 25%, 50%, or 65% pervious. Lowered costs would favor the most pervious type of windbreak.

Light. When chicks are young they need more than the normal photoperiods (day lengths); see Fig. 36-2. It has been suggested that this is associated with the size of the crop and the fact that chicks sometimes do not learn to eat enough, at an early age, during the period of normal daylight. After approximately 4 weeks of age, chicks actually grow better when not given too much light. As they approach maturity, 20 or 22 weeks of age, they may be given the full amount of light.

By reducing the amount of light given in the growing period, egg production can be improved in winter-hatched chickens. Decreasing day lengths

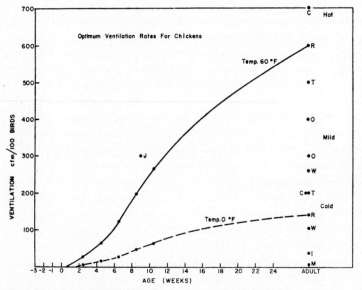

Fig. 36-1. Ventilation rates vary with age of chickens and outside temperatures.

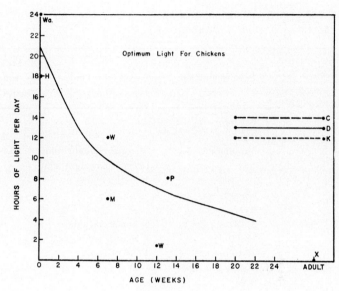

Fig. 36-2. Light requirements are higher for very young chicks and for early sexual maturity.

per se will delay sexual maturity. Once the birds are in production the cardinal rule is to avoid exposing the layers to decreasing day lengths.

Recommendations for the use of light for the various species of poultry are shown in Table 36-1.

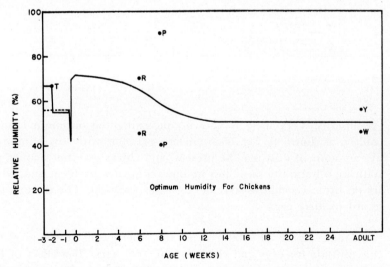

Fig. 36-3. High relative humidity is required for hatching and early feathering.

TABLE | *Recommendations for the use of light for poultry expressed as photo-*
36-1. | *periods and intensities.*

Species and Age (weeks)	Light: Dark (hours)	Minimum Intensity (foot-candles)
I. *Chicken fryers*		
0–3	24:0	1.0
3 to market	Seasonal daylight (plus intermittent night light, 1:3)	0.1–0.5
Chicken layers		
0–3	24:0	1.0
3–12	Seasonal daylight	0.5
12–20	8:16 or 6:18*	0.5
20 to market	14:10 or 16:8*	1.0
II. *Turkey meat birds*		
0–3	24:0†	2.0
3 to market	Seasonal daylight (plus intermittent night light, 1:3†)	
Turkey layers		
0–3	24:0†	2.0
3–24	Seasonal daylight	
24–28**	6:18	1.0
28+	14:10	2.0
III. *Ducks, geese, and pigeons‡*		
Jan. through April	14:10	2.0

* Avoid decreasing amount of light from Oct. to Feb.
† These are estimates. Data not available.
** Precondition with 10 hours or less for 4 weeks before egg production; 14 hours or more to bring into egg production.
‡ Very little known of actual requirements.

Humidity. Very little is known concerning the optimum humidity for poultry, as shown in Fig. 36-3. On one extreme, with low humidity, excessive amounts of dust may be present, and chicks may not feather properly. With high humidity, heat loss becomes a greater problem and, when birds are on litter, coccidiosis may be a greater problem. The same is true with regard to dirty eggs.

Altitude. Figure 36-4 differs from the other graphs, for it gives the tolerable altitude for eggs and chicks at different ages. The effect of high altitudes is mainly one of incubation. Once hatched, chickens and turkeys may be reared successfully up to 12,500 feet. The hatchability of turkey eggs is more sensitive to altitude than chicken eggs.

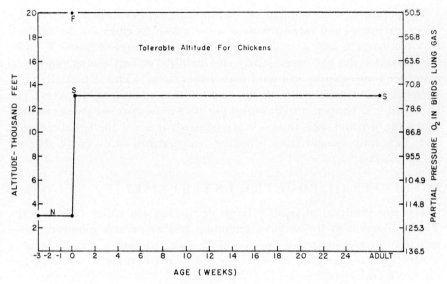

Fig. 36-4.   Chickens and turkeys can be grown at high elevations.

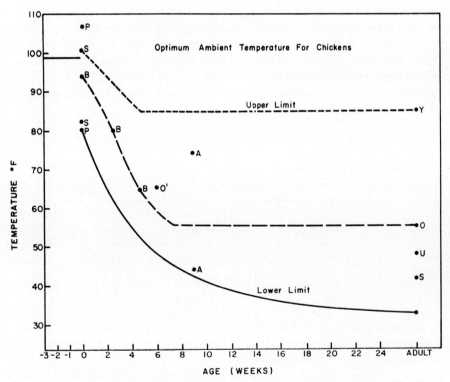

Fig. 36-5.   High temperatures are required for hatching and brooding.

Temperature. The ambient or surrounding temperature is usually the major environmental factor involved in heat loss. Its effect can be modified by air movement and humidity. Brooding temperatures of 90–95°F under the hover for the first week reflect the inability of very young poultry to maintain homeothermy (constant body temperature). This is partially physiological and partially due to the lack of insulation from feathers. The upper limit of temperature shown in Fig. 36-5 represents the temperature at which egg size and shell thickness are reduced; it is not the lethal temperature. Sick birds benefit from brooding temperatures in excess of that for normal chicks.

36-3. TYPES OF POULTRY ENTERPRISES

The end products of poultry farms or ranches are either meat or eggs. The production of by-products, including feathers, is not important commercially in any species of poultry. With specialization a limited number of ranches may specialize in the rearing of "started" pullets for subsequent egg production.

Types of poultry enterprises for chickens include fryer or broiler production, egg production, and rearing started pullets. Turkey enterprises include meat production and hatching egg production. Ducks as a source of meat or eggs have never been popular in the United States, though a notable exception is the Long Island duck farming area. Geese, pigeons, Guinea fowl, and other poultry are handicapped by a low rate of egg production, which seriously limits the numbers which may be produced.

The approximate distribution of costs of production of five common types of poultry enterprises are given in Table 36-2.

TABLE 36-2. | *Production costs of poultry enterprises, expressed as per cent of total cost.**

	Chickens			Turkeys	
	Fryers	Layers	Pullets (16 wk.)	Meat	Hatching eggs
Feed	60.9%	59.9%	46.9%	63.6%	50.9%
Stock	17.4	8.2	30.8	14.1	17.2
Labor	7.6	14.2	12.3	8.4	16.3
Fuel	2.2		1.4	0.7	
Interest	1.1	4.1	1.0	6.5	1.8
Depreciation	4.3	5.3	3.8	2.5	2.8
Miscellaneous	6.5	8.4	3.8	4.2	11.0

*Source of information: University of California Agricultural Extension Service. The date and California counties represented for the columns in respective order are as follows: 1956–57 Los Angeles, 1960 State wide representing over 1 million layers, 1958 Orange, 1959 Los Angeles and 1960 Fresno, Tulare and Kings. Especial thanks are due W. F. Rooney and A. Shultis.

Meat production of chickens and turkeys is characterized by having a high percentage (60–70%) of the total cost represented by feed costs. The costs of production for fryer production may be biased because the sample included a number of growers who raised caponettes (fryers with implants of diethylstilbestrol). In all types of the enterprises feed costs were approximately half of the cost of production, by far the largest single item. Egg production in both chickens and turkeys shows a relatively high labor cost since much of the routine work lacks mechanization. The percentage cost of the stock is high for pullet rearing because sexed pullet chicks of specialized breeding are used and because feed consumption to 16 weeks is low. Other costs of production include interest, depreciation, taxes, fuel, vaccination, and drugs. These, on a percentage basis, are minor.

Table 36-3 was prepared in order to give a bird's-eye view of production practices. The values are neither standards nor optimums. The figures will vary from year to year as the result of economic conditions and location, and as improvements are made in nutrition, breeding, and management.

36-4. BROODING AND REARING

It is not within the scope of this chapter to discuss this all-important stage in the growth and development of the chick. It is a stage during which proper environmental surroundings are most important. The rearing period begins when brooding ends—on the average, when the birds are 6–8 weeks old. Rearing is no longer a seasonal job. To maintain a constant supply of eggs one needs to count on a year-round replacement program. Fryers are produced, processed, and sold every week of the year.

36-5. REPLACEMENT SCHEMES

When the entire flock replacement is made at one time in the spring, wide variation in seasonal egg production is common. Such a procedure was formerly justified because fall and winter egg prices were always the highest of the year. Spring-hatched chicks were the only ones available from many hatcheries. Such a program provided full poultry houses only in the fall months. The pendulum swung to hatching the year around—in fact, brooding every three weeks became a common practice for early cage operators. However, such a scheme is hard to maintain in view of the work of disease prevention. Production from pullet flocks is more profitable than older hen flocks.

The specialized pullet rearing farm may be independent or connected with a hatchery or feed company in order to increase sales and have pullets for an integrated organization. With very large poultry farms this may be under the management of one man or a corporation.

In a program suggested by Arthur Shultis, Extension Economist, Uni-

TABLE 36-3. | *Summary of poultry production practices.*

		Chicken			Turkey hatching eggs
	Chicken fryer	Laying flock	Pullet production	Turkey meat	
Breeds	Crosses, NH or WR females, X Cornish, or Synthetic males	W. Leghorn or hybrid crosses	W. Leghorn or hybrid crosses	BB Bronze, heavy white and hybrid	BB Bronze, heavy white and hybrid
Housing (a) Space requirements	Floor-confined (1 bird/ft²)	Wire cages (0.5–1 ft²/ bird)	(1 bird/ 2/3/ft²)	Floor brooded (1 bird/ft²)	Confined (1 bird/6 or 8 ft²)
Housing (b) Space requirements		Litter floor (2.5–3 ft²/ bird)	(1 bird/ 2 ft²)	Range reared (1 bird/ 50 ft², bare lot)	Range (1 bird/ 50 ft²) bare lot
Land (acres)	5	5	1	20	10
No. birds/family/ cycle	20,000	5000	16,000	5000	2000
Investment/bird ($)	1.00	5.00	1.25	2.00	5.00
Hatches/yr	4	2–5	3	1+	2
Weeks/cycle	10	to 18–19 months	16	26	20–24
Probable receipts/ yr (No.)	4	52	3	1 or 2	40
Money required for stock each cycle	$3000 at 15¢	$9000 at $1.80	$5600 at 35¢	$3500 at 70¢	$12,000 at $6.00
Money required for feed each cycle	$7092 at $4.50 cwt	$21,000 at $4.00 cwt	$7219 at $4.00 cwt	$14,765 at $3.75 cwt	$7800 at $4.00 cwt
Management Standards Feed/bird/cycle (lb.)	8	95	12	80	100
Mortality (%)	3	12	5	6	5
Labor/bird (hr)	0.02	0.7	0.1	0.3	1
Eggs/hen		250			65
Culling rate (%)		90			

* Shade (1 bird/2 ft²)

versity of California, Berkeley, and Stanley Coates, Farm Advisor, Alameda County, one specialized pullet-raising enterprise may contract to supply egg farms with pullets by a four-year, written contract. Such a program has certain advantages: operator specialization, production of quality products, use of improved disease prevention techniques, and cooperative supervision and decision. In addition, increased volume and orderly marketing could be accomplished, which would also lead to full use of equipment. It is important that the operators in this program have a written contract in which the terms of operation are spelled out and agreed to by each party. Where people are mutually dependent, one on another, for success in operation, it is important that these be people who can work together, who can get the job done, and who solve problems as they arise.

Another plan has been developed for an individual, rather than a group, to make efficient use of housing and equipment and to help keep egg production on a high year-round level. In this plan, the laying houses are divided into 5 equal sections, to house 5 age groups of layers. There is a complete replacement of each laying section within a period of 15 months. Each unit is kept as a one-age-group section for the 15-month period. One unit or section becomes empty and ready to house a new group of 5-month-old replacement pullets every 3 months. Thus, 4 groups are replaced in a 12-month period. At any time laying birds in the flock would range in age from 5–20 months—an average age of about 12 months. The plan allows one to carry out vaccination and other disease-preventive measures during the growing period to insure healthy pullets. No birds are carried through a complete molt into the second year for commercial egg production.

When economic conditions are unfavorable, as at a time of low egg prices, hens may be kept longer by canceling one or more replacement orders. Layers over 18 months of age should be culled sufficiently to maintain a 60% rate of lay. The pullets 6–12 months of age should be laying 72% or better, and birds 12–18 months of age, 66% or better. The average flock rate of production 6–18 months of age should be at least 65%. The best way to bring up the flock rate of production is by weekly culling of old hens.

36-6. FEEDING AND WATERING SYSTEMS

When feeding poultry one feeds to suit the needs of the flock rather than the individual. No set of rules can be given as to the best feeding method, but whichever system is used, the birds usually have some type of feed at all times. With large-sized flocks and hired labor, all-in-one rations are often used to reduce to a minimum the possibility of incorrectly balanced rations.

Mechanical feeders and continuous watering are commonly accepted practices. Bulk handling has replaced most of the sacked feeds. Since it is hard to feed whole grains and mash in the same mechanical feeder many growers use either pellets, crumbles, or mashes which are complete in all nutrients except perhaps for calcium, which may be fed as oyster shell or limestone grit. Because of the extra labor involved in feeding, green feeds, wet mash, and other supplemental feeds are generally no longer part of the feeding program. There are good reasons for feeding pellets or crumbles to broilers, but there is an added cost which may or may not be justified.

While mechanical feeders are popular with birds on the floor, birds in cages and colony cages may be fed nearly as fast with the use of a power cart and a traveling feed hopper. In a time-and-travel study made in California in 1957, it was found that feeding required the most travel time. The use of a power cart and mechanical feeding halved the feeding time. The use of large hoppers which hold several days' supply of feed also reduces the feeding time for birds kept on litter-floored houses. Turkeys on range are often fed by a tractor-trailer arrangement whereby feed is augered into feeders.

While poultry rations are very similar in many respects, rations designed for a given age and type of poultry should be fed as directed. Young turkeys or poults should not be given a chick starter mash. Within a given type of ration there is little reason for hesitating to change the grains in a mash. With nutritional consultants to supervise, changes in rations may be safely made, based on the use of computers for poultry feed formulations.

Although water is necessary for all classes of livestock, it was recently discovered that hens given water only 3 times a day, 15 minutes each time, did as well as birds given water continuously. The hens use their crops as storage, instead of drinking frequently. The problems of disposal of wet droppings under wire floors is simplified by this practice.

Growth and feed consumption guides are only useful in helping to set up budgets and measure results (see Table 30-1). Poultry breeders working with broiler stocks have already passed the planning stage of having 3-pound males at 6 weeks of age. Poultry nutritionists will soon have developed broiler rations that will require only $1\frac{1}{2}$ lb. of feed to produce 1 lb. of grain to marketing time.

36-7. DISEASE PREVENTION AND CONTROL

The individual bird loses its identity in poultry management; one is concerned with the health of the flock. The depopulation procedure for controlling poultry diseases is very costly unless it is a planned part of normal management procedure. The all-in-all-out system of fryer or pullet raising has the inherent advantage of controlling certain poultry diseases.

The role of sanitation in disease prevention is always important. But merely to say that sanitation is a good management practice is similar to "the sounding brass and a tinkling cymbal." Sanitation has been defined as keeping the bird—and everything the bird comes in contact with—clean. The producer can carry on from there.

Vaccination is effective against certain poultry diseases: fowl pox, laryngo-tracheitis, Newcastle, and bronchitis. Since fowl pox is spread by insects, such as mosquitoes, seldom if ever does it pay not to vaccinate against this disease. Whether or not to vaccinate against the other diseases depends upon the local situation. Only a flock in good health should be vaccinated and, preferably, with only one vaccine at a time. The vaccination program should be completed before the pullets are 4 months old and before they start to lay. It should be done by, or under the supervision of, a qualified individual. Since most vaccines are live viruses, capable of causing disease if improperly used, they must be treated carefully.

Coccidiosis occurs in floor-reared birds. Prevention is helped by keeping the litter dry and by following other management practices such as using wire around the watering and feeding areas. Medication with coccidiostats is effective if an outbreak occurs. Low levels of such drugs are usually added to fryer rations as a preventive measure. For replacement birds reared on litter they are often added to the starter and growing mashes.

CRD (chronic respiratory disease), known as air-sac infection and sinus-itis, occurs in both chickens and turkeys. It is more serious with turkeys. Prevention is based on keeping the birds free from stresses of all kinds— other diseases, multiple vaccinations, lack of water, or unfavorable environmental conditions.

The proper treatment of a disease has as a prerequisite the identification of the disease by a pathological laboratory or a qualified veterinarian. A few diseases such as fowl pox may be recognized by the caretaker.

Among the most frequent parasites is roundworm, which may be a problem if chickens are reared on old litter or contaminated ground. Heavily infested birds should be treated with nicotine or piperazine preparations. Tapeworm control is indirect and can be accomplished by controlling intermediate hosts such as flies and beetles. A major step toward fly control is keeping the droppings dry.

Mites, both red and fowl mites, are often a problem in flocks, especially where wild birds are present. Insecticides approved by the Food and Drug Administration may be used. A DDT spray will control red mites and malathion used for spraying the birds is effective against fowl mites; malathion will also control lice.

36-8. EGG HANDLING

The gathering and processing of eggs for market is one of the most time-consuming chores on a poultry ranch. The production of clean eggs is the goal of every poultryman. The number of birds he may keep in a given area is dependent on the litter conditions. Clean eggs are associated with clean litter.

Nests of many shapes and sizes are used for poultry. Up to the present time the limiting factor in litter-floored housing has been the lack of a nest adaptable to mechanical egg gathering. Wire roll-away nests have been used with limited success in litter houses, but all too often the hens prefer to lay in the litter. For cages and colony cages these nests are suitable and greatly reduce the time and travel of gathering eggs.

Cracked eggs in excessive numbers may be associated with the season, age of layers, type of nests, nutrition, and gathering procedures. Egg gatherers can save a tremendous amount of time if it is possible to pack the eggs as clean without their having to be rehandled. In a California survey made in 1957, when egg gathering and cleaning were combined, the time required for egg handling chores was halved.

Many operations are performed in the egg room, some by the common mechanical sizers and graders. In order to market clean eggs, many poultry-men find it necessary to wash their eggs. However, even when carefully washed such eggs should not be placed in cold storage. Some poultrymen use dry-type egg-cleaning machines. Eggs cleaned by these machines are less likely to spoil, but more labor may be required than for washing. Eggs may also be packed in cartons on the farm for marketing through chain stores and so forth. The trend is toward greater efficiency in the handling of fresh ranch-produced eggs. The use of underlit, bulk, roller-table candling to remove eggs with defects is proving to be less costly than hand candling each egg. This is a practice which is working out quite satisfactorily for fresh ranch-produced eggs where the care and age of the egg is known. It is being used by a number of dealers and processors.

This practice of machine candling shows promise primarily because con-siderable labor is saved. However, if such a program is to be used, the fol-lowing management practices are desirable, to maintain egg quality:

1) Purchase replacement stock from a breeder whose stock has good egg quality.

2) Gather eggs twice a day—on warm days, gather three times.

3) Cool rapidly and hold eggs under temperature of 50–60°F in refriger-ated egg rooms.

4) Depend upon pullet egg production and cull old hens out of the flock, for both their shell quality and interior quality deteriorate.

5) Move eggs rapidly from ranch producer to consumer outlets so that consumers obtain fresh-laid quality eggs.

6) Oil spray eggs to cut down on evaporation if eggs are to be kept without refrigeration.

36-9. COST ANALYSES

Data from poultry cost-account studies can be applied by the individual poultryman. With the extension of business methods to poultry production it becomes necessary for the poultryman to keep records and use them in order to survive in competition with poultrymen who do. In some states these cost accounts have been encouraged by the Agricultural Extension Service.

Poultry management studies are conducted in California in the following way. Cooperators send their monthly cost-of-production information to the Agricultural Extension office. In turn a monthly progress report is published, giving production-cost information of each cooperator by code. At the end of the year, a detailed report is published, giving all production and income data. The report includes a poultry management supplement describing management practices followed on each ranch, and helps the cooperator to analyze his poultry enterprise and to determine the strong and weak spots in his management.

The individual cost-account studies of a poultryman, if he does it on his own, may be compared with those of the Agricultural Extension Service, random-sample egg-laying tests, and various county and state poultry management studies. The records provide the basis and set the standards from which to work for improvement. For example, poor egg production quickly shows up in the study but requires analysis on the ranch to pinpoint the cause. High mortality and high feed costs are other examples.

When considering published cost-account data it should be remembered that these are not true averages; they are likely to be biased in favor of the better poultryman. Poorer poultrymen do not bother to keep records. "They aren't farming as well as they know how already."

The summarized material of Table 36-4 was obtained from San Diego County, California, from Farm Advisor Robert H. Adolph.

While all the data is of interest to the poultryman who wants to know how he stands, there are a number of important production factors in the egg business: number of eggs per hen, pounds of feed per hen, average flock replacement, culling and mortality, labor per hen, and egg size. Economic factors include feed cost, price received for eggs, and miscellaneous costs per hen.

36-10. PROBLEMS OF POULTRY MANAGEMENT

Lest the student think that all problems of poultry management have been solved, current problems are listed with suggestions for alleviating the condition. Better control methods are urgently needed.

Flies. The use of wire floors on poultry ranches, although it encourages large flocks in a small area, creates a fly problem. When only one bird is kept in a cage, with proper drying conditions the manure can be dried. But such is seldom the case. At times county health officials require the manure be cleaned out every week, and this imposes an additional cost on the poultryman.

TABLE | *San Diego County, California cost study averages.*
36-4.

	1957	1958	1959
Number of cooperators participating	36	42	40
Average number of layers per ranch	5685	6426	7177
Production, egg sales, and net cost			
Eggs produced per hen	235	239	243
Rate of lay (%)	64	65	67
% large and ex-large eggs	70	68	68
Price received per cull hen	$0.40	$0.46	$0.30
Price received per av. doz. eggs sold	36.3¢	37.0¢	29.8¢
Net cost per dozen sold	30.8¢	28.3¢	28.1¢
Laying flock data			
% of average flock during year			
Died	14	14	14
Culled	68	79	82
Added	100	105	107
% hens in flock over 18 months of age	18	16	14
Feed and labor			
Lb. feed—includes replacements	114	115	115
Estimated feed—layers only	91	91	90
Lb. all feed per doz. eggs sold	5.9	5.8	5.7
Feed cost ¢ per dozen	20.2¢	19.3¢	18.5¢
Labor per hen (hrs)	0.96	0.78	0.66
Costs per hen, dollars			
Feed costs	$3.91	$3.80	$3.72
Chick replacements	0.44	0.48	0.48
Supplies, taxes and services	0.45	0.52	0.42
Hired labor	0.47	0.48	0.38
Less { Cull sales	0.29	0.34	0.25
{ Stock inventory difference	0.23	0.27	0.10
Net cash costs of production	4.75	4.67	4.65
Overhead and home labor allowances	1.20	0.92	0.99
Net cost of eggs	6.95	5.59	5.64
Income and costs per hen			
Egg income	$7.00	$7.32	$5.97
Net cost of eggs	5.95	5.59	5.64
Management income	1.05	1.73	0.33
Depreciation	0.34	0.29	0.29
Interest on capital investment	0.26	0.25	0.26
Family labor	0.60	0.38	0.44
Farm income	2.25	2.65	1.32

Dust. Turkeys create a dust problem when raised in large numbers on small acreages in a dry climate. Sprinkling the area with water and strip cropping are the two control measures, to date, which work best.

Dirty Eggs. Dust increases the number of dirty eggs in cages and in roll-away nests; removal of this dust from the wire or protection of the wire with covers or lids over the egg trays reduces the problem. Damp litter also increases the incidence of dirty eggs. Clean nest litter is a partial remedy, but the solution goes beyond that, to consideration of ample space per hen, good ventilation, suitable waterers, and sometimes removal of excessive water from the chicken house by pit cleaners.

Cannibalism. Much evidence has been presented to show that nutrition, genetics, and management all may contribute to solving this problem. Cannibalism defies experimentation for one cannot always get the experimental lots to cannibalize one another. Debeaking or removing one-half or more of the upper beak with a debeaking machine has given the best results so far.

Low Winter Egg Production. Lighting that provides 14 hours of light per day and housing that prevents exposures to temperatures below 35°F will help to maintain winter egg production. Improvements in breeding, feeding, and management—for example hatching more than once a year—have helped to reduce this problem.

Hot Weather Problems. Every new poultryman must learn that hens in cages are more susceptible to heat prostration than birds on the floor. When temperatures exceed 95°F for four hours or more, some unacclimated birds may die. The new poultryman should remember that heat loss must equal heat production, or fever—and eventually death—will result. One may use "foggers" or mist sprayers to dampen the birds with water, thus cooling them by evaporation. (Wetting the birds with a hose is too time-consuming for a large farm.) Cool drinking water helps to reduce the bird's internal heat.

Predators and Stampeding. Unless kept confined, poultry and their eggs may become prey to predators. With turkeys and other poultry the number of birds killed by piling up or stampeding in fright often exceeds those killed by the predator. The key word is vigilance.

36-11. WHY POULTRY RANCHES FAIL

When looking for the cause of financial failure, the poultryman may find it by looking in the mirror. There are failures among poultrymen because there are failures among people, and for various causes.

(1) Lack of fundamental poultry know-how and failure to keep up-to-

date and to change production and marketing methods. There is no substitute for keeping accurate records and using them as bases for management
decisions.

(2) Lack of adequate marketing. Many steps are necessary to get eggs
from ranch to consumer. Usually it pays to produce a quality product and
obtain the highest price, but producing without an assured market can
result in distress prices.

(3) High feed costs. Use the lowest-cost feed available, consistent with
good performance, and avoid waste.

(4) Low egg production. Purchase chicks from a proven source.

(5) High mortality. Follow a vaccination or disease-control program
tailored to fit the ranch and its conditions. Obtain accurate diagnoses from
a qualified veterinarian.

(6) Inadequate financing. Take advantage of discounts, loans, and quantity purchases. Long- and short-time debt loads should not exceed $5.00 and
$1.00 respectively, per layer. Maintain a reserve in case of many months of
poor prices.

(7) Zoning and population pressure. Flies and odors are considered
public nuisances and can force the poultryman from a neighborhood. See
that manure and moisture are properly handled.

(8) Location. It must not be too distant from centers of population and
must afford good transportation.

(9) Lack of volume. High production per bird is not enough. Volume is
very important not only in making the total return to the individual greater
but also in finding a market.

(10) Inefficient use of labor and equipment. Keep the ranch filled to
capacity. Use as a motto for efficient labor: "Pick up an egg only once."
Process it before it is put down. Taxes may be reduced by planning ranch
operations and keeping complete accounts. Buildings and equipment should
be designed to reduce labor.

REFERENCES AND SELECTED READINGS

Asmundson, V. S. and F. H. Kratzer, 1951.
Turkey production in California. Calif.
Agr. Ext. Circ. 110.

Bankowski, R. A. and A. S. Rosenwald,
1956. Poultry vaccination—why and how.
Calif. Agr. Expt. Sta. Circ. 455.

Card, L. E., 1960. *Poultry Production.* 9th
Ed. Lea and Febiger, Philadelphia.

Hart, S. A., T. Cleaver, W. O. Wilson and
A. E. Woodard, 1958. Housing and oper-
ational studies on California egg farms.
Poultry Sci., 36:1386–1395.

Hartman, R. A. and D. F. King, 1956.
Keeping Chickens in Cages. 4th Ed. Ro-
land C. Hartman, Redlands, Calif.

Longhouse, A. D., H. Ota, and W. Ashby,
1960. Heat and moisture design data for
poultry housing. *Agr. Eng.* 41:567–576.

Shultis, A., 1959. The egg production business in California. Calif. Agr. Expt. Sta.
Circ. 483.

Section VII

Classification, Grading, and Marketing of Livestock and their Products

Chapter 37

Classification and Grading of Meats

37-1. INTRODUCTION

One of the primary reasons for the development of our present efficient methods for marketing meat has been the widespread understanding and use of a system of identifying its market acceptability. This system involves the process of classification and grading.

The purpose of a classification and grading system for meat is to provide the means for identifying—or grouping together—carcasses which have similar characteristics that are important in determining their market value. The widespread use of such a system by the various market agencies—packers, wholesalers, jobbers, and retailers—very materially facilitates trading and reduces marketing costs.

Class, as used in a broad sense, is a designation that identifies—or groups together—carcasses or cuts that have a similar commercial use and which come from the same species or kind of animal. For example, lamb and mutton are both derived from the ovine species. However, since they are not interchangeable from the standpoint of their commercial use, they are considered as two distinct classes of meat. Subclasses of carcasses within a specific class or kind of meat usually refer to the sex condition of the animal from which the meat was derived. Most of the characteristics upon which the determination of class and subclass are based are rather clearly developed and are widely understood and accepted.

Grade is a designation that identifies carcasses or cuts of the same class on the basis of certain utility or value-determining characteristics. A grade

647

includes a sufficiently narrow range of grade-determining factors such that the individual units have a high degree of interchangeability.

The origin of meat classification and grading probably dates back to the time when men first started trading in this commodity. Even in those times, in appraising the relative merits of different carcasses, buyers and sellers applied some of the basic principles of the presently used system of classification and grading. The early markets in this country were highly localized, and almost all trading was based on personal inspection of the meat by the buyer. In this connection, a distinct terminology was developed in each market area to describe preferences and trade practices. The growth of large urban centers and the improvement in shipping facilities stimulated the rapid growth of large competitive livestock markets and packing companies. Consequently, there likewise developed a need for a nationally recognized system of classes and grades for livestock and meat, in order that prices among competitive markets could be equitably compared.

Federal class and grade standards for livestock and meat were first formulated and issued in tentative form by the U.S. Department of Agriculture (USDA) in 1916. They were immediately put to use as the basis for the National Meat Market Reporting Service conducted by the Department. These original standards were based on much of the earlier research done on market classification and grading of livestock and meat by the University of Illinois.

Since their inception, the federal meat grade standards have been used by the USDA as the basis for a meat market reporting service. These standards also serve as the basis upon which the Federal Meat Grading Service grades beef, veal, calf, lamb, mutton, and pork.

The federal class and grade standards for meat are published and thus generally available to all segments of the industry. However, their use by the industry has always been strictly voluntary, except for two periods of national emergency, during World War II and the Korean conflict, when the federal grading of beef, veal, calf, lamb, and mutton was compulsory under federal maximum price regulations.

The federal grading of meat grew out of a request of a producer group known as the Better Beef Association. That group organized in 1926 for the primary purpose of getting a federal program established for the grading of the higher qualities of beef. It was the contention of that group that if a reliable identification of excellence were placed on these better grades of beef, consumers would buy them with greater confidence and that this would stimulate the production of better beef cattle. Accordingly, in May, 1927, the USDA inaugurated the federal grading of beef on a voluntary, experimental basis for one year. At the end of this first year, the program was continued on the same voluntary basis but the users of the service were charged fees to cover the operating costs of the service. The service was later expanded to include the grading of other meats. Federal meat grading is now available in all of the principal marketing centers of the country.

The federal class and grade standards have been revised from time to time as new research information became available, for purposes of clarification of the standards, and to meet changes in consumer preferences and in production and marketing practices.

The marketing and distribution of meats in the United States is a complex process, and classification and grading are likewise very specialized functions in this process. For these reasons, only a very brief treatment of this subject can be included in this chapter.

Individual meat packers and retailers may, and often do, use their own brand names for identifying the meat they sell. Although these private branding systems generally include many of the same factors as those upon which the federal standards are based, the standards used by private companies are not published. Since there are no controls over the use of brands by private companies, these may vary from one company to another and they may also differ from federal grades. Therefore, the following discussion of classification and grading will be limited to the federal standards as published and used by the USDA.

37-2. BASIS FOR GRADE

The two basic considerations utilized in grading meat are: (1) to reflect differences in the proportion of the more desirable to the less desirable parts of the carcass and in the ratio of meat to bone; and (2) to evaluate the characteristics of the meat that are associated with its ultimate consumer acceptability. Grade, as a measure of these considerations, is based on the development of three major factors—conformation, finish, and quality. However, since variations in finish are expressed indirectly by variations in development of quality and conformation, the manner in which these factors are evaluated and combined into a grade can best be explained by considering that there are only two major factors—conformation and quality.

Conformation. Conformation refers to the proportionate development of the various parts of the carcass and to the ratio of meat to bone. It is primarily a function of the relative development of the muscular and skeletal systems. Carcasses that have thick, plump muscles in relation to their skeletal structure are considered to have good conformation, provided they are particularly well muscled in the regions of the most valuable parts. The overall thickness and fullness of a carcass may be affected materially by the quantity of external fat. However, since the evaluation of conformation is essentially an indication of muscularity, the quantity of outside finish should not be a consideration.

Fig. 37-1. Degrees of marbling.

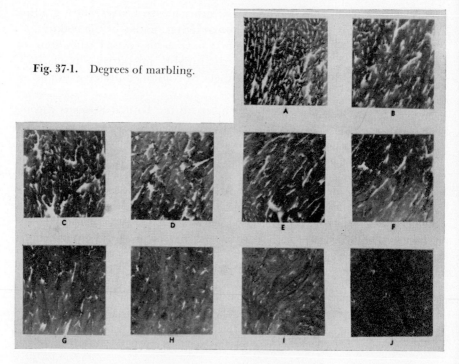

Quality.[1] Quality, as used in grading meat, refers to its expected consumer acceptability. Among the meat characteristics considered in evaluating quality are the texture, firmness, and marbling of the meat, and the indications of maturity of the animal from which it was produced. The evaluation of texture, firmness, marbling, and, to some extent, maturity is complicated by the fact that most meat is graded in unribbed carcasses, without the benefit of observation of a cut surface of the lean. It is necessary, therefore, to evaluate these characteristics indirectly, on the basis of other characteristics that are closely related to their development. Finish is one of the most important of these. Finish refers to the amount, character, and distribution of external, intermuscular, and intramuscular fat or marbling. Marbling—the interspersion of fat within the muscles—makes by far the greatest contribution to the palatability of meat. Figure 37-1 illustrates ten of the degrees of marbling referred to in the official standards.

As the amount of external fat is increased on a carcass, the amount of marbling also tends to increase. However, carcasses are quite variable in this respect, and it is not unusual for carcasses that have a thick layer of external finish to have very little marbling in the meat. For that reason, the quantity of external fat is given practically no consideration in determining

---

[1] The term "quality" is also used, at times, to refer to the general excellence or acceptability of meat for a specific purpose. When used in this less restrictive sense "quality" may also include such factors as proportion of fat and lean, color of fat, and so forth.

quality. Color of fat is a price-determining factor in some instances, but since it has not proven to be closely related to quality, it is not used as a factor in grading. However, the character of the fat is a factor associated with quality. Firm, brittle fats indicate a higher degree of quality than do soft, oily, or "powdery" fats. The development of certain interior fats— feathering between the ribs, fat streaking in the inside flank muscles, fat covering over the diaphragm, and overflow fat over the ribs—are the most reliable indicators of marbling and are thus used extensively in grading intact carcasses or sides. In grading ribbed carcasses, the degree of marbling is the only aspect of finish that is considered.

The evaluation of the degree of maturity is also an important consideration in evaluating quality. The principal evidences of maturity are the color, size, and shape of the rib bones; the ossification of cartilage (particularly the "buttons" on the ends of the chine bones and the cartilaginous connections of the sacral vertebrae); and the color and texture of the lean.

Since high finish and advancing maturity have opposite effects on quality, the federal standards permit increased marbling to compensate, within certain limits, for advancing maturity. Excellent quality in meat, as evidenced in the cut surface, usually implies a full, well-developed, firm muscle of fine texture and bright color containing a liberal amount of marbling and a minimum of connective tissue.

USDA Meat Grades. The following tabulation summarizes the applicable grades for the various kinds of meat for which the USDA has issued official standards. (These are listed as references at the end of this chapter.)

Class and subclass	*Grade*
Beef—steer, heifer, cow*	Prime, Choice, Good, Standard, Commercial, Utility, Cutter, Canner
Bull	Choice, Good, Commercial, Utility, Cutter, Canner
Stag	Same as bull
Calf	Prime, Choice, Good, Standard, Utility, Cull
Veal	Same as calf
Lamb	Prime, Choice, Good, Utility, Cull
Yearling mutton	Same as lamb
Mutton	Choice, Good, Utility, Cull
Pork carcasses	U.S. No. 1, U.S. No. 2, U.S. No. 3, Medium, Cull

37-3. BEEF GRADING

In grading bovine carcasses, the class, or kind—veal, calf, or beef—is determined first. Despite the fact that the federal standards for these three kinds of meat are contained in three separate standards, it is intended that

---

* Cow carcasses not eligible for the Prime grade.

they be considered a continuous series. Therefore, the grade of a carcass that is near the borderline in maturity between two of these groups would be essentially the same regardless of the standard under which it were graded. Beef includes meat from animals ranging in age from about nine months to the oldest animals that come to market.

Sex condition is also an important consideration in grading beef carcasses. Carcasses from steers, heifers, and cows are graded by the same standards, whereas those from stags and bulls are each graded on the basis of their own respective standards.

Steer carcasses are recognized by the rough, rather irregular fat in the region of the cod, the small pelvic cavity, the small "pizzle eye," the curved aitchbone, and the small area of lean above the aitchbone.

Heifer carcasses are identified by the smooth udder fat, the slightly larger pelvic cavity and straighter aitchbone than in steers, and by the much larger area of lean above the aitchbone.

Cow carcasses are characterized by a large pelvic cavity and a nearly straight aitchbone. The udder is usually removed, but in some cows that are not lactating at the time of slaughter, the udder will be left on the carcass. Cow carcasses usually have at least slightly prominent hips, and since most are rather advanced in age when marketed, the bones and cartilages usually are hard and white.

Bull carcasses are recognized by their disproportionately heavy muscling in the round, the heavy crested neck, and the large, prominent "pizzle eye." The cut surface of the meat is usually dark and coarse. Stag carcasses exhibit characteristics somewhat intermediate between those of steers and bulls.

After the class and subclass are determined, the quality and conformation are evaluated and combined into a final grade based on the appropriate grade standards. Since federally graded beef is largely that produced from steers, heifers, and cows, this will be the only aspect of beef grading discussed.

The grade standards for beef describe the quality requirements in terms of texture, firmness, and marbling of the rib-eye muscle (or indications thereof) for different degrees of maturity. In the Prime, Choice, Good, and Standard grades, which are restricted to carcasses from young cattle, the requirements are described for two maturity levels—for very young carcasses and for those approaching maximum maturity for the grade. However, the two maturity groups do not cover the entire range in maturity for cattle in the Prime, Choice, Good, and Standard grades. Thus, a third group is recognized between these two groups. The requirements for this intermediate maturity group are intermediate between those of the other two groups. Very young beef carcasses have red, porous chine bones that have soft, pearly white cartilages. Rib bones tend to be narrow, round, and slightly red, and there is usually some evidence of separation and cartilage between the sacral vertebrae. The lean is usually fine and smooth in texture and rather light in color. Within these grades, carcasses that are approaching the maximum maturity permitted have flatter rib bones and rather hard, white chine bones; and the cartilages on the chine bones may show distinct ossification. The lean in such carcasses is usually not as fine or as smooth in texture as that of younger carcasses, and the flesh is darker. The Commercial grade is restricted entirely to carcasses older than those eligible for Good and Standard, whereas the Utility, Cutter, and Canner grades include carcasses within the full range of maturity.

After the maturity of a carcass is determined, the other indications of quality—the feathering between the ribs,

DEGREE OF MARBLING	MATURITY		
	Very young	Inter-Mediate	Approaching* max. maturity
Extremely abundant			
Very abundant			
Abundant			
Moderately abundant	PRIME QUALITY		
Slightly abundant			
Moderate	CHOICE QUALITY		
Modest			
Small	GOOD QUALITY		
Slight			
Traces	STANDARD QUALITY		
Practically devoid			
Devoid			

*Approaching maximum maturity for Prime, Choice, or Good as specified

Fig. 37-2. Marbling requirements for various quality grades.

the overflow fat, the streaking of fat in the flank, the protrusion of fat between the chine bones, and the character of the fat—are evaluated. These are important only as an indication of the amount of marbling in the rib eye and are used only in grading unribbed carcasses. If a carcass is ribbed, the only quality characteristics considered are the marbling, color, texture, and firmness of lean and the evidences of maturity. A quality grade for a carcass may be determined by evaluating the quality characteristics in relation to the requirements of the various grades. Since marbling and maturity are of such importance in determining quality, Figure 37-2 shows how these characteristics are combined into the quality grade, provided other quality-determining characteristics, such as firmness, color, and texture of the lean have an equivalent degree of development.

The standards for each grade also give detailed descriptions of the conformation requirements. By evaluating the conformation of the various parts of the carcass, an overall appraisal of conformation can be made in terms of grade.

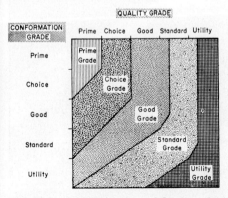

Fig. 37-3. Determination of final grade from conformation grade and quality grade.

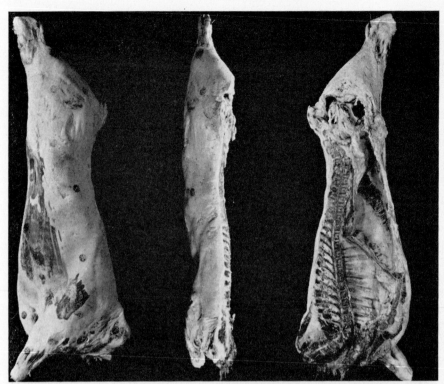

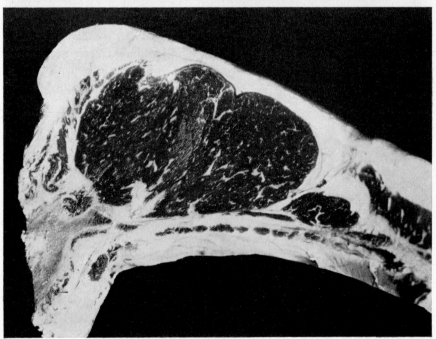

Balancing Grade Factors. To arrive at the final grade of a carcass, the "quality" grade and "conformation" grade must be combined. The relative importance given to each of these factors varies somewhat with grade. For example, in the Prime and Choice grades, a superior development of conformation is not permitted to compensate for a deficient development of quality, whereas in the lower grades this type of compensation is permitted to a limited extent. In all grades a superior development of quality is permitted to compensate for a deficient development of conformation. This, again, is at a somewhat different rate in different grades. Figure 37-3 shows diagrammatically how conformation grade and quality grade are combined to arrive at the final grade. For example, a carcass with average Choice quality and average Choice conformation would be graded Choice. Another carcass having high Standard quality and average Choice conformation would be graded Good. The underlying reason for these variable rates of compensation is that buyers of the Prime and Choice grades are primarily interested in quality, whereas the consumers that normally use the lower grades are less interested in quality but more interested in the proportion of edible meat.

Differences in beef carcasses are illustrated in Figs. 37-4 to 37-9; the accompanying legends briefly describe the characteristics of the carcasses in relation to the official standards.

37-4. VEAL AND CALF GRADING

One of the most difficult decisions to make in grading bovine carcasses concerns their proper classification as veal, calf, or beef. These classes are distinguished on the basis of the color and texture of the lean, the character of the fat, the size, shape, and color of the bones, the degree of ossifi-

---

Figs. 37-4 and 37-5. U.S. Prime beef carcass. This very young carcass, as indicated by the red chine bones, the large cartilaginous "buttons" on the thoracic vertebrae and the distinct separation of the sacral vertebrae tends to be blocky and compact and is thickly fleshed and plump throughout, thus slightly exceeding minimum Prime grade conformation requirements. The moderately abundant feathering, numerous streakings of fat in the inside flank muscles, the nearly completely covered skirt, the liberal protrusion of fat between the chine bones, the liberal intermixing of fat within the brisket, and the apparently firm, high quality of external and interior fats are indicative of moderately abundant marbling in the rib eye. This degree of marbling together with the development of conformation would thus qualify this carcass for average Prime before ribbing. After ribbing, however, the rib eye (Fig. 37-5) exhibits only slightly abundant marbling and the carcass is therefore limited to the lower limits of the Prime grade.

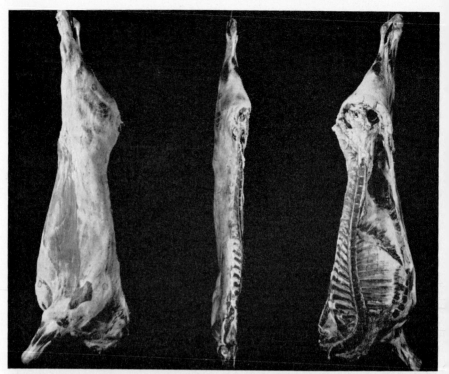

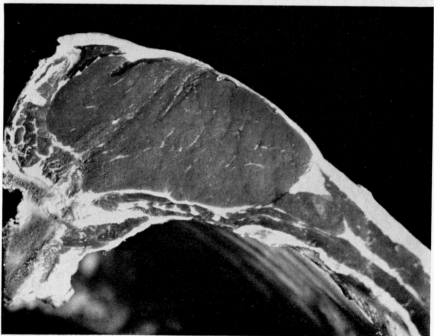

cation of the cartilage, and the carcass size. Although typical carcasses of each class have distinctive characteristics, carcasses near the borderlines between these classes seldom show an equal development of each of these characteristics. Hence, there may be some overlapping of these characteristics between groups. The final determination must represent a composite evaluation of all characteristics.

Color of the lean is the most important characteristic used in differentiating between veal and calf. The lean of typical veal carcasses is grayish-pink and it is very smooth and velvety in texture. Such carcasses also have slightly soft, pliable fat and round, red rib bones. Most veal carcasses weigh less than 150 lb., but some exceed this weight, particularly in the higher grades.

The lean of typical calf carcasses is grayish-red and is usually somewhat firmer than that of veal. The fat is drier and flakier and the rib bones are flatter and lack some of the redness characteristics of veal carcasses. Calf carcasses usually weigh from 150 to 275 lb. and rarely exceed 350 lb., even in the higher grades.

Sex condition does not materially affect the quality of the flesh of veal and calf. Therefore, all sexes are graded on the same standards. Also, because of their immaturity, veal and calf carcasses have a decidedly lower degree of finish than comparable grades of beef. Practically all veal and calf carcasses are graded without ribbing, so there is seldom an opportunity to view a cut surface of the lean.

Balancing Grade Factors. Since the standards for veal, calf, and beef are considered as a continuous series, conformation and quality are evaluated in exactly the same way as previously explained for beef. After the conformation and quality grades are determined, these are combined into a final grade in exactly the same manner as for beef.

37-5. LAMB AND MUTTON GRADING

Ovine carcasses are divided into three classes or maturity groups—lamb, yearling mutton, and mutton. Lamb carcasses always have "break joints"

Figs. 37-6 and 37-7. U.S. Standard beef carcass. This very young, red-boned carcass is very rangy and narrow and has a thin, tapering, slightly concave round-conformation only slightly better than the midpoint of the Utility grade. However, the slight amount of feathering, the slight protrusion of fat between the chine bones, and the slight streaking of fat in the inside flank muscles indicate that the rib eye will have traces of marbling and thereby qualify the carcass, before ribbing, for the minimum of the Standard grade. The characteristics of the rib eye (Fig. 37-7) coincide with their exterior indications.

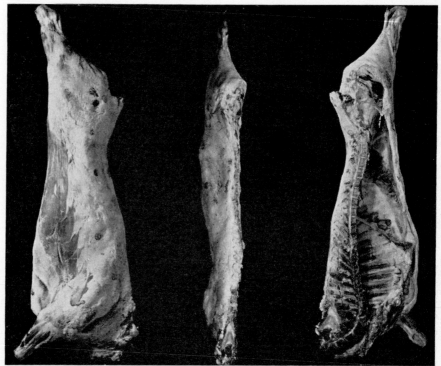

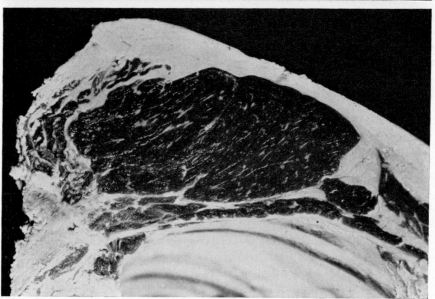

on their front shanks and these are moist and fairly red and show well-defined ridges. The rib bones are moderately flat and slightly wide; the lean is light red and has a fine texture.

Yearling mutton may have either break joints or spool joints on their front shanks; the rib bones tend to be flat and moderately wide and the lean is slightly dark red and is slightly coarse in texture.

Mutton carcasses always have spool joints on the front legs and have wide, flat rib bones. The lean is dark red in color and coarse in texture. Figure 37-10 illustrates a break joint and a spool joint.

The grade standards apply to all carcasses without regard to their sex. However, carcasses that show heavy shoulders and thick necks typical of uncastrated males are discounted in grade from less than one-half a grade to two full grades, depending on the extent to which these secondary sexual characteristics are developed. Grade is determined on the same general basis as for beef—by considering variations in conformation and quality.

Except for one important difference, the combination of quality grade and conformation grade into a final grade is much the same as for beef. In lamb and mutton, carcasses which have at least midpoint Choice conformation are permitted to have a development of quality equivalent to the minimum of the upper third of the Good grade and still be graded Choice. This type of compensation is not permitted in Choice beef.

Another difference between the standards for these two species relates to the extent to which a superior development of quality can compensate for a deficiency in conformation. The lamb and mutton standards specify that, regardless of how high a degree of quality a carcass may have, it will not be considered for a given grade if it does not have a development of conformation equivalent to at least that of the next lower grade. For example, a carcass could not be graded Choice if it had less than Good grade conformation. (There is no such minimum conformation specified for beef.) Also, the lamb and mutton standards provide for a minimum external fat

---

Figs. 37-8 and 37-9. U.S. Commercial beef carcass. This hard-boned carcass with cartilages on the ends of the chine bones which are completely ossified and barely visible has rather typical, minimum Commercial grade conformation with its slightly thick but slightly concave round, its prominent hips, sunken loin, slightly thin chuck, and rough, irregular contour. However, despite the apparent rather firm, high quality exterior fat covering, the interior fats—feathering, overflow fat, and fat streaking in the inside flank muscles—are very scanty and insufficient to indicate that the rib eye will have the required moderate degree of marbling to qualify it for the Commercial grade. Therefore, the carcass is eligible only for the Utility grade before ribbing. After ribbing, however, the rib eye (Fig. 37-9) exhibits a moderate amount of marbling and the carcass thereby qualifies for the lower limits of the Commercial grade.

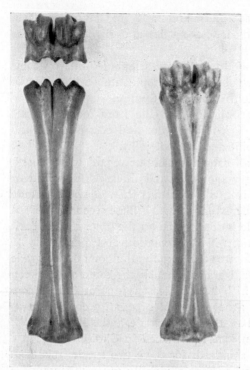

Fig. 37-10. Ovine break joint and spool joint.

covering for carcasses in the Prime and Choice grade. Figures 37-11 through 37-14 illustrate differences in two grades of lamb carcasses; the accompanying legends describe the characteristics of the carcasses in relation to the official standards.

37-6. PORK CARCASS GRADING

Pork carcass grading also involves identification of differences in "quantity" and "quality," as is the case with other meats. The grades are based on (1) differences in yields of lean cuts—hams, loins, picnics, and Boston butts, and (2) differences in quality of cuts. The yield or quantity factor assumes greater importance in pork grading at this time than it does in other meats. This, of course, is reflected in the expressed consumer preference for the lean cuts rather than the fat cuts of pork.

Sex classification is important in the grading of pork carcasses, since barrow and gilt carcasses are graded on one set of standards and sow carcasses on another. There are no official standards for grades of stag and boar carcasses.

Barrow carcasses have the typical pocket in the split edge of the belly (where the sheath was removed) and have a small "pizzle eye." Gilt carcasses have a smooth split edge of the belly but do not show any development of mammary tissue. Sow carcasses have a smooth belly edge similar to gilts but show a rather pronounced development of mammary tissue as a result of advanced pregnancy or lactation.

Boar carcasses have a somewhat larger belly pocket than barrows and have a large, coarse "pizzle eye." The shoulders are heavy, and the skin and joints are coarse. The lean is dark red and is coarse in texture. Stag carcasses have characteristics somewhat intermediate between those of barrows and boars.

In general, carcasses in U.S. No. 1, U.S. No. 2, and U.S. No. 3 grades all have an acceptable degree of quality of lean. Differentiation between these grades is based solely on characteristics associated with differences in the yield of lean cuts. This is primarily a function of fatness in relation to weight or length. Thus, a U.S. No. 1 carcass has about the minimum degree of fatness required to produce an acceptable quality of pork. Carcasses of U.S. No. 2 grade are overfinished; U.S. No. 3 carcasses are decidedly overfinished. There is a progressive reduction in the yield of lean cuts between U.S. No. 1, U.S. No. 2, and U.S. No. 3 carcasses. Medium grade

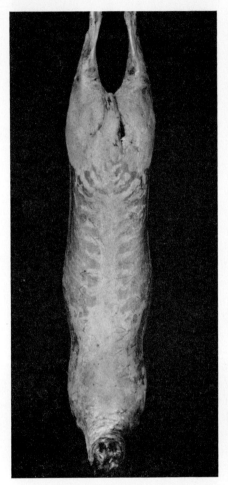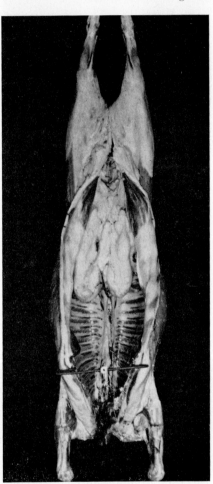

Figs. 37-11 and 37-12. U.S. Prime lamb carcass. The conformation of this young lamb carcass, especially through the back, exceeds the minimum specified for the Prime grade. The moderate amount of feathering between the ribs, the modest streaking of fat on the inside flank muscles, and the moderately thick and full flanks and firm lean also slightly exceed the minimum quality requirements for Prime and qualify the carcass for the lower third of the Prime grade.

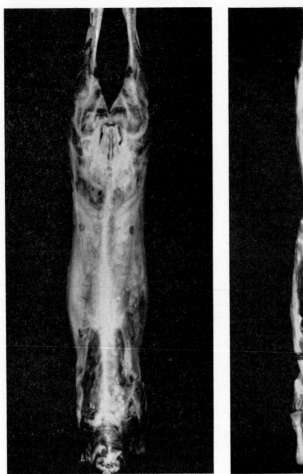
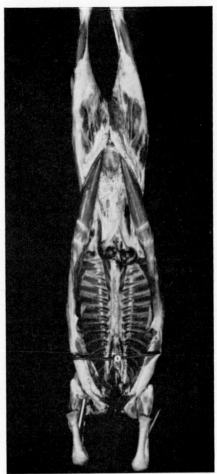

Figs. 37-13 and 37-14.   U.S. Utility lamb carcass. The conformation of this lamb carcass exceeds the requirements for the midpoint of the Utility grade. However, its development of quality—devoid of feathering and fat streakings and very soft, watery lean—is equivalent to only the Cull grade. The superior development of conformation is sufficient to qualify this carcass for the lower third of the Utility grade.

carcasses are underfinished, and, although the ratio of lean to fat is higher than in the U.S. No. 1 grade, the quality of the lean is not generally acceptable. Cull grade carcasses are decidedly underfinished and have a correspondingly lower quality of lean.

Objective guides are incorporated in the standards for grades of pork carcasses. Those applicable to barrow and gilt carcasses are presented in Table 37-1. This approach to grading pork carcasses is in contrast to the grading of other meats, in which the standards are presently subjective in

TABLE 37-1. | *Weight and measurement guides to grades for barrow and gilt carcasses.*

Carcass weight or carcass length*	Average backfat thickness in.† by grade				
	U.S. No. 1	U.S. No. 2	U.S. No. 3	Medium	Cull
Under 120 lb. or under 27 in.	1.2–1.5	1.5–1.8	1.8 or more	0.9–1.2	Less than 0.9
120 to 164 lb. or 27 to 29.9 in.	1.3–1.6	1.6–1.9	1.9 or more	1.0–1.3	Less than 1.0
165 to 209 lb. or 30 to 32.9 in.	1.4–1.7	1.7–2.0	2.0 or more	1.1–1.4	Less than 1.1
210 or more lb. or 33 or more in.	1.5–1.8	1.8–2.1	2.1 or more	1.2–1.5	Less than 1.2

* Either carcass weight or length may be used with backfat thickness as a reliable guide to grade. The table shows the normal length range for given weights. In extreme cases, where the use of length with backfat thickness indicates a different grade than by using weight, final grade is determined subjectively as provided in the standards. Carcass weight is based on a chilled, packer-style carcass. Carcass length is measured from the forward point of the aitch bone to the forward edge of the first rib.

† Average of measurements made opposite the first and last ribs and last lumbar vertebra.

nature. Studies of measurement and cutting data for barrow and gilt carcasses have established that the average thickness of backfat in relation to either carcass length or weight is a reliable guide to the yield of cuts and quality of meat.

However, other characteristics are also considered in grading to achieve a more accurate evaluation of yields and quality. The use of these other characteristics is restricted to the grading of carcasses which, on the basis of their fatness and their length or weight, are near the borderline between two grades. In no instance may these other characteristics be used to change the grade of a carcass more than one-half a grade from that indicated by its thickness, back fat, and weight or length.

The U.S. No. 1, U.S. No. 2, and U.S. No. 3 grades differ only in their yield of cuts. Therefore, the only factors other than backfat thickness in relation to length or weight used in grading carcasses near these borderlines are quantitative characteristics, such as meatiness, conformation, and fat distribution. On the other hand, the U.S. No. 1, Medium, and Cull grades differ only in their quality. For this reason, the only factors other than back fat thickness in relation to length or weight used in grading carcasses near these borderlines include only quality characteristics such as firmness, quantity and distribution of internal fats, and belly thickness.

Firmness of fat, as related to the degree of finish, is also considered in grading. However, carcasses whose fat is soft or oily, owing to the type of feed consumed, are graded without consideration of this characteristic, but are identified as soft or oily along with the grade. Differences between U.S. No. 1 and U.S. No. 3 pork carcasses are shown in Figs. 37-15 and 37-16. The

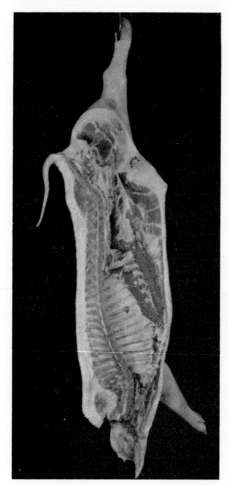 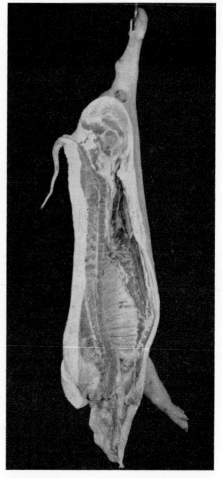

Fig. 37-15. U.S. No. 1 pork carcass. Average thickness of backfat, 1.4 inches; length of body, 29.8 inches; estimated yield of ham, loin, picnic, and Boston butt, 52.6%.

Fig. 37-16. U.S. No. 3 pork carcass. Average thickness of backfat, 2.1 inches; length of body, 27.5 inches; estimated yield of ham, loin, picnic, and Boston butt, 45.1%.

legend accompanying each picture indicates the average thickness of back fat and length of body.

Sow carcasses are graded on exactly the same basis as described for barrow and gilt carcasses, except that the objective guides to grades are based entirely on thickness of back fat without reference to length or weight. This relationship was established through measurement and cutting data on sow carcasses. Table 37-2 shows the range in average thickness of back fat for each of the grades of sow carcasses.

TABLE 37-2. | *Backfat thickness guide for grades of sow carcasses.*

Grade	Average backfat thickness* (inches)
U.S. No. 1	1.5–1.9
U.S. No. 2	1.9–2.3
U.S. No. 3	2.3 or more
Medium	1.1–1.5
Cull	<1.1

* Average of three measurements, skin included; made opposite first and last ribs and last lumbar vertebra.

REFERENCES AND SELECTED READINGS

References marked with an asterisk are of general interest.

*United States Department of Agriculture, Official United States standards for grades of carcass beef. Service and Regulatory Announcement No. 99. Issued June 1926; reprinted June 1956.

*———— Official United States standards for grades of veal and calf carcasses. Service and Regulatory Announcement No. 114. Issued September 1928; reprinted September 1956.

*————. Official United States standards for grades of lamb, yearling mutton, and mutton carcasses. Service and Regulatory Announcement No. 123. Issued March 1931; reprinted April 1960.

*————. Official United States standards for grades of pork carcasses (barrow and gilt; sow). Service and Regulatory Announcement No. 171. Issued September 1952; reprinted April 1958.

Chapter 38

Classification and
Grading of Livestock

38-1. INTRODUCTION

As pointed out in the previous chapter, in the early growth of our country the main agricultural production areas moved progressively farther away from the large urban areas. Concurrent with this relocation, large, highly competitive central livestock markets and packing plants were developed adjacent to these areas. This was made possible largely as a result of the improvement in transportation facilities. However, it was also materially facilitated by the development and widespread use of a nationally recognized and understood system of *classes* and *grades* of livestock.

To a somewhat greater extent than has been the case with meat, the livestock industry has adopted and used the system of classification and grading of livestock as developed and published by the U.S. Department of Agriculture. Although there has never been an official federal livestock grading program, the federal standards are used by the USDA as the basis for conducting a nationwide livestock market news service. Some states, however, conduct official livestock grading programs in which state employees officially grade livestock at the time it is offered for sale—usually at auctions. In most such programs, the federal standards are used as the basis for the service.

The trend toward increased selling of livestock through auctions and by direct sales at the ranch, farm, or feed lot means that some producers are assuming a responsibility in marketing their livestock, which they formerly delegated to commission agents when livestock was sold on a central market. To the extent that this development has taken place, it becomes increasingly important that livestock producers have as much understanding as possible of the market desirability of their livestock—primarily their class and grade. Federal class and grade standards have been developed for

666

slaughter animals of all species; for some species, standards have also been developed for feeder animals.

The class and grade standards for slaughter livestock are based on the class and grade of carcass they will produce. The class and grade standards of feeder animals are based on the class and grade of slaughter animals they will produce under normal feeding and management practices. This closely interrelated system of standards thus provides the means of communication whereby consumers' wants and preferences for meat can be relayed back through the entire marketing channel to the producers. This enables producers to more intelligently plan their production and marketing program.

Class, as used in its broader sense, is a means for identifying animals for their commercial use. Thus, there are two general classes of livestock—slaughter and feeder. Subclasses of livestock usually are based on their sex condition. Thus, in cattle, steers, heifers, cows, bulls, stags are considered subclasses.

In formulating standards for these various classes of livestock, some of the subclasses may be grouped together. For instance, grade standards for slaughter steers, heifers, and cows are combined in the same manner as are the standards for grades of slaughter barrows and gilts.

38-2. GRADES OF SLAUGHTER LIVESTOCK

Basis for Grade. Since the grade of a slaughter animal is the estimated grade of carcass it will produce, the characteristics used in grading are the same as used in grading carcasses—(1) conformation and (2) quality of meat.

In evaluating conformation, the primary emphasis is placed on estimating the ratio of lean meat or muscle to bone and the ratio of the more demanded to the less preferred parts. Animals that have thick, plump muscles in relation to their skeletal structure are considered to have good conformation—particularly if this muscling is well developed in the region of the most valuable parts. Since the actual thickness and plumpness of the animal is influenced greatly by the fatness of the animal, plumpness and thickness of muscling can best be appraised from those parts of the animal on which there is relatively little fat deposited. Thus, the round in cattle, the ham in hogs, and the leg in sheep are particularly useful parts to observe closely in evaluating conformation. Other parts of the carcass should not be ignored, but their evaluation—particularly in highly finished animals—should be made with appropriate adjustments for the fat that may be present. The loin and back are two parts of the animal over which fat is deposited at a relatively fast rate; in rapidly fattening animals, the contour of these parts changes very rapidly. Since an animal's carcass is made up only of muscle, fat, and bone, two animals of the same weight and scale or skeletal structure but which differ considerably in fatness necessarily will show a difference in muscular development. The fatter of these two will normally have the least thickness of muscling and thus the poorest conformation.

An accurate appraisal of a live animal for the quality of meat that will be contained in its carcass is usually more difficult to make than is an appraisal of its conformation. This results from the fact that the criteria that are useful for estimating marbling and other quality characteristics of the lean are, at best, only moderately accurate indicators of these characteristics. The degree of finish carried by an animal is, of course, the best single criterion of the quality of the meat in its carcass. However, the distribution and firmness of the finish are probably fully as important as the amount. Maturity is likewise a very important consideration in grading slaughter livestock. Among the criteria that are useful in evaluating maturity are: (1) the size of the animal, (2) the width of the muzzle (this reflects differences in the number of small, temporary teeth and of the larger, permanent teeth), (3) the length of the tail (in vealers and calves the hair on the tail is relatively short, since it has not had time to grow long), (4) the general symmetry and smoothness of outline (as animals advance in maturity they frequently develop more prominent hips and become irregular in contour) and, (5) in horned cattle, the size of the horns. As animals advance in maturity, they are required to have greater degrees of finish to qualify for a given grade.

USDA Grades for Slaughter Livestock. The following tabulation summarizes the applicable grades for the various kinds of slaughter livestock for which the USDA has issued official standards. (The official United States standards for grades of livestock are listed as references at the end of the chapter.)

Kind of animal	Subclass	Grade
Cattle	Steer, heifer, and cow*	Prime, Choice, Good, Standard, Commercial, Utility, Cutter, and Canner
	Bull	Choice, Good, Commercial, Utility, Cutter, and Canner
	Stag	Same as bull
Calf		Prime, Choice, Good, Standard, Utility, and Cull
Veal		Same as calf
Lamb		Prime, Choice, Good, Utility, and Cull
Yearling mutton		Same as lamb
Mutton		Choice, Good, Utility, and Cull
Hogs	Barrows and gilts	U.S. No. 1, U.S. No. 2, U.S. No. 3, Medium, and Cull
	Sows	Same as barrows and gilts

* Cows are not eligible for the Prime grade.

38-3. GRADING SLAUGHTER CATTLE

The various sexes of slaughter cattle are defined as follows.

Bull: an uncastrated male.

Steer: a male castrated when young, prior to development of the secondary sexual characteristics associated with a bull.

Stag: a male castrated after it has developed, or has begun to develop, the secondary sexual characteristics associated with a bull.

Cow: a female that has developed, through reproduction or with age, the relatively prominent hips, the large middle and other physical characteristics typical of a mature female.

Heifer: an immature female that has not developed the physical characteristics typical of a cow.

The determination of the grade of the live animal—that is, the grade of its carcass—requires well regulated judgment. Each animal graded will likely present a somewhat different combination of grade-determining characteristics. It is not unusual for an animal of one grade to have some characteristics that are associated with animals of one or more other grades. A composite evaluation of the total inherent characteristics of the animal is essential for accuracy in determining grade.

As previously indicated, maturity is one of the important factors considered in grading slaughter cattle; there are maximum maturity limitations for each of the four higher grades. Since evidences of maturity in beef carcasses vary among animals of the same approximate age, only general maximum age limitations can be indicated for these grades. These are as follows: Prime, 36 months; Choice, 42 months; Good, 48 months; and Standard, 48 months. The Commercial grade is restricted to steers, heifers, and cows that are over 48 months. There are no age limitations for the Utility, Cutter, and Canner grades.

The general fatness of the animal is a very important consideration in evaluating the expected quality of its carcass. However, distribution of fat is probably equally as important as the total fatness. For instance, a steer with considerably more fat in the cod, flank, and brisket than another steer will frequently have a higher quality of meat, even though the two steers may have a very similar degree of fatness over their loin and back. Animals do differ markedly in the relative amount of fat they deposit as marbling and in the amount they deposit over the outside of their carcass and around their kidneys. This is a characteristic that may be influenced by feeding, but it is likely an inherited trait. The variable distribution of fat is of tremendous economic importance, and the identification of factors responsible for it is worthy of much more research effort than has been directed to it in the past.

Excellent conformation in slaughter cattle is evidenced by a wide, thick back, full square rump, and a deep, wide, full quarter. Fullness and thick-

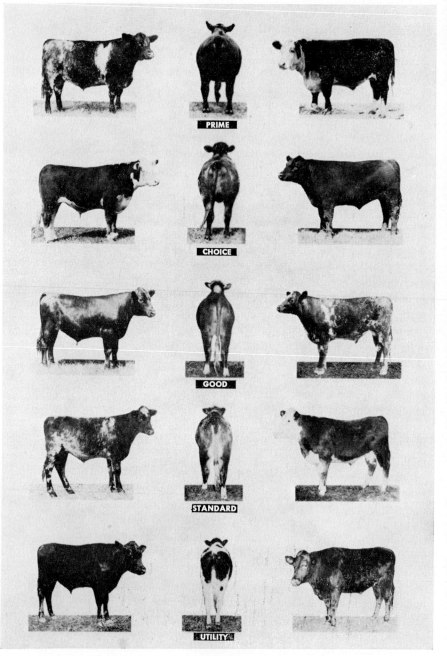

Fig. 38-1. Steers illustrative of slaughter cattle grades.

ness should be especially evident in the portions of the body producing the more desirable cuts—loin, rib, and round. Inferior conformation is evidenced by a decided lack of fullness and thickness, and the various parts are frequently angular, sunken, or even concave. Since conformation relates to proportions of the more valuable to less valuable parts and to the ratio of meat to bone, it cannot be appraised directly from the actual width, depth, and thickness of an animal. Rather, these factors must be appraised in relation to the size or scale of the animal.

The most logical and accurate way to determine the grade of a slaughter steer is to separately evaluate its conformation and its expected quality of carcass in terms of grade. These then can be combined into a final grade in the same manner as indicated for beef carcasses in the previous chapter. Unless this procedure is followed, there is a distinct tendency to permit conformation to exert a greater influence on grade than it should. This is particularly true in grading thick muscled, high quality cattle whose conformation is relatively better developed than their carcass quality. Figure 38-1 illustrates slaughter steers that qualify for the indicated grades.

38-4. GRADING OF VEALERS AND SLAUGHTER CALVES

Vealers and slaughter calves are young bovine animals. They are differentiated primarily on the basis of their age and evidences of types of feeding. Typical vealers are less than three months old and have subsisted largely on milk. Since vealers have consumed little or no roughage, they have the characteristic trimness of middle that is associated with limited paunch development. Calves are usually 3–8 months of age, have subsisted partially or entirely on feeds other than milk for a considerable length of time, and have developed the larger middles and other physical characteristics associated with maturity beyond the vealer stage. Most bovines that are 9 months of age or older are considered as cattle. Differences in sex condition between steers, heifers, and bulls are usually unimportant in vealers and calves; for this reason, the federal grade standards for these types are combined.

Vealers are usually of dairy breeding and, in most instances, are considered as somewhat of a by-product of the dairy industry. Slaughter calves, on the other hand, are usually of predominately beef breeding. In general, they are produced in the southern and southwestern parts of the country and are marketed in greatest numbers in the summer and fall months. The factors considered in grading vealers and slaughter calves, and the emphasis placed on variations in development of conformation and quality, are identical with those previously discussed for slaughter cattle.

Although there are separate federal standards for grades of vealers, slaughter calves, and slaughter cattle, these are actually considered a continuous series. This means that, for each grade, the quality-indicating requirements that vary with changes in maturity increase progressively with increasing maturity, from veal through calf and beef. In standards based on this premise, changes in maturity that occur at the junction of these three age groups are relatively unimportant. Thus, the requirements for a Choice calf that is approaching beef in maturity are practically the same as those for a Choice slaughter steer or heifer that is just beyond calf in maturity. A similar blending of the standards is intended for vealers approaching calf in maturity and for calves that are just beyond vealers in maturity.

38-5. GRADING SLAUGHTER LAMBS, YEARLINGS, AND SHEEP

The various sex and age groups of slaughter ovines are as follows.

Ram: an uncastrated male ovine.

Wether: a male ovine castrated when young and prior to developing the secondary sexual characteristics of a ram.

Ewe: a female ovine.

Lamb: an immature ovine usually under 14 months of age that has not cut its first pair of permanent incisor teeth.

Yearling: an ovine usually between one and two years of age that has cut its first pair of permanent incisor teeth, but which has not cut the second pair.

Sheep: an ovine usually over 24 months of age that has cut its second pair of permanent incisor teeth.

Since the grade of slaughter ovines is based on the grade of their carcass, the same principles must apply to grading the animals prior to slaughter as apply to grading carcasses. These are discussed in detail in the previous chapter.

The accurate determination of the grade of a slaughter lamb or sheep requires handling in addition to visual observation. This is necessary since the length and density of the wool is quite variable between individuals, making it almost impossible to accurately appraise the conformation and the thickness and firmness of finish without handling. Experienced graders may find one quick handling satisfactory. This usually is done by placing one open hand over the back and ribs with the thumb extended just over the backbone. The fingers are held close together and cover the rib section. Applying pressure very lightly, the hand is moved with a slight lateral and forward–backward motion.

If time permits, it is usually desirable to handle forward along the back from the dock to the neck. In doing this, the hand should be open and nearly flat and the fingers should be together. Pressure of the hand should be very light and the motion should be slightly lateral. Both hands may then be used in a similar manner along each side to determine the fleshing

Fig. 38-2. Lambs illustrative of the slaughter grades.

over the shoulders, ribs, and hips. Figure 38-2 shows slaughter lambs that qualify for the indicated grades.

38-6. GRADING SLAUGHTER SWINE

The various sex conditions of slaughter swine are defined as follows.

Barrow: a male swine castrated when young, before development of the secondary sexual characteristics associated with a boar.

Gilt: a young female swine that has not produced young or has not reached an advanced stage of pregnancy.

Sow: a mature female swine that has reproduced or has reached an advanced stage of pregnancy.

Boar: an uncastrated male swine.

Stag: a male swine castrated after development of the secondary sexual characteristics of a boar.

Grade standards for slaughter swine have been developed only for barrows, gilts, and sows. Those for barrows and gilts are combined into a single standard, since, when they are marketed, sex condition has not yet exerted an influence on the market acceptability of their carcasses.

The grades of slaughter swine are based on the corresponding grades of carcasses. Therefore, the same principles of evaluating grade must be considered in grading slaughter swine as are used in grading pork carcasses. Since thickness of back fat is such an important factor in grading carcasses, this likewise becomes the most important factor in grading slaughter hogs. Swine are much fatter when marketed than other species of meat animals. Therefore, the variable rate of deposition of fat on various parts of the body is more evident than in other animals, and this can be used to good advantage in estimating fatness. As hogs fatten they tend to deposit fat at a faster rate over their back than they do over the lower part of their body or over the lower part of their hams or shoulders. As a result, hogs with a high degree of finish usually will appear wider over their loin and back than through their underline, and they are wider through their loin than through the center or lower part of their ham. They also tend to taper slightly down their back from their shoulders to their hams. In such hogs, the contour of the back from side to side is frequently nearly flat, and there may be a decided break into the sides. The flanks are very deep and full, and the jowls are usually very thick and full.

By contrast, hogs with relatively little fat will appear rather peaked along their top and usually will be wider through their underline than through their back. The hams will be wider than either the shoulders or the loin; the flanks will be thin and the jowls thin and flat. Some of these characteristics are evident in Fig. 38-3, which illustrates the various grades of slaughter barrows and gilts.

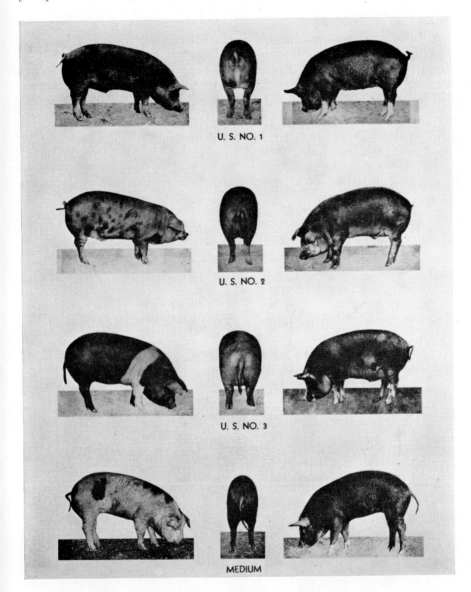

U. S. NO. 1

U. S. NO. 2

U. S. NO. 3

MEDIUM

Fig. 38-3. Animals illustrative of the grades of slaughter barrows or gilts.

38-7. GRADES OF FEEDER LIVESTOCK

The determination of whether a particular animal is considered a feeder or slaughter animal on the market is determined not by his characteristics but, rather, by the use for which he is purchased. If he is purchased for immediate slaughter, he is considered a slaughter animal. If he is purchased for further feeding, he is considered a feeder animal. Although certain combinations of characteristics in animals almost always result in their being purchased either for slaughter or for further feeding, there are also many animals whose characteristics make them best suited for feeding under certain economic conditions, whereas under other economic conditions they would be purchased for immediate slaughter.

Animals that are in thin condition—particularly those which have a good meat type—will practically always be sold as feeders, since under most economic conditions they will make profitable gains and thereby return a profit to their feeder. Since animals make their most economical gains dur-

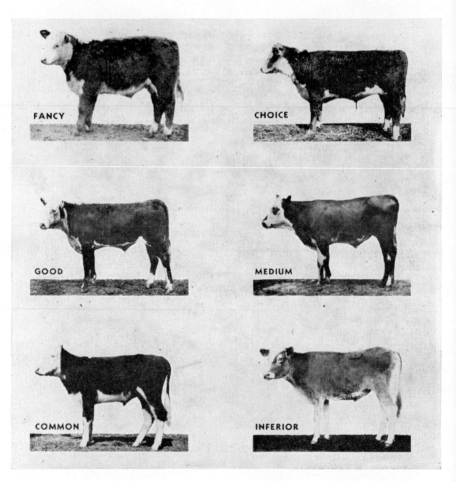

Fig. 38-4.   Steers illustrative of the feeder cattle grades.

ing the early stages of fattening, it is usually most advantageous to purchase animals for further feeding that have only a limited degree of finish. Livestock whose value is almost the same to slaughterers or feeders are frequently referred to as "two-way" or "warmed-up" animals.

The grade of a feeder animal is based upon the grade of slaughter animal it will produce at its "logical slaughter potential" and on its thriftiness or its likely efficiency of gain. The "logical slaughter potential" is the stage in an animal's development when its conformation and carcass quality have an equivalent degree of development.

When animals are fed beyond their "logical slaughter potential" their carcass quality becomes relatively more highly developed than their conformation. This means that when an animal is fed beyond its "logical slaughter potential" it takes a considerably greater increase in quality to make a given increase in the slaughter grade than it does to make a similar increase in slaughter grade prior to the time the "logical slaughter potential" is reached. For example, it is entirely possible for an animal with Good grade conformation to be fed until it has developed Prime grade quality. The slaughter or carcass grade of such an animal would be Choice. However, this would normally require a longer feeding period and would require a more expensive feeding regime, whereas feeding an animal with Choice grade conformation to produce a Choice grade slaughter animal would require feeding to develop only Choice—instead of Prime—grade quality. Thus the feeder grade of the first animal is Good, whereas the feeder grade of the second is Choice.

Conformation in feeder cattle is evaluated in terms of the conformation of the slaughter animal at its "logical slaughter potential." Since most feeder animals are in thin condition, they do not have as thick or as plump an appearance as they do at their "logical slaughter potential." For this reason, the conformation grade descriptions of a particular grade of feeder animal require less thickness, fullness, and so forth than the conformation descriptions of the corresponding grade of slaughter animal. This is especially true in the higher grades of feeder animals.

Thriftiness, or the likely efficiency of gain by an animal, is considered in grading feeder animals, but it is not used to raise the feeder grade beyond the animal's grade at its "logical slaughter potential." For example, a feeder animal with a "logical slaughter potential" of Good, but which gave the appearance of being unusually thrifty, would not be graded Choice. On the other hand, a feeder animal with a "logical slaughter potential" of Choice might be graded Good if it appeared to be unthrifty and likely to have a low efficiency of gain. Figure 38-4 illustrates the tentative standards for grades of feeder steers.

REFERENCES AND SELECTED READINGS

USDA. Official United States standards for grades of slaughter cattle. Service and Regulatory Announcement No. 112. Issued September 1928; reprinted June 1956.

———. Official United States standards for grades of vealers and slaughter calves. Service and Regulatory Announcement No. 113. Issued September 1928; reprinted May 1957.

———. Official United States standards for grades of slaughter lambs, yearlings and sheep. Service and Regulatory Announcement No. 168. Issued April 1951; reprinted November 1960.

———. Official United States standards for grades of slaughter swine (barrows and gilts; sows). Service and Regulatory Announcement No. 172. Issued September 1952; reprinted April 1958.

———. Market classes and grades of feeder and stocker cattle. Circular 505. Issued October 1938; revised August 1942.

Chapter 39

Marketing of Livestock and Meats

Livestock is a national commodity. It is produced and marketed in every state of the Union. The distribution of livestock and meats takes place on a national scale; cattle raised on the plains of Texas may be fattened in an Iowa feed lot, slaughtered in Chicago and the steaks therefrom served in a New York restaurant. Spring lambs produced in California may be slaughtered kosher style in Brooklyn and consumed in Boston. Meat and lard from hogs raised in Illinois may be sold in Philadelphia, San Francisco, and New Orleans. Livestock marketing must therefore be viewed as a national industry rather than as a purely local business.

This huge national industry developed from small beginnings. When the first settlers arrived, no livestock existed in this country. All of our domestic livestock, as we know it today, was originally imported. George Washington, as well as many other famous Americans, was an importer of livestock. In an average year, our annual slaughter of meat animals now totals about 25 million head of cattle, 10 million head of calves, 80 million head of hogs, and 15 million head of sheep and lambs. When this volume of meat is divided among all the people of the country, we have yearly about 87 lb. of beef, 6 lb. of veal, 65 lb. of pork and $4\frac{1}{2}$ lb. of lamb and mutton for every man, woman, and child in the United States.

39-1. THE MARKETING PROCESS

Marketing may be defined as the performance of services necessary to move goods, after they have been physically produced, into the possession and ownership of final consumers. The services usually required in the successful marketing of agricultural products are: (1) assembling, (2) grading and standardizing, (3) packaging, (4) processing, (5) storing, (6) financing, (7) transporting, (8) selling, and (9) risk-bearing. Some of these services are performed more than once in the marketing process; others, such as packaging or processing, are not involved for certain products. In the livestock industry, marketing the live animals, slaughtering and processing operations, and moving the resulting meat products through trade channels to consumers are as essential to the completion of the production process as is the work of the primary producer.

Marketing Stages. Marketing of agricultural products can logically be grouped into three major stages: (1) concentration of supplies at shipping points, (2) equalization of supply and demand in wholesale transactions, and (3) distribution to consumers through retailers. Livestock generally passes from the hands of a large number of producers into the hands of a much smaller number of buyers; the slaughter animals are then sent to packers for slaughter and processing and on to retailers; from the retailer, the final product goes to the consumer.

Sales Channels for Livestock and Meats. The customers or buyers to whom a livestockman or middleman sells his product are his sales outlets. The term sales outlet may be used either to indicate different kinds or classes of buyers or a series of specific persons or firms.

A sales channel is a series of marketing agencies through which a product

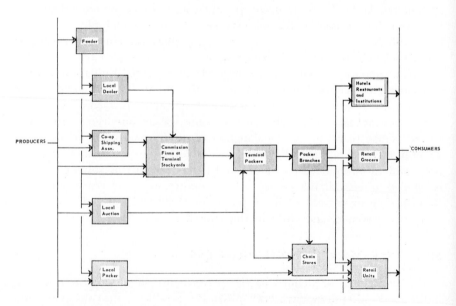

Fig. 39-1.   Principal sales channels for livestock and meats.

moves from the producer to the consumer. Sometimes sales channels are called trade or marketing channels. Figure 39-1 shows the principal sales channels for livestock and meats. When these sales channels are traced in reverse, they indicate the various sources of supply used by each class of middleman.

Direct Marketing Increasing. During the first quarter of this century, terminal livestock markets at Chicago, Kansas City, Omaha, Denver, and other railroad centers dominated the marketing of livestock. In 1923, the earliest year for which data are available, the following proportions of federally inspected slaughter were purchased at terminal markets: cattle 90%, calves 86%, sheep and lambs 86%, hogs 77% (USDA, 1923).

In recent years, an increasing volume of livestock has moved directly from producers, country dealers, and auctions to packers. The proportion marketed through the terminals has declined. Several terminal markets, such as those at Los Angeles and San Francisco, have ceased operation entirely. The volume of livestock moving through the Chicago terminal market has likewise been reduced materially. In California, for example, it is estimated that in 1960 approximately 90% of the cattle fed for slaughter moved directly from the feed lot to the packer—bypassing the terminal market. Indications are that in all parts of the United States the trend toward more direct marketing is increasing.

Among the more important changes that have contributed to this trend are improved motor truck transportation, improved market-news facilities, and increased development of large feed lots, which feed and market animals to meet the specifications of packers, who in turn sell meat to fit the more discriminating specifications of large-volume retailers. Also, there has been a decentralization of packing plant facilities away from the terminal markets to minimize the high costs associated with central-terminal traffic congestion, high land values, labor problems and so forth. New and more specialized and efficient interior packing plants, located closer to sources of livestock supply, have received an increasing proportion of the livestock marketed by producers. Country livestock auctions have increased in recent years to approximately 2,300, whereas terminal markets have declined from over 65 in number to 49 in 1960 (Livestock Marketing Journal, 1960).

39-2. PRESENT METHODS OF SELLING LIVESTOCK

Selection of Sales Outlets. One of the major marketing problems is to decide which outlet or combination of outlets best fits the needs of the individual producer. The following are the most important factors to be considered in making such a choice.

(1) Sales volume handled.
(2) Quality of livestock usually preferred.
(3) Kind of livestock usually handled.

(4) Net returns to producer.

(5) Location or distance and transportation facilities available.

(6) Financial resources of seller and/or buyers.

(7) Personal abilities and preferences.

(8) Established trade connections.

Production and marketing situations differ widely. The relative importance of the above factors are thus likely to differ considerably in importance from one producer to another.

Local Markets, Country Dealers or Traders. Local markets may also be called assembly yards, buying points, or reload stations. They may be operated by a local dealer, a cooperative, or a packer.

Country dealers or traders are independent operators who buy and sell livestock on a full or part time basis for profit. They may vary considerably in their scale of operation. They usually buy from producers at the farm, but many also buy at auctions or concentration yards. Country dealers or traders conduct their activities in all livestock areas of the country.

Auction Markets. The auction is one of the oldest systems of selling. An auction may be defined as a public market at which an article is offered for sale simultaneously to several prospective buyers and is sold by the auctioneer to the highest bidder.

A livestock auction may be a proprietorship, partnership, general business corporation, or a cooperative association. The rapid rise in the volume of business handled by auctions indicates that farmers have found that the advantages of this method of sale outweigh its disadvantages.

Central or Terminal Markets. Terminal markets (also referred to as central markets) differ from other livestock markets principally in the scope and type of activity conducted. However, it is difficult to draw a clear-cut distinction between terminal markets and all other livestock markets.

Originally, our seaboard livestock markets were terminal markets in the true sense of the term. These markets were located on the east coast, in such cities as Baltimore, Philadelphia, and Jersey City, and were truly the end of the line at that time. Once livestock reached the coast it was rarely shipped to any other point.

Now, however, the term "terminal market" is only relative. In general, the term implies a market about the size of the one in Chicago, where there is a concentration of livestock for sale, a concentration of buyers, and a concentration of meat plants and other related services. Not all livestock shipped to terminal markets, however, is sold or processed there; a sizeable volume is shipped to other markets for sale. Another portion may be purchased and shipped to meat-packing plants located in other cities.

It is commonly thought that market transactions at terminal markets are the greatest single influence in determining livestock prices from day to day. Market-news agencies usually base their reports on the terminal markets. In recent years, however, with a declining volume moving through central markets, more information is needed concerning direct and final transactions in the country and in the feed lots to obtain a more complete picture of prices and movements.

Commission Firms at Central Markets. Commission firms at central markets receive livestock on consignment from producers, local dealers, or co-operative associations, and act as the shipper's agent in selling the livestock to buyers, chiefly packing companies. When a consignment of livestock has been sold, the yardage, feed, selling commission, and any other marketing charges are deducted from the total receipts for the animals, and the net receipts are forwarded to the shipper. The basic service of the commission firm is to supply highly skilled specialists in the sale of each class of livestock in order that the actual selling be done by a person whose technical competence is on a par with the buyer's experience.

Commission firms usually assume full charge of the livestock from the time of delivery by the consignor. The animals are sorted and penned by species, and sometimes by class. Sorting may also be done by weight and grade to provide for more effective sale. Commission firms also keep their patrons informed on the market situation and assist in the collection of claims against carriers for losses in transit. Commission firms are bonded under supervision of the Packers and Stockyards Division of the United States Department of Agriculture.

Selling on Contract for Future Delivery. Contracting for purchase or sale of livestock in advance is commonly practiced in the western livestock country. This system offers one means of insuring against possible price changes.

There are times when the producer gains by contracting to sell his livestock in advance or to purchase feeders or replacements, especially if he is able to interpret market trends correctly. On the other hand, if the producer misjudges market conditions, sale by contract for future delivery may have a distinct disadvantage.

Studies made of contract selling of livestock seem to show that the advantages of contracting are usually more with the buyer than with the producer. The buyer usually has more complete information and is able to interpret market trends more accurately than the average producer.

Stockmen who sell their animals on contract should be thoroughly familiar with the fundamentals of good livestock purchase contracts. Taylor (1953) and Stucky (1952), who have made separate studies of selling cattle on contract, point out the advantages and disadvantages of this type of selling and some of the pitfalls that might be avoided.

Cooperative Marketing of Livestock. In their day-to-day marketing operations, livestock cooperatives function within the same competitive framework as all other segments of the livestock industry. The cooperatives deal with the same livestock interests, trade with the same buyers, and are subject to the same industry-wide customs and practices. On the surface their operations do not vary greatly from those of non-cooperative livestock marketing agencies.

Cooperative associations are owned and controlled by producers. Control is exercised through a board of directors elected by the membership. To become a member and to be eligible to vote for directors, a producer must patronize the association and apply for membership. Membership is restricted to bona fide livestock producers. The primary purpose of the cooperative is to market livestock for members in the most effective way possible and to serve the members' interest in particular. Where the livestock cooperatives handle sufficient volume to set the competitive pace, they are instrumental in bringing about improvements in practices and in pricing for the benefit of producers. Capable management, adequate volume, and loyal membership support are vital to their success.

39-3. HOW LIVESTOCK PRICES ARE DETERMINED

Stated in simple terms, the prices of meat (and therefore of livestock) are determined by supply and demand—supply, the number of animals raised and sent to market and the yield of meat from these animals; demand, the number of dollars that consumers are able and willing to spend for beef, pork, lamb, and veal. It must be realized further that a great many factors—all of them constantly changing—affect both supply and demand. It is the complex interplay of all those factors that determines the price that livestock producers get for cattle, calves, hogs, or lambs on the day, and at the place, they are sold.

Illustrations of the Price-Making Process. The biggest single reason for the fluctuation in livestock prices is that the amount of total meat slaughtered and offered for sale by the packers varies from day to day or from week to week.

Meat is a perishable product that cannot be stored economically. Hence, there is strong pressure for it to be sold each day. There is really no such thing as a stored surplus of meat. Most of it is moved into the channels of trade within two weeks of the time it is slaughtered. Of course, small amounts may be stored as canned meat or in some other processed form, but only the lower grades of meat are handled this way.

If, during a particular week, supplies of a certain class and grade of livestock are large and haven't been sold by the end of the week, the holdover causes that particular class of livestock to sell for less when the market opens. This will be especially true if the current market run turns out to be heavy.

Changes in the meat prices that the packers get in the wholesale market are, in turn, almost immediately reflected in the prices that packers will bid for livestock. The prices that packers can pay for livestock are also greatly dependent on the prices they receive for by-products, such as tallow, hides, tankage, lamb pelts, and the like. Changes in the market price of these products can make a sizeable difference in the price a packer can pay for livestock.

On the demand side, the amount of money spent for meat depends mostly on the number of dollars available for consumer spending of all kinds. As disposable income goes up, the consumer tends to spend more money on meat. The livestock producer should recognize, however, that his product is competing with other meats such as poultry and fish as well as with plant foods. Thus, to maintain his market, he must present a superior product to the consumer at an attractive price. Furthermore, promotion is essential in order that meat can compete successfully with other consumer expenditures.

Consumer income changes very gradually. It does not increase or decrease nearly as often or as much as does the number of livestock raised and marketed. Whatever their incomes may be, consumers tend to spend, within rather narrow limits, about the same percentage of their income for meat. Accordingly, about the same amount of money is available for buying meat from one day, week, or month to the next. This means that when livestock marketings increase significantly, prices must go down in order to stretch the same number of consumer dollars over a larger meat supply. And when marketings are lighter, consumers will pay higher prices for the smaller supply of meat. This emphasizes the importance of orderly livestock marketing in helping to prevent violent price changes.

Competition from poultry, fish, eggs, cheese and many other products also has a great influence on meat prices. An increasing supply and variety of such items are available in convenient form at reasonable prices, and the consumer will continue to buy red meat only if she can buy the quality she desires at what she considers to be the right price.

Such things as weather, seasonal habits, and religious beliefs also affect the demand for meats. Weather conditions, which may either cause drought or increase grass supplies, can also greatly influence the movement of livestock to slaughter. Each of these factors has its particular influence on livestock and meat prices and must be considered by the alert producer.

Seasonal Marketing Patterns and Price Trends. Seasonal trends in prices of meat animals reflect the seasonality of production and of market sales.

SEASONALITY IN LIVESTOCK MARKETINGS*

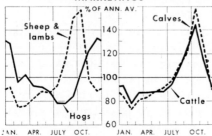

Fig. 39-2. Marketings are highly concentrated at the end of the grazing season for all meat animals except hogs. A November–January high in hog marketings reflects large March–April farrowings.

To a large extent, cattle and sheep are born in the spring and marketed in the fall, although there are many variations in different parts of the country. Their prices are usually lowest in the fall, when supplies are abundant, and climb to a spring high, when supplies are scarce.

Farrowing of pigs is concentrated in two seasons, spring and fall. Marketings and prices of hogs accordingly have two up-and-down swings each year. A major price peak occurs in late summer; a secondary peak in late winter.

Figure 39-2 shows how marketings are highly concentrated at the end of the grazing season for all meat animals except hogs. A November–January high in hog marketings reflects large March–April farrowings.

Within these broad trends are many separate seasonal patterns for individual grades and classes of livestock. Differences are especially great for the various kinds of cattle. Those that are not fed—lower grade steers and

Fig. 39-3. Sheep offered for sale at a typical country auction market.

cows, as well as all stocker and feeder cattle and calves for slaughter—conform to the pattern of peak supply and lowest prices in the fall. Feeding raises the grade of cattle and delays the peak supply for the higher grades until progressively later seasons.

Feeding of lambs smooths out the slaughter supply, but not as much as cattle feeding. Lamb prices retain the same general pattern as do lower grade cattle prices—lowest in the fall, highest in the spring.

Seasonal patterns change with time, as innovations are made in livestock production and marketing. Seasonal trends in prices of veal calves were markedly different in the 1950's than they were in the 1920's because marketings have since been affected by a shift from spring calving of milk cows to year-round calving. Likewise, seasonal marketings of fed cattle have been smoothed out, particularly in California, where cattle feeding has expanded over 500% since 1945 and is now done on a year-round basis. With such developments, seasonal fluctuations in slaughter cattle prices are not nearly so great because marketings are more uniform from month to month.

39-4. VERTICAL INTEGRATION IN THE LIVESTOCK INDUSTRY

In recent years, the subject of integration in its various forms has been one of growing interest and concern in livestock circles.

Definition and Trends. There are two general types of integration—horizontal and vertical. Horizontal integration is the combination of businesses that are alike into one larger business concern, for example, the merger of two or more ranches under one management. Vertical integration means the control of two or more stages in the chain of production, processing, and distribution under one single management or decision-making unit. It may come about either through cooperative arrangements, through contracts, or through ownership of the various steps in the process.

Integration in the livestock industry is not new. At one time, livestock production and meat consumption were completely integrated. All of the stages in the chain of production were under the control of one man, namely, the farmer. This chain included growing the feed, producing and butchering the livestock, and consuming the meat on the farm or selling it directly to consumers. Since those early days, however, we have had much specialization in various stages of production, processing, marketing, and distribution.

In recent years, many significant changes have occurred in food marketing that have also influenced trends toward integration. For example, food retailing is becoming controlled by an increasingly smaller number of larger firms. These large supermarkets depend upon uniform quality and continuous supply. To be assured of the desired uniformity and quantity of meat, they are interested in integration or in contracting with suppliers in advance for future delivery. Specifications of final products can be more closely controlled through some form of integration.

Forces Influencing Integration. Kramer (1958) indicates that the following forces have been important causes of the trend toward integration in the livestock and meat industry.

(1) Efforts of slaughterers and distributors to assure themselves of an adequate and stable supply of livestock, poultry, or meat.

(2) Efforts of slaughterers and distributors to control the quality of livestock, poultry, and meat.

(3) Efforts of farmers to spread or reduce risks and to reduce production costs.

(4) Efforts of farmers to obtain additional production capital.

(5) Efforts of feed companies and other farm suppliers to expand the market for their supplies.

(6) Efforts of slaughterers and distributors to reduce dependence upon others.

(7) Efforts of slaughterers and distributors to reduce transaction costs. In summary, it might be said that today's emphasis on vertical integration has grown out of the struggle of the agencies engaged in production and marketing to shorten the gap between the producer and the consumer. The primary ends sought are cost reduction and more market power of influence over supply, quality, and price. This is the basis for the growth of integration. For society in general, it means better quality; more uniform products at lower prices; more stability of supply and price throughout the year; and a smoother seasonal and geographical flow of product. In conclusion, it can be said that the success of integrated programs will be determined largely by the quality and effectiveness of management and by efficiency in the use of capital. Integration poses a threat to the inefficient, high-cost producer because he can't sell and make a profit on the same market as can the more efficient, integrated operation. On the other hand, it holds promise for many capable producers who will find opportunity to expand their business, reduce their risk, and increase their profits.

39-5. LIVESTOCK MARKET NEWS AND OUTLOOK INFORMATION

Market News. Market news, in a strict sense, consists of market supply, demand, and price information pertaining to daily trading in livestock and livestock products. This information is assembled from daily coverage of principal shipping points and terminal markets. Timeliness is the essence of market news. To be of most use to the producer, the information must be gathered during the most active trading period of the day and be made available almost immediately.

Accuracy of market news is always important, but there are often conflicts between timeliness and completeness. For this reason, some kinds of market news can be assembled and distributed daily, whereas other information cannot be sufficiently complete except on a weekly or monthly basis.

Owing to the different needs of farmers, packers, wholesale handlers, and retailers, several kinds of prices and price reports are issued.

Federal-State Market News Service. The Market News Service of the USDA, in cooperation with the states, is the largest and most important livestock market-news-gathering agency in the country. It operates on all the important livestock markets through a system of leased wires covering thousands of miles of teletype lines, which link scores of field and terminal markets. Reports are made available through radio, television, daily newspapers, wire news services and the mail. Most of these reports are available to producers free of charge upon written request to the offices that issue them. For all publications issued at Washington, addresses should be sent to the Office of Information, Agricultural Marketing Service, United States Department of Agriculture, Washington 25, D.C. For publications issued elsewhere, address the request to the originating office. These offices will also furnish a list of the various types of reports released as well as the date of release. In addition to market news issued by government agencies, often some of the most timely and accurate information regarding transactions is disseminated to clients by commission firms and other market-agency personnel actively engaged in market trading.

Outlook Information. Market outlook projection begins where fact collecting leaves off. Whereas market news is often thought of as information that needs to be available on an hourly or daily basis, outlook information generally relates to the next month, quarter, or year. It contributes to a better understanding of current market news. Basic facts are necessary for an understanding of the economic structure of the livestock industry, but facts alone are not enough. They must be interpreted, analyzed, and related before they have true meaning.

Farmers and ranchers must constantly make decisions concerning production and marketing practices. However, the results of most decisions will affect income at some future date rather than at the time the decision is made. Therefore, the outcome of the decision often depends not upon the prices and market conditions prevailing at the time the decision is made but rather on prices and market conditions at some future date. Thus, reliable outlook information is very important in assisting the livestock producer to arrive at sound conclusions. By studying various outlook reports, the livestock man should be able to arrive at a conclusion as to what the general level of prices and the price risks or advantages will be. By weighing these against his costs he can select the course of action that would be most likely to provide him with the greatest net income.

Livestock outlook reports are issued periodically from nearly all land-grant colleges and extension services as well as from livestock organizations, trade journals, and business sources. Producers may receive such reports by request to their nearest Land-Grant College Department of Agricultural Economics or by contacting their favorite livestock journal or reporting service.

39-6. LIVESTOCK MARKET TERMS AND DEFINITIONS

Important to the accurate understanding of market news and outlook reports is a proper understanding of market terminology and trading terms. The federal and state Market News Services have made market reporting clearer by adopting standard usages in their reports. With time, these terms have come into general use by newspaper reporters and others who prepare market news reports. Some of the most common definitions of terms used in Agricultural Marketing Service reports (USDA) to describe "market" and "demand" are as follows:

MARKET STRONG: A condition of increasing confidence on the part of the buyer; the term expresses the likelihood that the present demand will exhaust present supplies and that the supplies in sight can be absorbed at prevailing or at slightly higher prices.

MARKET ACTIVE: This represents a condition of quick sale, good demand, and a generally healthy condition. Although there may be no decided change in prices, it usually indicates an upward trend.

MARKET FIRM: This term reflects strong confidence in general conditions, often resulting in the strengthening of a price range but seldom in actual price advantages.

MARKET STEADY: A normal movement; steady, consistent trading, showing no definite trends.

MARKET UNSETTLED: Uncertainty on the part of the buyer There may be no actual price changes. It represents a waiting attitude; with spasmodic trading.

MARKET WEAK: This term may be used to describe a condition of actual price decline with a possibility of further decline, reflecting a decided lack of confidence on the part of the buyer. It may also be used when no actual price declines have taken place, but when large supplies are on hand and heavy supplies are in sight, it expresses the prevailing opinion that a decline is inevitable.

NO DEMAND: Indicates a condition of extreme inactivity and lack of trading. It represents a decided lack of confidence on the part of the buyer and suggests a downward tendency in prices.

DEMAND LIGHT: This indicates a feeling of hesitancy with few sales. There may be no price change, but the tendency, if any, is downward.

DEMAND GOOD: Indicates firm confidence in general market conditions on the part of the buyer. Represents a healthy condition with steady, consistent trading, although no actual change in price may occur.

DEMAND ACTIVE: This term indicates that buyers are rapidly absorbing available supplies at prevailing prices; upward trend in prices.

An understanding of these and other well-defined market terms greatly aids the producer in accurately interpreting the market reports that are issued.

39-7. LIVESTOCK TRADING TERMS

In addition to the specific terminology used to describe the market condition, livestock producers and handlers have developed a set of commonly understood trading terms that are also used extensively in conducting business. Many of these terms have developed over the years and have acquired specific meanings in the livestock trading vocabulary. A few examples will serve to illustrate what is meant.

LONG FEDS: Cattle that have been on corn or concentrated feed for 6–9 months or longer.

ORDER BUYERS: Men employed to act as buying agents for packers or other members of the industry.

SHE STUFF: Cows and heifers.

TOPPY: Stock of very good quality that should command the top of the market.

WARMED UP: Cattle that have been on a grain ration for a short period.

The alert livestock producer will have a good working knowledge of these and other terms that will aid him in better understanding market transactions.

39-8. HANDLING LIVESTOCK IN TRANSIT

Almost every market day, many tons of beef, lamb, and pork are destroyed or wasted due to carelessness in handling livestock. Directly or indirectly, such losses are absorbed by the producer. He loses money any time livestock is mishandled, crowded, or mistreated in any way.

Bruises may be caused at loading time by whips, canes, clubs, fork and nail punctures, bumping, crowding through gates and doors, and horn damage from other animals. Bruising, crippling, and death may also occur on the road by loading too few or too many in carriers. Rough handling in the truck or in the railroad car will cause bruising, crippling, and death loss. Good handling practices during transit by rail or truck will bring increased net returns to livestock shippers.

The following general practices will reduce injuries and weight loss and protect the health of animals:

(1) Keep railroad car or truck in good condition. Keep it reasonably clean and dry, free from projecting nails and bolts, and include proper bedding.

(2) Avoid undue excitement or excessive exercise in assembling, loading, and unloading animals.

Fig. 39-4.   Proper handling of livestock in transit pays dividends.

(3) Keep bruising to a minimum by dehorning, by unhurried movements through gates and narrow passages, and by using canvas slappers or electric prods instead of sticks or clubs.

(4) Use proper precautions in loading; loading chutes and other facilities should be in good condition. Use proper partitions or bracing between large and small animals and avoid overloading.

(5) Choose experienced, dependable carriers who will give proper attention to these fundamentals.

(6) Select a direct route for rapid delivery.

(7) Provide rest, water, and feed on long hauls. See that the carrier follows proper instructions regarding the handling of your livestock. Such practices will pay off in more net returns in the end.

39-9. DISTRIBUTION OF MEATS AND MEAT PRODUCTS

The meat distribution system in the United States has been changing rapidly. Changes in the meat industry include development of large-volume retail firms, mass buying of meat by retailers on a specification basis, widespread use of the federal meat trade standards, and adjustments in the distribution system. Packers using national systems of distribution have declined relatively in volume of meat sales. On the other hand, the number of independent packers and independent wholesale distributors have increased. At the same time, the specifications of the large-volume retail buyers have brought about changes in the methods of operation and in the principal types and qualities of meat handled by packers and wholesalers. The increased use of federal grade standards for beef, veal, and lamb, especially by large food chains, has also affected the entire meat industry.

Trends in Retailing and Merchandising. The big changes in meat marketing and merchandising have come in the organization of the marketing system and in the introduction of packaging and selling technologies. The development of self-service meat merchandising accelerated the move from the small grocery store to the giant supermarket. Self-service merchandising has enabled processors and retailers to take advantage of advances in packaging, such as heat-shrunk, transparent film and nitrogen-gas-filled film containers for packaging cured beef and pork products. Today, nearly 50% of the meat sold in the United States is purchased at a self-service counter. This trend is likely to continue.

Through prepackaging and maintaining high quality, processors and retailers have been able to carry product branding through to the consumer level. These new packages permit visual inspection of the product and enable the processor to identify his brand at the consumer level. Because of these developments in packaging methods, meat processors have been increasing the amount of product-branding at the retail level, the goal of each packer being, of course, to capture as much of the consumer market for his individual product as possible.

Retailers have found, since the advent of self-service and centralized packaging, that they are able to stock a greater variety of meat and processed products. This means that consumers have a greater variety of meat cuts and meat products available to them. They also have more built-in food services available than ever before. This wide differentiation of products has helped to broaden the market for meat.

One of the impacts of self-service on meat merchandising has been to increase the demand for higher quality. This development, of course, has had its influence on the producer and his management practices. Self-service meats have also led to closer trimming standards for retail cuts. Consumers are becoming better judges of values as a result of their self-service experience. As they shop in different stores, they recognize when the retailer is not doing as good a job of trimming as his competitor.

In recent years, several major meat processors have made attempts to process and package meat cuts at the plant and distribute them as packaged, boneless, defatted, frozen meat cuts. In general, however, consumers have not been willing to accept such meat cuts at current price levels. On an edible meat basis, the cost per pound of boneless frozen fresh meat cuts may not be any higher than the cost per pound of traditional unboned, untrimmed, fresh meat cuts. However, the cost per pound is considerably higher than that of an equal number of pounds of regular fresh meat cuts —thus, more consumer resistance.

Consumer Preferences. The introduction in recent years of these many new products in new forms has coincided with significant changes in consumer income and consumption patterns for meat. The combination of these and other changes has tended to increase the complexity of the choice-making process facing the consumer.

It is important for any industry to gear itself to produce what the customer wants. Although the average housewife has little concept of what makes high quality meats, she does know that the family likes tender, flavorful meats. Furthermore, she is very conscious of excessive fat on the meat. First, from the standpoint of efficient buying, she desires to cut down on waste; second, from the standpoint of health, she is extremely sensitive to obesity. Usually housewives want 'thin-skinned steaks' and light, meaty roasts. They want some marbling in the beef, and they like a bright red color in the lean meat. The key to the future is to give the consumers the kind of product they prefer in the form, quality, and place preferred. These points are significant to producers, handlers, and merchandisers all throughout the trade. Each must keep abreast of new developments and run his operations on an efficient basis or competition will take its toll.

REFERENCES AND SELECTED READINGS

Kramer, R. C., 1958. What is integration and its current status? Proceedings, Eighth National Institute of Animal Agriculture, Purdue Univ., April.

Livestock Marketing Journal, 1960. Swan, Texas. July 18.

Stucky, H. R., 1952. Contracting vs. selling at delivery time. Mont. Agr. Ext. Service, Bozeman, Montana. Mimeographed report.

Taylor, M. H., 1953. Livestock purchase and sale contracts. Utah Agr. Ext. Bull. 211, Logan, Utah.

USDA, 1923. Reports of Agricultural Marketing Service. Washington, D.C.

Chapter 40

Classification, Grading, and Marketing of Wool and Mohair

40-1. INTRODUCTION

The production of wool on a world-wide basis (Table 40-1) fluctuates from year to year as a result of periodic droughts in some of the major sheep-producing areas, notably Australia and South Africa. Approximately one-

TABLE 40-1.	*World wool production, 1960–61.**	

Area	Grease basis (millions of lb.)
World	5560
Australia	1600
Soviet Union	773
New Zealand	593
Argentina	450
United States	297
Uruguay	175
United Kingdom	120
Turkey	100

* Estimated world wool production. *World Wool Digest*, 11:171–172.

half of the 300 million lb. of U.S. wool production comes from the 11 western states. Texas, Wyoming, California, Montana, Colorado, South Dakota, Utah, and Idaho rank in descending order in wool production.

There are many different breeds and crosses of sheep in the world. Each produces wool of certain specific characteristics. In addition, fleeces from animals of a single breed may be quite variable. Moreover, each fleece does not contain uniform fiber throughout but varies in length, fineness, color, purity, and shrinkage according to the region of the body from which it comes. Raw wool, then, is not a uniform product.

On the other hand the manufacturer must have uniformity in order to insure that, after processing, his textile will have the necessary appearance, handle, drape, and wearing and insulating properties characteristic of the particular fabric. The ultimate uses of a specific type of wool are dependent to a large degree on its properties. For this reason, raw wool is divided into uniform lots at some step in the marketing process, before it reaches the manufacturer.

40-2. FACTORS DETERMINING THE VALUE AND UTILITY OF WOOL

Grading Systems and Standards Based on Fiber Diameter. Wool is divided into different grades on the basis of the diameter of its fiber. In the United States, two different grading systems are used. One of these is the American blood system. This system arose from the introduction of Merino sheep, which produced fine wool, and from their crossing with the common, coarse-wooled, somewhat hairy sheep of the colonies, which were imported earlier from the British Isles. The wool from this first cross with the common sheep was coarser than that from Merinos and was termed *half blood*. Wools of descending degrees of fineness were designated as $\frac{3}{8}$ blood, $\frac{1}{4}$ blood, common, or braid, the latter being the coarsest. Ultimately, the origin of these terms was forgotten, and they came to mean wools of a certain fiber size.

The other grading system, which is used throughout the world, is the counts, or Bradford, system. This system was originally based on the number of "hanks" of yarn that could be spun from one pound of clean wool. A hank of yarn is 560 yards long. Thus, from a pound of clean "60's" wool the manufacturer can spin 60 hanks of yarn—33,600 yards, or slightly over 19 miles, of yarn.

This counts system is now used more specifically to designate wools of a definite range in fiber diameter. Table 40-2 shows the blood and counts grades and their specifications in terms of average fiber diameter.

Carpet wool is not a grade of wool in the strict sense of the word, but comprises wools that are highly variable in fiber length and diameter. Practically all carpet wools used in the U.S. are imported from other countries and are shorn mostly from unimproved hairy breeds of sheep.

TABLE 40-2. | *Proposed measurement standards for grades of grease wool.**

Blood system	Grade	Average fiber diameter (microns)	Fiber diameter dispersion (measurement in microns)	
			Not less than	Not more than
Fine	80's	17.7–19.1	92% 10–25	8% 25.1 and over
				1% 30.1 and over
	70's	19.2–20.5	85% 10–25	15% 25.1 and over
				3% 30.1 and over
	64's	20.6–22.0	93% 10–30	7% 30.1 and over
				1% 40.1 and over
Half blood	62's	22.1–23.4	89% 10–30	11% 30.1 and over
				1% 40.1 and over
	60's	23.5–24.9	81% 10–30	19% 30.1 and over
				2% 40.1 and over
Three-eighths	58's	25.0–26.4	74% 10–30	26% 30.1 and over
				1% 50.1 and over
	56's	26.5–27.8	66% 10–30	34% 30.1 and over
				1% 50.1 and over
Quarter blood	54's	27.9–29.3	58% 10–30	42% 30.1 and over
				2% 50.1 and over
	50's	29.4–30.9	49% 10–30	51% 30.1 and over
				2% 40.1 and over
	48's	31.0–32.6	81% 10–40	19% 40.1 and over
				1% 60.1 and over
Low quarter	46's	32.7–34.3	74% 10–40	26% 40.1 and over
				1% 60.1 and over
Common	44's	34.4–36.1	66% 10–40	34% 40.1 and over
				2% 60.1 and over
Braid	40's	36.2–38.0	58% 10–40	42% 40.1 and over
				3% 60.1 and over
	36's	38.1–40.2	48% 10–40	52% 40.1 and over
				4% 60.1 and over

* Adapted from Wool Standards, 1955. Agricultural Marketing Service, USDA. *Federal Register*, 20:1891–1893.

Commercial wool grading is done by visual inspection. Wool graders are highly trained individuals whose experience enables them to grade wools rapidly and accurately. They check their visual standards periodically by inspecting standard sets of samples from wools that have been sectioned and measured for fiber diameter.

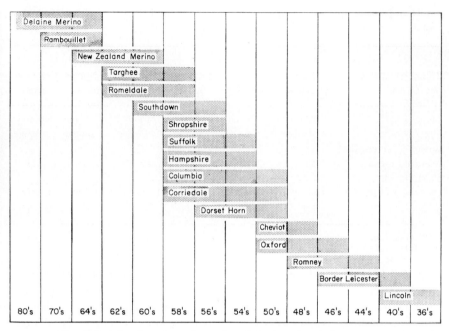

Fig. 40-1. Grades of wool produced by breeds of sheep common in the United States.

Production of Grades by Breeds. A fairly wide range of wool grades is commonly found among fleeces from any single breed of sheep, though most fleeces from a given breed will fall within a narrower range. Figure 40-1 lists common American sheep breeds together with the range of grades commonly found among their fleeces.

Length Classification. In addition to being graded on the basis of fiber diameter, wool is classified on the basis of staple length. The staple or combing length refers to the necessary length that permits a particular grade to be combed on the English or Noble comb. This length standard varies with wool grade. Shorter wools must be combed on the French or Heilman comb; wools that are too short to comb are known as clothing wools and go into woolen rather than worsted manufacture. Longer wools are more valuable on a per pound basis. Table 40-3 shows the length classification of wools accoridng to grade.

Shrinkage. Raw wool consists of wool fibers, suint from the suint (sweat) glands in the skin, wool grease (the waxy secretion from the sebaceous glands in the skin), as well as moisture, dirt, vegetable matter, and other foreign material. Wool grease protects the growing fiber from wear and

TABLE 40-3. | *Staple length designation by grade.* [E. M. Pohle et al., 1953. USDA Oct. Mimeo., Washington, D.C.].*

Commercial length class	Fine inches	$\frac{1}{2}$-blood inches	$\frac{3}{8}$-blood inches	$\frac{1}{4}$-blood inches	Low $\frac{1}{4}$-blood inches	Common inches
Staple	2.5 and longer	3.0 and longer	3.5 and longer	4 and longer	4.5 and longer	5.0 and longer
Good French combing	2.0	2.5	3.0	3.5		
Average French	1.5	2.0	2.0	2.5		
Short French	1.0	1.5				
Clothing and stubby	Under 1.0	Under 1.5	Under 2.0	Under 2.5	Under 4.5	Under 5.0

* The length designations are based on unstretched staple length and represent a minimum length for the bulk of the staples in a sample.

weathering. In purified form it is known as lanolin, a common component of salves, cosmetics, and skin lotions. The weight of the clean wool fiber content of the fleece, calculated as a percent of the total fleece weight, is known as the clean yield. This represents the proportional weight of clean wool fiber weighed at standard conditions (65% relative humidity and $70 \pm 2°F$). These conditions have been set up as standard for wool by the American Society for Testing Materials because wool changes in weight, diameter, and other properties with small changes in temperature and humidity.

In commercial practice the wool buyer usually estimates shrinkage by manually hefting representative fleeces from a given lot and by inspecting them for dirt, grease, and vegetable content. A recently developed apparatus is used to remove a series of sample cores from bags or bales of wool of a given lot. These cores are then enclosed in plastic bags and sent to a testing laboratory to ascertain the clean yield of the samples. This procedure permits the buyer or seller to evaluate a certain lot of wool as to shrinkage on a more accurate basis. Today, many large lots of wool are purchased at a price that is subject to core-test results.

Purity. Purity refers to the relative amount of foreign material present in the wool. This term is useful in describing wool as to estimated shrinkage or to damage to the clip due to the presence of such substances as certain seeds and unscourable branding paint, which lowers the wool value.

Soundness. Healthy animals will produce wool fiber that is sound throughout its length. When animals have been suffering from senility, prolonged malnutrition, or chronic disease, the wool will be fragile throughout its length. This is known as tender wool. Some wool will show a line of weakness at a specific point in its staple such that if a lock of wool is pulled, it will break at this point. In other wools, the break occurs spontaneously, and the animal may shed portions of its fleece. This shedding usually indicates that either severe starvation or high fever has recently affected the animal. Tender or broken wools are of low value, since such wool will break apart in being carded or combed with the result that the final processed fiber will be shorter than desired.

Color. Pigmented wool, as well as hair fibers, are common in some breeds of sheep and are found in certain individuals of other breeds. From a manufacturing viewpoint anything other than white wool is undesirable, the inclusion of pigmented fiber limits the use of the wool. A white fabric cannot be made from brown or black fleeces. Even minor variations in color cannot be tolerated in the manufacture of white or pastel-shaded garments.

Some wools will show permanent staining from a variety of causes, such as from bacterial or fungal damage to the fleece when on the animal, from sacking wet wool, or from drugs spilled on the animal during treatment for disease. The most common color defect in unpigmented wools is known in the trade as "canary yellow"—a bright yellow stain thought to be due to a combination of moisture and heat or light on the suint in the fleece.

Character. Grease wool that has a bright lustrous appearance, a desirable color (usually white to creamy), crimp pattern characteristic of the grade, and large well-defined locks is said to have excellent character. The term is used to denote all of the recognized characteristics that contribute to the general attractiveness of a fleece or clip.

Crimp. Wool from the improved breeds of sheep shows a wavy pattern. The distinctness of this waviness or crimp pattern varies somewhat with animal and breed and is greatly influenced by nutrition and health. This is a useful characteristic of wool and contributes to the springiness of the finished fabric. Menkart and Detenbeck (1957) noted that wools of identical fiber diameter, but which have more crimps per inch of unstretched length, can be made into a fabric with more desirable drape, handle, and shape retention characteristics than wools with less crimp.

Uniformity of Product. Wool from some animals varies in fiber diameter and in length from one part of the fleece to another. Furthermore, such animals commonly show a wide variation in length and fineness of fiber within the lock of a given area. This is primarily an hereditary defect.

The fleeces of primitive sheep and of occasional animals in improved breeds may contain dead-white, opaque fibers that are hollow (medullated), uneven in diameter, and very weak in tensile strength. These are called kemp fibers. Other undesirable fibers are either coarse and hair-like, white or colored. Animals whose fleeces contain such fibers should be culled from the flock. Lack of uniformity decreases desirability of the fleece from a manufacturing viewpoint.

40-3. MARKETING WOOL

If the sheep breeder knows the uses to which his clip may be put, he will understand the reasons behind his management procedures and will obtain a clearer idea of the value of his wool. The following paragraphs outline the general steps involved in processing wool from the time it leaves the sheep until it is made into a fabric.

Shearing. Sheep are shorn in such a manner that the fleece comes off as one single piece (see Fig. 40-1). This job should be done as smoothly and quickly as possible. The animals should be held in the proper position to avoid unnecessary struggling. Good shearers are able to shear over 100 mature ewes daily in 8 hours. Almost all sheep in this country are shorn by power machine rather than by the older hand blade method.

Much harm can be done to the clip at shearing time through improper packaging and handling of the wool. The grower should see that the shearing shed is free of straw and dirt so that none gets in the clip. Fleeces should be tied only with paper twine (fleece twine). Sisal or jute fibers from binder twine or old sacking can get mixed in with wool and cause extensive damage, since these fibers are virtually impossible to remove in processing. Black or colored sheep should be shorn last, and their fleeces packed separately. Fleeces from black-faced animals, lambs, rams, and yearling ewes, and any cotted or damaged wools should also be packed separately. Tags and dung locks, as well as floor sweepings, should be sacked separately. During shearing, the shearers should be instructed not to make any second cuts over the same area of the sheep, since this adds bits of short wool to a full length clip. Branding fluids used for marking animals should be of a type guaranteed to scour out of the wool.

Tying Fleeces. The person tying the wool gathers up the fleece and folds it belly in and the flesh-side out. It is then tied with special paper twine, which is easily removed from the fleece at scouring. The fleeces are thrown into a loft or into bins from which they can be sacked later. Because lambs' wool and some very short reshorn wool will not hang together in the fleece, it is not tied but is handled in boxes or baskets or is picked up with two small boards hinged together at one end.

Sacking. In the U.S., wool is ordinarily sacked in large burlap bags about 7 feet long, each holding 250–300 lb. The sacks are suspended in a frame, and fleeces are tossed in and tramped down in one tier or layer. The finished sack is sewed to keep out dust, and the sack is labeled as to ownership and type of wool. This wool is then either sold directly off the ranch or is taken to a warehouse for storage.

Grading (Classing). At a wool warehouse belonging to a wool cooperative, wool merchant, or commission merchant, the wool is commonly classed by a reputable wool grader. As the fleeces are examined, they are thrown one at a time into large baskets or bins marked for individual grades, lengths and types of wool. This is ordinarily the first step in making up lots, or lines, of wool. There is usually a black (or colored) line, a tender (or broken) line and, if wools from different areas are being graded, there may be a high-shrinking as well as a low- or medium-shrinking line. Division, however, is primarily made on the basis of fiber diameter, length, color, and soundness.

Graded lines of wool are resold from such a warehouse to mills. The classing process permits a particular mill to buy just the grade and length of fleece required for its particular operations. Some lots of wool from large, uniform flocks are highly desirable in that they do not require grading. These are called original-bag wools and may be sold off the ranch directly to a mill.

Sorting. Graded lines and original-bag wools are still not uniform enough for a certain specific mill use. Each fleece must be untied, tossed flesh side up onto a special table, and divided into its component types of wool. The sorting process involves skirting or removing the soiled, heavy-shrinking edge of the fleece, removing the seedy, high-shrinking belly, and, finally, the principal grade areas of the fleece. The fleece from the legs and britch area is commonly the coarsest. Each type of wool goes into a different sorting line destined for a particular use.

Scouring. Wools are usually run through an opener, duster, and burr picker, which serves to tear open the locks, remove some of the dust, and pick out larger burrs and seeds. In scouring, wool is passed through successive baths of solution to remove dirt, suint, and wool grease. The solution may be a mixture of detergent, sal soda, and warm water; in a few scouring plants, fat solvents are used. Efforts are made to disturb or agitate the wool as little as possible to avoid cotting or felting.

Scoured wool comes out of the final rinse as a white product in contrast to the dirty appearance of raw wool. Particularly seedy lots may be subjected to strong sulfuric acid (carbonized), which attacks materials of plant origin and breaks them down. The remaining residue crumbles easily and can be dusted from the wool. Since the wool is slightly affected by the acid, the reaction to dyes may be altered somewhat. Carbonization may be done on scoured wools or on rolls of finished fabric. In recent years, most seed removal has been accomplished through the use of Peralta rolls—heavy steel cylinders through which the wool is passed subsequent to carding. The rolls crush and powder the plant material, but allow the wool to pass through virtually undamaged.

Manufacturing. The following is a résumé of the general steps involved in wool manufacturing. Subsidiary steps, such as oiling, fulling, or the many finishing operations, have been left out in the interest of brevity.

CARDING. A wool card is a machine that consists of a succession of cylinders studded with needle-like points between which the wool is passed. The card serves to homogenize the wool fibers and to distribute them in a smooth strand of carded wool called card sliver.

WORSTED, WOOLEN, AND FELT MANUFACTURE. There are three principal methods of wool manufacture, each of which includes a great variety of specialized procedures and utilizes different wools or blends of wool in the finished product. Wools for these manufacturing systems all go through the carding process.

In worsted manufacturing, the card sliver is combed on a special machine that arranges the fibers parallel to each other in the resulting strand of sliver, which is called wool top. In the combing process, short fibers that are somewhat smaller in average diameter than others in the wool are combed out. This material is called noil and is used in either felt or woolen manufacture. Some manufacturers stop their processing at this point and sell wool top in the ball to other mills. Such manufacturers are called topmakers. Wool top is spun into yarn, woven, and dyed to make the finished fabric. Worsteds are usually tightly woven, hard-finished fabrics that are made into such garments as men's suits. Fine worsteds, used in sheer, summer-weight fabrics, are made from long wools that are extremely fine in diameter.

Woolen yarns are spun directly from the card sliver and do not go through the combing process. The wools used in the woolen process are shorter and are usually coarser than those used in worsted processing, although the principal difference is in length rather than in diameter of fiber. Because lambs' wool is short and has a soft feel, it is highly desired for the manufacture of soft woolens. Woolen yarns are larger in diameter than worsted yarns and are rougher to the feel. Woolen fibers do not lie parallel to each other as do those of worsted yarn. This is because the wool has not been combed into top before spinning. After having been spun into yarn, the wool is woven into fabric and dyed. Woolens are usually bulkier, more loosely woven and rougher to the feel than worsteds. A wide variety of fabrics is woven; these, in turn, are subjected to many different finishing processes. In the end, it may be difficult to distinguish some finished woolen garments from worsteds. Blankets, sweaters, some types of suiting, coat and dress materials, and socks are typical examples of woolen products.

Felt making is the oldest type of wool manufacture known to man. This process rests on the well-known ability of the wool fibers to mat or pack together into an unwoven fabric when subjected to heat, friction, and moisture. In the process, the fibers become so tightly interlocked that separation is difficult.

There are two principal types of modern felts. One is manufactured from carded wool, which is often mixed with cotton or other plant fibers, hair, or artificial fibers. In some felts a large amount of reprocessed wool and noil are used in felt manufacture. Wool up to $1\frac{1}{2}$ inches long is used, including all grades from 64's down to coarse carpet wool.

In processing, the fibers are mixed, thoroughly carded, and made into batting, which in turn is steamed and subjected to friction and heat. Fulling agents are worked into the batting, which is hammered repeatedly, after which the felt is washed to remove the fulling agent. Finally, this fabric is dyed and subjected to a variety of finishing processes. Felts are most familiar to us in the form of hats, felt washers, and rug pads.

Woven felts are made from wool and other fibers which are carded, combed, spun, and woven into heavy fabrics that are in turn felted and finished to make the final product. Some of our finest wool felts, such as billiard cloth, are made in this way.

KNITWARE. Knitting yarns may be either worsted or woolen yarns. The knitting industry is large and turns out a great variety of materials. Knitting is accomplished on intricate machines, which, depending on the model, can manufacture a tubular or flat fabric in a variety of stitches. Common examples are stockings, knit dresses, and sweaters.

40-4. MARKETING CHANNELS FOR WOOL

Some clips are sold by the grower directly to the manufacturer. These clips consist mostly of large, original-bag lots, which require relatively little classing or grading before mill use. Other clips are sold to *local buyers* engaged to buy wool for a particular *wool merchant*. Wool merchants grade or class wools and resell the graded lines to manufacturers. Wool merchants also act as commission merchants and may have wool consigned to them for grading and even for scouring, thus acting as *wool handlers* for the original growers. From the final sales' receipts they deduct a charge for their commission as well as the cost of the operations they perform.

In recent years *cooperative wool marketing* has grown rapidly. In a wool cooperative growers combine and pool their clips for sale and handling purposes. In some instances nothing is done with the wool except that it is all for sale at one location; individual owners of the cooperative merely have the advantage of volume sales for buyer attraction.

Some cooperatives, however, maintain a complete warehousing and grading facility where wools are classed and sold to mills in uniform graded lots. Here each grower's wool may be weighed into the different lots. He is paid for each lot according to the amount of wool he has in it. The cooperative method works well if the management is efficient, honest, and well acquainted with the needs of different mills in order that grading can be tailored to meet specific mill needs. Such a system is a particular advantage to the small grower, whose clip is not large enough to attract bids from several buyers. Large growers benefit by having their wool graded on a cost basis.

40-5. COMPETITION BETWEEN WOOL AND SYNTHETIC FIBERS

Wool producers face a difficult problem in the competition between wool and synthetic fibers. Thus far, no one synthetic fiber has all the desirable properties characteristic of wool. Some of them, however, do have certain properties similar to wool and can be made into fabrics simulating wool. A number of synthetics are used in wool blends.

Synthetic fibers do have some advantages over wool. Since they are manufactured by extrusion from small openings, synthetic fibers are exceedingly uniform in diameter. This is not true of wool. Furthermore, synthetic fibers can be made in any length, whereas wool fibers are limited to the growth provided by the sheep in 12 months. Some sheep have difficulty in producing wool of combing length (that is, fine wool, $2\frac{1}{2}$ inches long) in 12 months. Moreover, synthetics can have a crimp or wavy pattern imparted to them mechanically and can be made in a variety of cross-sectional forms. Fibers can be extruded that are oval, round, square, or W-shaped or U-shaped in cross section. Each one of these cross-sectional shapes will impart a slightly different handling characteristic to the fabric. Modern wool research is currently changing the wool fiber to compete with synthetics more efficiently. (See Chapter 4.) Wool growers can help meet competition from synthetics by selection for uniformity of wool growth in their sheep, by selection for increased length of staple, and by growing and marketing their product in the best way possible.

40-6. MOHAIR

Origin of Mohair. The mohair goat was originally from Angora, Turkey. It was first introduced to this country in 1849, in South Carolina; with continued importation, it gradually spread to the south and west, where it has proved most popular. Texas furnishes approximately 95% of the mohair produced in the U.S.

As noted by Corkery (1957), the mohair industry uses the following standards and grade names for mohair.

| | *Average diameter* |
Grade name	*(microns)*
Super kid	25.7
Baby kid	27.0
Kid 36	28.7
Kid 32	30.0
Adult 28	32.3
26	34.0
24	35.7
20	41.5
low	to 55.0

The USDA Wool Laboratory at Denver, Colorado (Federal Register, 1950) published a notice of proposed standards for seven grades of mohair including 40's, 36's, 32's, 28's, 24's, 20's and 16's. These standards are based upon samples held by the USDA. Thus far, the proposed grades have not been adopted as official nor have the diameter requirements for the grades been published.

Improvement of the Mohair Clip. Mohair is a beautiful, smooth, very lustrous fiber that is somewhat coarser than wool and which has a less pronounced waviness or crimp. Mohair tends to be more uniform in diameter than wool within the lock. By comparison with wool, the fiber feels slick, owing to its smooth scale pattern.

The goats are usually shorn twice a year (spring and fall); shedding may occur if this is not done. In addition, animals thrive better in shorter fleece. Improved strains are able to produce clips averaging one inch per month in growth, and have grease fleece weights up to 12 lb. per year (two shearings). In 1959, the yearly average U.S. grease fleece weight was 6.4 lb. per animal.

Light clips of weak or fuzzy fiber, excessive variability in diameter and length, shortness of staple, the presence of undesirable fibers, such as kemp or pigmented fibers, and the presence of foreign materials in the clip, such as grass seeds, awns, or burrs are considered defects in Mohair clips. Mohair should not shrink more than 12–15%, but some clips greatly exceed this due primarily to the practice of oiling the goats before shearing, which is done as a parasite control measure and to increase grease fleece weight.

IMPROVEMENT THROUGH BREEDING. Selection of superior breeding stock will do much to increase clean fleece weight and desirability of mohair fleeces. This can best be accomplished by the sue of outstanding bucks as flock sires and by careful culling of the nanny flock. Some breeders are mating outstanding sires to selected superior nannies and next best sires to next best nannies. A third group is sold or maintained for commercial production; all offspring are sold.

Mohair goat breeders recognize three general kinds of fleece on the basis of lock type (Gray, 1958). The ringlet (C-type) sometimes shows some twist or spiral but typically hangs in long, tight locks or curls about the diameter of a pencil. This type of fleece usually has sufficient length, but may lack density, thus allowing excessive penetration of dirt into the fleece. A second category is the flat lock (B-type), which hangs in flat, wavy locks. According to Gray, long-continued selection for this type of fleece may result in a shortening of staple length and, therefore, lighter fleece weights.

The third lock type, called the web lock, or round lock, is intermediate between the other two. Goats having web lock fleeces are said to produce heavier fleeces of good staple length for a greater number of years than goats having the other two fleece types. Since light and heavy or coarse and fine fleeces are found within each of these three fleece types, some growers are still not convinced of the superiority of any one type, although the web lock type seems to be most favored.

Breeding stock should be selected for dense, long, heavy fleeces of uniform mohair. Usually, finer mohair is preferred, as long as fleece weight or body size is not markedly affected by selection in this direction. Attention must be given to the uniformity of mohair in grade and in length over the body as well as within the lock. Flocks should be carefully culled for animals showing the weak, hollow, dead-white kemp or other medullated fibers, as well as pigmented fibers (usually reddish, black, or brown). Fleece length is very important, since longer staple is desired and is worth more on the market. Furthermore, selection for length increases clean fleece weight. Billies sold for breeding are usually marketed at 16–20 months of age. Fleece and body characteristics at this age (18 months) are considered to be the most reliable index of lifetime production in these animals.

Selection for body conformation and size should, of course, accompany selection for fleece characteristics, since a portion of the flock income is derived from the sale of kids for slaughter. Goat meat is called "chevon" on the market and is particularly favored by population centers of Spanish or Greek ancestry. Young kids of 30–40 lb. live weight are considered a delicacy and are sold as "cabrito" (the Spanish word for little goat). The meat is tender and highly flavored. It is particularly good for barbecuing.

OTHER MANAGEMENT PROCEDURES. Mohair goats are particularly sensitive to severe storms following shearing; heavy death losses have occurred when range flocks have been without access to shelter. This has led to the practice called "caping," in which a strip of mohair 3–4 inches wide is left on the back of the goats to help keep them warm until the new fleece grows out. However, it is best to either provide shelter or to change the shearing date to some less variable weather period.

The mohair left as a cape on the goat is ordinarily mixed in with the new fleece grown following shearing. This results in two different lengths of fiber in the succeeding fleece and is very undesirable in processing. If the cape is shorn off separately several weeks after shearing, shorter fibers will be mixed with the new fleece. As with sheep, it is often possible to avoid ranging the animals in burry or very seedy pasture areas, at least during the period preceding shearing. If this can be done, it will lessen the amount of "seed defect" in the clip at selling time.

Fleece branding fluids used on goats should be of a readily scourable type. Oiling goat fleeces as a parasite control measure is an undesirable practice. Buyers are aware of the practice and lower their prices accordingly. In some instances dirty crank case oil has been used, and this is difficult or impossible to remove at scouring. Several dips and sprays are available that can be used for the efficient control of lice, ticks, and other external parasites.

Marketing Mohair. Mohair is sold in much the same way as wool, usually by companies that act as warehousers, buyers, and handlers for both products. Some producers sell the clip on a graded basis; for this reason, a handling company often maintains a grading or classing service. The sale of graded lots from the clip is credited to the account of the consigning owner. Relatively little mohair is marketed through grower-owned co-operatives.

The most valuable raw mohair is that shorn from the kids in fall or spring. Kid hair shrinks less and is softer and finer than that from mature goats. Yearling mohair clipped at about 18 months of age is more desirable than adult mohair.

Sixty percent or more of the U.S. mohair clip is exported annually, principally to the United Kingdom; some is sent to other European countries and Japan.

Use of Mohair in Textiles. A résumé of the characteristics and uses of mohair has been given by Marincowitz (1959). Mohair is used in the production of fine velvets and in the manufacture of plush upholstery fabrics for cars and furniture. It is highly desired for such uses because it is stiff and lustrous, holds up well under long continued use, and shows off color to advantage, owing to its glossy appearance. Since the fiber is stiff, it is noted for its role in shape retention; in some uses, it imparts a slick, hard finish to the fabric. Finer grades of mohair are used as a component in the manufacture of suits, gowns, robes, and ties, where it furnishes crease resistance, durability, and excellent drape characteristics. The slickness of the fiber requires that spinning be performed carefully, since fibers tend to slide past each other quite easily. Large quantities of mohair are used in rugs and carpets.

REFERENCES AND SELECTED READINGS

Corkery, A. G., 1957. Properties, sources and grades of mohair. *Sheep and Goat Raiser.* July, p. 8.

Gray, J. A., 1958. Texas Angora goat production. *Sheep and Goat Raiser.* Dec., p. 10.

Menkart, J. and J. C. Detenbeck, 1957. The significance of wool fiber crimp. Part I.

A study of the worsted system. *Textile Research J.,* 27:665–689.

Marincowitz, G., 1959. High prices have been paid for mohair. *Sheep and Goat Raiser.* Nov., p. 30.

USDA, Agr. Marketing Service, 1950. Notice of proposed U.S. standards for grades of Mohair. Federal Register, Oct. 18, p. 6969.

Chapter 41

The Marketing of Milk and Dairy Products

Many there be who from their mothers keep
The new-born kids, and straightway bind their mouths
With iron tipped muzzles. What they milk at dawn,
Or in the daylight hours, at night they press;
What darkling or at sunset, this ere morn
They bear away in baskets—for to town
The shepherd hies him—or with dash of salt
Just sprinkle, and lay by for winter use.

VIRGIL, *Georgics, III*

Compared to the marketing of livestock and meats or poultry and eggs, the marketing of milk and dairy products is an extremely complex subject. The dairy industry may be considered as a collection of industries, each member having its own unique marketing problems and systems. The differences depend upon the type of product and geographical and time factors.

First we will consider in a general way the nature of dairy products as a part of the food industry. Milk, because of its universal use by infants, has been made the object of legislation to control its quality. State, municipal, and federal laws have been devised to control its composition and bacteriological quality at both producer and consumer levels. Quality of product and quality of package and knowledge of the importance of milk in nutrition have made milk and its products highly acceptable to the public. It is recognized generally in the industry that it is impossible to get a high-

711

TABLE | *Per capita consumption of dairy products, 1959. (USDA Statistical Bul-*
41-1. | *letin, 1960.)*

	Pounds of product
Fresh whole milk	297.0
Cream	7.0
Sweetened condensed milk	0.5
Unsweetened condensed milk	2.1
Evaporated milk	11.8
Butter	8.0
American cheese (Cheddar)	5.2
Other type cheese	2.8
Cottage cheese	5.2
Dry whole milk	0.3
Nonfat dry milk	6.2
Dry whey	0.2
Evaporated and condensed skim milk	4.3
Malted milk	0.2
Dry buttermilk	0.4
Frozen desserts (net milk used)	52.4
Ice cream	18.7
Sherbet	1.5
Ice milk	3.9
Other frozen products	0.1
Mellorine type (imitation)	1.2

quality product from low-grade raw milk. Hence the quality of the raw milk going to the processor of fluid milk or of manufactured dairy products is the first step in the successful marketing of dairy products.

The dairy industry may be considered to be made up of two major divisions—fluid milk, including fluid by-products, and manufactured products. Table 41-1 lists the per capita consumption of the principal dairy products.

Fluid milk and cream utilize slightly more than 50% of the total milk production. In 1959 the total per capita consumption of milk in all forms was 678 lb., of which 341 lb. was in the form of fluid milk and cream. Table 40-1 lists the 18 manufactured products that accounted for 337 lb. per capita.

41-1. FLUID MILK MARKETING

Fluid-milk marketing will be considered under two subdivisions: marketing of the raw milk to the processors and the marketing of the finished products to consumers via retail and wholesale channels. Before discussing these two aspects of the problem we will characterize the nature of this market and differentiate it from the marketing of manufactured milk products.

Fluid milk is bulky in comparison to its solids content, and it is perishable as compared to manufactured products. Because of these two factors it must be produced fairly close to the point of consumption. However, in recent years improved refrigeration, better transportation equipment, and faster highways have extended the area of production of fluid milk for a given market. The extension of the production area has contributed to the complexity of the marketing problem in terms of state and federal regulations of fluid milk marketing. Hardin (1960) has stated the problem well in a review of barriers to trade in fluid milk, "Economics and politics meet in the production and distribution of fluid milk."

Producer's Markets. The milk producer must find a market for fluid milk in his area. Since processors have increased in size and decreased in number, the bargaining power of individual dairymen has decreased. In order to compensate for the loss of bargaining power, most dairymen belong to a cooperative marketing association, which we may classify on the basis of its activities:

1) An association strictly for bargaining with no processing facilities.

2) A bargaining association, with processing facilities for handling surplus.

3) A cooperative distributing association, usually competing with private processors.

PRICE PLANS. The present complex price structures used in the purchasing of milk in the large markets have been gradually evolved from the experience of the past forty years. Because of the large fluid-milk surpluses at certain seasons, producers have sought a price plan that would permit payment of milk on a use basis and yet reward those who attempted to limit the seasonal surplus by maintaining a fairly even production throughout the year.

It is impossible to discuss each price plan in detail, but a list and brief description of the principal plans that have been used will indicate the many solutions tried for special situations (Roadhouse and Henderson, 1950; Spencer, 1956).

The flat rate plan, common before 1918. The producer was paid a uniform price for all milk purchased, regardless of use.

The use classification plan. Milk was assigned a class according to its use: Class I (fluid milk), Class II (cream), Class III (ice cream and other products). Class I, the highest in price, is usually the negotiated price. In this plan the producer receives a blended price, depending on the use of the milk. It involves the use of a dealer pool or a market pool. The dealer pool is operated in the absence of a cooperative association or a federal or state board, functioning to operate a market-wide pool. The use classification plan is most frequently combined with the two plans that follow.

The basic surplus or quota plan is a variation of the pooling system of the use classification plan. The purpose of the plan is to attempt to favor producers who will regulate their production to sales requirements. Many variations of the plan are used.

The formula plan is based on cost of feed, labor, and other costs.

Federal and State Control of Price to Dairymen. Both state and federal laws have been established to regulate the price, and in some cases the market area, for Class I milk.

FEDERAL MARKET ORDERS. The federal laws are known as Federal Market Orders. As of January, 1960, there were 79 market orders in operation. About two-thirds of the nonfarm population of the United States now resides in marketing areas defined by Federal Market Orders, operating under the minimum price terms to dairymen. One of the basic functions of Federal Milk Orders is to encourage the production of milk adequate to supply the needs of a given market (Bartlett, 1956). The orders define marketing areas, classify milk sold in such areas according to its use, fix prices for each classification, and provide for pooling of receipts and the ascertainment of blend prices so that producers will be paid equally (except for the differentials for quality and transportation). The plan is operated by a federal official. The processors pay the entire cost of the Federal Market Orders program.

STATE AND MUNICIPAL CONTROL. During 1933–1935, 17 states passed laws which attempted to control wholesale, retail, and producer prices of milk. Since 1935, 28 states have instigated similar legislation. Today 16 states fix the minimum prices to be paid to producers; 10 of these states also fix minimum retail and wholesale prices (Spencer, 1956). Municipal control has largely been related to inspection of sanitary requirements. It appears that many sanitary codes are needlessly detailed and serve to "build a wall" around their local markets in favor of their own dairymen and processors.

Processing and Distribution. Processing and distribution facilities and methods are important in considering the marketing of fluid milk.

PROCESSING FACILITIES. A review of changes in the market milk industry in the last 50 years traces the factors that have converted the industry from a simple, nearly cottage-type operation to an industrial factory type (Henderson, 1956). The following types of operations now exist.

Producer-distributor. In the face of increased labor and other costs, this type of operation is decreasing in importance. In certain isolated areas, however, the producer-distributor is able to compete with larger operators.

Single independent plants. Before 1925 the single plant was the most important form of organization. Many single-plant operations are too small for economical processing unless they have unique operating methods or market outlets. Consolidation of production facilities may be expected to continue to favor multiple-plant operations.

Multiple-plant operations. The trend is toward consolidation of plants into local or regional chains and to national chains. The increased costs of processing and distribution favor this type of operation since it contributes to better utilization of labor and capital. Large plants have automation in many departments, which reduces processing costs. The largest 8 dairy chains of the United States, regional and national, probably handle 40% of the fluid milk and cream.

DISTRIBUTION. Distribution of fluid milk is classified as retail or wholesale.

Retail distribution is of three types: company-owned trucks, driver-owned trucks, and distributors who may have a fleet of trucks serving a specific area. Retail distribution is the most expensive type of delivery since it does not lend itself to the most efficient use of labor and equipment. In recent years, however, certain procedures have been introduced to increase the output of labor and equipment. Some of these practices are delivery every other day or three times a week, discounts for increased quantity of product delivered at one time, and additional products handled—eggs, ice cream, and other food items. In many large cities approximately 30–35% of milk is sold from retail trucks. Most of the retail milk is packaged in glass bottles.

Wholesale distribution. Approximately 65% of the milk sold in many urban areas is distributed from food stores, some types of which are discussed here.

Independent or chain dairies—local, regional, or national in scope. The fluid milk and by-products may be packaged in the brand of the dairy or in the private brand of the retailer. Smaller stores are usually served every other day; supermarkets, at least once a day and often several times. Wholesale delivery is usually limited to a 5-day operation to conform with the 40-hour week required in most union contracts. Quantity discounts are usually on the basis of volume delivered at one time. Nearly 100% of the milk sold in stores is packaged in single-service fiber cartons.

Captive dairies. A group of small supermarket chains or a voluntary group of single supermarkets may control a dairy that processes and distributes exclusively to the members of the chains. The business is conducted like the independent chains discussed above, with the exception that a sales force is not needed and advertising is usually included in the store advertising.

Dairy chains owned by supermarket chains. A number of large national grocery chains operate a chain of dairy plants in their principal marketing areas. Their operation is similar to that of the captive dairy, with the difference that the ownership is in the control of one large chain rather than being the joint venture of a group of smaller chains or a voluntary group of single large supermarkets.

Trends in Fluid-milk Marketing. Fresh fluid milk will doubtlessly continue to dominate the market but technological developments are making other products acceptable as substitutes and introducing new forms of milk that tend to increase the overall consumption. Some of these developments are instant nonfat dry milk, instant powdered whole milk, canned sterilized whole milk, aseptic concentrated milk, frozen and fresh 3:1 concentrated milk, recombined milk made with low-heat nonfat dry milk, and anhydrous (pure) milk fat. Efforts to cut costs of processing and delivery of fluid milk or acceptable alternates will dictate the future trends in this segment of the dairy industry. We can expect increases in the size of producer dairies but fewer of them, and parallel changes in the processing plants. Automated operations of many parts of the process will further reduce labor costs. Five-day processing in plants will become a general practice and equipment will be designed to permit rapid handling of large volumes of milk. Retail delivery will be less frequent as quantity discounts become more general. Household dispensers will doubtless increase in importance and delivery only once or twice a week is probable.

Vending machines for $\frac{1}{2}$ pint, $\frac{1}{3}$ pint, quart, and $\frac{1}{2}$ gallon—in factories, apartment areas, depots, and other central locations—will make milk more available. Many surveys have shown also that increased total consumption of milk results from such distribution.

41-2. MANUFACTURED PRODUCTS

With the exception of cottage cheese and frozen desserts, most manufactured dairy products are characterized by the fact that they can be produced in areas remote from consumption centers, that they are reduced in bulk and weight, and that they can be held for relatively long periods of time without deterioration. Table 41-1 lists 18 manufactured products, which will be discussed under the classifications of butter, cheese, dried milk, condensed and evaporated milk, and frozen desserts.

Butter. The production and marketing of butter has undergone many changes in the last fifty years. Before the introduction of cream separators in 1878, much of the butter was made on the farm, where cream was secured by gravity separation. The separators made it possible for the dairyman to sell cream to a centralized butter plant and to retain the skim milk at home for feeding to pigs, chickens, and calves. Cream was often delivered after it had undergone some deterioration, and the resultant "centralizer" butter was of poor quality. With the development of evaporators and driers to utilize skim milk for human food, creameries were established to receive whole milk from farms and to convert it into butter and nonfat dry milk. This development resulted in an improvement in the quality of butter and in better utilization of the skim milk. This development was accelerated during World War II.

The per capita consumption of butter is approximately 8 lb. per person. The consumption of oleomargarine is slightly higher. This relationship has been maintained for a number of years and it is likely that the improved quality of butter and advertising supported by the dairy industry will maintain consumption at the current level. The public's concern with fat in the diet will tend to restrict the per capita consumption of all fats in major markets.

Cheese. Many types of cheese are manufactured and sold in the United States. Some foreign types of cheese are imported, principally from Switzerland, Holland, France, Italy, and Denmark.

AMERICAN CHEESE (CHEDDAR TYPE). This type accounts for approximately 65% of the cheese sold in the United States. The per capita consumption is 5.2 lb. In recent years considerable improvements have been made in the packaging and the merchandising of American cheese. Large wheels of cheese bandaged with cheesecloth and treated with paraffin are largely being replaced by rindless blocks. This type of package lends itself to cutting into wedges, slices, or bricks; the blocks are more attractive in appearance and aid in better merchandising.

OTHER TYPES OF CHEESE. This list would include all other varieties except cottage cheese. The per capita consumption is 2.8 lb., or approximately one-half that of Cheddar cheese. Swiss type, blue cheese, Monterey, Gorgonzola, and many other interesting cheeses can be effectively merchandised and increase the utilization of milk.

COTTAGE CHEESE. While cottage cheese is a manufactured product, it is usually sold along with fluid milk in both retail and wholesale outlets. The cottage cheese consumption, as shown in Table 41-1, is 5.2 lb. per capita. In one state the consumption is nearly 10 lb. per capita. This high rate of consumption is due to a high-quality product, effectively merchandised over a period of years.

Dry Milk. The development of the evaporator and drier for dairy products has resulted in increased use of milk products for human food and has made it possible to provide milk in many parts of the world where it would not otherwise be available. Some types of dry milk products have been designed for special purposes.

NONFAT DRY MILK. Nonfat dry milk is made by either the spray or roller process. The spray process is by far the most common. The U.S. Department of Agriculture has established commercial grades for both spray and roller powder. Spray powder is available in three classifications, depending upon the heat treatment used in processing. High-heat powder is used in making bread and in producing many other foods; low-heat powder is used for beverage purposes and for making cottage cheese, recombined milk, and ice cream; intermediate-heat powder is used where either the high- or low-heat product is not indicated. The American Dry Milk Institute has been instrumental in developing standards for dry milk and in preparing educational material to promote its use in foods.

The per capita consumption of nonfat dry milk is 6.2 lb. and consumption is increasing rapidly. The growth has been accelerated by the introduction of instant nonfat dry milk in consumer packages.

DRY WHOLE MILK. Dry whole milk shows a low per capita consumption —only 0.3 lb. The recent development and introduction of instant whole milk will doubtless result in a significant per capita increase in the dry product. It doubtless will be used to augment and supplement fluid milk in many areas, especially where a dependable quality of fluid milk is not available at a competitive price. Foreign markets will be an important factor in utilizing milk in the form of instant dry whole milk.

MISCELLANEOUS DRY MILKS. The per capita consumption of dry whey is now 0.2 lb. The utilization of edible dry whey in many products will increase this consumption. The lactose (milk sugar) and protein of whey are valuable food constituents and many applications for their use for human food are being developed.

Dry buttermilk is a by-product of butter manufacture. The per capita consumption of 0.4 lb. is likely to remain constant, since butter production is not expected to increase. Dry buttermilk is used in ice cream and in many types of packaged food.

Condensed and Evaporated Milk. Evaporated and condensed milk plants are generally located in manufacturing milk-production areas rather than in the milk shed of a large urban marketing area. Freight rates, however, make it essential that evaporated milk plants be not too far removed from the areas of consumption.

EVAPORATED MILK. The evaporated milk industry is in the hands of a few large companies because the factory requires a large investment and the product is an item of large volume and low margin. The per capita consumption of evaporated milk is 11.8 lb., but the trend is downward. A new development in the field, an aseptic product, may reverse the decline in consumption. Evaporated milk is sold exclusively through grocery stores and is handled at a low margin.

CONDENSED MILK. Sweetened condensed milk in cans is no longer an important form of manufactured milk used in the United States. Considerable amounts, however, are still manufactured for sale in the Orient. Sweetened condensed whole milk in bulk is manufactured for use in candy and to a lesser extent for use in ice cream. Condensed skim milk is used for milk solids in ice cream and other foods.

Frozen Desserts. Frozen desserts such as ice cream and ice milk, as Table 41-1 shows, accounts for a per capita consumption of 52.4 lb., in terms of milk. In terms of gallons of ice cream and ice milk, the per capita consumptions are 4 and 0.9 gallons, respectively. Ice cream is no longer regarded as a luxury—it is a stable food item. The advent of the half-gallon container, the increase in home freezers, and the wide distribution of ice cream at attractive prices in stores and especially in supermarkets will accelerate the per capita consumption of ice cream and other frozen desserts. The increase in the sale of ice milk in recent years has accompanied the interest of the general public in foods that are low in fat, high in protein, and low in total caloric value. This trend was noted in the discussion of fluid products, including nonfat milk fortified with milk solids and in connection with the "900 diet foods."

Imitation ice cream of the mellorine type continues to grow and depress the margins on all frozen desserts. This type of product can now be legally manufactured in 12 states.

41-3. BASIC FACTORS INFLUENCING THE MARKETING OF MILK AND DAIRY PRODUCTS

Quality. Dairy products, like all foods, must have quality appeal if they are to be successfully merchandised. The dairy industry is the most regulated of any food industry with respect to sanitation of producers' and processors' premises and to the bacterial quality and composition of the finished products. Most dairy companies attempt to control the quality of the product from the cow to the consumer. Plant laboratories in most companies maintain constant checks on incoming milk and finished products.

Knowledge of Nutritive Value of Milk and Dairy Products. Scientific interest in milk as a food began with the discovery of vitamin A by Dr. E. V. McCollum in 1913. This study stimulated research on the other nutritional factors in milk. The work of Dr. H. C. Sherman on the nutritional factors required to achieve "buoyant" health dramatically illustrated the benefits of drinking milk regularly in adequate amounts.

The National Dairy Council program brought the nutritional benefits of milk to the attention of doctors, dentists, nurses, nutritionists, and teachers. In 1924 the council initiated the program for serving milk in schools. Today about $2\frac{1}{2}\%$ of the total milk production—154 half pints per child in the participating schools—is utilized in the school milk program. The school milk and lunch programs have made teachers and children acquainted with the benefits of milk drinking and have undoubtedly done much to stimulate the use of milk.

Advertising and Sales Promotion. A third factor in marketing dairy products is advertising and the effort made in sales promotion. All food products are competing for a market limited by the amount of food a person will consume. It is essential that the story of milk and its advantages be continually kept before the potential customer in order that the dairy industry will receive its "fair share" of the food dollar.

The American Dairy Association was organized to advertise and promote the sale of all types of dairy products. Millions of dollars are collected from the dairy producers each year to finance the program of the ADA. All types of media are used—TV, radio, newspapers, billboards, point-of-sale material, and printed booklets on many dairy product subjects. Such advertising is for the benefit of the whole industry, increasing the sale of all types of dairy products. Many dairy companies, however, use the ADA material and tie it in with their own advertising programs to take advantage of the well-developed ADA programs.

Independent companies also spend millions of dollars a year in advertising their own brand name and the merits of their products. Attractive cartons and point-of-sale material, in addition to a quality product, are necessary to make an advertising program a continuing success.

41-4. PARTICIPATION OF UNITED STATES GOVERNMENT IN DAIRY PRODUCTS' MARKETING

Marketing. A discussion of the marketing of dairy products should recognize the part that government plays in this area. The government is committed to support the price of milk at not less than 75% or more than 90% of parity. In order to implement this law, milk products are purchased rather than milk. Before April of each year an estimation is made as to what price manufacturing milk and milk fat must be sold to reach 75 to 90% of parity. The Secretary of Agriculture determines the per cent of parity to use, depending upon supplies of milk and other factors. The products purchased are butter, Cheddar cheese, and nonfat dry milk. The prices paid for the products are determined by the price of milk per 100 pounds that would attain the desired parity. The Department of Agriculture must buy all milk products offered that will meet their specifications. The program is to support the market.

The disposal of the products purchased is accomplished in a number of ways. (1) The products can be sold in the domestic market if the price paid (plus storage and handling costs) is recovered. (2) The school lunch program receives some of the supported products. (3) The Army and Navy can use the products if the use will not interfere with commercial operation. (4) The products can be given to charities. (5) The mutual aid program for foreign countries disposes of large amounts of the products, especially nonfat dry milk. (6) The products may be sold to commercial interests at reduced prices if they are exported from the United States and reduced in price to equal world market prices.

REFERENCES AND SELECTED READINGS

References marked with an asterisk are of general interest.

Bartlett, R. W., 1956. Government control of the dairy industry other than health measures and standards. *J. Dairy Sci.,* 39:892–899.

*Dairy statistics-supplement for 1959 to statistical bulletin No. 218, June, 1960. Agricultural Marketing Service, USDA, Washington, D.C., p. 91.

Hardin, C. M., 1955. Political and institutional barriers to trade in fluid milk. Marketing efficiency in a changing economy. A report of the National Workshop on Agricultural Marketing, University of Kentucky. Agricultural Marketing Service, USDA, Washington, D.C.

Henderson, J. L., 1956. Market milk operations, 1906 vs. 1956. *J. Dairy Sci.,* 39:812–818.

*Roadhouse, C. L. and J. L. Henderson, 1950. *The Market Milk Industry.* 2nd Ed. McGraw-Hill, New York, pp. 534–547.

Spencer, L. 1956. Significant developments in the distribution and pricing of market milk in the United States, 1900–1956. *J. Dairy Sci.,* 39:884–891.

Chapter 42

Marketing of Poultry and Eggs

What's the use? Yesterday an egg, tomorrow a feather duster.
MARK FENDERSON, *"The Dejected Rooster"*

42-1. INTRODUCTION

Marketing of poultry and eggs has changed rapidly during the past few years. From a pattern of institutions, agencies, and procedures seemingly well established, a nearly complete alteration has occurred or is in the process of taking place in the production and distribution of poultry and egg products, including the channels of distribution and the marketing agencies involved in moving the product to market.

There are a number of reasons for this change. First, the average size of broiler and egg-producing flocks has increased. Small producers have been declining in numbers for some time, but the rate of withdrawal increased materially during the 1950's. Not only have many small producers gone out of business, but many of those who remained substantially increased the average size of their flocks. The increased size of production units has led to a shift in the markets and market agencies used and to an adoption of grades and standards for poultry and egg products. The large producers are considerably more quality-conscious than were the earlier small producers.

The second factor that has been instrumental in changing the poultry and egg marketing pattern has been a shift in the location of the production areas, the most noteworthy of which has been the development of broiler meat and egg production in the southern states. These states, formerly a deficit area, are now producing a surplus of poultry meat and are rapidly reaching a comparable production of eggs. As this area further develops its production facilities, and as other major production areas attempt to gain premium outlets for their products, through the reorientation of their marketing programs, increased attention will be given to the production of quality products and to the wider use of grades and standards in selling products.

A third factor is the change in size and location of marketing firms handling poultry and egg items. In the poultry and egg field the marketing firms were historically small in size. In recent years, however, there has been a marked shift to larger firms, headquartered, usually, in the production rather than the consumption areas. This particular type of shift—size and location—means that marketing firms must emphasize quality and grade standards to facilitate the marketing of large quantities of uniform products in distant areas and in premium markets.

A fourth factor in the changing marketing program is the pronounced shift to more direct marketing in many areas. Producers follow this practice by selling direct to retail stores or to chain store warehouses. Formerly they sold to country buyers, who in turn sold to larger egg handlers; these men sold to city wholesalers, who eventually sold to the chain store warehouses or to retail stores. Marketing firms likewise are engaging in more direct marketing through the packaging of poultry and eggs in consumer packages at country processing points and shipping them directly to either stores or chain store warehouses. In direct marketing the wholesale market facilities, formerly used to a large degree for all poultry and eggs, have been bypassed.

Direct marketing is of real economic advantage to producers and processors. However, it presents the industry with a lack of large central wholesale markets wherein the movement and pricing of poultry and eggs can be measured effectively, as was done in earlier years. The net result is that the wholesale markets have declined substantially in volume and many producers have become extremely critical of the validity of prices established in these markets when the bulk of the product moves direct to stores or chain warehouses. Two requirements for successful direct marketing of poultry and egg products are the maintenance of a high standard of uniform quality and the availability of a sufficient volume of the product to meet the needs of the buyers throughout the year.

Contract farming has made its most noticeable progress in the poultry field, where the bulk of the broilers or fryers are now produced on a contract basis, but increasing attention is being given to contract production of other poultry products. Although contract farming is essentially a means of financing production, it has led to the more uniform flow of production and to improved quality of the products. The more uniform flow results because producers are essentially working on a salary basis; they tend to keep their facilities at full operation rather than change the volume to follow the market prices. Moreover, in typical contracts, specifications are included concerning the management of the flock and the handling of the products. This in turn has encouraged and facilitated the development of uniform, high-quality products.

Last, throughout the poultry and egg industry, renewed attention has been given to developing new poultry and egg products. The industry has for years relied upon the sale of shell eggs and of broilers, fryers, roasters, and stewing chickens, but more recently the number of products has been reduced to shell eggs, fryers, and occasionally stewing chicken. The widespread trend to develop convenience food items for modern housewives caught the poultry industry lagging seriously. Chances are good that the next few years will see the production of many new products, which will broaden the market for poultry meat and eggs.

42-2. CONSUMPTION

Consumption data are available for eggs, chickens, and turkeys (Table 42-1). Data for the first two items are available from 1909; those for turkeys first became available in 1929.

Eggs. The consumption of eggs has varied widely during the past 50 years. Peak consumption—402 eggs per capita—was reached in 1945. The lowest rate of consumption occurred in 1935, at 280 eggs per capita. From 1910 to 1941, except for World War I and the Great Depression, egg consumption has averaged slightly more than 300 eggs per capita. With the outbreak of World War II, consumption rose to its peak level, held relatively high during the late 1940's and early 1950's, then declined. Estimated consumption in 1960 was 324 eggs per capita, the lowest in nearly 20 years.

Although the demand for eggs has declined in recent years, during the 1940's poultrymen were favored by a rising demand for eggs (Fig. 42-1). During the 1950's the chart data show a movement downward and to the left. Not only were consumers using fewer eggs, but, relative to their incomes, they were paying less for them. Also, the data indicate a less elastic demand for eggs. This simply means that consumption remains relatively steady even with major price concessions or that prices respond sharply to important changes in the actual supply of eggs.

Of the total egg consumption, about 7% are consumed as frozen and dried eggs, and the remainder as shell eggs. According to data available, approximately three-fourths of the shell eggs purchased by consumers are used as table eggs and the rest are used in cooking (Pincock, 1952, 1957).

TABLE 42-1.	*Average civilian per capita consumption of eggs, chickens, and turkeys, U.S., 1910–1960. [Egg and Poultry Statistics Through 1957, Statistical Bulletin No. 249, May 1959; and The National Food Situation, May 1960. Both published by the United States Department of Agriculture.]*

Year	Eggs	Chickens* (lb.)	Turkeys* (lb.)
1910–14	309	15.0	
1915–19	296	13.8	
1920–24	313	13.9	
1925–29	334	14.5	
1930	331	15.7	1.5
1931	333	14.1	1.4
1932	313	14.4	1.7
1933	296	14.7	2.0
1934	289	13.5	1.8
1935	280	13.1	1.7
1936	289	13.7	2.2
1937	308	13.6	2.3
1938	310	12.7	2.3
1939	313	14.1	2.5
1940	319	14.1	2.9
1941	311	15.4	2.9
1942	318	17.7	3.0
1943	327	23.0	2.7
1944	354	20.4	2.7
1945	402	21.6	3.5
1946	379	19.4	3.7
1947	383	18.1	3.6
1948	389	18.3	3.1
1949	383	19.6	3.3
1950	389	20.6	4.1
1951	392	21.7	4.4
1952	390	22.1	4.7
1953	379	21.9	4.8
1954	376	22.8	5.3
1955	371	21.4	5.0
1956	368	24.6	5.2
1957	358	25.6	5.9
1958	349	28.3	5.8
1959 †	347	28.8	6.0
1960 **	324	28.8	6.1

* Equivalent ready-to-cook, includes giblets.
† Preliminary, excludes Alaska and Hawaii.
** Preliminary, estimates for 1960; Alaska and Hawaii excluded.

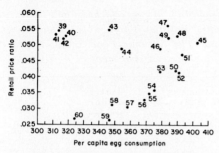

Fig. 42-1. Changes in the demand for eggs and in the retail price ratio (retail egg price divided by the per capita disposable income) for the period 1939 to 1960 inclusive. The data for 1960 are preliminary.

Chickens. From 1910 to the beginning of World War II the consumption of chicken held relatively steady at about 13 to 15 lb. per capita (Table 42-1). During World War II consumption rose to a peak of 23 lb. per capita and then declined somewhat after the war ended. During the 1950's consumption rose to a new all-time high level of nearly 29 lb. The development of the present-day commercial broiler has been important in increasing the consumption of chicken. Certainly there was little or no indication of an increase in chicken consumption during the time when cull hens made up the bulk of the chicken meat supply. With the advent of the broiler, which now makes up the bulk (about two thirds) of the poultry meat supply, plus favorable price considerations, consumption of poultry meat has been stimulated and may be expected to increase still further in the years ahead. Unlike the consumption of beef and pork, which tends to fluctuate cyclically, the consumption of chicken has shown a rather steady upward trend since the late 1930's (Fig. 42-2).

A study conducted by the U.S. Department of Agriculture (USDA, 1957) showed that 93% of the homemakers served or bought broilers or fryers during the preceding year and nearly 60% served broilers or fryers during the previous week. This indicates the present widespread use of broilers. The most popular way of using broilers or fryers is to serve them fried, as reported by 94% of the housewives who had served this item during the previous year. Other popular ways of preparing this type of chicken meat are baked or roasted, broiled, and barbecued. Broilers and fryers are usually purchased either whole or cut up. In the purchase of broilers and fryers housewives consider such things as freedom from bruises, discoloration, plumpness, pinfeathers, fat covering, and skin tears.

Turkeys. The consumption of turkeys in the early 1930's averaged about 1.5 lb. per capita. Beginning in the late 1930's, and continuing to date, the consumption of turkey meat has been moving upward (Fig.

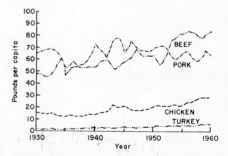

Fig. 42-2. Consumption of chicken, turkey, beef, and pork in the United States, 1930–1960.

42-2). Estimated consumption for 1960—6.1 lb.—is the highest on record. Here again the development of a lighter-weight bird, the marketing of turkeys at lighter weights, and the recognition that turkey meat is good at times other than during the fall holiday season, have encouraged consumption.

42-3. CLASSES AND GRADES

The reasons for classifying and grading poultry and eggs are numerous. Some of the major reasons are listed here.

(1) Classifying and grading facilitate exchange of products, especially under circumstances where the product is offered for sale by distant sellers.

(2) Products can be grouped according to their best and most efficient use.

(3) Premium markets can be found for best quality.

(4) Price comparisons are made easy.

(5) Buying and selling on description are possible.

(6) Risk of fraudulent market practices is eliminated.

(7) Pooling of shipments is made possible.

In general the grades for poultry and eggs are established by visual inspection, or candling. The process involves twirling the egg in front of, or rolling it over, a strong light in such a way that the light rays penetrate and illuminate the interior of the egg. In some of the modern plants, machines to detect eggs with cracked shells or blood spots are used to supplement the candling process.

Eggs (adapted largely from USDA, 1958, 1960)

MAJOR PARTS OF AN EGG. To understand the basis of our egg grades and to develop a limited knowledge of egg grading, one must be at least reasonably familiar with the four major parts of an egg: shell, yolk, albumen or white, and air cell. (A more detailed discussion of these parts is given in Chapter 5.)

The shell is the outer covering of the egg. It is a calcareous layer deposited around the outer shell membrane. In egg grading, the shell is considered from the viewpoints of cleanliness, shape, and texture.

The air cell, usually at the large end of the egg, is the space which results when the contents of the shell shrink upon cooling after being laid. Air passes through the shell and fills a space between the inner and outer shell membranes. When the egg has just been laid and cooled, the space is quite small. As the egg ages and the water evaporates, the air cell becomes larger.

The albumen or white of an egg is the nearly colorless material surrounding the yolk. It consists, in order, of a thin watery outer layer, a thick layer, a thin watery inner layer, and finally a thin layer of thick albumen surrounding the yolk, which branches out on two sides of the yolk to form the cordlike chalaza. When the egg is laid, the albumen is generally firm, with enough of the thick albumen to hold the yolk in the center of the egg. With time, the albumen becomes thinner or more watery, thus permitting the yolk to move freely from its normal center position in the egg. In grading eggs, albumen characteristics considered are freedom from foreign bodies, freedom from blood, and firmness.

The yolk is normally in the center of the egg, held there by the thick albumen. Because of its relatively high fat content, it moves upward and closer to the shell and becomes flatter as the albumen becomes thinner and weaker—just as cream rises to the top in milk. The yolk also becomes enlarged through the absorption of moisture from the albumen. Thus the size, shape, and position of the yolk in the egg are important indices of egg quality. Yolk factors considered in grading eggs are position in the egg, shape of yolk, outline of yolk, freedom from defects, and germ development.

GRADES. The basis for egg grades is resemblance to normal new-laid eggs. For this reason, care has been taken to explain briefly the characteristics of new-laid eggs and the changes occurring with age. Quality standards have been established for individual eggs, which provide for four main classes:

TABLE 42-2. | *Summary of United States standards for quality of individual shell eggs. (Standards effective Dec. 1, 1946; amended Mar. 1, 1955.)*

Quality Factor	AA Quality	A Quality	B Quality	C Quality
Shell	Clean, unbroken, practically normal	Clean, unbroken, practically normal	Clean to slightly stained; unbroken; may be slightly abnormal	Clean to moderately stained; unbroken; may be abnormal
Air cell	$\frac{1}{8}$ inch or less in depth; practically regular	$\frac{2}{8}$ inch or less in depth; practically regular	$\frac{3}{8}$ inch or less in depth; may be free but not bubbly	May be over $\frac{3}{8}$ inch in depth; may be free or bubbly
White	Clear, firm	Clear; may be reasonably firm	Clear; may be slightly weak	May be weak and watery; small blood clots or spots may be present
Yolk	Well centered; outline slightly defined; free from defects	May be fairly well centered; outline may be fairly well defined; practically free from defects	May be off center; outline may be well defined; may be slightly enlarged and flattened; may show definite but not serious defects	May be off center; outline may be plainly visible; may be enlarged and flattened; may show clearly visible germ development but no blood; may show other serious defects

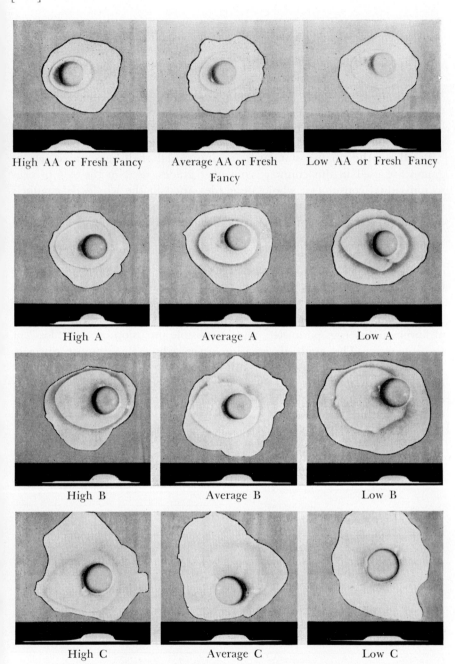

High AA or Fresh Fancy   Average AA or Fresh Fancy   Low AA or Fresh Fancy

High A   Average A   Low A

High B   Average B   Low B

High C   Average C   Low C

Fig. 42-3. The interior quality of eggs that meet the specification of the U.S. Standards for Quality of Individual Shell Eggs with respect to albumen and yolk quality. [From Poultry Division, Agricultural Marketing Service, USDA.]

AA quality

A quality

B quality

C quality

In addition, three other quality standards—dirty, check, and leaker—are established for eggs with dirty or broken shells. A summary of the standards for individual shell eggs is given in Table 42-2. The four major grades are illustrated in Fig. 42-3.

Based on the quality standards for individual shell eggs, three sets of grades are used in this country: consumer grades, used in the sale of eggs to individual consumers; wholesale grades, used in the wholesale channels of trade; and United States procurement grades, used for institutional buying and Armed Forces purchases. Attention in this chapter will be focused on the commercial and wholesale grades.

Consumer grades. These are used for lots of eggs that have been carefully candled and graded for retail sale. The four consumer grades of eggs are Grade AA or Fresh Fancy Quality, Grade A, Grade B, and Grade C; see Table 42-3.

Wholesale grades. These differ from consumer grades in the tolerance of lower quality eggs permitted, and in possible inclusion of some "loss" or inedible eggs. The grade designation given wholesale eggs are Specials, Extras, Standards, Trades, Dirties, and Checks. In general, Specials consist of 20% AA quality eggs and 80% A quality eggs; Extras, 20% A quality eggs and 80% B quality eggs; Standards, 20% B quality eggs and 80% C quality eggs; and Trades, 83% C quality eggs.

TABLE 42-3. | *Summary of U.S. consumer grades for shell eggs.*

U.S. consumer grade	At least 80% (lot average) * must be—	Tolerance permitted †	
		Percent	Quality
Grade AA or fresh fancy quality	AA Quality	15 to 20	A
		Not over 5 **	B, C, or Check
Grade A	A quality or better	15 to 20	B
		Not over 5 **	C, or Check
Grade B	B quality or better	10 to 20	C
		Not over 10 **	Dirty or Check
Grade C	C quality or better	Not over 20	Dirty or Check

* In lots of two or more cases, no individual case may fall below 70% of the specified quality, and no individual case may contain more than double the tolerance specified for the respective grade (that is, in lots of Grade A, not more than 10% of the qualities in individual cases within the sample may be C or Check, provided the average is not over 5%).

† Within tolerance permitted, an allowance will be made at receiving points or shipping destination for ½% leakers in Grades AA, A, and B and 1% in Grade C.

** Substitution of higher qualities for the lower qualities specified is permitted.

TABLE | *U.S. weight classes for consumer grades for shell eggs.*
42-4.

Size or weight class	Minimum net weight/dozen (oz.)	Minimum net weight/30 dozen (lb.)	Minimum weight for individual eggs at rate/dozen (oz.)
Jumbo	30	56	29
Extra large	27	$50\frac{1}{2}$	26
Large	24	45	23
Medium	21	$39\frac{1}{2}$	20
Small	18	34	17
Peewee	15	28	

Weight classes. In the marketing of eggs, weight and quality are often confused. Weight is separate and distinct from quality, however. Large eggs may be either Grade AA, A, B, or C. So may a jumbo or a small-sized egg. The weight classes established for consumer grades of eggs are those shown in Table 42-4. Weight classes for wholesale grades of eggs have been established by the USDA.

Producing quality eggs.[1] Egg quality is at its peak at the time the egg is laid. It has not been possible to improve the original quality. The most that can be done is to produce a high-quality product and then exercise the necessary precautions through proper practices to maintain as much of the original quality as possible. In general, the major considerations in producing and marketing high quality eggs are as follows:

1) Management practices:
   (a) Whether males are in the flock.
   (b) The number of times eggs are gathered each day.
   (c) Whether the laying flock is confined.
   (d) The condition of the nest and floor litter.
2) Holding conditions:
   (a) Temperature in the egg room.
   (b) Humidity in the egg room.

Flocks with males generally market lower-quality eggs than those without males. Males should be in the flock for hatching egg production only. The removal of males is especially important on farms where eggs are gathered only once each day, or where the egg-laying flock runs loose in the barnyard. Confinement of the flock when there is one daily gathering of eggs helps quality but it is even more helpful to gather eggs twice or, better still, three times daily.

[1] Adapted largely from L. B. Darrah, *Business Aspects of Commercial Poultry Farming.* Ronald, 1952.

Frequent gathering of eggs is essential in maintaining quality under the usual types of nesting arrangements. Gathering eggs twice each day rather than once gives a substantial boost in quality. Gathering them three times a day rather than twice further improves quality, but the gain is not as great as that obtained by twice-daily gathering rather than once-daily gathering.

Holding conditions of temperature and humidity are always important but especially so when other practices are poor. In general, egg rooms should be held at 45° to 55°F. The rooms should be kept moist; 80% or higher relative humidity is recommended.

While not listed as a factor, the temperature at which the eggs are candled or graded is important in the interpretation of egg quality. Under warm temperatures, eggs appear worse; under cool conditions, better than they are.

Poultry. Poultry, like eggs, has a multiplicity of classes and grades. Although this may seem unnecessary and confusing, it is necessitated by the wide variety of poultry meat items offered for sale (USDA, 1960).

CLASSES. The classes of chicken commonly used are the following.

Broiler or fryer. A young chicken (usually under 16 weeks of age) of either sex, tender-meated, with soft, pliable, smooth-textured skin and flexible breastbone cartilage.

Roaster. A young chicken (usually under 8 months of age) of either sex, tender-meated, with soft, pliable, smooth-textured skin and breastbone cartilage that is somewhat less flexible than that of a broiler or fryer.

Capon. An unsexed male chicken (usually under 10 months of age), tender-meated, with soft, pliable, smooth-textured skin.

Stag. A male chicken (usually under 10 months of age), with darkened

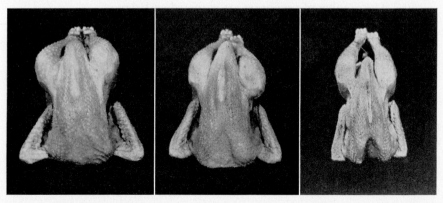

Fig. 42-4. Grades of dressed chickens. Left, A Quality. Center, B quality. Right, C quality. [From Poultry Division, Agricultural Marketing Service, USDA.]

flesh and considerable hardening of the breastbone cartilage. Stags show a condition of fleshing and a degree of maturity intermediate between that of a roaster and a cock or old rooster.

Hen or stewing chicken or fowl. A mature female chicken (usually more than 10 months old), with meat less tender than that of a roaster and non-flexible breastbone.

Cock or old rooster. A mature male chicken, with coarse skin, toughened and darkened meat, and hardened breastbone.

GRADES. The standards of quality used with poultry are applicable to individual birds. Factors considered in establishing standards for live poultry are: health and vigor, feathering, conformation, fleshing, fat covering, and degree of freedom from defects. The grades used for live poultry are Grade A or No. 1 Quality, Grade B or No. 2 Quality, and Grade C or No. 3 Quality. Grade names for dressed and ready-to-cook chicken are A Quality, B

TABLE 42-5. | *Summary of standards of quality for live poultry on an individual bird basis.*

Factor	A or No. 1 quality	B or No. 2 quality	C or No. 3 quality
Health and vigor	Alert, bright eyes; vigorous	Good health and vigor	Lacking in vigor
Feathering	Well covered; feathers show luster or sheen	Fairly well covered with feathers	Complete lack of plumage; feathers on back
Conformation	Normal	Practically normal	Abnormal
Breastbone	Slight curve, $\frac{1}{8}$ in. dent		
Back	Normal (except slight curve)	Moderately crooked	Crooked or hunched back
Legs and wings	Normal	Slightly misshapen	Misshapen
Fleshing	Well fleshed; moderately broad and long breast	Fairly well fleshed	Poorly developed, narrow breast; thin covering of flesh
Fat covering	Well covered; some fat under skin over entire carcass; no excess abdominal fat	Enough fat on breast and legs to prevent a distinct appearance of flesh through skin; hens or fowl may have excessive abdominal fat	Lacking in fat covering on back and thighs; small amount in feather tract
Defects	Slight	Moderate	Serious
Tears and broken bones	Free	Free	Free
Bruises, scratches and calluses	Slight skin bruises, scratches, and calluses	Moderate (except slight flesh bruises)	Unlimited to extent no part unfit for food
Shanks	Slightly scaly	Moderately scaly	Seriously scaly

TABLE 42-6. | *Summary of standards for quality of dressed and ready-to-cook chickens.*

Factor	A Quality		B Quality		C Quality
Conformation Breastbone	Normal Slight curve, $\frac{1}{8}$ in. dent		Practically normal Dented; curved; slightly crooked		Abnormal Seriously crooked
Back	Normal (except slight curve)		Moderately crooked		Seriously crooked
Legs and wings Fleshing	Normal Well fleshed, moderately long and broad breast		Moderately misshapen Fairly well fleshed on breast and legs		Misshapen Poorly fleshed
Breastbone Fat covering	Not prominent Well covered; some fat under skin over entire carcass; broilers or fryers with only moderate covering		Not prominent Sufficient fat on breast and legs to prevent distinct appearance of flesh through skin		May be prominent Lacking in fat covering over all parts of carcass
	Breast and legs	Elsewhere	Breast and legs	Elsewhere	
Pinfeathers	Practically free	Practically free	Relatively few	Slight scattering	Numerous
Ready-to-cook:					
Nonprotruding pins	Practically free	Practically free	Few scattered	Few scattered	Scattering
Hair	Practically free	Practically free	Few scattered	Few scattered	Few scattered
Protruding pins	Free	Free	Free	Free	Free
Cuts and tears	Free	$1\frac{1}{2}$ in.	$1\frac{1}{2}$ in.	3 in.	No limit
Missing skin	None		3 areas totaling not more than $\frac{3}{4}$ in.	Tail to hipbones width of feather tract	No limit
Disjointed bones	1		2		No limit
Broken bones	None (except 1 nonprotruding wing bone if fryer)		1 nonprotruding		No limit
Missing parts	Wingtips		Wingtips, and if readyto-cook, 2nd wing joint and tail		Wingtips and if ready-to-cook, wings and tail
Discolorations (aggregate)					
	Inches	Inches	Inches	Inches	
Flesh bruises	0	$\frac{1}{2}$	$\frac{1}{2}$	$1\frac{1}{2}$	No limit
Skin bruises	$\frac{1}{2}$	$\frac{3}{4}$	$\frac{3}{4}$	$1\frac{1}{2}$	No limit
All discolorations	1	$1\frac{1}{2}$	$1\frac{1}{2}$	3	No limit
Freezer burn	Few small ($\frac{1}{2}$ in. diameter) pockmarks		Moderately dried areas not in excess of $\frac{1}{2}$ in. diameter		Numerous pockmarks and large dried areas

Quality, and C Quality. A summary of the standards for live poultry is given in Table 42-5; for dressed and ready-to-cook chicken, Table 42-6. The three grades of dressed chicken are illustrated in Fig. 42-4.

The wholesale grades for dressed and ready-to-cook poultry are Extras, Standards, and Trades. Extras consist of at least 90% A Quality birds, with the remainder of B Quality; Standards, 90% B Quality, the remainder C Quality; and Trades, all C Quality.

Production of quality poultry meat is largely the result of starting with good stock, proper feeding, proper housing and sanitation, and attention to other phases of good management.

42-4. MARKETING CHANNELS

The channels used in the marketing of eggs and poultry have changed rapidly during the past few years. Twenty years ago most eggs moved from producers to country buying stations, or to huskers and peddlers, then to central assembling plants and shippers, whence they were shipped in large quantities to city wholesalers and jobbers. The latter sold to chain store warehouses or retail stores. In recent years the desire to sell to premium outlets has had a major impact on the channels used in the areas close to market. In these areas a substantial proportion of the eggs are moving either direct to consumers or from producers to retail stores. Because of this manner of marketing, country assembling plants and city wholesalers are gradually being eliminated. In the surplus-egg-producing states located long distances from market, direct marketing is relatively less important, but selling to large assembling plants rather than to country buying stations is growing in importance. These large plants in turn ship to wholesalers in distant cities or direct to chain store warehouses. A few firms are making arrangements for sales direct to retail stores, even in distant areas.

Poultry marketing, too, has changed rapidly in recent years. This is the result of a substantial increase in commercial broiler production and a change in the way of preparing poultry for the retail market—from New York dressed (blood and feathers removed only) to ready-to-cook birds or parts. Formerly, poultry moved through country buying stations and then largely to country shippers, to be sold to wholesalers of live chickens. These wholesalers moved the chickens to city processors and then either to wholesalers of dressed chickens or direct to retail stores. The wholesalers, of course, sold to retail stores. Today, two major patterns exist. In the heavy-producing areas birds are moved directly from farms to the processing plants and then to chain store warehouses or direct to retail stores. In other areas the buying station type of agency still plays an important role in assembling the small quantities of poultry from individual producers for sale in larger quantities to city or country processing plants.

In summary, one of the most striking developments in poultry and egg marketing is the simplification of the marketing channels. Formerly, many agencies were necessary because the poultry and eggs had to be collected from the millions of small farms that produced these items, and then assembled in large quantities for processing and for sale in distant markets. Today, with fewer but larger flocks, sales are becoming much more direct. Many small country buyers as well as numerous city wholesalers and jobbers are no longer needed or used.

42-5. MARKETING COSTS

The cost of marketing eggs has fluctuated widely over the years. In general, though, costs declined during the 1920's and early 1930's and reached the lowest point on record in 1935, when the average marketing margin for eggs was 9.3 cents per dozen (Table 42-7). Thereafter, marketing costs rose and reached a high of more than 20 cents per dozen in 1951 and 1952. Since then costs have declined somewhat, but remain at about 19 cents per dozen.

The cost of marketing eggs, as with other farm products, is "sticky"; that is, it changes slowly with price changes. As a result, marketing margins tend to remain relatively steady over short periods of time, even though farm prices and retail prices fluctuate greatly. In 1959, for example, farm and retail prices were considerably lower than in 1958, but marketing costs actually increased.

Because eggs require relatively little processing and relatively simple packaging, the farmer's share of the consumer's dollar spent for eggs has always been relatively high. During the period for which data are available, the farmer's share has ranged from a high of 75% of the consumer's dollar in 1943 and 1945 to a low of about 61% during the 1931–1933 period. In periods of prosperity the farmer's share is relatively high; in periods of depression, relatively low.

The biggest single cost item in marketing eggs is the retail operation. Although the retail margin varies widely, it generally averages close to 10 cents per dozen, which represents about a half of the total marketing margin. Other important cost items are labor, cartons, and transportation from the farm to the retail market.

Marketing margins for ready-to-cook chicken are available for the period 1950–1959 (Table 42-7). During this 10-year period, marketing margins averaged slightly over 20 cents per pound. The farmer's share of the consumer's dollar, however, has been declining. In the early 1950's the farmer's share averaged about two-thirds of the consumer's dollar. In the most recent year for which data are available, the farmer's share averaged just over half of the consumer's dollar spent for chicken.

The make-up of the marketing margin for chicken is difficult to assess because of the tremendous impact that loss-leader sales have on the marketing of the chicken. Evidence available indicates that a substantial share

TABLE 42-7.	*Marketing margins for eggs and chickens. [Farm-Retail Spreads for Food Products. Misc. Pub. 741, Agricultural Marketing Service, USDA; and The Marketing and Transportation Situation. AMS, USDA, January, 1960.]*

	Eggs				Chickens (broilers and fryers, ready-to-cook)			
Year	Retail price/ dozen (Cents)	Farm value* (Cents)	Farm- retail spread (Cents)	Farm- er's share (%)	Retail price/lb. (Cents)	Farm value† (Cents)	Farm- retail spread (Cents)	Farm- er's share (%)
1920–24	49.4	34.8	14.6	70				
1925–29	26.3	32.1	14.2	69				
1930	39.8	25.9	13.9	65				
1931	31.3	19.1	12.2	61				
1932	27.0	16.5	10.5	61				
1933	25.5	15.8	9.7	62				
1934	29.0	18.9	10.1					
1935	34.1	24.8	9.3	73				
1936	33.8	23.6	10.2					
1937	33.2	22.4	10.8	67				
1938	32.9	21.9	11.0	67				
1939	29.8	19.0	10.8	64				
1940	30.7	19.7	11.0	64				
1941	36.8	25.8	11.0	70				
1942	44.7	32.3	12.4	72				
1943	53.0	39.8	13.2	75				
1944	50.4	34.8	15.6	69				
1945	53.9	40.2	13.7	75				
1946	55.3	40.4	14.9	73				
1947	65.8	47.8	18.0	73				
1948	68.4	49.4	19.0	72				
1949	65.9	46.8	19.1	71				
1950	57.1	38.0	19.1	67	57.0	37.4	19.6	66
1951	69.7	49.4	20.3	71	59.7	39.0	20.7	65
1952	63.6	43.2	20.4	68	60.0	39.7	20.3	66
1953	66.8	49.0	17.8	73	58.5	37.0	21.5	63
1954	58.1	40.1	18.0	69	54.8	34.6	20.2	63
1955	58.1	40.1	18.0	69	54.8	34.6	20.2	63
1956	57.7	39.8	17.9	69	47.8	26.9	20.9	56
1957	54.9	36.6	18.3	67	46.7	25.9	20.8	55
1958	57.9	39.5	18.4	68	46.1	25.4	20.7	55
1959**	50.9	31.9	19.0	63	43.2	22.3	20.0	53

* Payment to farmers for 1.03 dozen eggs.
† Payment to farmers for 1.37 pounds live chicken.
** Preliminary.

of the chicken is sold during special sale periods of chain stores and that a relatively small part is sold otherwise. Thus margins are appreciable when sales are low, but practically nonexistent when sales are high. In general, however, about half of the marketing margin, as with eggs, consists of the gross markup at retail. Operations of processing plants, including assembling of chickens and distribution of processed items to consuming centers, averages 7 to 8 cents per pound; wholesale operations account for the remainder of the margin.

In general, assembling costs in the marketing of poultry and eggs have declined as production has become more concentrated in certain areas and as flocks have become larger. On the other hand, the rising cost of labor, as well as the demand by the consumer for new and better services and products, have more than offset the reduction in assembling costs. Thus, total marketing costs have tended to rise over the years.

REFERENCES AND SELECTED READINGS

Reference marked with an asterisk is of general interest.

*Darrah, L. B., 1952. *Business Aspects of Commercial Poultry Farming.* Ronald, New York.

Pincock, M. G., 1952 and 1957. Consumer purchasing practices and quality recognition for eggs. A.E. 1073, Dept. of Agricultural Economics.

USDA, 1957. Selected highlights from a study of consumer's use of and opinions about poultry. AMS-159.

——, 1958. Regulations governing the grading and inspection of shell eggs and United States standards, grades, and weight classes for shell eggs. Poultry Division, AMS.

——, 1960a. Regulations governing the grading and inspection of poultry and edible products thereof and United States classes, standards, and grades with respect thereto. Poultry Division, AMS.

——, 1960b. Farm-retail spreads for food products. Misc. Publ. 741, AMS.

——, 1960c. The marketing and transportation situation. AMS.

Livestock Diseases

Chapter 43

Infection and Its Effects on Livestock Production

There is nothing, Sir, too little for so little a creature as man. It is by studying little things that we attain the great art of having as little misery and as much happiness as possible.

JOHNSON *to Boswell for his Private Journal*

Infectious diseases have plagued mankind and his domestic animals throughout the ages. History is replete with accounts of mysterious sicknesses which affected large populations of people or animals. These maladies changed history by influencing the success or failure of wars and the material progress of nations. The results of infection are multiple: the human host may be directly attacked or infectious diseases may indirectly affect man by attack on animals. In the latter instance, the general plane of human nutrition is lowered by loss of meat, milk, and eggs, and the economy is harmed by inefficiency in livestock production. When disease is prevalent, the yields of animal products may be far too small in relation to the effort expended. Animal losses by disease in the United States have been estimated at a billion dollars annually. Consider the importance of these problems in less favored parts of the world where efforts at control are minimal and the population involved must bear the full impact of disease attacks.

Though much remains to be done in infectious disease control, we can look back with satisfaction at what has been accomplished. It was only near the end of the last century and the beginning of our twentieth century that man began to understand the nature of these problems. The scientific giants

741

of the early developments were people such as Pasteur, Koch, and Ehrlich. These are familiar names to all of us because their accomplishments opened the way for a great period of progress in improving the health of man and animals.

In this chapter we want to explore the problem of the infectious diseases of domestic animals and see how various areas of science have contributed in the past and presumably will contribute in the future. The interrelationship of livestock production, veterinary medicine, and public health will become obvious as we proceed.

43-1. PARASITISM

Infection is a drama involving two main actors, the host and the parasite. The hosts that concern us here are the domestic mammals and birds which man has selectively bred and trained for various specialized purposes. The parasites are creatures who have become dependent on the host for their existence. They have lost the capacity to survive as independent forms of life. Therefore they spend all or part of their life cycles either on the surfaces or in the tissues of the host. There are many forms of parasites. A partial list includes, in order of increasing structural complexity: viruses, bacteria, fungi, protozoa, helminths (worms), and arthropods (insects). It must be remembered that the parasitic forms constitute a very small part of the total number of species in a given biological group. For example, very few of the fungi found on earth are parasitic in comparison with the total number. The viruses are an exceptional group, wherein all forms are parasitic.

These various forms of life have given rise to several fields of science—virology, bacteriology, mycology (study of fungi), and parasitology (this last term includes the study of protozoa, helminths, and insects). When dealing with infectious diseases, physicians and veterinarians may contribute as professional men trained in the healing arts as well as scientific specialists in a particular field of knowledge. Other scientists prepare themselves by intensive basic study in one of these sciences. The best progress in research is made when knowledge from disease-oriented educations (M.D. or D.V.M.) and scientific specialty educations (Ph.D.) are combined among investigators working together.

To exist, parasitic forms of life have restrictions on their freedom of development, determined by four requirements for perpetuation.

The Parasite Must Gain Entrance to the Host. The portal of entry is limited to body orifices and the skin and varies among different parasites. The mouth and nose are probably the most important since they provide approaches to the respiratory and gastrointestinal tracts, and thus indirectly to the blood. The tissues of mouth and nose are constantly exposed to contamination from feed, water, and inhaled air. An important aspect of good livestock management, therefore, is to prevent contamination of feed and water with animal excretions. Certain disease organisms gain access to the host during the act of breeding; these cause the venereal diseases. Although the skin is usually an effective barrier against the entry of parasites, some organisms do penetrate the skin and others enter at sites of skin abrasions. Biting insects may serve as vectors for disease organisms by penetrating the skin and thus depositing the parasite in the tissues.

The Parasite Must Multiply and Adapt to the Environment. Following entry, the contest between host defenses and parasitic adaptation begins. It is in this phase that injury to the host is created—the period during which a disease is in progress. It has been the usual center of interest in veterinary medicine.

The Parasite Must Have a Satisfactory Portal of Exit. The parasite must have a means for leaving the host because each individual host will eventually die—either because of the parasitism or from other causes. The organisms affecting the respiratory tract usually escape in respiratory excretions. This may occur from coughing or sneezing. Parasites entering by way of the digestive tract are frequently shed from the host in the droppings or feces. Those entering by insect bite usually escape by gaining access to the tissues of a new insect when the host is bitten.

The Parasite Must Have an Effective Mechanism for Transmission to a New Host. Many disease agents pass constantly from the infected excretions of one individual to another of the same species. In their evolutionary development, such parasites frequently become limited to a single host. Numerous parasites have more involved mechanisms of transmission—for example, the formation of resistant spores. This is a dormant physical state of the parasite which does not require prompt transmission to a new host. The spore can lie in soil and other places for prolonged periods, awaiting the arrival of a new host animal. Some worms and protozoa have very complex life cycles, which may depend upon development in one or more intermediate hosts before gaining access again to the domestic animal host.

43-2. DEFENSE MECHANISMS OF THE HOST

The science of immunology concerns the study of means by which the host may protect itself from parasites. Immunologists continuously search for additional ways to aid the host defense mechanisms. Certain infectious diseases affect only one host; hog cholera in swine and diphtheria in man are examples. Man has high, natural resistance to hog cholera virus but is susceptible to the diphtheria organism. The opposite situation pertains to the susceptibility of swine. Therefore, we see that some parasites have a high degree of host specificity; some hosts, on the other hand, have a high level of natural resistance to certain parasites. The natural resistance of the host manifests itself at the time the parasite is attemping to multiply and adapt to the host enviornment. Precise knowledge of the mechanisms of natural resistance is lacking, and the refractoriness of the host to a given parasite is simply considered a genetic endowment. Some parasites infect several species and are spoken of as organisms with a wide host range. Examples of diseases affecting both man and several domestic animals are rabies, psittacosis, tuberculosis, tetanus, and trichinosis. Not only are variations in resistance to parasites found between species but, furthermore, within a given species of susceptible host, one can find wide variations of susceptibility. This has been shown to be inherited resistance or susceptibility. Genetic selection of breeds or families of domestic animals demonstrating increased resistance to certain infections has been accomplished. It is one of the important hopes for the future that this work may be expanded to assist livestock production in this important way.

Normal Defenses of the Host. Many structures and body fluids of the host are ingeniously designed for the prevention of parasitic invasion (Raffel, 1953). The skin itself is not only a mechanical barrier but its secretions also have the property of killing some bacteria. The mucous membranes such as those lining the nasal chambers, respiratory tract, and digestive tract secrete a mucous film entrapping many parasitic organisms and mechanically sweeping them away. In addition, the secretions of such membranes may contain substances which act directly to destroy the parasite. The animal body has a remarkable series of cells—phagocytes—that are of central importance in preventing disease. These cells are widely distributed in such places as the liver, spleen, blood, and bone marrow. They have amoebalike behavior and appearance in that they are capable of taking particles into their cell substance. If the particle is an invading bacterium or some other parasite, it will very likely be destroyed within the phagocytic cell. Inflammation in the tissues is another important means for defending the host. Everyone has experienced the infection of a finger following a skin abrasion or the troubles associated with a "boil" in the skin. In these situations the affected tissue is swollen, painful, red, and warm; it is inflamed. The pathologist studies such affected tissues and knows that the inflammatory response of the host is walling off the invading microorganism and assisting in the destruction of the invader.

Acquired Immunity. Although the natural defense mechanisms play a great role in the prevention of disease among the domestic animals, it is common knowledge that these natural defenses may be overwhelmed. In speaking of acquired immunity, we are interested in knowing what can be added to the natural defenses to protect the host. It is convenient to divide acquired immunity into active and passive categories.

ACTIVE ACQUIRED IMMUNITY. In this condition the tissues of the host play an active part in bringing about an increase in resistance. Children recovering from measles or chickens recovering from an attack of coccidiosis are examples wherein the live disease organism grows in the tissues and is eventually destroyed, leaving the host with a higher degree of resistance than it had naturally. Since the natural disease frequently kills or leaves the animal in a useless physical condition for commercial purposes, this is not a satisfactory way to gain acquired immunity. Consequently, artificial means are sought for inducing the desired changes in the host which will not harm the health of the animal. This procedure is called immunization or vaccination. By vaccination procedures, the veterinarian induces the body to form certain kinds of antibodies and perhaps enhances the capacity of certain cells to combat the parasite. The antibodies are protein molecules formed by lymphoid tissues and discharged into the lymph and blood. We test for their presence by various procedures referred to as serological tests.

PASSIVE ACQUIRED IMMUNITY. The accumulation of protective antibodies for a specific organism in the serum means that a transfer of serum from an actively immunized animal to a normal animal may afford a degree of added protection. The recipient of the serum is passive in the sense that it did not form the antibodies. Passive immunity occurs naturally in the newborn animal because antibodies are received from the dam. In some species antibodies from the maternal serum pass across the placenta and reach the blood of the developing fetus in the uterus. In other species such as the horse, cow, and sheep, the maternal antibodies are stored in the colostrum and are taken up by the newborn when nursing begins. Only in the newborn animal do these antibodies escape destruction by the digestive fluids and enter the blood stream in appreciable amounts. Resistance thus acquired is lost in a matter of weeks or in a few months at the most. Passive immunity is induced artificially by the injection of antiserum, a procedure affording immediate increased resistance to diseases such as tetanus, botulism, swine erysipelas, and canine distemper. However, the passive protection afforded by serum injection is dissipated in a matter of weeks.

In the remainder of this chapter some of the important groups of parasitic organisms will be described and one or two examples from each group will be considered. The examples demonstrate the diversity of approaches required for infectious disease control, but the reader should realize that there are numerous infectious disease problems which must await future research before they can be brought to the advanced state of control depicted in the examples.

43-3. THE VIRUSES AND THEIR CONTROL

The viruses are a large group of very small microorganisms that can only multiply when inside a host cell (Pelczar and Reid, 1958). The unit of virus measurement is the millimicron (m_μ). This is $1/1,000,000$ of a millimeter or 1/25,400,000 of an inch. The viruses range in size from about 5 to 300 millimicrons. Many of them are within the size range of large molecules. Such structural simplicity does not permit them to live independently because they lack vital parts needed for growth and multiplication. Consequently, they are the most dependent and burdensome of all the world's creatures. A virus in a susceptible host will seek out certain cells for completion of its life processes. The cells chosen by the virus may then be injured, resulting in disease in the host. The nature of the disease depends upon the particular cells involved. Thus the clinical signs and the damaged tissue (lesions) can indicate to the veterinarian which virus is responsible.

The scientist working with viruses rarely sees the microorganism he is studying. How does he know what he is doing in such a situation? He can determine this by knowing the nature of the disease produced in experimental animals by the virus under study and by the use of serological procedures. The many serological techniques cannot be described here, but some procedures will be considered briefly in a subsequent section of the chapter.

We said that viruses can only grow in living cells and this means that the virologist must cultivate them in living cells in the laboratory. Two main methods are used for this. One procedure is to grow the virus in the living tissues of the developing chicken embryo. Another method of great current importance is virus cultivation in tissue culture. In this situation, cells from an animal are grown on a glass surface in bottles! If the virus grows in the kidney cells of the calf, then we may grow kidney cells of the calf in tissue culture and use these cells as hosts for virus.

Viral Encephalitis. Throughout the world there are several different viruses that cause inflammation of the brain (encephalitis) in vertebrate animals. However, our attention will focus on one of these, the Western equine encephalitis virus (W.E.E.). In the United States this virus has infected horses in every state west of the Appalachian Mountains. The virus was named after the horse (equine), but it was soon realized that man also suffered from this disease.

According to figures compiled by the U.S. Department of Agriculture, around 2,000 cases of equine encephalitis have been reported annually in horses in recent years. At certain times this reaches far greater proportions, as in 1938, when 184,662 cases occurred. The stricken horse first goes through a brief period when it has a fever and mild depression (Hagan and Bruner, 1961). The virus is in the blood of the horse at this time. Many infections are arrested at this early stage and go completely undetected. However, if brain invasion occurs, the animal shows many peculiar forms of behavior. It may shy from objects which ordinarily cause no concern, or it may walk in circles or force its way through fences. At these stages it will refuse to take feed and water and may develop a sleepy attitude, in which case it will rest its head on any convenient structure such as the manger. Paralysis follows and the horse eventually collapses and remains down until death ensues. Events similar to those described for the horse also occur in man.

What is the source of the virus that causes this bizarre and frequently fatal disease? In search of an answer to this question, scientists have uncovered many interesting facts which provide a basis both for understanding the infection and for attacking the control problem (Fig. 43-1). The greatest number of cases occur in August and September, and this information led workers to look for an insect vector. We now know that certain mosquitoes play a key role in transmitting this virus among vertebrates. But where does the mosquito get the virus? Does the horse serve as the reservoir and, therefore, the source of infection for man? Research has indicated that the

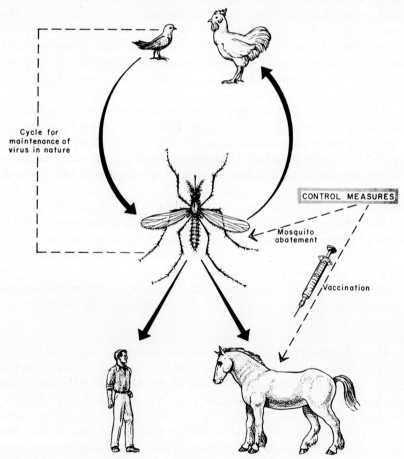

Fig. 43-1. The parasitic cycle of the western equine encephalitis virus and the places where control efforts are directed. Transmission from horse to man is not considered an important part of the infection chain.

horse plays a very limited role in this respect, but that wild and domestic birds are the probable sources of infection for the mosquito vector. High percentages of domestic chickens have been shown to carry antibodies against the virus in places where epidemics occur among horses and man (Hammon *et al.,* 1945). Wild migratory birds may also carry antibodies. Experimental infection of these bird hosts demonstrates that they develop high yields of virus in their blood for brief periods but show no signs of sickness. This, therefore, is infection without disease! Mosquitoes biting birds when virus is in their blood can readily pass it on to man or to the horse.

A two-pronged effort at control is used. The first control effort is to block the infection chain at the point of transmission from the wild bird host to the horse or man. This means control of the mosquito vector. In several parts of the United States mosquito abatement programs are in effect for control of viral encephalitis and as a pest control measure in their own right. Though costly, this procedure will undoubtedly become more common as additional lands go under irrigation and create environments for the breeding of mosquitoes. Many problems concerning the operation of large mosquito abatement programs remain unsolved.

The other control measure is directed toward raising the resistance of the susceptible host. In the case of the horse, this is done by annual vaccination with killed encephalitis virus. Virus is grown in embryonating chicken eggs. The chicken embryos die within 24 hours of the virus inoculation, at which time the embryo tissues are heavily saturated with virus. The embryo is ground into a paste and the virus is killed with formalin. This suspension is then injected between the layers of the skin in the horse. Vaccination of horses is performed in the late spring or early summer so that a high level of resistance will be in effect during the peak of the mosquito season.

In summary it can be said that the outlook for viral encephalitis suggests that this will become an increasingly important problem as more lands are irrigated. This will be associated with a need for better methods of mosquito control and improved methods for the immunization of horses and possibly man.

Hog Cholera. Hog cholera is the most important disease of swine in the United States. It occurs throughout the country but is most prevalent in the concentrated swine raising areas of the Midwest. This very costly and destructive disease can kill nearly 100% of susceptible animals in a given outbreak (Hagan and Bruner, 1961). The pigs suffer from degeneration in the walls of the small blood vessels in numerous parts of the body and depression of the number of phagocytic cells. This latter effect decreases the resistance of the host to a variety of other parasites. Death from hog cholera is therefore often associated not only with the virus infection itself but with pneumonia and inflammation of the intestinal tract, secondary processes caused by other organisms.

How does this parasite persist in nature and continue to cause its great losses to livestock production? To perpetuate itself in nature, the virus must be protected from the deleterious effects of drying and sunlight. Characteristically in a hog cholera outbreak, a few animals in the drove sicken initially. In a matter of a few weeks nearly all the swine in the immediate environment become ill The virus leaves the infected host in a variety of secretions and excretions. Once the first pig in a drove of swine develops hog cholera, the remaining pigs will become infected by direct transfer of virus to their digestive tracts. But how did the first pig contact the virus? Frequently, the virus may be tracked from farm to farm on contaminated footwear and other objects. It is unfortunate that swine are often slaughtered for food purposes at the beginning of a hog cholera outbreak to limit economic loss. Virus-laden pork trimmings from infected carcasses may thus be present in garbage that is fed to susceptible swine. This can initiate a new outbreak of the disease. These methods all explain how the disease outbreaks may spread from one farm to the next during an epidemic season, but there has long been a question of how the virus persists in the relatively long periods which often intervene between outbreaks. Shope (1958) demonstrated that the swine lungworm may serve as a reservoir and intermediate host for the virus of hog cholera. Lungworms in virus-infected swine may take up the virus and pass it on to a new generation of lungworms through the eggs. The newly hatched larval lungworms may in turn survive for many months in the soil as parasites in the common earthworm. Thus, months later, completing this rather complicated cycle, rooting swine may ingest earthworms and take up the virus.

With this knowledge, what means are available for controlling hog cholera (Fig. 43-2)? Certainly rigid use of quarantine to prevent direct transfer of virus from farm to farm is an obvious step. The cooking of garbage to prevent the ingestion of live virus in pork scraps is another important control procedure, now required throughout the United States. Laws requiring the cooking of garbage also have beneficial effect for the control of several other diseases.

Paramount in importance for control is the immunization of swine. The passive immunity afforded by antiserum is very valuable at the beginning of hog cholera outbreaks to block the entrance of virus into the cells of susceptible swine. The development of means for inducing active immunity is an important chapter in veterinary medicine which goes back to the work of Dorset, McBride, and Niles (1908). These investigators showed that virus injected simultaneously with antiserum would cause the swine to develop a long lasting immunity. This procedure required a delicate balance between the killing power of the virus, the protective capacities of the serum, and the general state of health of the host animals. The procedure has

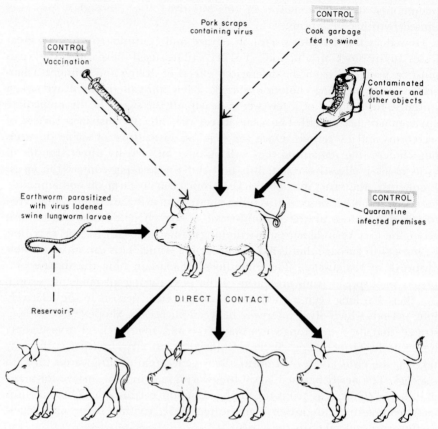

Fig. 43-2. Different ways in which hog cholera may start on a farm and the control measures used for its prevention.

been a tremendous boon to the swine industry but it has not always been free of difficulties. So called "virus breaks" and "serum breaks" have resulted in the loss of animals from hog cholera following the immunization procedure. This kind of vaccination procedure requires a good deal of judgment on the part of the veterinarian in deciding when and how to proceed. Unfortunately, the vaccination has frequently been performed without the aid of expert opinion, and losses have, not uncommonly, been extensive. The goal of the veterinary profession has been to eradicate this disease, and it was long recognized that this could not be done when the immunization procedure required the use of live virus, because vaccination kept virus in the environment. Work was undertaken to prepare vaccines made with killed viruses, and two vaccines of this kind are now used in the United States. They have not replaced the simultaneous serum and virus vaccination procedure because they do not stimulate immunity for as long a period; 2 to 3 weeks are required following vaccination for immunity to develop fully.

Work continued in search of yet a better means for immunizing swine. Adaptation of the hog cholera virus to multiply in the domestic rabbit was an important development (Baker, 1947). By alternately passing the virus between the rabbit and the pig, it was eventually trained to grow and multiply in the tissues of the rabbit. This rabbit-adapted virus produced little more than fever in the rabbit host, and likewise it had lost its disease-producing capacity in the pig. This paved the way for a new chapter in hog cholera control. Tamed hog cholera virus can be used to immunize swine and induce a resistance greater than that obtained with killed virus. The tamed or modified virus can be used with simultaneous injection of anti-serum. This means not only that protection is afforded immediately—rather than waiting the 2–3-week period necessary with killed virus vaccination—but, more importantly, it obviates the use of the live, dangerous, disease-producing virus. The prospects for complete control of hog cholera are now very good. The significant discoveries leading up to the tamed hog cholera virus vaccine afford an excellent example of how advances in disease control are achieved.

43-4. THE BACTERIA AND THEIR CONTROL

The bacteria constitute a large group of single-celled organisms considered to be the smallest form of plant life. In size the bacteria may be a little smaller or a little larger than a micron; that is, they are only about 1/1,000 of a millimeter in a given dimension. Bacteria usually reproduce by binary fission, the formation of two cells from a single cell (Pelczar and Reid, 1958). They may take numerous shapes: spheres, rods, or spirals. Extracts or broths made from the tissues of animals support the growth of bacteria very well. Thus, the bacteria thrive on the same nutrients required for the maintenance of higher animals. Nutrients prepared in the laboratory for growing bacteria are referred to as media, many of which are in the liquid state and are called broths. Substances may be added to broths which cause gel formation; these media are referred to as solid media. The use of media for the cultivation of bacteria permits diagnosis of diseases by growing the organism from infected tissues and then recognizing the cultivated organism as a disease agent. Of the many thousands of bacterial species on earth, only a few cause disease. Therefore, special knowledge is required to detect a disease-producing organism since nearly all bacteria will grow quite readily on media.

Brucellosis. Brucellosis is an important disease affecting both man and animals on a world-wide scale. There are three main species of bacteria which cause brucellosis. These closely related organisms incite a similar disease process but have different species of animals as principal hosts. Thus *Brucella abortus* primarily affects cattle, *Brucella suis* primarily affects swine, and *Brucella melitensis* primarily affects goats. However, all three species cause brucellosis in man, frequently called undulant fever because the human host is likely to have a series of daily fever peaks over an extended period.

Let us consider in some detail the problem of *Br. abortus* infection in cattle. This disease has been given several different names—contagious abortion, infectious abortion, Bang's disease, and brucellosis. The main clinical effect is indicated by the term contagious abortion (Hagan and Bruner, 1961). The cattleman may suffer extensive calf crop losses due to abortions late in gestation. Some weak calves are born alive, but die during the first few days of life. The reason for early expulsion of the calf from the cow's uterus can be explained on the basis of the habitat of this bacterial parasite. The organism multiplies within the cells of the placental membranes surrounding the calf in the uterus. The membranes become inflamed and undergo degenerative changes. This unhealthy state of the tissues interferes with the nourishment of the calf and finally results in the act of abortion. After aborting once or twice, infected animals may carry a normal calf to full term even though the uterine fluids are contaminated with the organism at the time of calving. Though the host has developed some increased resistance, it is still unable to rid its tissues of the parasite. The udder constitutes the other important site for long-term survival of the *Brucella* organism. The important aspect of infection in this tissue is the frequency with which the bacteria are shed in the milk. The implication of contaminated milk for transmission of the disease to man is obvious.

The *Brucella* organism has become a well-adapted parasite in the vertebrate host, persisting for years in an infected animal. How can we know when an animal is infected? To detect the organism in milk, we can inject milk into guinea pigs and see if disease develops in that experimental animal. We can examine the membranes and fluids from the calf by staining them and studying the cells under the microscope, or by culturing these materials on media in an attempt to grow the *Brucella* organism. These methods are useful for study of the disease but they are too laborious and time-consuming for large-scale diagnosis. Therefore, we use serology as the major diagnostic procedure, utilizing our knowledge that the serum of infected animals contains antibodies. There are many different serological procedures for the diagnosis of infection by the detection of antibodies. The one used for detecting *Brucella* antibodies is called agglutination. It is the least complex serological test to perform and it has been the cornerstone for brucellosis diagnosis. The essential features of such a test will be described.

Blood is taken from the animal to be tested for brucellosis and allowed to clot. As the clot contracts, serum will separate from it and this serum is then tested to determine the amount of antibody activity present. To do this we dilute the serum out through a series of tubes (Fig. 43-3); the fluid used for diluting is a special salt solution. The *Brucella* antibodies are protein molecules whose presence cannot be detected unless we put them in contact with the organism. A suspension of killed *Br. abortus* is placed in each tube containing the serially diluted serum. The surface of the bacterial cell is not smooth, but has a pattern like the tread on an automobile tire. Even though the parts of the pattern are very tiny, they are repeated several times over the surface of the organism. This pattern is characteristic and specific for the organism under study. When antibodies are in the serum, they attach to a portion of the surface pattern because they have the mirror image of that pattern on a portion of the antibody surface. You could compare this to the perfect fit of a lock and key. The antibody has two places on its surface which can attach to the bacterial cell; therefore each antibody can link two bacteria. This makes it possible to form a network if one mixes large numbers of bacteria with large numbers of antibody molecules. As this linking occurs, the masses of bacteria become large enough to settle out of suspension and appear as granular masses in the bottom of the tube. In a negative test, this does not occur and the cells

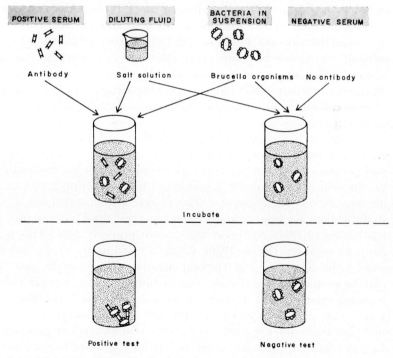

Fig. 43-3. The tube agglutination test as used in the diagnosis of Brucellosis. All reacting components are represented diagrammatically.

remain in suspension giving an opaque appearance to the solution. The agglutination test may be modified so that it can be performed on the surface of a glass plate. In this case, a few drops of serum and bacteria are mixed and the test is read within ten minutes. Visible clumping occurs in a positive reaction. This rapid plate test is commonly used in large disease-control programs.

The reaction of agglutination is also used when seeking antibodies in secretions from the mammary gland. This may be done by separating the casein from the whey and testing the whey in a manner similar to serum testing. Another procedure, called the milk ring test (MRT) is very useful for detecting antibodies in bulk milk. Whole milk is mixed in a tube with *Brucella* organisms that have been stained with a purple dye. If the milk contains antibodies, agglutination will begin, and as the cream layer rises the entrapped masses of bacteria will be carried with it. Thus, a positive test demonstrates a purple cream layer with white milk below. A negative test is exactly the opposite; the cream layer is white and the milk is diffusely purple because the stained bacterial cells are still in suspension.

Brucellosis is controlled for two important reasons. One is for the prevention of economic loss to the livestock producer from abortions and infertility in his cattle. The other reason relates to the public health problem of brucellosis in man. Great numbers of *Brucella* organisms are shed at the time of calving. When susceptible cattle eat or drink in an area contaminated by infected fluids or lick an aborted fetus, they in turn are infected. Transmission among cattle commonly occurs in this way, although venereal transmission is also possible. Man may contract brucellosis by ingestion of contaminated milk, by working around infected animals at the time of calving or abortion, or by handling parts of infected carcasses in slaughterhouses.

In 1935 the United States began a disease-control program aimed at the eventual eradication of bovine brucellosis. This is a cooperative federal-state program which has two approaches—vaccination and test-and-slaughter. Vaccination of young cattle is performed by inoculating a vaccine containing live *Br. abortus* organisms. The vaccine is prepared from a particular strain, chosen because it produces an increased level of resistance in cattle but has no ill effect on the animals, when properly used. This is a tamed *Brucella* organism (Buck, 1930). Cattle are ordinarily vaccinated as calves, and by the time they reach sexual maturity (time for the first calf) they may be resistant to the disease. Vaccination has been of great assistance in reducing economic loss to the livestock industry from brucellosis. However, vaccination alone will not eradicate the disease, and when the level of infection reaches a low percentage, the test-and-slaughter program is used. In this situation, cattle are diagnosed as having brucellosis on the basis of agglutination tests. Animals reacting positively to the test are removed from the herd. As compensation for loss of the animal, the owner receives the full carcass value from slaughter plus an additional sum (indemnity) from the government. The brucellosis eradication program has made extensive progress. When begun in 1935, more than 11% of the cattle in the United States were infected, whereas the figure is around 1% at this writing. This decline has been paralleled by similar reductions in the number of human cases of brucellosis.

Tuberculosis. Tuberculosis is well recognized as one of the most serious diseases affecting man. However, it is less commonly known that various forms of tuberculosis plague nearly all vertebrate animals. Even reptiles may suffer from tuberculosis, but we shall devote our attention to the important problem of this disease in cattle. The bacterium responsible is named *Mycobacterium bovis,* a different species from the so-called human tubercle bacillus, *Mycobacterium tuberculosis.* These organisms are so closely related that a dispute existed in the past as to whether they are separate species. The bovine tubercle bacillus will cause tuberculosis in man just as readily as the human tubercle bacillus. The reverse is not true; cattle are quite resistant to the human tubercle bacillus.

Tuberculosis is a chronic or long-lasting disease resulting in weight loss, general lack of vigor, and eventually death. Similarity of the control problems to those in brucellosis are readily seen. Infection causes extensive loss to the livestock producer and is likewise an important threat to human health. Again in this disease, man may contract the infection by drinking the milk of the cow or by handling infected animals.

Diagnosis of bovine tuberculosis is difficult because animals appear quite normal until they are in advanced stages of the disease. Therefore, detection of the infected individual in an early stage of the disease process is the key problem. The agglutination test, as used in brucellosis, is unsatisfactory for diagnosing this disease; an entirely different phenomenon is used as the basis for testing. Certain diseases, such as tuberculosis, induce a form of allergy or hypersensitivity in the infected individual. The host becomes allergic to the protein portions of the bacterial cell and will react quite violently to the proteins. The veterinarian uses this allergic state as the basis for diagnosis. Tubercle bacilli are grown in liquid media, and, as they grow, protein from the cells is extruded into the liquid. This liquid, after processing, is called tuberculin. If a small amount is injected between the layers of the skin of an infected individual, the allergic reaction manifests itself as an inflammatory lesion showing swelling, redness, and sometimes necrosis of the cells in the skin. Such a reaction would be called positive and would indicate infection by the *Mycobacteria.*

In 1917 a federal-state cooperative program for the eradication of tuberculosis in cattle was begun. The program is based on a test-and-slaughter procedure. The tuberculin test is used for diagnosis and is usually performed on cattle by injecting tuberculin into the skin near the base of the tail or the side of the neck. Animals that are allergic to the tuberculin are removed from the herd. The livestock producer is compensated by receiving the salvage value of the carcass and an indemnity payment, as described for brucellosis control. In 1917, about 5% of the cattle in the United States were tubercular; by 1940 this figure was reduced to less than 0.5%. This important accomplishment has been described in a book entitled *Man's Greatest Victory Over Tuberculosis* (Myers, 1940). Nevertheless, the battle with tuberculosis in cattle has not ended because scattered herds with active infection continue to appear. If care is not exercised, these foci of infection can readily spread to other herds. As the number of tuberculous herds has been reduced, the problem of accurate diagnosis among the remaining infected animals becomes more critical. Additional procedures for refining the diagnosis are being sought in the research laboratories.

A vaccine is available for immunization against tuberculosis which is called BCG. This vaccine consists of live tubercle bacilli which do not cause the progressive fatal disease. This is a tamed organism similar to the one used for brucellosis vaccination. In many parts of the world BCG vaccination is used on both man and animals for the control of tuberculosis. The question may be asked, why not vaccinate for tuberculosis in the United States? The answer is very simple: vaccination makes the individual allergic to tuberculin. Obviously, vaccination would make our diagnostic test with tuberculin useless. The decision to vaccinate or use a test-and-slaughter procedure depends upon the density of tuberculous animals and the economic status of an individual country. The decision to use test-and-slaughter in the United States was wise since cases of human infection from the bovine tubercle bacillus are now very rare, and we are well along the way toward abolishing livestock loss from tuberculosis.

43-5. THE PROTOZOA AND THEIR CONTROL

The protozoa constitute the phylum of the simplest animals. The name explains this since the Greek word for first is *protos* and animal is *zoon*. These so-called single-celled animals are often complex in structure; they vary greatly in size, shape, and physiological characteristics (Pelczar and Reid, 1958). The protozoa are divided into four classes and parasitic forms are found among all classes. As an example, we shall consider the class Sporozoa, which contains several parasitic forms such as the agent of malaria in man, the cause of Texas Cattle Fever, the organism causing toxoplasmosis in man and animals, and the agents of coccidiosis.

Coccidiosis. The coccidia are an important group of protozoa; all are parasitic and produce disease in cattle, sheep, goats, swine, dogs, cats, rabbits, ducks, turkeys, chickens, and other animals. As these parasites are of great economic importance to the poultry industry, we will examine the problem of coccidiosis in chickens.

Many protozoa have complex life cycles. To understand coccidiosis one must know the developmental stages (Fig. 43-4). The infectious form of the parasite is called an oocyst. When the chicken swallows a mature oocyst, eight sporelike structures escape from it and enter the cells lining the intestinal tract. Inside these host cells the parasite begins to round up and become larger. This is followed by division of the larger structure into numerous, small banana-shaped bodies. The infected cell containing these organisms is very swollen and eventually ruptures, releasing the parasites. This increase in numbers is by asexual reproduction, wherein the parasite simply divides many times. The process of increase is called shizogony. The

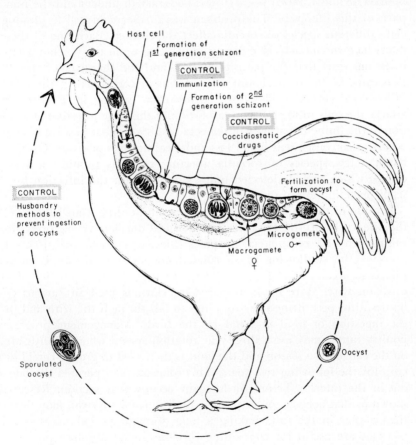

Fig. 43-4. The coccidial life cycle and measures used for control. The digestive tract of the chicken and infected host cells are represented diagrammatically.

released parasites enter new cells and repeat the cycle. Thus, there may be repeated generations of shizogony; the number varies with the species of coccidium concerned. This phase of the life cycle involves many cells in the lining of the intestinal tract and is, therefore, very destructive to the tissues. When this stage is completed, the parasite gives rise to male and female sexual forms called microgametes and macrogametes, respectively. As these forms are freed from their host cells, they unite in the intestinal canal to form a fertilized structure, an oocyst. The oocyst is passed from the bird in the droppings and represents the resistant form of the parasite which can serve to infect a new host. To become infective, the oocyst must undergo a period of maturation called sporulation. With the proper conditions of moisture, air, and temperature, sporulation can take place in about 24 to 48 hours. Obviously, much research was necessary to understand the numerous parts of this life cycle. The problem was further confused by finding that eight different species of coccidia affect the chicken. Each one of these produces its own characteristic disease depending upon the specific part of the intestinal tract that the parasite attacks, and the character of the damage thus caused. One of the more severe forms of coccidiosis in the chicken is called cecal coccidiosis because the organism causing it (*Eimeria tenella*) attacks the cells lining the ceca, a portion of the large intestine. The disruption to the lining membrane of the ceca is so severe that massive hemorrhage occurs, with consequent blood loss and local necrosis of tissue. On the other hand, a few species of coccidia affecting chickens produce a very mild disease which goes undetected unless one looks for the infection by microscopic examination of droppings.

Because of the importance of coccidiosis in poultry, knowledge regarding the life cycle of the parasite has modified husbandry methods used in raising birds for commercial purposes (Biester and Schwarte, 1959). If one prevents the swallowing of sporulated oocysts, the disease is prevented. Efforts to accomplish this are the basis for the common practice of raising birds on wire. Wire mesh or hardware cloth is used in various poultry houses, thus permitting the droppings to fall through the wire and prevent the ingestion of fecal material by the birds. Management programs for poultry ranges may use a three-year rotation system wherein birds are kept on the range for a season and the land is then used to grow a cereal or grass crop for the following two years. This rotation plan permits the oocysts to die in the interim, before birds again occupy that section. Research has shown us that oocysts, under proper conditions for survival, may live longer than a year in the soil, making a long dormant period necessary. These methods are useful for controlling coccidiosis, but absolute prevention of infection is not possible even under these strict circumstances. Because of this limitation, investigators have continued looking for additional ways to control the disease. Development of the sulfonamide drugs and certain other nitrogen-containing compounds opened a new chapter in the control of coccidiosis. These drugs are referred to as coccidiostats. Most of them do not prevent the beginning of the life cycle stages of parasitic growth, but they stop the process after the initial shizogony cycle has been completed. This is important for two reasons. Interruption of the life cycle at the second generation of shizogony prevents the highly destructive effects of the disease on the individual bird. The second important effect is that the drugs allow the infection cycle to begin, thus stimulating a response in the bird to form resistance or immunity.

That birds can develop immunity to coccidia, if they are able to survive an initial infection, has been known for some time. In a haphazard way, this can occur during the usual husbandry methods wherein some individuals in the flock will receive a light, natural infection and thus develop resistance to a larger dose of challenging organisms which may reach them later. However, by leaving this to chance the poultryman is never sure when he will unintentionally create the circumstances for a massive build-up of coccidial organisms that can be highly destructive to the flock. Another factor in coccidial immunity is that it is highly specific. This means that immunity to one of the eight species of coccidia affecting the chicken does nothing to induce resistance to the other seven species. Investigators have tried to use all of this knowledge for the practical immunization of poultry. The procedure is to make a preparation containing known numbers of oocysts of the important species affecting the health of the bird. Birds receive this dose of organisms and are then placed on a coccidiostatic drug which will prevent the immunizing organisms from causing disease but permit immunity to develop (Dickinson *et al.*, 1951). Immunizing procedures of this kind are expected to have an important place in coccidiosis control in the future.

In summary, coccidiosis is controlled by efforts from three directions; (1) efforts to prevent the swallowing of sporulated oocysts by various husbandry methods, (2) the use of coccidiostatic drugs for the treatment of birds to prevent overwhelming losses during an outbreak, and (3) procedures to immunize the birds.

43-6. WORMS (HELMINTHS) AND THEIR CONTROL

There are many free-living forms of worms, such as the common earthworm, but our concern is with the parasitic worms which we call helminths. There are numerous species of helminths, and it is certain that all of the earth's vertebrates are subject to some form of helminth infection. The helminths occur as flatworms and roundworms. The flatworms include the tapeworms and flukes while the roundworms include many cylindrical forms such as the common roundworms of the dog and pig (ascarids).

Trichostrongylidosis. The trichostrongylids are a family of roundworms (Lapage, 1956). Five genera from this family contain species which inhabit the stomach and intestinal tract of sheep and cattle, producing a disease condition called trichostrongylidosis. This disease, which may masquerade in many forms, causes extensive losses in the livestock industry. The extremes of parasitism by these worms may cause intestinal irritation with diarrhea, anemia due to blood-sucking worms, great loss of general condition, and eventually death. Many milder patterns of disease are seen, including infections with no apparent damage to the host. These variations in the disease pattern are governed by the size of the worm burden and the resistance status of the animal. By far the greater number of trichostrongyle infections do not kill the host, and one might ask what their importance is in this case. It must be remembered that the livestock producer is concerned not only with the survival of his animals, but he is obliged to have healthy animals capable of making economic weight gains as he prepares them for a competitive market. The greatest economic loss from trichostrongyle infections is the result of their effect on the general thriftiness of the animals.

The life cycle of a typical trichostrongyle is both interesting and involved (Fig. 43-5). The male and female adult worms mate within the intestinal tract of the host, and the female then begins laying eggs. The eggs are passed from the host in the feces or droppings. The parasitologist can determine which of the numerous trichostrongyles are affecting the host by microscopically studying the eggs. Eggs on the pasture hatch into larvae and then begin a period of nonparasitic existence. The larvae eat bacteria found in their environment and live as free organisms on the grass and soil. Stages of development follow wherein the larvae become somewhat larger and more complex in structure. They go through a molting process at each developmental stage. When molting, the outer skin or sheath is usually cast off in a manner similar to the shedding of the outer skin by a snake. Third-stage larvae that retain the skin of the second stage as a protective sheath are infective to sheep and cattle. These larvae are located on grass and soil and are ingested by grazing animals. The larvae emerge from the protective sheath, burrow into the mucous membrane lining the intestinal tract, and undergo another molt to become fourth-stage larvae. Fourth-stage larvae molt once more to a fifth stage, and in this last form they increase in size to become adult worms. Even as adults these worms are only about $\frac{1}{2}$–1 in. in length; thus an observer must use care to avoid overlooking them when examining tissues with the naked eye. They make up in numbers what they lack in size; a lamb showing signs of disease may be carrying 60,000 parasites.

As in many kinds of infectious disease, much can be accomplished in terms of minimizing trichostrongyle infections by the use of wise management practices. Eggs passed in the feces may give rise to infective larvae in 5 to 7 days, and presumably the larvae may survive for 6 months. Obviously the livestock producer should avoid overstocking and continuous use of pasture

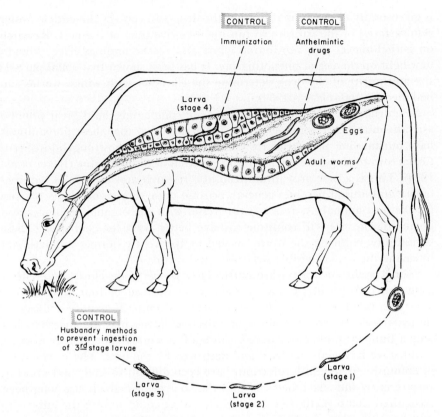

Fig. 43-5. The life cycle of a trichostrongylid worm and measures used for control. The digestive tract of the calf is represented diagrammatically.

lands; these practices permit a build-up of infective larvae, particularly around places of animal concentration. A wise procedure, if it can be adapted to practical circumstances, is to keep animals moving frequently to new pastures. Studies of the host indicate that this group of worms infect cattle, sheep, goats, and deer, but they do not usually affect species such as the horse, pig, or chicken. The contaminated land may be used for grazing animals that are not susceptible to this form of parasitism or for growing another crop while waiting for the larvae to die.

It is common knowledge that success in avoiding parasitism is highly variable and we must deal with great numbers of animals carrying worm burdens that affect their health. In these situations one must resort to other means of control—for example, the use of drugs to kill the worms. Such drugs are called anthelmintics, and currently the most valuable one for the control of the trichostrongyles is phenothiazine. Since this drug can have toxic effects on sheep and cattle, the achievement of useful results from its administration requires skill on the part of the veterinarian. Phenothiazine is given orally to the animals so that the drug will contact the cuticle (outer skin surfaces) of the parasite within the digestive tract of the host. Research on anthelmintics is a continuing effort and recent findings have brought new light on the use of phenothiazine. It has been shown that small particle size and purity of the drug determine the efficiency with which worms can be killed (Douglas *et al.*, 1959).

New drugs, such as the organophosphate compounds, hold great promise as anthelmintics. Preliminary studies have indicated that these preparations have outstanding properties for the treatment of trichostrongylidosis, particularly in cattle where phenothiazine is often of limited value (Baker *et al.*, 1959). This is a new area in anthelmintic research and caution is required before application becomes general, because these compounds have toxicity for the host animal. As research progresses with the organophosphates and phenothiazine, we will continue to have better ways for controlling these parasites by reducing the worm burden in apparently normal animals, and by saving the lives of visibly sick sheep and cattle.

Young lambs and calves are particularly prone to develop severe effects from the trichostrongyles. After they reach the age of four months and older they become increasingly resistant. They eventually acquire a resistance status wherein many thousands of infective larvae may be ingested, but only a limited number will develop into adult worms. The greater number of infective larvae are repelled and destroyed by the host. The mechanisms of immunity to helminth infections have been difficult to study and up until very recently they have been beyond the control of man. It has long been recognized that a small dose of infective larvae could induce the animal to undergo these changes toward a resistance status. This means of immunizing by natural infection is untrustworthy because of the lack of control over the numbers of ingested larvae. Efforts made to immunize animals by injecting extracts prepared from dead worms have not been successful. The evidence suggests that certain substances released from the worm while it is viable and growing in the tissues are necessary to induce resistance. As the larvae go from one stage to another during the molt, they release certain fluids which are apparently important for inducing immunity. Research workers have conceived the idea of inducing the immune response by infecting animals with irradiated larvae (Soulsby, 1961). Such larvae burrow into the mucous membrane and go through the molt but do not complete their life cycles. During the period of viability, they would excrete the substances necessary for immunization. These research findings are very encouraging and indicate that we will one day artificially immunize against helminth infections.

43-7. INSECTS AND THEIR CONTROL

The insects belong to an extensive class of organisms, including lice, gnats, bugs, mosquitoes, fleas, and flies. Most of these are known to the reader for the role they play as insect pests and for their important place in disease transmission. Our attention will be focused on the important insect problem of myiasis, the infestation of host animal tissues by fly maggots.

The Screwworm Problem. Several species of flies deposit their eggs in animal wounds as well as decaying vegetable or animal material (Herms, 1950). Larvae hatch from the eggs and, when the deposition is on a live animal, the resultant myiasis can be quite troublesome. A special form of myiasis, however, is caused by the fly *Callitroga americana*. This is the screwworm fly, whose larvae must hatch on the tissues of a warm-blooded animal and obtain their nutrition by eating the living flesh. This characteristic of the screwworm fly has made it a persistent threat to economical livestock production. Any time a break occurs on the body surface of an animal it becomes subject to attack by the screwworm. Common sites for screwworm infestations include castration wounds, docking wounds, shear cuts, dog bites, dehorning wounds, the navels of newborn animals, and all manner of snags and scratches.

The female fly, which is a bit larger than the common housefly, attacks and deposits as many as 400 eggs along the edges of the wound (Fig. 43-6). In less than one day the eggs hatch into larvae which begin to eat host tissues. The larvae have rings of spines encircling the body which give them the appearance of a wood screw—thus the name screwworm. Extensive damage can be done, as the larvae feed on the tissues for a period of 5 to 6 days. After this feeding period, they drop from the wound and burrow into the ground, where they take a new form, called the pupae. After about 8 days they emerge as flies and in an additional 6 days are ready to lay eggs. The whole life cycle is completed in about 24 days.

Efforts to prevent extensive losses from screwworms have required continuous vigilance on the part of livestock men for many years. Good management practices will do much to limit the problem. Screwworms are especially active during the warm months and this period requires frequent inspection and prompt treatment of all wounds. Entomologists have developed preparations such as smear 335 and smear EQ-62, which are useful for killing screwworms in wounds and repelling flies to avoid reinfestation. The organophosphate compounds, mentioned previously for the control of helminths, are an additional weapon in the fight against the screwworm fly. Sprays containing these compounds may be used at the time animals receive wounds or skin abrasions. Sprays have certain advantages over the smear preparations: (1) longer-lasting action, (2) sufficient power of penetration to reach and kill larvae that may be deep within the wound, and (3) no interference with normal wound healing. Thus, we do have means for combating this problem, but the control measures require extensive effort and vigilance on the part of the livestock producer.

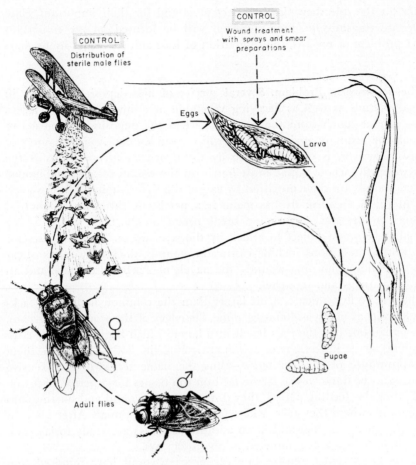

Fig. 43-6. The life cycle of the screwworm fly and methods used for its control.

The Agricultural Research Service of the U.S. Department of Agriculture estimates the annual loss from the screwworm among the southwestern states at approximately 20–25 million dollars. The southeastern United States was not concerned with this problem until 1933, when infested animals were brought in from the drought-stricken southwest. Estimated yearly losses in the southeast soon amounted to about 20 million dollars. These extensive losses further stimulated research on the part of entomologists, and eventually an important new control procedure for parasite eradication was developed.

The screwworm fly is a semitropical insect. This means that it is particularly important in states which have winters sufficiently mild to permit year-round activity. During the warm months this parasite ranges into the central and northern states, but such far-ranging insects are invariably killed during the colder months of the year. The over-wintering areas constitute a far more restricted region of the United States than is apparent from the distribution of the organism at certain times. Observation on the life cycle revealed that the female fly mates only once. Early work had shown that X-radiation of fruit flies would cause a change in the sperm of the male so that their progeny, or offspring, would not survive. Studies by Bushland and Hopkins (1953) showed that radioactive cobalt-60, which emits gamma radiation, would sterilize the insects—eggs fertilized by an irradiated male failed to hatch.

With this background the parts of the puzzle could now be put together. In the over-wintering areas sterilized male flies were to be turned loose in great numbers. These flies would seek out and mate with fertile females but the deposited eggs would not hatch. Competition by the sterile males would, after a period of time, tend to overwhelm fertile males found in the environment. Eventually this could cause the eradication of the screwworm. This novel eradication plan was first tried on a small island in the Caribbean Sea, the Island of Curaçao. The island was geographically isolated by water, which prevented reinfestation, and it was soon demonstrated that eradication could be accomplished. The southeastern United States was thought to be a favorable place for an eradication program because the over-wintering region was limited to the peninsular part of Florida. This meant that the focus of infestation was limited by water on three sides and by colder winters in the region to the north. Early in 1958 a federal-state cooperative program was begun for the extensive release of sterile flies in that region (Agricultural Research Service Report, 1959). A laboratory was set up in which great numbers of flies were produced under artificial conditions and subjected to gamma radiation in the pupal stage. The sterile flies were then carried to various parts of the eradication region by airplane and distributed from the air. The control program in that region has been eminently successful, and in November of 1959 the program in Florida was discontinued because eradication had been accomplished. This was a remarkable achievement in livestock disease control and one wonders whether the same procedure can be followed in the extensive areas of the southwest, which are similarly plagued by the screwworm fly. Unfortunately, the problem is more complicated there because the great land mass is contiguous with Mexico. The cost of such a program would be staggering. It would require maintenance of a large buffer zone across the whole width of Mexico, in which sterile male flies would have to be continuously present. In Florida there were only 50,000 square miles of over-wintering area, but the southwestern area requiring eradication is about 145,000 square miles. At present it does not appear feasible to attack the problem in this way. More research and new ingenious ideas will be required before complete eradication of this disease can be accomplished.

REFERENCES AND SELECTED READINGS

References marked with an asterisk are of general interest.

Agricultural Research Service, USDA, October, 1959. Report on the screwworm problem in the southwestern United States and northeastern Mexico.

Baker, J. A., 1947. Attenuation of hog-cholera virus by serial passage in rabbits. *J. Am. Vet. Med. Assoc.*, 111:503–505.

Baker, N. F., P. H. Allen, and J. R. Douglas, 1959. Trial with a new organic phosphate as an anthelmintic in cattle. *Am. J. Vet. Research*, 20:278–280.

*Biester, H. E. and L. H. Schwarte, 1959. *Diseases of Poultry*. 4th Ed. Iowa State Univ. Press, Ames, Iowa.

Buck, J. M., 1930. Studies of vaccination during calfhood to prevent bovine infectious abortion. *J. Agr. Research*, 41:667–689.

Bushland, R. C. and D. E. Hopkins, 1953. Sterilization of screw-worm flies with X-rays and gamma rays. *J. Econ. Entomol.*, 46:648–656.

Dickinson, E. M., W. E. Babcock, and J. W. Osebold, 1951. Coccidial immunity studies in chickens I. *Poul. Sci.*, 30:76–80.

*Dorset, M., C. N. McBryde, and W. B. Niles, 1908. Further experiments concerning the production of immunity from hog cholera. U.S. Bur. Animal Indus. Bull. 102.

Douglas, J. R., N. F. Baker, and W. M. Longhurst, 1959. Further studies on the relationship between particle size and anthelmintic efficiency of phenothiazine. *Am. J. Vet. Research*, 20:201–205.

Graham, O. H., B. Moore, M. J. Wrick, S. Kunz, J. W. Warren, and R. O. Drummond, 1959. A comparison of Ronnel and Co-Ral sprays for screw-worm control. *J. Econ. Entomol.*, 52:1217–1218.

Hagan, W. A. and D. W. Bruner, 1961. *The Infectious Diseases of Domestic Animals*. 4th Ed. Comstock Publishing Associates, Ithaca, N.Y.

Hammon, W. McD., W. C. Reeves, S. R. Benner, and B. Brookman, 1945. Human encephalitis in the Yakima Valley, Washington, 1942. *J. Am. Med. Assoc.*, 128:1133–1139.

Herms, W. B., 1950. *Medical Entomology*. 4th Ed. Macmillan, New York.

Lapage, G., 1956. *Veterinary Parasitology*. Charles C. Thomas, Springfield, Ill.

Myers, J. A., 1940. *Man's Greatest Victory Over Tuberculosis*. Charles C. Thomas, Springfield, Ill.

Pelczar, M. J. and R. D. Reid, 1958. *Microbiology*. McGraw-Hill, New York.

Raffel, S., 1953. *Immunity-hypersensitivity-serology*. Appleton-Century-Crofts, New York.

Shope, R. E., 1958. The swine lungworm as a reservoir and intermediate host for hog cholera virus. I. The provocation of masked hog cholera virus in lungworm-infested swine by ascaris larvae. *J. Expt. Med.*, 107:609–622.

Soulsby, E. J. L., 1961. Mechanism of immunity to helminths. *J. Am. Vet. Med. Assoc.*, 138:355–362.

Index